Design of Robust
Control Systems

Design of Robust Control Systems
From Classical to Modern Practical Approaches

MARCEL SIDI

Holon Academic Institute of Technology
and
Tel-Aviv University

KRIEGER PUBLISHING COMPANY
MALABAR, FLORIDA
2001

Original Edition 2001

Printed and Published by
KRIEGER PUBLISHING COMPANY
KRIEGER DRIVE
MALABAR, FLORIDA 32950

Library of Congress Cataloging-in-Publication Data

Sidi, Marcel J.
    Design of robust control systems : from classical to modern practical
approaches / Marcel Sidi.
        p.   cm.
    Includes bibliographical references and index.
    ISBN 1-57524-143-9 (hardcover : alk. paper)
    1. Robust control.   I. Title.

TJ217.2. S53 2000
629.8—dc21   00-035464

10 9 8 7 6 5 4 3 2

To my wife Raya

Preface

One of the main motivations for writing this book is the growing disregard of classical design theory in the face of the tremendous development in control theory over the past twenty years. Too frequently, the student of today skips classical design approaches and focuses directly on modern advanced theories. This is unfortunate. A thorough understanding of classical fundamental feedback theory is essential for understanding advanced design procedures such as the H_∞-optimal control. In order to remedy this deficiency, our approach is to progressively introduce the reader to modern control design techniques through the presentation of more traditional and classical oriented control theory.

The second motivation for writing the book is of practical importance. Advanced works on control theory concentrate on theoretical developments and in reading such books, one is fascinated by the writer's exposition, the mathematical proofs and so on. Too frequently, however, according to this author's experience with students, the essence of the studied material is never completely grasped and understood, unless the student is faced with illustrative problems and their solution. Then the applicability of the stated and proven theorems becomes apparent. In **Design of Robust Control Systems,** less importance is attached to proofs of theorems-these can be found in many excellent books on control theory. On the other hand, each newly treated item is followed by an example that fully illustrates the design issues, enabling the reader to repeat the solution and acquire the needed experience and understanding of the presented technique.

The book emphasizes the practical aspects in designing feedback control systems in which the plant may be nonminimum-phase, unstable and also highly uncertain. Early anticipation and correct interpretation of these effects can considerably shorten the design process. The plant uncertainty property is closely related to what is today called 'robustness'. A major task in automatic control is to design well-behaved feedback controlled systems which remain 'robust' and satisfy formally defined quantitative performances for the entire uncertainty region of the plant. 'Classical' and 'modern' design approaches for uncertain plants are explained side-by-side and used to solve similar design examples. This allows the reader to compare results obtained by both approaches. From here stems the name of the book.

The design approaches presented in the text strongly emphasizes the principle of 'design to quantitative specifications'. This approach partially removes the need for multiple cut-and-try design iterations until a satisfactory solution is achieved.

The fundamental 'classical' design approach presented here and which has been developed from the beginning of the seventies, is a research area that is linked to industrial needs. It also emphasizes the importance of designing for robust capability to the exact amount of plant uncertainty, but not more, thus saving on bandwidth and on cost of feedback. The design technique is performed in the frequency-domain, which is very transparent to tradeoffs between different system requirements. Fortunately, there are also good approximations for translating time-domain into frequency-domain specifications.

The reader is directed in how to efficiently solve control problems by hand calculations. Although excellent, inexpensive software can be used today for control design purposes, its efficient use depends heavily on practical design experience by hand calculations. For instance, the QFT-Matlab toolbox is used to solve the highly uncertain plant feedback problem in the frequency-domain. However, this software can never be used efficiently unless the designer has experience in solving such problems by hand calculations, drawing by hand permissible bounds on the nominal open-loop transmission function in the logarithmic complex plane, etc.

Of special interest are the gain bandwidth limitations when the plant to be controlled is not minimum-phase, but rather contains unstable poles, and/or right-half-plane zeros. It is important that students familiarize themselves with these theoretical bandwidth limitations prior to attempting a detailed design.

The state-space theory and design techniques that emerged in the end of the fifties are formulated in the time-domain, but they, too, are closely linked to the frequency-domain and thus allow us to mix design requirements and techniques in both domains. Design technique such as the LQR (Linear Quadratic Regulator) and LQG (Linear Quadratic Gaussian) have been in common use for a long time. They are presented in the text with some fully solved illustrative examples. The deficiency of these celebrated design techniques lies in their inability to cope with the uncertainty of constrained plants. This deficiency motivated the use of the H_∞-norm optimization paradigm to solve the uncertain plant control problem. The H_∞-control approach, which emerged in the early Eighties, is today spreading rapidly among the control community. Fundamental features of these new design approaches are also treated in the book. Basic control problems solved with the classical frequency-domain techniques are also solved with H_∞-norm optimization design techniques. It is our desire to give the reader the opportunity to grasp the common features of both design philosophies, as well as to appreciate the superiority, if any, of each approach in regard to this detail or that. In the author's opinion, it is logical to look upon all these design techniques as complementary. A right and correct solution of a feedback control system with the H_∞-control design approach requires knowledge of classical control theory in the frequency domain. To illustrate this point, knowledge of how to translate technical requirements from the time-domain into the frequency-domain and how to choose optimally the weighting transfer functions is of utmost importance if the H_∞-control design approach is to emerge with the best 'practical' solution. Also, deficiencies in one technique can be compensated with superior features of the other. These important points are underlined in the book by the problems presented and their detailed solutions. Moreover, an attempt is made in the text to use a kind of combined QFT/H_∞ design technique for both SISO and MIMO two-degree-of-freedom, highly uncertain feedback systems.

The book is the result of my teaching experience at the Tel-Aviv University, and also of my practical experience as development control engineer at Israel Aircraft Industries Ltd., where for more than 25 years I designed flight control feedback systems for aircraft, missiles and spacecraft.

A prerequisite for reading this book is a first course in automatic control, continuous and sampled-data, and an introductory to linear systems and to linear algebra. The book is intended for advanced undergraduate students, graduate students, as well as for practicing engineers.

Most of the examples were solved by software produced by MATHWORKS Inc., including the MATLAB programs related to control, such as Control System, Robust Control, QFT, μ-Analysis and Synthesis and LMI Control Toolboxes.

APRIL 1999

Acknowledgments

It is very difficult to me to write the following few sentences because I do not really know where to begin. My interest in feedback control theory was sparked by the classical book of Professor Truxal on Automatic Control, written in 1955, for which I thank him. Next I was faced with sensitivity problems in feedback control systems, and I found a very rich source on these subjects in the book of Professor Horowitz, published in 1963. This book is, so to speak, the first one in which a control problem is treated quantitatively in a systematic way. Much later, in the beginning of the seventies, the philosophy of quantitative design and synthesis of uncertain feedback control systems was developed under the name 'Quantitative Feedback Theory' (QFT). I had the privilege to work with Professor I. Horowitz on the invention and development of QFT when studying toward my Ph.D. degree, and I am also greatly grateful to him for encouraging my fundamental understandings in Automatic Control. The book by Bode (1945) also strongly influenced my understanding of the fundamental theory of automatic control, especially when system sensitivity and feedback constraints are concerned. Later, I was greatly influenced by what is known today as Modern Control Theory, presented in such fine and excellent books as those by Anderson and Moore (1971, 1990), Kwakernaak and Sivan (1972), and many others. In the Seventies and Eighties, a great effort was initiated to develop new theories and design techniques related to MIMO feedback problems. I was much influenced on this subject by such great scientists as Professors Rosenbrock, MacFarlane, Postlethwaite, Brockett, Zames, Doyle and many others whom I hesitate to list entirely for fear of possibly forgetting someone whose impact upon me has been profound. In writing the book, I was also strongly influenced by the books of Maciejowski (1989), Doyle , Francis and Tannenbaum (1992), Dorato, Abdallah and Cerone (1995), Skogestad and Postlethwaite (1996), Zhou and Doyle (1998) and many others in which advanced feedback control theory is treated. Many thanks to all the mentioned scientists from whom I have learned so immensely.

Contents

Abbreviations

BW   -bandwidth
dB   -decibel (xdB $= 20 \log_{10} x$)
deg   -degree
DOF   -degree-of-freedom
GM   -gain margin
IBC   -Ideal Bode Characteristic
LHP   -left-half-plane (real (s) < 0)
LQG   -linear quadratic Gaussian
LQR   -linear quadratic regulator
LTI   -linear time invariant
LTR   -loop transfer recovery
LTV   -linear time varying
NC   -Nichols chart
NMP   -nonminimum phase
MIMO   -multi-input multi-output.
MISO   -multi-input single-output.
MP   -minimum phase
NP   -nominal performance
NS   -nominal stability
ODOF   -one-degree-of-freedom
PM   -phase margin
QFT   -Quantitative Feedback Theory
rad   -radian
RHP   -right-half-pane (real(s) ≥ 0)
RP   -robust performance
RS   -robust stability
SISO   -single-iput single-otput.
SS   -state-space
TF   -transfer function.

TM   -transfer matrix
TDOF   -two-degree-of-freedom

Symbols

Capital italic letters denote SISO transdfer functions, for instance: *P, G, H, F*. Signals and their Laplace transforms are denoted by the same lower case italic letter; if confusion is expected,'*s*' or '*t*' are added as argument. For example: r, $r(t)$, $r(s)$, y, $y(t)$, and $y(s)$.

The capital letter '*P*' is used for 'plant' in all its versions: $\mathbf{P}, \mathbf{P}_k, P, P_k$

Bold capital letters denote matrices; the same italic low case letters stand for matrix elements: $\mathbf{M} = [m_{ij}]$

Bold low case letters stand for vectors; the same italic low case letters stands for vector elements:

$\mathbf{v} = [v_i]$	-vector
$\mathbf{P} = [p_{ij}]$	-plant transfer matrix with elements p_{ij}
$\mathbf{G} = [g_{ij}]$	-controller transfer matrix with elements g_{ij}
$\mathbf{F} = [f_{ij}]$	-prefilter transfer matrix with elements f_{ij}
$\mathbf{W} = [w_{ij}]$	-weighting transfer matrix with weighting elements w_{ij}
$\{\ \}$	-sets are denoted by $\{\ \}$ parenthesis, for example $\{P\}$ is a set of plants.
$(^T)$	-the superscript T denotes transpose of a matrix or of a vector.
$\sigma(\mathbf{A})$	-square root of the eigenvalue of $(\mathbf{A}*\mathbf{A})$
$\bar{\sigma}(\mathbf{A}) \equiv \sigma_{max}$	-the largest singular values of a matrix $\mathbf{A}$
$\underline{\sigma}(\mathbf{A}) \equiv \sigma_{min}$	-the smallest singular values of a matrix $\mathbf{A}$
$\mathcal{R}$ and $\mathcal{C}$	-the set of real and complex matrices
$\mathcal{RH}_\infty$	-the set of rational proper transfer matrices analytic in Re(s) $\geqslant 0$
$\mathcal{S}$	-the set of all stable, proper, real-rational functions
$\rho(\mathbf{A})$	-spectral radius of $\mathbf{A}$ (the largest magnitude of its eigenvalues)
$\lambda(\mathbf{A})$	-eigenvalue of $\mathbf{A}$
$\mathbf{A}*$	-complex conjugate of $\mathbf{A}^T$
$\det(\mathbf{A})$	-determinant of a matrix $\mathbf{A}$
$\text{tr}(\mathbf{A})$	-trace of matrix $\mathbf{A}$
$\|\mathbf{A}\|$	-norm of a matrix $\mathbf{A}$ ($=[\lambda_{max}(\mathbf{A}*\mathbf{A})]^{1/2}$)
$\|\mathbf{A}\|_S$	-spectral norm of $\mathbf{A}$: $\|\mathbf{A}\| = \bar{\sigma}(\mathbf{A})$
$\|\mathbf{A}\|_2$	-H_2 norm of a transfer matrix $\mathbf{A}(s)$
$\|\mathbf{A}\|_\infty$	-H_∞ norm of a transfer matrix $\mathbf{A}(s)$
$\|\mathbf{x}\|$	-Euclidean norm of a vector
$\text{diag}(a_i)$	-diagonal matrix with elements a_i
$\mathbf{I}_n \equiv \mathbf{I}(n, n)$	-unity diagonal matrix of order $n \times n$
$\mathbf{0}_n \equiv \mathbf{0}(n, n)$	-null matrix of order $n \times n$

Chapter 1

Introduction

The first known analytic study of stability was performed by Maxwell in 1868 when he analyzed the stability of James Watt's flyball governor for controlling speed, developed in 1788. The theory of automatic control as perceived today has its beginning in the early thirties when feedback amplifiers for communication appeared in commercial use. The use of 'feedback' was initiated with the objective of rendering the amplifier characteristics less sensitive to the uncertainties and physical anomalies of common electronic components in use at that time. Feedback also provided defined properties to the 'amplifier' as a whole.

As is well known today, feedback creates serious stability problems. The first work dealing with instability was published by Nyquist (1932) who revealed the famous **Nyquist stability criterion.** His work was extended by Black (1934), who investigated and analyzed stability of feedback amplifiers. The theory of automatic control was substantially advanced due to the very fundamental work of Bode (1945).

In World War 2, feedback theory was oriented toward solving control problems related to war equipment, such as the then-new 'radar instrumentation', the control of submarines and so on. Control theory quickly advanced and by the end of the fifties, what is called today 'classical control theory', enabled the design of many complex control systems based on feedback principles. (See, for instance, James et al. 1948 and Truxal 1955). With the subsequent appearance of very sophisticated hardware such as advanced aircraft, missiles, spacecraft, complex chemical plants and nuclear power stations, control theorists had to seek and develop new design approaches based on what we call today 'modern control theory', which is in some sense a natural continuation of the classical control theory. Thus, a good understanding of classical control theory is a prerequisite in understanding the complexities inherent in modern control design techniques.

Both classical and modern feedback control theories treated initially processes with known and fixed parameters. Unfortunately, complex plants are generally uncertain in the sense that their parameters are not known precisely, i.e., only the ranges of their values are known. The feedback system must behave according to

1

quantitatively specified performances, in other words, to behave 'robust' despite uncertainties of the plant.

The objective of this book is to apply classical and modern practical design approaches to uncertain feedback control systems. The material in the book deals with linear time-invariant uncertain systems only. However, for engineering purposes, the material is also applicable to slowly-varying plant parameters.

1.1   The Structure and Components of a Feedback Controlled System

A feedback control system is a combination of physical components that together perform a defined mission. A generalized structure of a feedback controlled system (SISO or MIMO) is shown in Fig.1.1, followed by an explanation of its various components.

The components of a feedback controlled system.

We distinguish, basically, between two kinds of functional components:

(i) The components pertaining to the defined physical *plant* which are to be controlled, so that specified system objectives are achieved. The *plant* denotes the constrained part of the system whose outputs are the system outputs. It can be described by a single transfer function block, or, if necessary and feasible, by several blocks of sub-plants, $P_1, P_2, ..., P_n$, so that additional control benefits can be obtained by measuring their outputs.

(ii) The components belonging to the *controller* of the feedback system, which are inherent and an indispensable part of the controlled system, are described by the transfer function blocks S, H, G, F_f, F_c:

G—a dynamic compensator whose primary task is to provide the feedback system with the necessary dynamical stability and the defined steady-state error coefficients. The dynamic compensator is also used to satisfy defined closed-loop specifications. This is an essential control component in any feedback system.

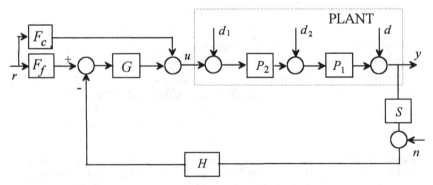

Figure 1.1.   A general two-degree-of-freedom feedback structure.

G is sometimes called *control network, control compensator,* or just the *controller,* or the *compensator.*

S — sensor hardware that measures the plant outputs which are used for controlling the feedback system.

H — a dynamic filter whose primary objectives are to process the sensors outputs. Its main task is to attenuate the inherent sensors noise and the structural dynamics signals of the plant (if these exist), etc.

F_f — a prefilter used to conveniently shape the input-output tracking performances of the controlled feedback system. If it can be physically implemented, it gives the system a second degree-of-freedom for design purposes.

F_c — a precommand filter that intentionally speeds the system's output by directly accessing the plant input.

Needless to say, these controller components can be implemented by electronic hardware or by microprocessor software.

The signals in a feedback controlled system

We distinguish between different basic signals, such as external reference and disturbance input signals, system outputs and control signals at the input to the plant:

- Reference inputs can be of two kinds, (i) command inputs generated by human operators, such as a pilot for instance, or (ii) command inputs generated by the kinematics of a moving body, such as in a radar system tracking a flying body.

- Disturbance inputs are unwanted signals that tend to affect the controlled system, acting on the plant at different input points.

- Noise signal inputs are produced inside the physical sensors. They can cause a deterioration within the controlled feedback system.

- Output signals are the variables to be controlled. In a MIMO feedback system, the output is a vector whose elements are the dynamic variables of the plant. In general, not all of them are measured and specified as controllable. (Some of them may even not be measurable).

- Input control signals, sometimes called the *control effort,* are generated by the control compensator *G* and injected into the input to the plant. Their amplitude level should be kept as low as possible in order to prevent saturation of the plant input.

1.2. Why Feedback?

Why do we need to apply feedback in order to control a physical system whose plant is mathematically known? In order to give a simple answer to this somewhat naive question, we simplify the feedback structure of Fig.1.1 to that of Fig.1.2a, where *P(s)* is assumed to be a SISO plant whose output is

$$y(s) = P(s)u_p(s) = P(s)[u(s)+d(s)] \qquad (1.1)$$

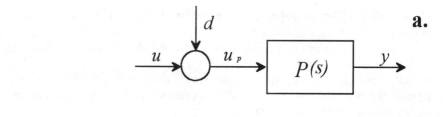

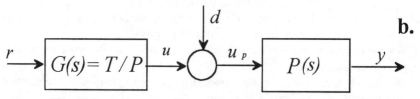

Figure 1.2.   Achievement of input-output characteristics with no feedback.

Suppose that our goal is to achieve for the controlled systems a specified input-output transfer function

$$T(s) = y(s)/r(s) \qquad (1.2)$$

If the disturbance $d(s) = 0$, we can achieve this goal by adding in front of the plant a control network $G(s) = T(s)/P(s)$ as in Fig.1.2b. This is equivalent to canceling of the plant dynamics and substituting the specified dynamics of $T(s)$. What is wrong with this approach? Although there are many arguments for using feedback, the two primary ones are presented here:

A- For a perfectly known plant, this procedure may be satisfactory. But, if the plant is not exactly known, then $G(s)$ will be an erroneous solution. Therefore, the input-output outcome will not be sufficiently similar to the desired one. In extreme cases, in which the plant $P(s)$ includes an unstable pole located at $+a$, if there exists even a very small uncertainty ε in $+a$, the input-output transfer function will comprise an unstable dipole of the form $(s-a+\varepsilon)/(s-a)$. (Because no perfect cancellation of the unstable pole can be then achieved). Consequently, the plant output will inevitably diverge.

B- If the disturbance $d(s)$ is known, its effort at the plant output can be annihilated by injecting the following corrected signal at the input to the plant

$$u_p(s) = r(s)T(s)/P(s) -d(s); \ y(s) = P(s)u_p(s). \qquad (1.3)$$

This is described schematically in Fig.1.2b. The output will then be the desired response $y(s) = T(s) \, r(s)$. Unfortunately, the disturbance $d(s)$ is seldom well-known, and its characteristics are generally not deterministic. Hence, the actual output can strongly deviate from the desired response $y(s)$ to the command input $r(s)$ only, as per Eq.(1.3).

1.3. Items to be Considered by Designers of Feedback Controlled Systems

A generalized feedback structure is shown in Fig.1.1. The advantages obtained by using feedback are invaluable. But feedback itself introduces practical problems. Suppose that we have to use feedback around a stable plant to achieve some desired characteristics of the feedback controlled system. If the feedback control system is badly designed, it may become unstable, although the plant is basically a stable physical system. Some insight into the feedback structure will help in understanding what the design problems are, and how they will be treated in this book.

Design specifications

Feedback is used in order to achieve specified characteristics and performances, which, as already explained, cannot be achieved in an open-loop mode of operation. These are mainly: (i) input-output tracking quantitative specifications, and (ii) the attenuation of the effect of expected (but not exactly known) external input disturbances at the output or input to the plant. LTI plants that do not include right half plane poles and zeros can be controlled by a LTI controller to achieve any desired closed-loop specifications, assuming that the sensor noise level is negligible and that the plant has the physical capabilities of providing the expected control effort. Stabilized feedback systems with plants containing RHP poles (but no RHP zeros) might suffer from a too high open-loop gain bandwidth that is intolerable from physical limitations point of view. The opposite is true for stabilized feedback systems in which the plant contains RHP zeros.

To summarize, when the plant contains RHP poles and/or zeros, theoretical limitations exist on achievable closed-loop specifications. One of the important tasks in this book is to treat these limitations quantitatively.

Uncertainty of plant parameters

The plant parameters are not known exactly. That is to say, they are uncertain and only the ranges of their values are known. The nominal closed-loop performances will not change drastically with small changes of the plant parameter values. However, if the parameters of the plant change significantly, this may cause serious problems in the design of feedback controlled systems in which 'stability' and 'specified design performances' are to be achieved despite the known plant uncertainty. This is the so-called 'robustness problem', a main analysis and design objective in the present book. It will be shown that if the uncertain plant includes RHP zeros, then there is no guarantee that initially defined system specifications can be achieved.

Saturation of the plant.

When tough specifications must be achieved, the needed control efforts may surpass the plant capabilities. In this case, nonlinear effects arise, which have to be adequately treated. If the plant can be subdivided physically into two or more cascaded sub-plants as in Fig.1.1, then there is an advantage in using the output of P_2, if this is measurable, with the aim of achieving ameliorated performances by closing an internal feedback loop.

Sensor noise amplification

Sensors always exist in a feedback controlled system. Unfortunately, they produce internal electrical noise which is superimposed on the measured and useful signal that is to be fed to the controller $G(s)$. This noise may have a tremendous effect on the design of any feedback system. As we shall see, in order to achieve both low sensitivity of the closed-loop system to parameter uncertainties as well as good external disturbance rejection, a high open-loop gain is needed in a wide frequency range. For instance, consider the problem of attenuating the disturbance $d(s)$ at the system output $y(s)$ in Fig.1.1:

$$y(s) = \frac{d(s)}{1 + G(s)H(s)P(s)S(s)} = \frac{d(s)}{1 + L(s)} \qquad (1.4)$$

It is clear that in order to keep $y(s)$ small due to the external disturbance $d(s)$, the magnitude of $L(j\omega) = G(j\omega)H(j\omega)P(j\omega)S(j\omega)$ must be large in a sufficiently wide frequency range. Since the plant $P(s)$ is constrained and cannot be altered, it is clear that the magnitude of $G(j\omega)H(j\omega)S(j\omega)$ must be increased in order to decrease the magnitude level of $y(s)$ (i.e, to achieve a good disturbance attenuation). But there is a major drawback in increasing the magnitude of $G(j\omega)H(j\omega)S(j\omega)$. This is explained qualitatively as follows: the sensor noise $n(s)$ is amplified at the input to the plant according to the following equation:

$$u(s) = \frac{-G(s)H(s)}{1 + G(s)H(s)P(s)S(s)} n(s) = -\frac{G(s)H(s)}{1 + L(s)} n(s). \qquad (1.5)$$

Let us consider two frequency ranges:
(i) the frequency range where $|L(j\omega)| >> 1$ (generally applicable in the low frequency range in which most of the disturbance energy is concentrated), in which case

$$u(s) \cong -n(s)/[P(s)S(s)]; \qquad |L(j\omega)| >> 1 \qquad (1.6)$$

Eq.(1.6) shows that in this frequency range, the noise amplification does not really depend on the designed controller $G(s)$ and on the sensor filter $H(s)$, but depends exclusively on the properties of the plant $P(s)$ and the sensor $S(s)$ hardware.
(ii) the frequency range where $|L(j\omega)| << 1$, in which case

$$u(s) \cong -G(s)H(s)n(s); \quad |L(j\omega)| \ll 1 \tag{1.7}$$

Eq.(1.7) shows qualitatively, that the higher the magnitude of $G(j\omega)H(j\omega)$ in this frequency range, the higher the effect of sensor noise amplification at the input to the plant will be. Generally, the energy of the sensor's noise is concentrated in this frequency range. Thus, higher bandwidth controllers increase the frequency range in which the effect of sensor white noise amplification is significant.

The conclusion from the above is that designing the control compensator to achieve good external disturbance rejection will inversely aggravate the sensor's noise amplification and all the problems associated with it. Hence, one of the most basic challenges in feedback control is to find satisfactory controllers that can achieve a compromise between the above different controversial problems existing in most real physical feedback systems. This is an important and major theme throughout this book.

To summarize, feedback design techniques must consider quantitatively the acceptable sensitivity of the input-output tracking transfer function to plant uncertainty; the external disturbance rejection; the system limitations due to RHP poles and zeros comprised in the plant; and the sensors noise amplification, which, if not adequately attenuated, may saturate the input to the plant.

1.4. Book Contents

The book deals with Single-Input/Single-Output (SISO) and Multi-Input/Multi-Output (MIMO) linear feedback systems. Fundamental feedback properties are most easily and clearly explained and understood with SISO systems. Moreover, since some of the MIMO design techniques to be treated rely on SISO design procedures, it is only natural to dedicate the first chapters principally to SISO feedback systems, although MIMO system will be mentioned where needed. The remaining chapters deal with MIMO feedback systems.

A brief description of the contents of each chapter is presented, taking care to point out the significant interrelationships between chapters.

Chapter 2. This chapter deals first with the definition of the feedback problem. Then basic feedback properties are treated and illustrated. The input-output sensitivity function, so important to the quality of the designed feedback control system, is next introduced and analyzed. The internal stability of feedback systems is then defined, and a basic theorem related to that subject is proven.

We review the basic concepts of design. Loopshaping principles are explained. The design approaches in the book are based very much on frequency-domain techniques. The fundamental Nyquist stability criterion is first stated, then the classical 'relative stability' is defined. Nyquist-oriented design techniques using the Bode plots, the Nichols chart, and the inverted Nichols chart are next treated.

Basic loopshaping design techniques for achieving stability margins, specified bandwidths, and sufficient attenuation of external input disturbances and of sensor noise are explained and illustrated with fully solved examples.

One and two-degree-of-freedom feedback system structures are discussed and, detailed loopshaping for such systems is exemplified. The limitations and superiority of both system structures are stated and compared.

Design tradeoffs in feedback systems are introduced. Performance requirements such as 'gain and phase margins' in terms of the sensitivity and the unity-feedback transfer functions are then analyzed. The definition of the 'weighted' and 'mixed sensitivities' is followed by the definition of the 'standard H_∞-optimal regulator problem'. Loopshaping by use of a H_∞-norm optimization algorithm is then illustrated with a solved example in detail.

Chapter 3. This chapter deals with basic features and practical topics in the design of SISO feedback systems. System design specifications are basically given in the time-domain. However, since the design techniques are performed mostly in the frequency-domain, the practical time-domain specifications for minimum and non-minimum-phase systems are first translated into frequency-domain specifications. Translation techniques for time-domain into frequency-domain are developed and the results are summarized in appropriate graphs and in approximated analytical relations. There exists direct and exact translation from the time-domain into the frequency-domain if the real part of a transfer function is known. Unfortunately, control engineers are mostly using, for practical reasons, transfer function magnitude information, for which only approximate frequency-domain into time-domain relations exist. Such approximations are stated and analyzed in this chapter.

The problem of achieving specified gain bandwidth of minimum-phase transmission functions in an optimal way is discussed via the so called Ideal Bode Characteristic. Systems including RHP zeros and/or poles, and/or pure time delay suffer from inherent limitations in achieving desired bandwidths. These limitations are analyzed, and analytic results are derived for predicting the best achievable bandwidths when such RHP poles and zeros are included in the plant transfer function. Some new results are discussed and exemplified with detailed numerical solutions.

Stabilization is a subject that deserves special attention. The Youla-parametrization (or Q-parametrization) is a synthesis technique for finding all the stabilizing controllers for a given plant. This technique, explained here for SISO feedback systems, is illustrated with solved examples. When the plant includes several RHP poles and zeros, it is generally difficult to choose the correct mathematical structure for the compensator that will stabilize the feedback system. The mechanization procedures presented in the literature for dealing with this problem emerges as a stable solution in which the open-loop gain has in general very limited bandwidth and phase and gain margins. This means poor feedback properties. Design processes for achieving the best feedback properties out of a difficult unstable non-minimum-phase plant are explained and illustrated with detailed examples.

Chapter 4. The material in the previous chapters treats the synthesis and design of feedback systems in which the plant is well-defined and has parameters with fixed and known values. In real systems, the parameters are neither well-known, nor can they be treated as completely time invariant. When the linear plant is highly uncertain, the design techniques treated in chapters 2 and 3 cannot be used successfully. In Chapter 4, we introduce a highly uncertain plant whose parameters are not precisely known. Only the ranges of their values are known. We develop design techniques to satisfy the design specifications despite the plant uncertainties. At this point the subject of 'robustness' is introduced. The theory behind this technique is today known as Quantitative Feedback Theory (QFT), which is based on classical frequency-domain control theory. The fundamental design technique for minimum-phase uncertain plants, which is presented, can be used to obtain an engineering solution for any a priori specifications for the controlled system (naturally at the cost of a wide bandwidth loop transmission function).

When plants including RHP zeros or sampled-data feedback systems are treated, the fundamental design techniques must be slightly modified. Moreover, because of inherent limitations on feedback systems that include RHP zeros, it may even happen that the design cannot fulfill all the a priori stated system specifications. Completion of the design requires for easing the initially specified performances and trying an additional design. The fundamental design technique, with all its variations for nonminimum-phase and for sampled-data systems, are illustrated with practical design examples solved systematically and evaluated by simulations in the time- and in the frequency-domains.

Design of uncertain feedback systems based on the H_∞-optimal control approach is also treated in this chapter. Plant uncertainty models compatible with the H_∞-norm paradigm are introduced and illustrated. Design for robust stability and for robust performance is treated next, also with detailed examples. Finally, the two-degree-of-freedom feedback system problem for uncertain linear SISO plants is solved with the H_∞-optimal control approach using QFT principles. Both QFT and QFT/H_∞ control designs end with solutions of comparable qualities.

Chapter 5. This chapter deals with single-input, cascaded plants. The existence of an additional measurable internal variable can be used in the design of a single-input/multi-output (SIMO) feedback control system in order to achieve the specified design performances with a reduced level of amplified sensor noise at the input to the plant. Each additional measurable variable allows an additional internal feedback loop to be closed, thus reducing the control burden on the main, outer feedback loop. The above possibility is of special importance when dealing with uncertain plants.

Chapter 6. This chapter deals with synthesis and design of LTI MIMO feedback systems. The subject of controlling MIMO systems is one of the most highly researched areas in the past twenty years. It is treated in the state-space, or in the frequency and the s-plane frameworks.

First, some common design techniques for 'certain' MIMO feedback systems in the *s*- and in the frequency-domain (such as diagonalization of the open-loop transfer function matrix, noninteraction by inversion of the plant transfer function matrix, sequential loop-closing, etc.) are explained and illustrated.

General results about 'internal stability' for MIMO feedback systems are also stated. Next, Q-parametrization is explained as a prelude to the theory of algorithms that solve the standard H_∞ optimal regulator problem.

The primary objective of this chapter is to present quantitative design tools for synthesizing a controller around a highly 'uncertain' MIMO plant with the aim of achieving desired input-output tracking specifications. When uncertain plant MIMO feedback systems are treated in the QFT framework, the basic idea is to break the design process into a sequence of *n* SISO feedback control designs, where *n* is the order of the MIMO system. A solution to the original problem is a combination of the solutions of each sequential step with the SISO design techniques treated in Chapter 4.

Chapter 7. The main purpose of Chapter 8 is to solve the MIMO TDOF uncertain plant feedback problem in the context of H_∞-norm optimization. It is true, that in this case too, the technical performance requirements are defined in the frequency-domain. However, the fundamental H_∞-optimization algorithms have their roots in the state-space formulation. In addition, since we are faced with a MIMO feedback problem, it is essential to have at least a superficial but close insight into the basic optimization theory for MIMO feedback control design, culminating with the solution of the Linear Quadratic Regulator (LQR) problem. This is done in Chapter 7. The LQR design techniques are then adapted to solve tracking control problems, such as the 'implicit' and 'explicit' model following. Next, the Linear Quadratic Gaussian (LQG) problem is reviewed briefly in regard to those cases in which some of the states are not measurable. Since these states are not measurable, they must be estimated in some optimal way in order to allow implementation of the optimal control law derived with the LQR design technique. The solutions of these problems are linked with the solution of matrix Riccati equations. Proofs of stated important theorems are generally omitted since they can be found in excellent textbooks and technical papers, which are referenced where needed.

Understanding of the above-mentioned subjects is a very necessary stage before we undertake the solution of the MIMO TDOF uncertain plant feedback problem within the H_∞-norm optimization context.

Chapter 8. This chapter deals with the general MIMO uncertain feedback problem solved with the paradigm of H_∞-norm optimization.

First, some elementary facts are explained about singular values, and also about their use in measuring transfer matrix size, as well as in defining performances of MIMO feedback systems. The Standard H_∞-Regulator Problem is then posed, and the mathematics of an optimization algorithm to solve it is outlined. A design technique for solving the MIMO TDOF uncertain feedback problem is finally presented. The same MIMO uncertain plant example solved in Chapter 6 with the classical QFT design technique is solved in this chapter within the H_∞-control paradigm, complemented with QFT principles. The achieved performances of both design techniques are compared.

Appendices: The appendices in the book are intended to summarize some well-known important aspects in linear system theory used in the book. It goes without saying, that rigorous proofs are not included.

Appendix A: Signal flow graphs are treated in this appendix. The final result is the well-known Mason gain formula. This formula for solving graphically linear simultaneous equations is of help when computing transfer between signals and systematically calculating transfer functions of complicated feedback system structures.

Appendix B: When MIMO feedback problems are treated, especially those solved with H_∞-norm optimization algorithms, vector and matrix norm notions are extensively used. Singular value equalities and inequalities are stated and explained for use in the related chapters.

Basic notions in the state-space formulation are defined and explained.

Eigenvalues and eigenvectors of real transfer function matrices are defined for use in connection with the generalized Nyquist stability criterion.

Linear fractional transformations and related relations are defined for use in the solution of the H_∞-optimal regulator problem.

Appendix C: When the control design is performed in the frequency-domain, the control compensator is obtained in the loopshaping stage by adding real, first-order poles and zeros, and complex second-order poles and zeros, but also lead-lag or lag-lead networks. Another very useful control network consists of two poles and two zeros located in such a way that special gain and phase characteristics can be obtained in the loopshaping process. Useful graphs and tables are prepared and included for that purpose. The Nichols chart and its inverted version are defined, and an explanation of how to use them in practice is presented.

Appendix D: For the convenience of the reader, some basic definitions and theorems from the Theories of Fourier, Laplace and Z transforms are presented.

Appendix E: Feedback control theory deals with analytic functions $F(s)$ in the s-plane. $F(s)$ can be a function describing the dynamics of a linear process, usually called a *plant,* or it may stand for the open- or closed-loop transmission function in feedback systems. In fact, all control theories in the s-domain are based on these kind of functions.

When treated in the practical frequency-domain, to each value of $s = j\omega$ there corresponds a value of the function in the complex plane, expressed as $F(j\omega) = A(\omega) + jB(\omega)$. The real and imaginary parts of these functions play an important part in the analysis of linear systems. Moreover, there exist some very important relationships between the real and the imaginary parts of such functions, with strong impact on practical feedback properties, such as maximum achievable bandwidth, etc.

The present appendix intends to summarize some useful relations of practical nature between real and imaginary parts of analytic functions used in control theory, but also to point on some important results concerning theoretical restrictions on these functions. The material follows closely the very fundamental work of Bode, 1945, also use is made of the works of Guillemin (1949), Seshu and Balabanian (1959) and Horowitz (1963).

Appendix F. This appendix investigates what the minimum order of a compensator for achieving stabilizability of a specific feedback system is, when a pole placement procedure is used in a design technique presented in Chapter 3.

Appendix G. Steady-state error coefficients play an important role in preparing specifications for a feedback controlled system. The usual error coefficients for position, velocity and acceleration inputs are defined and illustrated with different types of feedback systems.

Chapter 2

Basic Properties and Design of SISO Feedback Systems

Chapters 2 to 5 deal with SISO feedback systems. Fundamental properties of feedback are best explained with SISO feedback systems. Most of them have their counterpart in MIMO feedback systems, and this will be indicated explicitly where needed. The feedback problem is defined in Section 2.1. Mathematical definitions of feedback are treated in Section 2.2. Practical analytic tools for investigating stability are explained in Section 2.3. Section 2.4 deals with design perspectives and tradeoffs in feedback systems. Loopshaping with H_∞-norm optimization algorithms is considered in Section 2.5.

2.1. Introductory Definitions

The basic feedback structure we shall deal with in this book is shown in Fig.2.1.1. It differs slightly from the structure postulated in Fig.1.1, in which $H(s)$ has been omitted, because from the point of view of feedback properties, it can be incorporated into $G(s)$. Feedback systems in which $H(s)$ is identically equal to 1 are called *unity-feedback* systems. The precommand $F_c(s)$ has also been omitted for simplicity, because it has no influence on feedback properties of the closed-loop system. Also, the cascaded plants P_1 and P_2 have been adjoined to form the single plant P. The remaining canonical two-degree-of-freedom structure is simpler to discuss, and will be used in this and in the following chapters. Basically, the designation *two-degree-of-freedom* (TDOF) feedback structure indicates a system in which the command input $r(t)$ in Fig.2.1.1 and the system output $y(t)$ can be independently measured. With this assumption, two design control compensators, $G(s)$ and $F(s)$, can be used to independently control **two** feedback system specifications. The structure shown in the figure is of course only one of many possible canonical TDOF feedback structures. However, this one is especially efficient for solving the uncertain feedback problem by use of the Nichols chart introduced in Section 2.3.3.

13

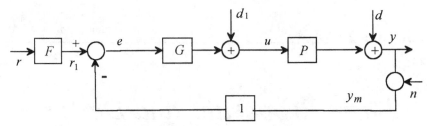

Figure 2.1.1. A canonical two-degree-of-freedom unity-feedback structure.

We are interested in the following transfer functions which are related to the feedback system shown in Fig.2.1.1.

$$T(s) \stackrel{def}{=} \frac{y(s)}{r(s)} = F(s) \frac{L(s)}{1 + L(s)} \; ; L(s) \stackrel{def}{=} G(s)P(s) \tag{2.1.1}$$

$$T_{d1}(s) \stackrel{def}{=} \frac{y(s)}{d_1(s)} = \frac{P(s)}{1 + L(s)} \tag{2.1.2}$$

$$T_d(s) \stackrel{def}{=} \frac{y(s)}{d(s)} = \frac{1}{1 + L(s)} \equiv S(s) \tag{2.1.3}$$

$$T_{un}(s) \stackrel{def}{=} \frac{u(s)}{n(s)} = \frac{-G(s)}{1 + L(s)} = -G(s)S(s) = \frac{-1}{P(s)} \frac{L(s)}{1 + L(s)} \tag{2.1.4}$$

$$T_1(s) \stackrel{def}{=} \frac{y(s)}{r_1(s)} = \frac{L(s)}{1 + L(s)} \equiv T_{uf}(s) \tag{2.1.5}$$

$$T_{ud}(s) \stackrel{def}{=} \frac{u(s)}{d(s)} = \frac{-G(s)}{1 + L(s)} \tag{2.1.6}$$

$$T_{yn}(s) \stackrel{def}{=} \frac{y(s)}{n(s)} = - \frac{L(s)}{1 + L(s)} \tag{2.1.7}$$

The initial stage in a feedback system design consists in correctly specifying the above transfer functions. Some important comments concerning these functions follow:
- $T(s)$ is the transfer function from r to y in a *two-degree-of-freedom* (TDOF) feedback system. $T_1(s)$ is the transfer function from r_1 to y in a *one-degree-of-freedom* (ODOF) unity-feedback configuration, in which the prefilter $F(s)$ cannot be imple-

mented physically. For obvious reasons, $T(s)$ and $T_1(s)$ may be called the *input-output tracking* (or just the *tracking*) transfer functions. These transfer functions are specified according to the desired tracking performances that are to be achieved.

- T_d is the transfer function from the disturbance d to the plant output y. In order to specify the needed disturbance attenuation by the transfer function $T_d(s)$, we must first acquire some information concerning the spectrum of the disturbance $|d(j\omega)|$. We also have to specify the permitted level of the output $|y(j\omega)|$ due to that disturbance. Once $|T_d(j\omega)|$ is defined, $T_d(s)$ can then be approximated.

Similar arguments exist when defining $T_{d1}(s)$ for the disturbance d_1 introduced at the input to the plant.

- $S(s)$ is of special importance when the sensitivity of $T(s)$ to plant uncertainty is treated. Since $S(s) = T_d(s)$, the most difficult design requirements of each will be retained in the definition stage.

- $T_{yn}(s)$ must be specified according to the assumed (or known from measurements) spectrum of the sensor noise, as well as from the permitted level of this noise reaching the system output y.

- $T_{un}(s)$ is the transfer function from the sensor noise source to the plant input u. The magnitude of $|T_{un}(j\omega)|$ must be as low as possible, especially at high frequencies where the sensor noise spectrum is the most pronounced, so that the amplified noise at the plant input u is minimized.

Since a good design of $T(s)$ and $T_d(s)$ *does not generally comply with a satisfactory* $T_{un}(s)$, design tradeoffs between achievable performances of these transfer functions become imperative.

$L(s)$, the *open-loop* transfer function, is also called the *loop transmission function*.

Remark. The subscript '$_{uf}$' in Eq.(2.1.5) is sometimes referred to as 'unity-feedback'. In someway this is misleading, because there is no signal f in Fig.2.1.1. However, when we treat the MIMO feedback system later, this subscript will become useful and meaningful for designating the unity-feedback closed-loop responses of the different input-output channels.

An additional, important relation follows from Eqs.(2.1.3) and (2.1.5), namely,

$$T_1(s) + S(s) = 1 \qquad (2.1.8)$$

This equation says simply that in an ODOF system the two most important transfer functions, the unity-feedback $T_1(s)$ and the sensitivity $S(s)$ cannot be specified and realized independently at will. (The prefilter $F(s)$ cannot be physically implemented if no reference command can be applied at its input, see Section 2.3.4).

$T_1(s)$ is also called the *complementary sensitivity function* because, from Eqs.(2.1.8), it follows that $T_1(s) = 1 - S(s)$.

Using the above definitions, it is instructive to express the plant output $y(s)$ and the plant input $u(s)$ in terms of the different external inputs to the feedback system, which are $r(s)$, $d_1(s)$, $d(s)$ and $n(s)$ in Fig.2.1.1. We find that

$$y(s) = T(s) r(s) + S(s) d(s) + P(s) S(s) d_1(s) - T_1(s) n(s) \qquad (2.1.9)$$

$$u(s) = F(s)G(s)S(s)r(s) - G(s)S(s)d(s) + S(s)d_1(s) - G(s)S(s)n(s). \qquad (2.1.10)$$

Some basic conclusions about feedback design can be derived from these equations:
1-To adequately attenuate the effect of the external disturbances $d_1(s)$ and $d(s)$, $|S(j\omega)|$ must be small in the frequency ranges at which the level of these disturbances is most pronounced. This usually happens in the lower and intermediate frequency ranges.
2- To keep the amplified sensor noise $n(s)$ low at the output $y(s)$, $|T_1(j\omega)|$ must be small in the frequency range at which the sensor noise spectrum is concentrated. Fortunately, in general the sensor noise is concentrated at high frequencies, so that in the intermediate frequency range, $T_1(s)$ can have a fairly large bandwidth, allowing good tracking characteristics.
3- To achieve a low level of control effort at the input to the plant due to the effect of disturbances and of sensor noise, $|G(j\omega)|$ must be small, specially in the high frequency range where the noise spectrum level is most pronounced, and where $|S(j\omega)| \to 1$. In the lower frequency range, where $|S(j\omega)|$ is small, a larger $|G(j\omega)|$ is less harmful from the point of view of the sensor noise amplification effect.

A major conclusion is that design tradeoffs are necessary in the different stages of shaping the transmission function $L(s) = G(s)P(s)$, so that large magnitude of $|L(j\omega)|$ (which leads to small $|S(j\omega)|$) is achieved in the frequency ranges where the input disturbances are most harmful, but small magnitude of $|L(j\omega)|$ is achieved in the higher frequency range where the sensor noise is concentrated.

Similar conclusions are presented in Chapters 6 and 8 for MIMO feedback systems.

Note that $1 + L(s)$ is the denominator of all the transfer functions defined in Eqs.(2.1.1) to (2.1.7). In this connection we will cite here, for the convenience of the reader, some very important definitions and theorems developed by Bode (Bode 1945 and Horowitz 1963).

2.2.   Mathematical Definition of Feedback

2.2.1.   *The Origin of Feedback Theory*

Feedback control theory has its origin in the design of feedback amplifiers, developed in the early thirties by Nyquist (1932), Black (1934), Bode (1945) and their co-workers. The primary motivation was to use feedback in order to reduce the sensitivity of the transfer function of communication amplifiers to uncertainties in the electronic hardware.

To demonstrate the reduction of the sensitivity of $T(s)$ to parameter variations inside the feedback loop, suppose that in Fig.2.1.1 $G(s) = k$, for which Bode defined the sensitivity function as follows:

$$S_k^T(s) = \frac{\partial \ln T}{\partial \ln k} = \frac{\partial T/T}{\partial k/k} \tag{2.2.1}$$

If we apply the above formula to the feedback system in Fig.2.1.1, we get

$$S_k^T(s) = \frac{1}{1 + kP(s)} = \frac{1}{1 + L(s)} \tag{2.2.2}$$

$S_k^T(s)$ is generally shortened to $S(s)$, as in Eq.(2.1.3). Eq.(2.2.2) shows that the relative uncertainty of the specified transfer function $T(s)$ to the relative uncertainties of the magnitude of the forward element k is reduced by the factor $1 + L(s)$.

The sensitivity function is of utmost importance to the theory of feedback, as we shall see on many occasions in the book.

2.2.2. Return Ration, Return Difference and the Invariance of its Numerator Polynomial

A feedback controlled system may consist of a large number of local feedback loops and forward paths, that finally can be converted to the canonical unity-feedback structure shown in Fig.2.1.1.

A multiloop feedback structure is shown in Fig.2.2.1. In this figure, a signal flow graph representation is used. Sometimes, analysis of feedback loop structures is more easily and efficiently carried on by using signal flow diagrams instead of the usual block diagrams. (See also Appendix A.)

The system shown in Fig.2.2.1a consists of several feedback loops. There is feedback gain around each one of the elements k_1, k_2, etc. Suppose that we wish to calculate the loop transmission for the element k_1. First, we nullify all external inputs to the feedback system such as r and d; then we cut this branch in two and we insert a source node on the forward side and a sink node on the return side of k_1; then we apply a unit-input signal at P_1 and calculate the signal returning at P_2 (as shown in Fig.2.2.1b). The ratio between the output and the input signals is called the *return ratio* for k_1 and is marked by T_{k1}. The difference between the inserted and the returned signals is $F_{k1} = 1 - T_{k1}$, which is called the *return difference*. We can also open the feedback system at other elements. For instance at the input to k_2, and calculate the return difference F_{k2} for that element too. Based on these definitions, a most fundamental theorem follows, whose proof is based on the Mason gain formula. The proof can be skipped by the reader, but not the theorem's result!

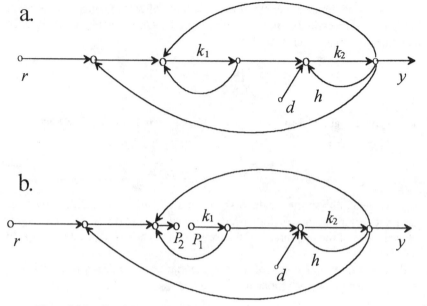

Figure 2.2.1.   Signal flow graph for calculating *Return ratio* and *Return difference*.

Theorem 2.1.   The numerator of the return difference $F_{ki} = 1 - T_{ki}$ is identical for all k_i chosen as references. (The theorem does not hold for trivial situations. For instance, if for an injected signal at P_1 there exist no path to P_2).

Proof: Suppose that we want to calculate the return difference F_{k1} . First, we cut the branch k_1 as in Fig.2.2.1b, and insert a unit signal at P_1. Since the analysis to follow is true for any branch k_i, let us use k for k_1 . By the Mason gain formula, Eq.(A.2), we can compute the return ration from P_1 to P_2.

$$T_k = \left(-k \sum_q G_q \Delta_q^k\right) \frac{1}{\Delta^k} \tag{2.2.3}$$

hence

$$F_k = 1 - T_k = 1 - \frac{1}{\Delta^k}\left(-k \sum_q G_q \Delta_q^k\right) = \left(\Delta^k + k \sum_q G_q \Delta_q^k\right) \frac{1}{\Delta^k} \tag{2.2.4}$$

We can rewrite Δ of Eq.(A.3) for any $k = k_i$ as follows (see also Seshu and Balabanian, 1959)

$$\Delta = \Delta^k + k \sum_q G_q \Delta_q^k \tag{2.2.5}$$

where Δ^k is derived from Δ by putting $k = 0$; G_q is the qth forward path gain from P_1 to P_2 (not including k) since k is open; Δ_q^k is the remaining part of Δ^k for the qth forward path after all loops having a common node with the qth path have been deleted from Δ^k. Eq.(2.2.4) together with Eq.(2.2.5) give

$$F_k = \frac{\Delta}{\Delta^k} \tag{2.2.6}$$

Δ, shown to be the graph determinant of the system in Fig.2.2.1a, does not depend on the chosen k_i (Bode 1945 and Seshu and Balabanian 1959). Eq.(2.2.6) is true for any forward or feedback branch k_i in Fig.2.2.1.

It is easily shown that the numerator of Δ is the system's characteristic polynomial in the complex variable s. The practical importance of Theorem 2.1 is that the *closed-loop poles* of the feedback system from any input to any output (except for degenerate cases), which are *the zeros* of $F_k(s) = 1 + L(s)$ in Eqs.(2.1.1) to (2.1.7), do not depend on which element k_i is chosen as reference when the return difference related to it is calculated. The following example illustrates the meaning of the above theorem.

Example 2.2.1.   Calculate the return difference for the elements k_1 and k_2 in the feedback structure of Fig.2.2.2.

First, we calculate the return ratio and then the return difference for k_1. Let us cut the loop at the input of k_1, and then inject a unit-input signal at P_1. The signal returning at P_2 can then be calculated in order to find the return ratio and the return difference for k_1

$$T_{k1} = \frac{-k_1}{Js^2}\frac{1}{1 + \dfrac{k_2}{Js}} = \frac{-k_1}{Js^2 + k_2 s}; F_{k1} = 1 - T_{k1} = \frac{Js^2 + k_2 s + k_1}{Js^2 + k_2 s} = \frac{D(s)}{Js^2 + k_2 s}.$$

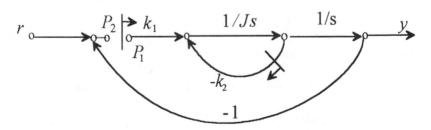

Figure 2.2.2.   Return difference calculation for reference elements k_1 and k_2.

The return ratio for k_2 and its return difference are similarly calculated to be

$$T_{k2} = \frac{-k_2 s}{Js^2 + k_1}; \, F_{k2} = 1 - T_{k2} = \frac{Js^2 + k_2 s + k_1}{Js^2 + k_1} = \frac{D(s)}{Js^2 + k_1}.$$

Thus, the numerators of F_{k1} and that of F_{k2} are exactly the same, namely, $D(s) = Js^2 + k_2 s + k_1$. (Notice that the denominators of both return differences are of course different! The denominator of F_{k1} can be obtained by putting $k_1 = 0$ in $D(s)$. The denominator of F_{k2} can be similarly obtained by putting $k_2 = 0$ in $D(s)$).

Notice also that the transfer function of the closed-loop from $r(s)$ to $y(s)$ is

$$T(s) = \frac{k_1}{Js^2 + k_2 s + k_1},$$

whose denominator is exactly the same as the numerators $D(s)$ of F_{k1} and of F_{k2}.

Example 2.2.2.   Consider the system of Fig.2.1.1. If we open the loop at the input to $G(s)$ and choose it as reference branch, we then get the following return ratio and return difference,

$$T_G = -G(s)P(s) = -L(s); \, F(s) = 1 - T_G = 1 + G(s)P(s) = 1 + L(s).$$

Note that $-L(s)$ is the return ratio, and that the same return difference $F(s)$ exists in the denominator of each one of the transfer functions in Eqs.(2.1.1) to (2.1.7). Clearly this result is true for any reference instead of $G(s)$. Nonetheless, it is important to note that the stability of the numerator of $1 + L(s)$ does not guarantee stability of all the input-output transfer functions that can be defined in Fig.2.1.1. This point will be discussed next.

Example 2.2.3.   Consider the system in Fig.2.1.1 in which $P(s) = (s + a)/[s(s - b)]$; $G(s) = (s - b)/(s + c)$. Consequently, $L(s) = (s + a)/[s(s + c)]$ and the return difference becomes: $1 + L(s) = [s^2 + (c + 1)s + a]/[s(s + c)]$. Clearly, for $c > -1$ and $a > 0$, the roots of the characteristic polynomial (the numerator of $1 + L(s)$) are stable. Also, when the prefilter in Fig.2.1.1 is equated to one, then:

$$y(s)/r(s) = (s + a)/[s^2 + (c + 1)s + a],$$

which is a stable transfer function. However,

$$y(s)/d_1(s) = (s + a)(s + c)/\{(s - b)[s^2 + (c + 1)s + a]\},$$

is clearly an unstable transfer function because of the unstable pole located at $s = b$.

The conclusion is that stability of the roots of the characteristic polynomial, which are the roots of the numerator of $F(s) = 1 + L(s)$, is not a sufficient condition for the stability of all the transfer functions pertaining to the feedback system in Fig.(2.1.1). An additional condition is necessary to guarantee stability of **all** these transfer functions. This condition is stated in a well known theorem, whose proof can be found in Vidyasagar (1985) or in Doyle et al.(1992).

2.2.3. Asymptotic Stability and Internal Stability

The most common, simple and useful definition for stability of LTI systems is the *asymptotic stability,* defined as follows.

Asymptotic stability:

When linear time-invariant systems are treated, stability is easily defined. In this category of systems, the plant and the control compensator can be expressed as rational transfer functions whose numerator's roots are the zeros, while the denominator's roots are the poles of the transfer functions. By definition, a transfer function is *asymptotically stable* if, and only if, all its poles are located in the open left half plane (LHP) of the s-variable. By this definition, poles on the imaginary axis are defined as unstable. Poles in the LHP have negative real parts. Thus, when a system having such poles is activated in the time-domain by any bounded input, the output will be also bounded. Moreover, the transient part of its time response will decay exponentially with time until it completely dies out. From these phenomena stems the term *asymptotic stability.*

Internal stability

Internal stability is defined in terms of the external input variables r, d_1, d, n and the internal and output variables e, u and y in Fig.2.1.1. The system is internally stable if, and only if, for each of the bounded external input signals r, d_1, d and n, the internal variables e, u and the output variable y are also bounded signals. In other words, for internal stability, all the transfer functions from r, r_1, d_1, d and n to e, u and y must contain poles located only in the open LHP of the s-variable. No poles on the imaginary axis $j\omega$ are allowed. For a more general and systematic analysis of internal stability, see Section 6.2.7, where similar arguments for MIMO systems are derived.

Theorem 2.2. The feedback system is internally stable iff:
a. The transfer function $1 + L(s)$ has no RHP zeros. (See Theorem 2.1).
b. There is no pole-zero cancellation in the closed RHP when $L(s) = P(s)G(s)$ is formed.

Part *a* of the theorem is a necessary condition, but not a sufficient one. Part *b* of Theorem 2.2 applies to cases similar to those in Example 2.2.3. It also states that when a feedback system with plants containing poles and zeros in the right-half-plane is designed, no pole-zero cancellations are allowed by the controller, and that the right-half-plane zeros and poles of the plant must remain explicitly in the open-loop transmission $L(s) = P(s)G(s)$. A simplified proof follows.

Proof: Suppose that the zeros of $1 + L(s)$ are in the LHP. With no RHP pole-zero cancellations when producing $L(s) = G(s) P(s)$, Eqs.(2.1.1) to (2.1.7) show internal stability. With RHP pole-zero cancellations in $L(s)$, Eqs.(2.1.1) (2.1.3) and (2.1.5) show that stability is preserved. However, Eqs.(2.1.2) and/or (2.1.4) show that since RHP poles remain in the transfer functions, internal instability occurs.

To illustrate this, let us admit one RHP pole in the plant transfer function located at $s = +p$. Define $P(s) = N_P/D_P = N_P/D_P'\,(s-p)$, where D_P' contains only LHP poles. If pole-zero cancellation is performed, the RHP pole is introduced in the compensator $G(s)$ as a RHP zero so that, $G(s) = N_G/D_G = N_G'(s-p)/D_G$ and $L(s) = N_P N_G'/D_P' D_G$ with no RHP poles. After insertion of these terms in Eq.(2.1.2), we get

$$
\frac{y(s)}{d_1(s)} = \frac{N_P}{D_P'(s-p)} \; \frac{1}{1 + \dfrac{N_P N_G'}{D_P' D_G}}
$$

$$
= \frac{N_P D_P' D_G}{D_P'(s - p)(D_P' D_G + N_P N_G')} = \frac{N_P D_G}{(s - p)(D_P' D_G + N_P N_G')}
$$

which is unstable, although the zeros of $1 + L(s)$ are designed to be in the LHP. In a similar way, it can be shown that if a RHP zero of the plant is canceled by a RHP pole of the compensator, then $y(s)/d_1(s) = T_{d1}(s)$ (Eq.(2.1.2)) will remain stable while $u(s)/n(s) = T_{un}(s)$ (Eq.(2.1.4)) becomes unstable, although the zeros of $1 + L(s)$ are designed to be in the LHP.

2.3.   Definition of Some Feedback Control Issues Using the Basic Feedback Equation

The transfer functions of interest in the context of the canonical feedback structure in Fig.2.1.1 are given by Eqs.(2.1.1) to (2.1.7). These transfer functions are of interest in any feedback control problem. They all have in common the return difference $F(s) = 1 + L(s)$. Suppose that $G(s)$ is designed to achieve desired specifications of one of the transfer functions in Eqs.(2.1.2) to (2.1.7). In this case, for a given plant $P(s)$, the designed compensator $G(s)$ automatically dictates all the remaining transfer functions in Eqs.(2.1.2) to (2.1.7). However, the input-output transfer function $T(s)$ in Eq.(2.1.1) can be further manipulated by the prefilter $F(s)$, which provides a second degree-of-freedom to the feedback structure.

It is a common practice in classical feedback control of LTI systems to design in the frequency-domain. In this context, the Nyquist stability criterion, Bode plots and the Nichols chart are extensively used. (As will be shown in Chapters 4, the

Nichols chart is very efficient in solving feedback control problems with highly uncertain plants.)

We shall now briefly review the main mathematical and graphical tools for designing loop transmission functions in the frequency-domain with the objective of achieving defined closed-loop specifications, including specified 'relative stability', to be defined later.

2.3.1. Asymptotic and Relative Stability Considerations in the s-Plane and in the ω-Domains

Asymptotic stability, defined in Section 2.2.3, is related to the location of the closed-loop poles in the *s*-plane. However, very efficient classical and modern design techniques are performed as well in the frequency-domain. The Nyquist stability criterion is the basic graphical test for determining closed-loop stability and relative stability from the frequency response of the loop transmission function $L(j\omega) = G(j\omega)P(j\omega)$.

The Nyquist stability criterion

The Nyquist stability criterion was invented originally in order to give the designer a graphical tool for analyzing and for ascertaining stability of communication amplifier systems.

Before we state the criterion, some definitions are necessary: Let Γ_N, known as the Nyquist contour, denote the closed contour in the *s*-plane that encircles the entire RHP as shown in Fig.2.3.1a, and let Γ_L be the mapping of Γ_N onto the complex plane by $L(j\omega)$ as shown in Fig.2.3.1b. The Nyquist stability criterion in its simplest form then states the following:

Let $L(s)$ be a rational loop transmission function that maps the Nyquist contour Γ_N in the *s*-plane onto the closed contour Γ_L in the complex plane which encircles the point $[-1 + j0]$ N times. Then the number of RHP zeros of $1+L(s)$ is

$$z = N + p \tag{2.3.1}$$

where p is the number of RHP poles of $L(s)$ located inside the Nyquist contour Γ_N and N is positive if the encirclements are in the same direction as that of the *s*-contour direction of Γ_N in the s-plane. Hence, stability is achieved if and only if $z = 0$, i.e., if $N = -p$. In other words, for a loop transmission $L(s)$ containing p unstable poles, stability of the closed-loop is attained only if the mapped contour Γ_L by $L(s)$ in the complex plane encircles the point $[-1 + j0]$ p times in a direction opposite to that of the direction of the Nyquist contour Γ_N in the *s*-plane. At this point it is important to emphasize that no RHP zero-pole cancellations are allowed in forming $L(s)$ by the plant $P(s)$ and the compensator $G(s)$, $L(s) = P(s)G(s)$. If such a cancellation is performed, the Nyquist criterion may show stability, while checking for internal stability as explained in Section 2.2.3 might show internal instability.

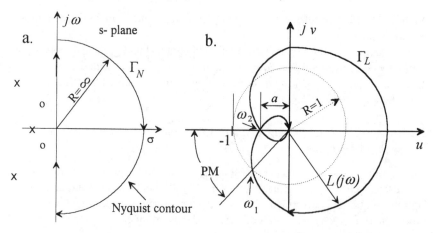

Figure 2.3.1.   Graphical interpretation of the Nyquist stability criterion.

The point $[-1, j0]$ on the complex plane is called the *Nyquist stability critical point,* or, in short, the *critical point.*

Relative stability (gain and phase margins)

Gain and phase margins are an indication of how far the open-loop transmission $L(j\omega)$ is from the stability critical point $[-1 + j0]$. These are defined as follows: A circle with radius $R = 1$ and centered at the origin is drawn in Fig.2.3.1b. Suppose for this explanation that there are no open-loop RHP poles included in $L(s)$. In Fig.2.3.1b, $L(j\omega)$ crosses the unity circle at ω_1, hence $|L(j\omega_1)| = 1$. Thus, $L(j\omega)$ will not encircle the critical point $[-1 + j0]$, unless the phase of $L(j\omega_1)$ is increased by a phase-lag larger than the angle *PM*. We shall then say that the *phase margin* of $L(j\omega)$ is *PM*, usually given in degrees. Definition of gain margin is done in a similar way. Let arg $L(j\omega_2) = -180°$ and $|L(j\omega_2)| = a < 1$. If we increase the gain of $L(j\omega_2)$ by a factor larger than $1/a$, then the loop transmission $L(j\omega)$ will encircle the critical point $[-1 + j0]$, thus causing instability of the closed-loop. In this case, we say that the *gain margin (GM)* of $L(j\omega)$ is $1/a$. It is common to call ω_1 the *crossover frequency,* $\omega_{co} \equiv \omega_1$, while ω_2 is called the *gain margin frequency,* $\omega_{GM} \equiv \omega_2$.

2.3.2.   Design in the Frequency-Domain Using Bode Techniques.

Some preliminary definitions are necessary, prior to discussing design techniques in the frequency domain.

Logarithmic magnitude.   The logarithm of a complex number is itself a complex number. For instance, if $P(j\omega) = |P(j\omega)|e^{j\Phi(\omega)}$, then, if log to the base 10 is used,

$$\log P(j\omega) = \log |P(j\omega)| + \log e^{j\Phi(\omega)} = \log |P(j\omega)| + j\,\Phi(\omega) \log(e)$$

The real part is equal to the logarithm of the magnitude, $\log |P(j\omega)|$, which is called the *logarithmic magnitude* (or *gain*) of $P(j\omega)$ (shortened usually to *log magnitude*). The imaginary part is proportional to the phase $\Phi(\omega)$.

Decibel. In practical work with feedback systems, the *decibel* unit is commonly used. The logarithmic gain is defined as $20 \log_{10} |P(j\omega)|$, where the units are in *decibel*, shortened usually to 'dB'.

Bode plots.

As is well known, any rational transfer function can be represented in terms of zeros and poles. The zeros are the roots of its numerator polynomial, while the poles are the roots of its denominator polynomial. Any rational transfer function can then be expressed in the form

$$
L(s) = \frac{k \overset{i}{\Pi}(s + z_i)\, \overset{n}{\Pi}(s^2 + 2\,\xi_n\omega_{zn}s + \omega_{zn}^2)}{s^l \overset{l}{\Pi}(s + p_l)\overset{m}{\Pi}(s^2 + 2\xi_m\omega_{pm}s + \omega_{pm}^2)} \tag{2.3.2}
$$

which consists of i real zero, n second-order complex zeros, I integrators, l real poles and m second-order complex poles. The frequency responses of each individual pole or zero transfer function can be displayed conveniently as a standard plot on semilog paper, where the magnitude in decibel units is plotted versus log ω. There is together with this plot an additional one, the corresponding phase versus log ω. These plots are known as the famous *Bode plots* (*logarithmic plots*.) (See also Appendix C.) Such plots greatly simplify the calculation of transfer function in the frequency-domain. The advantage of using Bode plots is that calculation of the overall logarithmic magnitude and phase-angle of a transfer function is obtained by adding and subtracting the magnitudes in dB and the phase-angles in degrees of each one of the individual zeros and poles belonging to the transfer functions. In this way, one can also represent separately the behavior of $P(j\omega)$ and of $G(j\omega)$ versus log ω, and obtain finally $L(j\omega)$ by simply adding their logarithmic magnitudes in dB and phases in degrees.

The gain and phase margins are easily identified on Bode plots. See Fig.2.3.2. (When the analysis or the design of the feedback system is performed in the Bode diagram, the gain margin is denoted in decibel units). If unstable poles exist in the loop transmission, the Bode plots are not sufficient for checking stability and care should be taken so that the number of negative encirclements of the critical point $[-1 + j0]$ in the complex plane conforms with the Nyquist stability criterion.

Design by using Bode plots consists of shaping $L(j\omega) = G(j\omega)\, P(j\omega)$ by the control network $G(j\omega)$, $P(j\omega)$ being given and known. The final $L(j\omega)$ must fulfill the usual characteristics such as steady-state error coefficients, adequate gain and phase margins, crossover frequency, and of course closed-loop stability.

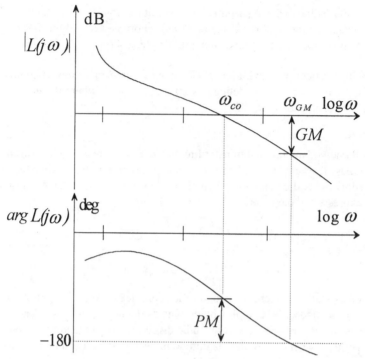

Figure 2.3.2.   Definition of gain and phase margins, ω_{co} and ω_{GM} on the Bode diagram of $L(j\omega)$

2.3.3.   The Nichols Chart and its Special Characteristics

Designing feedback systems with Bode plots is a very basic technique extensively used over the years. Bode plots of lead-lag, lag-lead networks, poles, zeros, differentiators, integrators, etc., can be efficiently used in shaping an adequate $L(j\omega)$. However, a small drawback arises in designing $L(j\omega)$ on the Bode diagram: The Bode plots of $\log|L(j\omega)|$ and of $\arg L(j\omega)$ do not show explicitly the behavior of the closed-loop transfer function. On the other hand, the Nichols chart, invented by Nichols in the forties, shows explicitly the behavior of the unity-feedback $T_1(j\omega)$ for given $\log|L(j\omega)|$ and $\arg L(j\omega)$ versus ω. The relative stability margins (*PM, GM*) are also easily identified on this chart. Later, we shall also see that the Nichols chart is an ideal medium for designing feedback around highly uncertain plants.

Unity-feedback constant gain contours on the Nichols chart.

The unity-feedback transfer function was defined by

$$T_1(s) = \frac{G(s)P(s)}{1 + G(s)P(s)} = \frac{L(s)}{1 + L(s)} \tag{2.3.3}$$

which is the transfer function in Fig.2.1.1 from r to y with $F(s) = 1$. (To facilitate the presentation in the book when the Nichols chart is used, the unity-feedback transfer function will be sometimes named just $T(s)$ instead of $T_1(s)$). The vertical and the horizontal Cartesian coordinates of the Nichols chart are the magnitude in dB units and the phase-angle in degrees of $L(j\omega)$. Contours of constant values of $|T_1(j\omega)|$ in dB and of constant values of arg $T_1(j\omega)$ in degree are superimposed on the Nichols chart. See Appendix C for their derivation, and for an accurate and detailed Nichols chart in Fig.C.6.2. Fig.2.3.3 displays contours of constant values of $|T_1| = 6, 3, 1, 0, -1, -3, -6$ and -12 dB. But, for visual clarity, no contours of constant unity-feedback phase-angle are shown. To find the unity-feedback $|T_1(j\omega)|$, draw $L(j\omega)$ on the Nichols chart by reading for each frequency ω the values of log $|L(j\omega)|$ and arg $L(j\omega)$ from the Bode plots of $L(j\omega)$. The resultant curve of $L(j\omega)$ has frequency as a parameter. For the $L(j\omega)$ displayed in the figure, we can easily obtain by inspection the unity-feedback $|T_1(j\omega)|$ at different frequencies. Moreover, the maximum peak value of $|T_1(j\omega)|$ is also obtained by inspection. In the case at hand, it equals $+3$ dB.

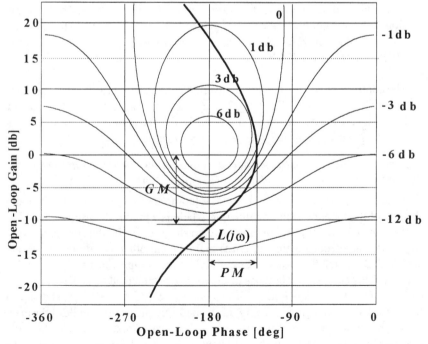

Figure 2.3.3.   Basic features of the Nichols chart: contours of constant $|L/(1+L)|$ (in dB). Contours of constant arg $L/(1+L)$ are here omitted for keeping the figure clear.

Location of the stability critical point and identification of phase and gain margins

It is easy to locate the Nyquist stability critical point $[-1 + j0]$ on the Nichols chart. The critical point is the intersection of the open-loop 0 dB horizontal axis with the open-loop $-180°$ phase vertical axis. On the same Fig.2.3.3, are shown the phase margin in degree and the gain margin in dB for an assumed $L(j\omega)$.

Inverted Nichols chart for disturbance analysis and design

Eq.(2.1.3) is the transfer function from the disturbance $d(s)$ to the output $y(s)$, named by $T_d(s) \equiv S(s)$. Contours of constant values of $|S|$ in dB units are displayed on the inverted Nichols chart.

To understand the meaning of this chart, let us define $l(s)$ as equals to $1/L(s)$. Therefore $l(j\omega) = 1/L(j\omega)$ and Eq.(2.1.3) reduces to

$$T_d(j\omega) \equiv S(j\omega) = \frac{l(j\omega)}{1+l(j\omega)} . \tag{2.3.4}$$

Eq.(2.3.4) is of the same form as Eq.(2.3.3) for which contours of constant values of $|T_1|$ have been plotted in Fig.2.3.3. However, $l(j\omega) = 1/L(j\omega)$, which means that the gain $|l(j\omega)| = 1/|L(j\omega)|$, and arg $l(j\omega) = -$arg $L(j\omega)$. Hence, the range $-360°$ to $0°$ of arg l becomes $+360°$ to $0°$ for arg L. Also, $|l|$ dB $= -|L|$ dB. The final conclusion is that the contours of constant values of $|S| = |1/(1+L)|$ are the contours of constant values of $|T_1| = |L/(1+L)|$ which are rotated by $180°$ about the [0dB, $-180°$] point. (See Fig.C.6.3). This is the origin of the name *inverted Nichols chart*.

The contours of constant $|S|$ of the inverted Nichols chart can be superimposed on the Nichols chart as in Fig.2.3.4. The contours of constant $|S| = +3, -1, -6$ and -12 dB are the dotted curves in Fig.2.3.4. For the assumed $L(j\omega)$ in this figure, we find that $|S(j\omega_3)| = |T_d(j\omega_3)| = +2.8$dB while $|T_1(j\omega_3)| = -6$dB.

Superiority of design based on Bode plots and on the Nichols chart over design based on the Nyquist plot in the complex plane

The frequency-domain design techniques seldom uses the complex plane for loop-shaping of the loop transmission function. There is a practical reason for this. For a given plant $P(j\omega)$, the design problem is to shape $L(j\omega)$ by the control network $G(j\omega)$ so that adequate gain and phase margins and other system properties are achieved. Although this task can be fulfilled in the complex plane, design in this plane is a difficult process because of the following practical considerations:

(i) Since $L(j\omega) = P(j\omega)G(j\omega) = |P(j\omega)||G(j\omega)|\ e^{j[\arg P(j\omega)\ +\ \arg G(j\omega)]}$, shaping of $L(j\omega)$ consists in changing its magnitude by multiplying the magnitude of the plant $|P(j\omega)|$ by the magnitude of the controller $|G(j\omega)|$ at a large number of frequencies, and by rotating $P(j\omega)$ by the argument of $G(j\omega)$ at the same frequencies. The multiplication renders the shaping process cumbersome. It is difficult for the de-

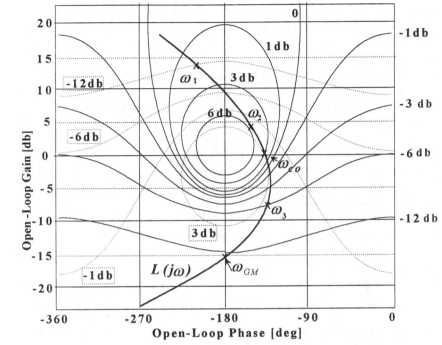

Figure 2.3.4.   Basic features of the inverted Nichols chart (dotted curves are contours of constant $|S| = |1/(1+L)|$) superimposed on the Nichols chart.

signer to predict mentally the overall change of $L(j\omega)$ by $G(j\omega)$ because of the simultaneous action of multiplication of $|P(j\omega)|$ by $|G(j\omega)|$ and of rotation of $P(j\omega)$ by arg $G(j\omega)$. (ii) In high frequencies, $|L(j\omega)|$ is very small and it is difficult to plot and shape it in linear scale.

The above difficulties do not appear when Bode plots and Nichols charts are used because: (i) log magnitude and phase (in degree) of $G(j\omega)$ are added arithmetically to those of $P(j\omega)$ to get $L(j\omega)$, which is a much easier computational process; and (ii), when the magnitude of $L(j\omega)$ is small, its logarithmic value in negative dB is large, so that it can be processed more accurately than in linear scale. Note that the frequency range where $|L(j\omega)|$ is comparatively small is very relevant for feedback design. Moreover the notion of relative stability is more easily foreseen on Bode plots and on the Nichols chart.

2.3.4.   Distinction between One and Two DOF Feedback Systems

The simple canonical unity-feedback structure in Fig.2.1.1 must be correctly interpreted in conjunction with the existence of the prefilter $F(s)$. Suppose that the feedback structure in this figure represents an aircraft flight control system. The control network $G(s)$ is designed so as to achieve defined disturbance rejection specifications, steady-state error coefficients, open-loop crossover frequency, stability margins, and so on. The bandwidth of the unity-feedback system as obtained from the Nichols chart will be a byproduct of the realization of the above mentioned specifications by the loop transmission function $L(j\omega)$. The obtained unity-feedback $|T_1(j\omega)|$ may not conform with desired closed-loop specifications as seen by the pilot. However, since in this feedback system the prefilter $F(s)$ can be physically implemented, $F(j\omega)$ can provide the input-output transfer function $|T(j\omega)|$ in Eq.(2.1.1) with any desired characteristics, independently of the control network $G(s)$ used in achieving $|T_1(j\omega)|$. This prefilter $F(s)$ supplies the system a second-degree-of-freedom. In fact, by using both $G(s)$ and $F(s)$, the transfer function in Eq.(2.1.1) and one additional transfer functions in Eqs.(2.1.2) to (2.1.7) can be independently specified and realized.

Contrary to the above example, let us suppose that the prefilter $F(s)$ cannot be physically implemented. In this case, only a one-degree-of-freedom exists, in the sense that only one of the transfer functions in Eqs.(2.1.2) to (2.1.7) can be independently specified and achieved. This situation exists, for example, in a radar tracking system, in which the input $r(t)$ is the kinematics of motion of a flying body, $y(t)$ is the position of the body in space which is not measured, and $e(t)$ is the boresight error of the flying body in the antenna axis frame. In this case, since only the error $e(t)$ is measurable, only the control network $G(s)$ can be implemented and used for design purposes. As a result, only $G(s)$ can manipulate the closed-loop transfer function $T(s)$ of the feedback controlled system.

At this point, it is important to note that there are approximate relationships between the frequency-domain response $|T(j\omega)|$ and its step time response. (See Chapter 3). But since the peak value of $|T_1(j\omega)|$ for ODOF feedback systems is closely related to the relative stability of the feedback system, so, too, is the peaking in the input-output unit-step response. By looking at the Nichols chart in Fig.2.3.3, we see that the smaller the phase margin, the larger the peak value of $|T_1(j\omega)|$ will be, (see also Section 2.5.2). In fact, a large peaking in the frequency-domain is accompanied by an approximated underdamped second-order complex pole. On the other hand, in a TDOF system, this underdamped complex pole of $T_1(s)$ can be canceled by the prefilter $F(s)$. Hence, an overall input-output transfer function can be realized at will, thus obtaining any desired time response, despite the fact that the stability margins of the feedback system may be very low. This leads to the conclusion that in TDOF systems there is no direct relationship between the stability margins of the feedback system and its time-domain response (In practice it is very important to have it).

Moreover, since we can use at most two control networks for both one and two DOF systems, some necessary tradeoffs must be performed between system requirements that can be defined by the seven transfer functions described in Section 2.1.

2.3.5.   Frequency-Domain Design of ODOF Feedback Systems

The initial stage in the design of a feedback control system consists of shaping the open-loop transmission function $L(s)$ so that it satisfies some described performances. Loopshaping of $L(j\omega)$ in the frequency-domain is the primary objective in the design process.

The general features of a loop transmission $L(j\omega)$ in the frequency-domain are shown in Fig.2.3.4. Several important and extensively used notations concerning $L(j\omega)$ and $T_1(j\omega) = L(j\omega)/[1+L(j\omega)]$ include the following:

Crossover frequency ω_{co}, and GM frequency ω_{GM}

We have already defined ω_{co} to be the frequency at which $|L(j\omega)| = 1 = 0$ dB (see Fig.2.3.2). This frequency is connected to the definition of loop bandwidth. By ω_{GM} we defined the frequency at which the argument of $L(j\omega)$ is $-180°$. The importance of these two frequencies will be emphasized later. Clearly, the gain and phase margins are easily detected in Fig.2.3.4 at ω_{co} and at ω_{GM} respectively. In this special case, $PM = 45°$, $GM = 15$ dB.

Conditional stability

The loop transmission $L(j\omega)$ in Fig. 2.3.4 is relevant to a feedback system which is *conditionally stable,* since the system will become unstable if the open-loop gain is lowered by more than 10dB.

Closed-loop performances and bandwidth ω_{-3dB}

In addition to the above definitions and features observed on the Nichols chart, closed-loop performance can be also detected. For instance, we see that the unity-feedback magnitude of the system is $|T_1(j\omega_2)| = 5.8$ dB at ω_2. Hence, $|T_1(j\omega)|$ has a peak value of ≈ 5.8 dB. Should this peak value be larger than permitted by the specifications of the problem, reshaping of $L(j\omega)$ on the Nichols chart can easily lower it to an acceptable value. Also $|T_1(j\omega_3)| = -6$ dB, and $|T_1(j\omega_{GM})| = -12$dB. The frequency at which the unity-feedback magnitude equals -3dB, below its $|T_1(j0)|$ value, will be named ω_{-3dB}. This frequency is also known as the *bandwidth* of the closed-loop system.

Disturbance rejection

As already indicated in this chapter, the inverted Nichols chart can be used to describe disturbance rejection performances sensed at the plant output. For instance, we see that at ω_1 in Fig.2.3.4, the attenuation of the disturbance d at the output y (Fig.2.1.1) is $|T_d(j\omega_1)| = -12$ dB. Also $|T_d(j\omega_{co})| = +3$ dB. By inspecting the figure, we can derive $|T_d(j\omega)|$ for all frequencies, and decide if the obtained $L(j\omega)$ fulfills the stated specifications on $|T_d(j\omega)|$. If it does not, a reshaping of $L(j\omega)$ may be necessary, until all specifications are satisfied.

An additional disturbance d_1 is also defined in Fig.2.1.1. The inverted Nichols chart does not give a direct insight into the attenuation of d_1 at the output y. However, it is possible to transfer the disturbance d_1 to the location of d by preceding it by the block P, which is the transfer function of the plant. This procedure will be pursued in Chapter 4, where synthesis of the highly uncertain feedback system by the QFT design technique is discussed.

Loopshaping

Loopshaping stands for the procedure of achieving a desired $L(j\omega)$ that satisfies stated specifications on the open-loop transmission and also on the closed-loop transfer functions. Once the plant is known, the procedure of loopshaping consists of adding in front of it dynamic control networks, so that the obtained $L(j\omega)$ satisfies simultaneously all specifications (such as phase and gain margins, bandwidth, disturbance attenuation, maximum peaking in the frequency response of the closed-loop system, steady-state error coefficients, etc). Since the loopshaping is actually performed by using the conventional integrator, poles and zeros, lead, lag, lead-lag, etc. control networks, the achieved controllers have basically the properties of the well known *PID controllers* (Proportional, Integral, Differential). To facilitate the matter for the reader, normalized graphs and tables of such control networks are presented in Appendix C.

To familiarize the reader with the loopshaping procedure we will present a number of examples. Loopshaping is an essential part in the synthesis of single and multivariable feedback systems with which the present book deals. It is true that the practicing engineer can today use available and very advanced commercial software that helps enormously in the loopshaping process, but he will never take full advantage of such software until he acquires sufficient experience in loopshaping by hand calculations. It is therefore important that compatible basic loopshaping procedures will be mastered and practiced.

The problems to be solved in this section will exemplify use of lag, lead and mixed lead/lag or lag/lead compensations for achieving defined, steady-state error coefficients, phase and gain margins, open-loop crossover frequency and closed-loop bandwidth.

Example 2.3.1.   Use *lag compensation* for achieving defined phase margin and velocity error coefficient K_v.

The constrained plant is $P(s) = 6/[s(s + 0.5)(s + 4)]$. The desired specifications are $K_v = 15$, $PM = 45°$ and maximum permitted peak value of $+3$ dB in $|T_1(j\omega)|$.

Solution: Since the plant is a Type 1 system, no addition of an integrator in $G(s)$ is needed in order to obtain a finite K_v. It is easily found that without compensation, $K_v = 3$, which is not satisfactory. Since the desired velocity constant is $K_v = 15$, we need to use a control network $G(s)$ in which $G(0) = 5$ (see Appendix G). In the first step of the design, we sketch Bode plots of

$$G(s)P(s) = 5 P(s) = 30/[s(s + 0.5)(s + 4)]$$

and we find that from the logarithmic magnitude and phase Bode plots in Fig.2.3.5, $PM = -21.7°$. This means that the closed-loop system will be unstable if uncompensated. In order to introduce the use of Nichols charts, the same $5P(j\omega)$ is plotted on the Nichols chart in Fig.2.3.6. It is clearly seen that the closed-loop system is unstable because of the encirclement of the critical point located at [0 dB, $-180°$]. Note that $|L(j\omega)| = +10$ dB wherein arg $L(j\omega) = -180°$.

The design process can be carried out on the Bode diagram or on the Nichols chart. For the less experienced reader, it is easier for him to use the Bode diagram. We are interested in achieving a phase margin of $PM = 45°$. According to Fig.2.3.5, we find that at $\omega = 0.38$ rad/sec, the phase-lag is about $-132°$, and the magnitude is 30 dB. If we can reduce it by 30 dB at this frequency, the PM will amount to about $48°$. The problem is how to achieve this reduction in magnitude without appreciably changing at the same time the phase at the crossover frequency (here $\omega_{co} = 0.38$ rad/sec). A compensator based on a lag-lead network (Fig.C.4.1) can be used with the following argument: to achieve an attenuation of 30 dB in the range $\omega \geq \omega_{co} = 0.38$ rad/sec, we have to choose $a = 30$ in Fig.C.4.1. However, the phase-lag that will accompany the magnitude attenuation must be equal or smaller than $3°$ at $\omega = 0.384$ rad/sec, in order not to degrade the phase margin specification. This means that we have to choose $u = 19$. Hence, $\tau = u/\omega = 19/0.38 = 50$, for which the compensating network becomes

$$G(s) = 5(1 + 50s)/(1 + 50 \times 30s).$$

The compensating network must have more poles than zeros in order to preclude a very high amplification of the sensor white noise at the input to the plant. This design item will be treated in detail in Section 2.4. Meanwhile, let us admit that we must add a far-off pole to the open-loop transmission function. This pole can be viewed as a high frequency noise filter.

In the present example, the far-off pole can be positioned at $\omega = 5$, so that it will add a very small additional phase-lag at $\omega = 0.38$ rad/sec. The overall phase-lag of $L(j\omega)$ will remain close to $-135°$, thus keeping unspoiled the specified $PM = 45°$. (Conceptually, the noise filter can be manipulated more efficiently and accurately by procuring in advance an additional, known reserve in phase-lead when designing the lag-lead network; this can compensate exactly for the phase-lag added by the noise filter). The final compensating network then becomes:

$$G(s) = 5(1 + 50\ s)/[(1 + 1500\ s)(1 + 0.2\ s)].$$

The final $L(j\omega) = P(j\omega)G(j\omega)$, is plotted in Figs. 2.3.5 and 2.3.6. The resulting phase margin, gain margin, and ω_{co} are clearly detected. Exact computation shows that at $\omega = 0.39$ rad/sec, the loop-gain is 0 dB, and the phase-lag is $-135°$, resulting in $PM = 45°$ as required. Also, at $\omega = 1$ rad/sec, the gain margin is 13.4 dB. The resulting $L(j\omega)$ is transferred from the Bode diagram to the Nichols chart in Fig.2.3.6 from which we can directly obtain $|T_1(j\omega)|$ and plot its log magnitude

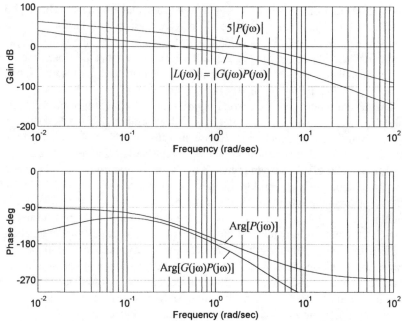

Figure 2.3.5.   Bode plots of $5P(j\omega)$ and the compensated $L(j\omega) = P(j\omega)G(j\omega)$

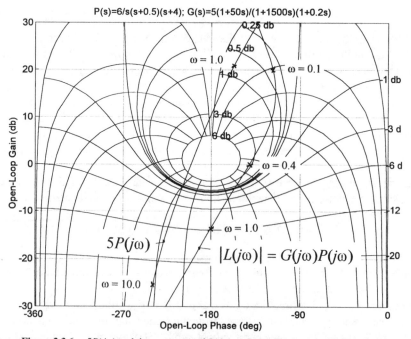

Figure 2.3.6. $5P(j\omega)$ and the compensated $L(j\omega) = P(j\omega)G(j\omega)$ on the Nichols chart.

versus log ω as in Fig. 2.3.7. The maximum unity-feedback peak value is about +3 dB, which satisfies the a priori specifications.

The next example illustrates how a lead-lag compensating network is used to simultaneously achieve desired phase margin and $\omega_{co,}$ but not steady-state error coefficients.

Example 2.3.2.   This example deals with the pitch orientation control system of an aircraft. Suppose that the longitudinal dynamics for elevator displacement of the aircraft are given by $P_1(s) = \theta(s)/\delta_e(s) = (s + 3)/[s(s^2 + 2.8s + 5.3)]$, and that the dynamics of the hydraulic actuator system deflecting the elevators of the aircraft is given by $P_2(s) = \delta_e(s)/V(s) = 5/(s + 10)$ ($V(s)$ is the voltage actuating the actuator). Design a closed-loop feedback system so that the crossover frequency $\omega_{co} = 3$ rad/sec, and that the $PM = 40°$. (No steady-state error coefficients are specified for the closed-loop, since these are inherently nullified by the pilot).

Solution: The Bode plots of the overall system plant

$$P(s) = P_1(s)P_2(s) = 5(s + 3)/[s(s + 10)(s^2 + 2.8s + 5.3)]$$

are shown in Fig.2.3.8. At ω = 3 rad/sec, the gain is $|P(j3)| = -23$ dB, and $\arg[P(j3)] = -175°$. Clearly, if we increase $|L(j\omega)|$ by 23 dB, its magnitude will

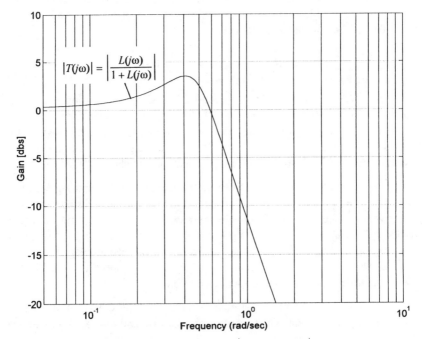

Figure 2.3.7.   Bode plot of $|L(j\omega)/(1+L(j\omega)|$.

be 0 dB at $\omega = 3$ rad/sec, but the phase margin will be only $PM = 5°$, which is insufficient according to the specifications of the problem. We have to add a lead-lag network that will provide at $\omega_{co} = 3$ rad/sec the missing lead-angle needed to increase the PM to at least 40°. We also have to take into consideration the small additional phase-lag that will be contributed by the far-off pole noise filter already mentioned, whose purpose is to limit the sensor noise amplification at high frequencies. Now, let us choose $a = 5$ from Fig.C.4.1 in order to obtain a lead-angle of about 40° at $\omega = 3$ rad/sec. (This choice provides 5° phase-lead reserve for the noise filter to be added later). To fix τ, if we choose $u = 0.3$, then $\tau = u/\omega = 0.3/3 = 0.1$, and the compensating network becomes $G(s) = K(1 + 0.1 \times 5s)/(1 + 0.1s)$, where K is still undefined. To fix K, we have to look once again at Fig.C.4.1, where we find that, since $u = 0.3$ and $a = 5$, the gain will increase by 5 dB at $\omega = 3$ rad/sec. Added to the original -23 dB of $P(j3)$, the magnitude of $|L(j3)|$ at this frequency will amount to $-23 + 5 = -18$ dB. Therefore, an additional increase of the log magnitude by $K = 18$ dB ($= 7.94$) is necessary. Consequently, the lead-lag compensating network becomes

$$G(s) = 7.94(1 + 0.5s)/(1 + 0.1s).$$

Next, we have to add the far-off pole for the high frequency sensor noise attenuation. If we locate this pole at $20\omega_{co}$, then an additional phase-lag of only about 3° will be added at $\omega_{co} = 3$ rad/sec. This is acceptable, because, in the stage of designing the lead-lag network, an intentional reserve of 5° phase-lead was provided. The final compensating network is then

$$G(s) = 7.94(s+0.5)/[(1 + 0.1s)(1 + 0.017s)].$$

The final $L(j\omega)$ is shown in Figs.2.3.8 and 2.3.9. Exact calculations show that $|L(j3)| = 0.05$ dB, and $\arg[L(j3)] = -139°$. This completes the design of the longitudinal pitch control system. The loop transmission $L(j\omega)$ is also shown on the Nichols chart in Fig.2.3.9. One can readily see that the peak value of the closed-loop amounts to $+3$ dB, so that all the specifications are satisfied.

The last two solved examples illustrate the use of lead-lag and lag-lead networks in achieving specified phase margin, together with another specification, such as steady-state error coefficients, or a crossover frequency. In most practical problems, loopshaping is more complicated than what has been observed in the above examples. In general, the combination of several lead and lag compensating networks are used in order to achieve additional design specifications. The following example will demonstrate such a situation.

Example 2.3.3.   This example is similar to that of Example 2.3.1, but some of the specifications are different. The specification $K_v = 15$, and $PM = 40°$ remain unchanged, but, a crossover frequency $\omega_{co} = 1.5$ rad/sec is necessary.

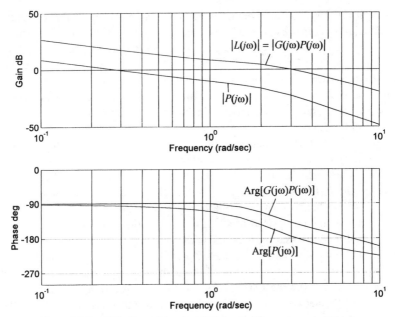

Figure 2.3.8. Bode plots of the plant $P(j\omega)$ and of the compensated $L(j\omega)$.

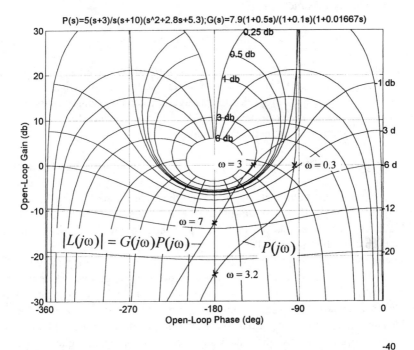

Figure 2.3.9. $P(j\omega)$ and the compensated $L(j\omega)$ on the Nichols chart.

Solution: it is possible to solve this example by using one single lag-lead and one single lead-lag networks. The lag-lead network can be designed to decrease the open-loop transmission magnitude close to zero dB near the specified crossover frequency; the lead-lag network is designed to provide enough phase-lead in the same frequency range in order to satisfy the phase margin specification. In this example, we shall proceed in a somehow different way, in order to make use of a combined lead-lag/lag-lead compensating network (described in Appendix C, and shown in Fig. C.5.4).

Fig.2.3.10 shows the open-loop uncompensated $KP(s)$, where $K = 5$, in order to satisfy the specification of the velocity error coefficient $K_v = 15$. Notice that at $\omega = 1.5$ rad/sec, $5|P(j1.5)| = 9.4$ dB and arg $5P(j1.5) = -182°$. In order to satisfy the $PM = 40°$ specification at that frequency, the combined compensating network has to provide the needed decrease in gain of 9.4 dB, together with an additional phase-lead of $42°$ at $\omega = 1.5$ rad/sec. Looking at Fig.C.5.4a, we see that a compensating network with normalized $z = 1.0$ and $p = 11.2$ is needed while the normalized frequency $u = 3.75$ should be located at $\omega = 1.5$ rad/sec. This means that the center of the combined network will be located at $\omega/u = 1.5/3.75 = 0.4$ rad/sec. For these values, the location of the poles and of the zeros of the network becomes $z = 0.4$ (because the normalized $z = 1.0$), $p_1 = 0.4/11.2$, and $p_2 = 0.4 \times 11.2$. The lead-lag/lag-lead compensating network will accordingly become

$$G_1(s) = 5(s + 0.4)^2 / [(s + 0.4/11.2)(s + 0.4 \times 11.2)].$$

We shall now add the far-off pole of the sensor noise filter, say, at $\omega = 40$ rad/sec, which is sufficiently distanced from the crossover frequency, so that the previously obtained phase margin is not spoiled. (Once again, when choosing the parameters of $G_1(s)$, a deliberate finite reserve in phase-lead can be provided for the noise filter). The final compensating network becomes

$$G(s) = G_1(s)/(1 + s/40) = 5(s + 0.4)^2 / [(s + 0.4/11.2)(s + 0.4 \times 11.2)(1 + s/40)].$$

To find $|T_1(j\omega)|$, locate the obtained $L(j\omega)$ on the Nichols chart in Fig.2.3.11, by reading the values of $|L(j\omega)|$ in dB and arg $L(j\omega)$ in degrees from the Bode plots of Fig.2.3.10 at several relevant frequencies. The resultant plot of $L(j\omega)$ on the Nichols chart enables us to find $|T_1(j\omega)|$ by inspection.

The purpose of Examples 2.3.1 to 2.3.3 was to demonstrate loopshaping procedures. The practical ways to implement the loopshaping process are innumerable, and rely strongly on the designer's experience. Practicing with different examples is mandatory in order to achieve the necessary maturity and a deeper understanding in loopshaping. Math Works has prepared a computerized program called *QFT Toolbox*, for assisting the designer in loopshaping, (Borghesani, Chait and Yaniv 1994).

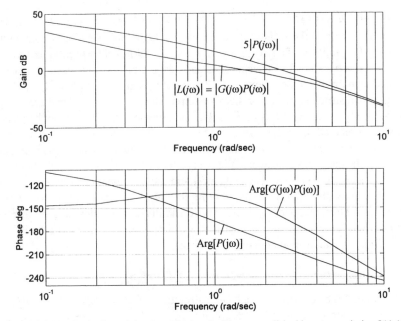

Figure 2.3.10. Bode plots of the plant $P(j\omega)$ and of the accomplished loop transmission $L(j\omega)$.

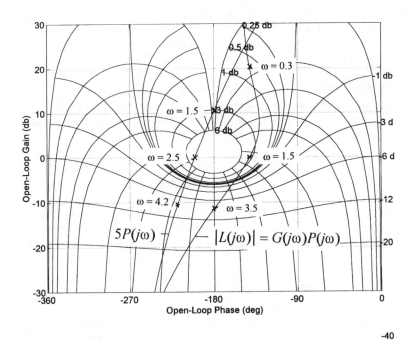

Figure 2.3.11. $P(j\omega)$ and the compensated $L(j\omega)$ on the Nichols chart.

Limitations of one degree-of-freedom feedback systems

As we have seen in the solution of Example 2.3.1, the unity-feedback bandwidth is about 0.7 rad/sec. The resulting $|T_1(j\omega)| = |L(j\omega)/[1+L(j\omega)]|$ shown in Fig.2.3.7 is a byproduct of the specified and designed loop transmission $L(j\omega)$. It has not been predicted or solicited in advance. It was already explained that if the real physical structure of the feedback system is such that no command can be applied directly at the input r as in Fig.2.1.1, then the prefilter $F(s)$ cannot be physically implemented. In such cases, since there is only one network $G(s)$ that can be used for design purposes, $L(s)$ and $T(s)$ cannot be independently specified and achieved. In these circumstances, the design will be based on tradeoffs between the properties of $L(s)$ (*GM, PM, ω_{co}*, etc.) and the specifications on $T(s)$. As explained previously, there is an inherent limitation in the design of such systems, known as ODOF feedback systems. This difficulty can be alleviated by using a prefilter $F(s)$ if the physical structure allows its implementation, thus obtaining for the designer an additional degree-of-freedom.

2.3.6. Design in the Frequency-Domain of TDOF Systems

If the system to be controlled is a TDOF structure, i.e., $F(s)$ can be physically implemented, then the closed-loop log magnitude versus frequency of the transfer function from r to y can be shaped so that it satisfies given specifications. Thus, if $T_1(s) = L(s)/[1+L(s)]$ is known, then the specified $T(s)$ in Eq.(2.1.1) can be achieved by adding the prefilter $F(s)$, since $T(s) = T_1(s)F(s)$. Now it is easily seen that the specifications on the transfer function in Eqs.(2.1.1) can be satisfied exactly and simultaneously with one of the transfer functions in Eqs(2.1.2) to (2.1.7).

Example 2.3.4.   This example is a continuation of Example 2.3.1. Suppose that an additional specification on the closed-loop bandwidth of $|T(j\omega)|$ is to achieve ω_{-3dB} = 1 rad/sec. To accomplish this new requirement, we have to add the prefilter

$$F(s) = \frac{(s^2 + 0.252s + 0.16)(s + 7)(s + 0.14285)}{(s^2 + 1.02s + 0.16)(s + 1)(s + 1)}$$

The final $|T(j\omega)| = |T_1(j\omega)F(j\omega)|$ is shown in Fig.2.3.12, for which $\omega_{-3dB} \approx 1.0$ rad/sec. Note also that the prefilter $F(s)$ might become very complicated, but this is the price that has to be paid in order to satisfy the input-output tracking specifications.

2.4.   Design Tradeoffs in Feedback Systems

The need for design tradeoffs between different system requirements during the shaping process of $L(j\omega)$ is caused by the demand to limit the sensor white noise amplification at the input to the plant, and to reduce the control efforts as much as possible. See Eq.(2.1.4). As already mentioned in Chapter 1, the sensor's noise

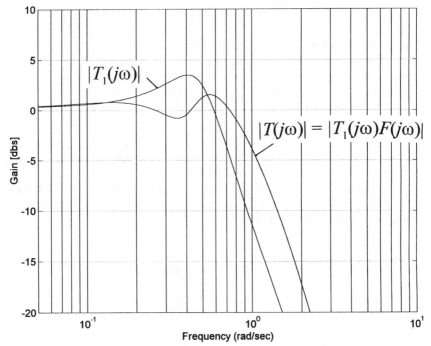

Figure 2.3.12.   Bode plot of $|T(j\omega)| = |T_1(j\omega) F(j\omega)|$.

amplification limits the achievable open-loop bandwidth. If the Root Mean Square (RMS) amplitude of the amplified sensor noise at the plant input is high relative to its inherent saturation level, the noise might saturate the input, and the feedback system will cease to function properly. It may even become unstable.

2.4.1.   The Sensor Noise Amplification Problem In Feedback Systems.

In the present section, we will analyze how the properties of the loop transmission $L(j\omega)$ influence the sensor noise amplification. From Eq.(2.1.4), the amplification of sensor noise at the input to the plant is

$$|T_{un}(j\omega)| = \left| \frac{G(j\omega)}{1 + L(j\omega)} \right| = \left| \frac{1}{P(j\omega)} \frac{L(j\omega)}{1 + L(j\omega)} \right| \qquad (2.4.1)$$

Let us separate the entire frequency range into the following three ranges which are typical of almost all feedback systems:
   (i) low frequency range, where $|L(j\omega)| \gg 1.0$
   (ii) intermediate frequency range, where $|L(j\omega)| \approx 1.0$, and
   (iii) high frequency range, where $|L(j\omega)| \ll 1.0$.

Clearly, in the low frequency range

$$|T_{un}(j\omega)| \approx |1/P(j\omega)|; \quad |L(j\omega)| >> 1. \tag{2.4.2}$$

Thus, the sensor noise amplification in this range is independent of the designed $L(j\omega)$, (as long as $|L(j\omega)| >> 1$), and is solely fixed by the plant characteristics, i.e., the higher its magnitude, the lower the amplification factor will be.

In the high frequency range we can approximate $|T_{un}(j\omega)|$ by

$$|T_{un}(j\omega)| \approx |G(j\omega)| = |L(j\omega)/P(j\omega)|; \quad |L(j\omega)| << 1. \tag{2.4.3}$$

This is the most important range from the sensor noise point of view, because the spectrum of the sensor noise is generally located in this range.

In the intermediate frequency range, if we admit that the loop transmission function does not cross the contours of constant $|T_1(j\omega)| \geq 6$ dB $= 2.0$, then the limit of noise amplification will be

$$|T_{un}(j\omega)| = \left| \frac{G(j\omega)}{1 + L(j\omega)} \right| = \left| \frac{1}{P(j\omega)} \frac{L(j\omega)}{1 + L(j\omega)} \right| \leq \left| \frac{2}{P(j\omega)} \right|. \tag{2.4.4.a}$$

If it also does not penetrate the contours of constant $|S(j\omega)| = |1/[1+L(j\omega)]| \geq 6$dB $= 2.0$, (inverted Nichols chart), then

$$|T_{un}(j\omega)| = \left| \frac{G(j\omega)}{1 + L(j\omega)} \right| = \left| G(j\omega) \frac{1}{1 + L(j\omega)} \right| \leq 2.0|G(j\omega)|. \tag{2.4.4.b}$$

Next we shall use Bode plots to sketch the approximated $|T_{un}(j\omega)|$ in the frequency domain, Fig.2.4.1. In Region 1, the plot of $|T_{un}(j\omega)|$ is approximated by $|1/P(j\omega)|$, while in Region 3 it is approximated by $|G(j\omega)|$.

We distinguish in Figure 2.4.1b between two cases which are $|T_{un}(j\omega)|$ and $|T'_{un}(j\omega)|$. In the first case, $|L(j\omega)|$ crosses $|P(j\omega)|$ at ω_b. It remains below it as ω increases above ω_b. Thus $|T_{un}(j\omega)|$, the log magnitude difference of the two functions, becomes negative in decibels, or smaller than 1, as shown in Fig.2.4.1a. To find the RMS value of the amplified white noise, the area under the solid line belonging to $|T_{un}(j\omega)|$ in linear frequency scale in Fig.2.4.1a is squared and integrated. Since $|T_{un}(j\omega)|$ decreases at least as fast as $1/\omega$ in the range $\omega > \omega_b$, the RMS value emerges finite.

For the case $|T'_{un}(j\omega)|$ (also shown in Fig.2.4.1 by the dotted line at high frequencies), the difference in dB between $|L'(j\omega)|$ and $|P(j\omega)|$ remains **constant** at the high frequency range. Thus, $|T'_{un}(j\omega)|$ is constant in linear frequency scale for the entire high frequency range, and the RMS value of the amplified noise tends to infinity.

The conclusion is that, in order to assure a finite RMS value of the amplified sensor noise reaching the input to the plant, $|L(j\omega)|$ must have a more negative slope than that of $|P(j\omega)|$ beyond some frequency. Since in the high frequency

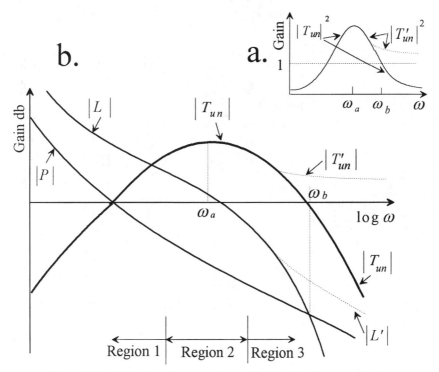

Figure 2.4.1. Generation of sensor noise amplification in the frequency domain.

range $|T_{un}(j\omega)| \approx |L(j\omega)/P(j\omega)| = |G(j\omega)|$, we conclude that $L(s)$ must have a larger excess of poles over zeros than that of $P(s)$, in order that $|T_{un}(j\omega)|$ will drop to zero as $\omega \to \infty$, thus, $G(s)$ must be strictly proper. Moreover, in order to minimize the RMS value of the amplified sensor noise at the input to the plant, we have to keep $|L(j\omega)|$ as small as possible at high frequencies.

2.4.2. RMS Computation of $|T_{un}(j\omega)|$

In order to get some idea of the RMS amplification factor, let us analyze the system in Example 2.3.2. The computed $|T_{un}(j\omega)|$ is shown in Fig.2.4.2, which also shows $|L(j\omega)|$ and $|P(j\omega)|$. To compute the RMS value of the amplified sensor white noise, the square of the magnitude of $|T_{un}(j\omega)|$ is displayed in Fig.2.4.3 on a linear frequency scale. After summing up graphically the area under the $|T_{un}(j\omega)|^2$ plot, we find that

$$|T_{un}(j\omega)|_{RMS} = \left[\frac{1}{\pi} \sum_{\omega} |T_{un}(j\omega)|^2 \right]^{1/2} = 201.6.$$

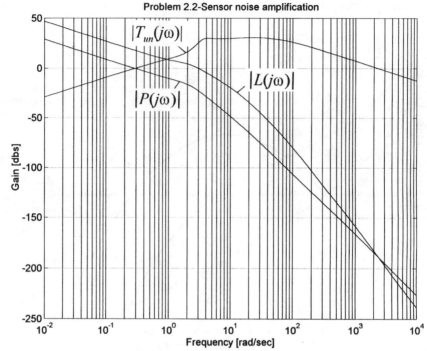

Figure 2.4.2.   Graphical calculation of sensor noise amplification $|T_{un}(j\omega)|$.

The exact calculation using Matlab software amounted to $|T_{un}(j\omega)|_{RMS} = 203.74$.

Note that we have purposely illustrated the white noise amplification problem with the results of Example 2.3.2 in which the magnitude of $L(j\omega)$ is appreciably higher than that of $P(j\omega)$ in a broad frequency range.

2.4.3.   *Optimization of the Loop Transmission Function L(jω)*

The loopshaping process described previously was presented in Examples 2.3.1 to 2.3.4. In each, several specifications were defined and achieved. However, the same results could be achieved with an unlimited choice of different $L(j\omega)$'s. We wish to define here what an optimal loop transmission $L(j\omega)$ is. This aspect will be dealt with in detail in Chapter 4, but it is instructive to explain here some basic facts concerning this optimization problem.

It can be easily concluded from Eqs.(2.1.1) to (2.1.7) that in the frequency range where $|L(j\omega)| > 1.0$ (most likely the low frequency range), the larger $|L(j\omega)|$ is, the better the feedback benefits are. The practical implementation of this optimization criterion is best discerned on the Bode diagram in Fig.2.4.4. Suppose that accord-

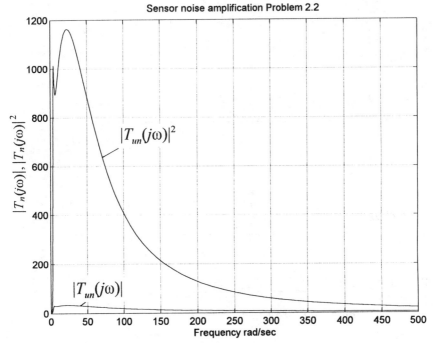

Figure 2.4.3. $|T_{un}(j\omega)|$ and $|T_{un}(j\omega)|^2$ on a linear frequency scale.

ing to the specifications concerning the loop transmission in the frequency-domain, the phase-lag is permitted to be as large as $(-180 + PM)°$ in Fig.2.4.4. We can add to the initially defined loop transmission $L(j\omega)$ a control network $N(s)$ whose basic characteristics in the frequency-domain are displayed in Fig.2.4.5. The theory of such idealized functions is amply described in Bode (1945). Practically, such a characteristic can be approximated by a lag-lead network, (see Fig.C.4.1). Such a network generates a phase-lag that can fill the gap between the line defining the permitted phase-lag value, and the initially achieved arg $L(j\omega)$ in Fig.2.4.4. However, according to the network characteristics in Fig.2.4.5, a simultaneous augmentation of the magnitude of $L(j\omega)$ will be achieved in this frequency range (see 'Improved $|L(j\omega)|$' in Fig.2.4.4). It is clearly seen in Fig.2.4.4 that the magnitude of $L(j\omega)$ is increased in the frequency range ($\omega < \omega_{co}$) in which the initial loop transmission $L(j\omega)$ has a magnitude larger than one, thus increasing the benefits of feedback in this range. An immediate consequence is that the performances of all the transfer functions in Eqs.(2.1.1) to (2.1.7) are improved in this frequency range.

Note that if the improved $L(j\omega)$ crosses the 0 dB line close to the [0 dB, $-180°$] point, then this argumentation may not be locally true, i.e., near ω_{co}. This means that, when 'improving' the open-loop transmission, care must be taken in keeping a satisfactory phase margin.

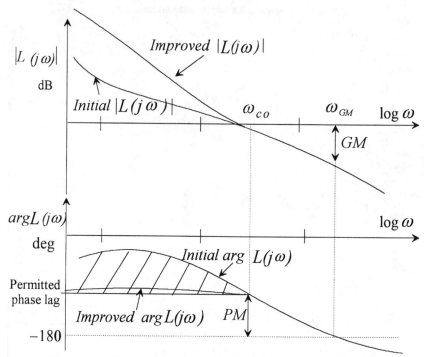

Figure 2.4.4. Implementation of the loop transmission optimization criterion.

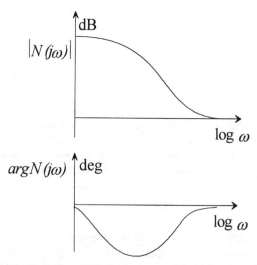

Figure 2.4.5. Bode diagram of a lag-lead network in the frequency-domain.

The gross conclusion is that in order to optimize the loop transmission, *the argument has to exploit the maximum permitted phase-lag* in the frequency range $\omega < \omega_{co}$ as long as the specified phase and gain margins remain satisfied.

2.5. Loopshaping Based on H_∞-Norm Optimization.

The H_∞-optimal control design techniques are introduced via SISO feedback systems. Their use in MIMO systems is treated in Chapter 8.

In the previous sections of this chapter, design of the feedback system was performed directly by shaping the loop transmission function $L(s) = G(s)P(s)$. The return difference $1 + L(s)$ was established as common to all the transfer functions in Eqs.(2.1.1) to (2.1.7). The sensitivity function was defined as $S(s) = 1/[1 + L(s)]$. It also should be remembered that $T_1(s) + S(s) = 1$. By virtue of these facts, it is possible to express the above transfer functions in term of $S(s)$ and $T_1(s)$ (see also Fig.2.1.1).

$$T(s) = F(s)T_1(s) \tag{2.5.1}$$

$$T_{d1}(s) = P(s)S(s) \tag{2.5.2}$$

$$T_d(s) = S(s) \tag{2.5.3}$$

$$T_{un}(s) = -G(s)S(s) = T_{ud}(s) \tag{2.5.4}$$

$$T_1(s) = 1 - S(s) = G(s)P(s)S(s) = -T_{yn}(s) \tag{2.5.5}$$

According to the redefined closed-loop transfer functions in terms of $S(s)$ and $T_1(s)$, it seems possible to design the feedback system by directly shaping the magnitude of these functions.

In this context, some important approximations can be observed,

$$|L(j\omega)| \gg 1 \Rightarrow S(j\omega) \approx 1/L(j\omega); T_1(j\omega) \approx 1$$

$$|L(j\omega)| \ll 1 \Rightarrow S(j\omega) \approx 1; T_1(j\omega) \approx |L(j\omega)|.$$

In the frequency range in which $|L(j\omega)| \approx 1$, no such simplifying relations exist between $T_1(j\omega)$, $S(j\omega)$ and $|L(j\omega)|$. In fact, should the phase-lag of $L(j\omega)$ be too large in the frequency range where this condition exists, (which means that $L(j\omega)$ is too close to $[-1 + j0]$) in the complex plane) large peak values may appear in the closed-loop magnitudes of $S(s)$ and of $T_1(s)$, even if stability is guaranteed. When the loopshaping of $L(j\omega)$ is performed in the Nichols chart, the peak value of $|T_1(j\omega)|$ is detected by inspecting what is the contour of constant $|T_1(j\omega)|$ with maximum value which is tangent to $L(j\omega)$. When the inverted Nichols chart (Fig.2.3.4) is also superimposed on the normal Nichols chart, then the maximum peak value of $|S(j\omega)|$ is similarly detected. Thus, when loopshaping of $L(j\omega)$ is performed on the combined Nichols and inverted Nichols charts, we can control simultaneously both $S(j\omega)$ and $T_1(j\omega)$. However, in the last decade, alternate design approaches have been proposed and extensively used to directly shape the magnitude of closed-loop transfer functions such as $S(s)$, $T_1(s)$ and $T_{un}(s)$. These design approaches are best formulated as an H_∞-loopshaping problem whose solution is obtained by use of standard H_∞-norm optimization algorithms. These can be found in existing commercial software, such as the Robust Control, the μ-Analysis and Synthesis and the LMI Control toolboxes, all belonging to The MATHWORKS, Inc.

2.5.1.   Definition of the H_∞ and H_2 Norms.

H_∞ is a norm, sometimes called the H_∞-norm. It is defined as the peak value $|F(j\omega)|$ of a stable, real-proper, scalar frequency dependent transfer function $F(s)$ (see Appendix B),

$$\|F(s)\|_\infty \overset{def}{=} \max_\omega |F(j\omega)| \qquad (2.5.6)$$

If this function has no maximum, then 'max' can be interchanged with 'sup' (the supremum, or least upper bound). Then, the definition is

$$\|F(s)\|_\infty \overset{def}{=} \sup_\omega |F(j\omega)| \qquad (2.5.6a)$$

This situation is very common in control theory, in cases where the maximum is approached only as $\omega \to 0$. By definition,

$$\max_\omega |F(j\omega)| = \lim_{p \to \infty} \left[\int_{-\infty}^{\infty} |F(j\omega)|^p \, d\omega \right]^{1/p} \qquad (2.5.7)$$

This expression is used to find the maximum magnitude over the frequency ω. When raising $|F(j\omega)|$ to an infinite power, the peak value of $|F(j\omega)|$ is overamplified and more easily detected. The H_∞-norm is in fact the peak (sup) value of the Bode magnitude plot of $F(j\omega)$. The symbol H stands for *Hardy space* (see Garnett 1981 and Appendix B). H_∞ is then the set of **stable, proper** transfer functions with bounded infinity-norm. To remind the reader, $F(s)$ is *stable* if it is analytic in the closed RHP plane; it is *proper* if $\lim_{s \to \infty} F(s) \to Const$ (the order of the numerator is equal to that of the denominator); it is *strictly proper* if $\lim_{s \to \infty} F(s) \to 0$ (the order of the numerator is smaller than that of the denominator); and it is *improper* if $\lim_{s \to \infty} F(s) \to \infty$ (the order of the numerator is greater than that of the denominator).

The H_2 norm, also called the 2-Norm in the text, is defined likewise as

$$\|F(j\omega)\|_2 = \left[\frac{1}{2\pi} \int_{-\infty}^{\infty} |F(j\omega)|^2 d\omega\right]^{1/2} \tag{2.5.8}$$

The following lemma follows for the defined H_2 and the norms H_∞ (see Doyle et.al, 1992).

Lemma 2.5.1: The H_2-norm of $F(s)$ is finite iff $F(s)$ is *strictly proper* and has no poles on the imaginary axis; the H_∞-norm is finite iff $F(s)$ is *proper* and has no poles on the imaginary axis.

Another important property of the H_∞-norm is:

$$\|F_1(s)F_2(s)\|_\infty \le \|F_1(s)\|_\infty \|F_2(s)\|_\infty \tag{2.5.9}$$

The H_∞-optimal design of control systems is performed in the frequency-domain, where the above definitions of norm will be extensively used. However, H_2 and H_∞ norms can be also defined for time-domain functions. Fortunately, by use of Parseval's theorem, relations between the time and the frequency versions of these norms can be found (see Appendix B).

Interpretation of H$_2$ and H$_\infty$ norms in real physical systems

A deterministic interpretation may be seen in the following. Let us suppose that $d(t)$ is the only input to the feedback system of Fig.2.1.1, and that it can be represented as an impulse $d(t) = \delta(t)$. A common objective of the control system in this figure might be to minimize the expected energy of the error $e(t)$ due to the external disturbance $d(t)$. But, in order to prevent excessive amplitude (energy) of the control effort $u(t)$, the *cost function*, or *performance index PI* may be defined in the following way:

$$PI = E\left\{\|e\|_2^2 + \beta^2\|u\|_2^2\right\} = E\left\{\int_0^\infty [\|e\|^2 + \beta^2\|u\|^2]dt\right\}$$

where E is the expectation and β is a scalar parameter that can be chosen so that a compromise is achieved between the error e and the control effort u expectations. In terms of the sensitivity transfer function $S(s)$, Eq.(2.1.3) and $T_{ud}(s)$, Eq.(2.1.6), we can write

$$E\left\{\|e\|_2^2 + \beta^2\|u\|_2^2\right\} = \left\|\begin{matrix} S(j\omega) \\ \beta G(j\omega)S(j\omega) \end{matrix}\right\|_2^2 = \left\|\begin{matrix} S(j\omega) \\ \beta T_{ud}(j\omega) \end{matrix}\right\|_2^2$$

which is a H_2-norm.

Quite different control objectives with real physical systems must sometimes be defined when explicit restrictions on the control effort amplitude must be observed. For instance, in terms of the previous terminology, we may wish to optimize

$$\sup_{\|d\|_2 \leqslant 1} \left\{ \|e\|_2^2 + \beta^2 \|u\|_2^2 \right\} = \left\| \begin{array}{c} S(j\omega) \\ \beta G(j\omega)S(j\omega) \end{array} \right\|_{\infty}^2 = \left\| \begin{array}{c} S(j\omega) \\ \beta T_{ud}(j\omega) \end{array} \right\|_{\infty}^2$$

which is a H_{∞}-norm.

2.5.2. Basic Relative Stability Performance Requirements

Design of feedback system control begins with definition of performance require-ments, such as maximal steady-state errors, speed, overshooting and ringing of the time responses. Some of these requirements are strongly related to the relative sta-bility properties of the feedback system, namely, the gain and phase margins on the Nyquist diagram (Fig.2.3.1) or on the Nichols chart (Figs.2.3.3). It will be shown in Chapter 3 that large peak values in the log magnitude versus frequency plot of a transfer function leads to large overshoots in the step time response, which is generally not acceptable. Therefore, this is a good reason to limit large peaking in the magnitude Bode plot. A look at the Nichols chart in Fig.2.3.3 shows qualitatively that the phase and gain margins decrease as the values of the contours of constant $|T_1|$ increase. In Fig.2.3.3, $L(j\omega)$ is tangent to the 3 dB unity-feedback constant gain contour. For this contour, $PM = 45°$ and $GM = 4$ dB at least. Hence, if $|T_1(j\omega)|_{peak} \leq 3$ dB, it is guaranteed that $PM > 45°$ and $GM > 4$ dB. The inverted Nichols chart in Fig.2.3.4, in which the dotted curves are contours of constant $|S(j\omega)|$, shows in a similar way that a maximum peak value of 3 dB in $|S(j\omega)|$ guar-antees that $PM > 45°$ and $GM > 11$dB. In other words, relative stability proper-ties can be expressed in terms of $|S(j\omega)|_{max}$ as well in terms of $|T_1(j\omega)|_{max}$.

Gain and phase margins in terms of $|T_1(j\omega)|_{max}$

1- Gain Margin (*GM*):
The gain margin of $L(j\omega)$ is defined at ω_{GM} where $\arg L(j\omega_{GM}) = -180°$. Hence $L(j\omega_{GM})$ is real and negative. The unity-feedback magnitude is then

$$|T_1(j\omega)| = \left| \frac{-L(j\omega_{GM})}{1 - L(j\omega_{GM})} \right| = \frac{L(j\omega_{GM})}{1 - L(j\omega_{GM})}.$$

Since $L(j\omega_{GM})$ is real, $GM = 1/L(j\omega_{GM})$ by definition. It readily follows that for any unity-feedback constant gain contour $|T_1(j\omega)|$,

$$GM = 1 + 1/|T_1(j\omega)|.$$

As a result, the minimum gain margin is expressed by the following equation:

$$GM \geq 1 + 1/|T_1(j\omega)|_{max} \qquad (2.5.10)$$

If *GM* and $|T_1(j\omega)|$ are expressed in dB, then it follows that:

$$GM[dB] \geq 20 \log_{10}\left[1 + 1/\text{antilog}_{10}\left(\frac{|T_1|_{max}[dB]}{20}\right)\right] \qquad (2.5.10a)$$

2-Phase Margin (*PM*):
To find the phase margin, remember that at ω_{co}, $|L(j\omega)_{co})| = 1 = 0$ dB, hence,

$$T_1 = \frac{e^{j\phi(\omega)}}{1 + e^{j\phi(\omega)}} = \frac{1}{1 + e^{-j\phi(\omega)}}; \phi(\omega) = \arg L(j\omega_{co}).$$

From the above equation, together with the relation $PM + \phi(\omega) = \pi$, it follows that:

$$|T_1|^2 = \frac{1}{2[1 + \cos\phi(\omega)]} = \frac{1}{2[1 - \cos(PM)]} = \frac{1}{4\sin^2(PM/2)}.$$

Consequently, for a unity-feedback system in which $|T_1|_{max}$ is known, we find that the minimum phase margin is equal to:

$$PM \geq 2\sin^{-1}\left[\frac{1}{2|T_1|_{max}}\right][rad] \qquad (2.5.11)$$

For instance, if $|T_1|_{max}$ [dB] = 3dB, then $|T_1|_{max} = 1.4125$. From Eqs.(2.5.10) and (2.5.11) we find that $PM > 41.46^0$ and that $GM[dB] > 4.649$dB. Check graphically these results in Fig.C.6.2.

Gain and phase margins in terms of $|S(j\omega)|_{max}$
1-Gain Margin (*GM*):
To calculate the gain margin in terms of $|S(j\omega)|_{max}$ we find that,

$$S(j\omega) = \frac{1}{1 - |L(j\omega_{GM})|} = \frac{1}{1 - \dfrac{1}{GM}}$$

from which it follows that for a given contour of constant $|S(j\omega)|$, the gain margin is:

$$GM = \frac{|S|}{|S|-1}.$$

Finally, for a known $|S(j\omega)|_{max}$, the minimum gain margin is expressed by the following equation:

$$GM \geq \frac{|S(j\omega)|_{max}}{|S(j\omega)|_{max} - 1}$$ (2.5.12)

In decibel units, the above equation becomes:

$$GM[dB] > 20 \log_{10} \frac{\text{antilog}_{10} \dfrac{|S|_{max}[dB]}{20}}{\text{antilog}_{10} \dfrac{|S|_{max}[dB]}{20} - 1}$$ (2.5.12a)

2- Phase Margin (*PM*):
  Since $|L(j\omega_{co})| = 1$, we can write

$$S(j\omega) = \frac{1}{1 + e^{j\phi(\omega)}} = \frac{1}{1 + \cos(\phi) + j \sin(\phi)}$$

from which it is easily derived that:

$$|S(j\omega)|^2 = \frac{1}{2[1+\cos(\phi)]} = \frac{1}{2[1+\cos(\pi-PM)]} =$$

$$= \frac{1}{2[1-\cos(PM)]} = \frac{1}{4 \sin^2(PM/2)},$$

so that, for any given $|S(j\omega)|_{max}$, the minimum phase margin is:

$$PM \geq 2 \sin^{-1} \left[\frac{1}{2|S(j\omega)|_{max}} \right]$$ (2.5.13)

For instance, if $|S|_{max} = 3dB$, then by Eqs.(2.5.12a) and (2.5.13) we get $PM > 41.46^0$ and $GM[dB] > 10.69$ dB. Check graphically these results in Fig.C.6.3.
  The relations in Eqs.(2.5.10), to (2.5.13) are important because they allow us to translate gain and phase margins to maximum admissible peak values of the magnitudes of the sensitivity transfer function $S(s)$ and also of the unity-feedback transfer function $T_1(s)$.

Remark. Eqs.(2.5.11) and (2.5.13) are solvable for $|T_1|_{max} > 0.5 = -6dB$ and for $|S|_{max} > 0.5 = -6dB$ respectively. This means that if $|T_1|_{max} < -6dB$ or $|S|_{max} < -6dB$, no phase margin exists. This fact is also clearly discerned in Figs.C.6.2 and C.6.3.

2.5.3. Weighted Sensitivity

The sensitivity function $S(s)$ is most important in feedback system design because it takes care of several design performance requirements. First, as its name indicates, changes in the input-output transfer function $T_1(s)$ due to uncertainties of the plant $P(s)$ depend directly on $S(s)$ (Bode 1945). The tracking error in following a reference command input also depends on $S(s)$. As we have already seen in the last section, relative stability directly depends on the peak value $|S(j\omega)|_{max}$. Moreover, disturbance attenuation properties also depends on $S(s)$ (see Eq.(2.5.3)).

To conclude, we ideally desire a sensitivity function with small magnitude in a relevant frequency range. For the above mentioned performances, we need to consider only its magnitude; the phase is of a lesser importance. Generally, $|S(j\omega)|$ is constrained to be small at low frequencies, but gradually tends to increase to unity as ω increases to ∞ for systems in which the loop transmission function $L(s)$ is strictly proper, a condition satisfied for most practical systems. A typical specification on $S(s)$ may be

$$\|S(j\omega)\|_\infty \leq M, \tag{2.5.14}$$

which complies with many system requirements. Nonetheless, this inequality is not sufficiently well defined. For instance, when the disturbance attenuation is considered, the frequency range in which $|S(j\omega)|$ is to be small depends on the frequency spectrum of the external disturbance signal. In practical terms, at frequencies in which the disturbance is large, $|S(j\omega)|$ must be small. In other words, M in Eq.(2.5.14) has to be frequency dependent. Moreover, it will be seen in Chapters 4 and 8, where highly uncertain plant feedback systems are considered, that quantitatively defined specifications on the sensitivity of the transfer function $T(s)$ to known plant uncertainties in $P(s)$ is guaranteed by achieving an adequately specified frequency dependent $|S(j\omega)|$. We are thus forced to specify a weighting function $W_S(j\omega)$ related to $S(j\omega)$, such that

$$|S(j\omega)| < 1/|W_S(j\omega)|; \quad \forall \omega. \tag{2.5.15}$$

The above equation is equivalent to satisfying the H_∞-norm inequality

$$\|W_S(j\omega)S(j\omega)\|_\infty < 1. \tag{2.5.16}$$

Therefore, the performance requirement is that the H_∞-norm of the weighted sensitivity function $W_S(j\omega) S(j\omega)$ will be smaller than 1. The above problem of optimizing the sensitivity function $S(j\omega)$ by H_∞-norm optimization was first proposed by Zames (1979). $|W_S(j\omega)|$ has a practical meaning. Since, according to the definition, $S(s) = 1/[1 + L(s)]$, we derive from Eq.(2.5.15) that (see also Doyle et al. 1992),

$$|1+L(j\omega)| > |W_S(j\omega)|. \tag{2.5.17}$$

But also, since $1 + |L(j\omega)| > |1 + L(j\omega)|$, we find that $1 + |L(j\omega)| > |W_S(j\omega)|$ and finally,

$$|L(j\omega)| > -1 + |W_S(j\omega)|. \tag{2.5.18}$$

We note in Fig.2.5.1 that according to Eq.(2.5.18), $L(j\omega)$ on the complex plane must be at each frequency ω outside a circle of radius $|W_S(j\omega)|$ centered at $[-1 + j0]$. Since $L(s)$ is assumed to be strictly proper ($|L(j\omega)| \to 0$ as $\omega \to \infty$), there must be a high frequency ω_h beyond which $|W_S(j\omega_h)| < 1$.

It will be later seen that appropriate weighting functions $W_1(s)$ and $W_{un}(s)$ can be defined for achieving desired specifications for other system transfer functions, such as $T_1(s)$ and $T_{un}(s)$ respectively.

2.5.4.   *Mixed Sensitivity*

The requirement $\|W_S(j\omega)S(j\omega)\|_\infty < 1$ is not the only one of interest when performances of a feedback system are defined. In general, the control engineer is interested in specifying and realizing all the seven (!) transfer functions in Eqs.(2.1.1) to (2.1.7) (The relative importance of each one was outlined at the end of Section 2.1). We may be interested in achieving simultaneously, for instance, the three H_∞-norms

$$\|W_S(j\omega)S(j\omega)\|_\infty < 1; \quad \|W_{un}(j\omega)T_{un}(j\omega)\|_\infty < 1; \quad \|W_1(j\omega)T_1(j\omega)\|_\infty < 1. \quad (2.5.19)$$

This is definitely impossible if the "<" sign is exchanged with the "=" sign, because, in a one-degree-of-freedom feedback system, only one compensator, $G(s)$

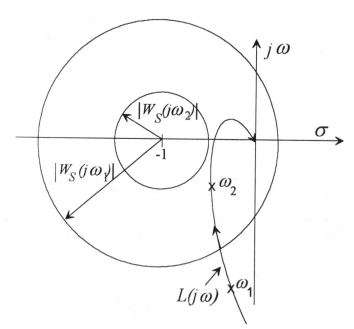

Figure 2.5.1.   Acceptable specifications on $S(j\omega)$ at ω_1 and at ω_2.

in Fig.2.1.1, is at our disposal for design purposes. The designer then has to compromise between partial achievements of the different specifications. Tradeoff is a common practice without which no engineering design can be completed.

Mixed sensitivity is a way of obtaining a design when more than one specification is to be achieved in a ODOF feedback system. In this case, we can define the specifications in a stacked vector form, in which all the important specifications in term of weighting functions are mixed together. For example,

$$\mathbf{PV} = \begin{bmatrix} W_S(j\omega)S(j\omega) \\ W_{un}(j\omega)T_{un}(j\omega) \\ W_1(j\omega)T_1(j\omega) \end{bmatrix} = \begin{bmatrix} W_S(j\omega)S(j\omega) \\ W_{un}(j\omega)G(j\omega)S(j\omega) \\ W_1(j\omega)P(j\omega)G(j\omega)S(j\omega) \end{bmatrix}. \quad (2.5.20)$$

We have in this case a *mixed sensitivity specification* (Verma and Jonckheere 1984, Skogestad and Postlethwaite 1996). In this and future discussions, all weighting functions are assumed to be stable and minimum phase. For SISO feedback systems, an Euclidean vector norm can be used for the overall design specification

$$\|\mathbf{PV}(j\omega)\|_\infty = \max_\omega \sqrt{|W_S S|^2 + |W_{un}T_{un}|^2 + |W_1 T_1|^2} < 1. \quad (2.5.21)$$

With this definition of the different weighting functions and of the performance vector **PV,** the H_∞ optimal controller $G(s)$ is obtained by solving the minimization problem

$$\underset{G(s)}{\text{minimize}} \; \|\mathbf{PV}(G)\|_\infty \quad (2.5.22)$$

where $G(s)$ is the stabilizing controller at our disposal. In the MIMO case treated in Chapter 8, **PV** is a matrix, and principal gains (frequency dependent singular values, Appendix B), are used to measure magnitudes of this matrix.

The solution of the inequalities in Eq.(2.5.19) is not exactly the solution of Eq.(2.5.21) which is both more attractive from a mathematical point of view and also more conservative. This is especially pronounced when the three involved functions have their peak values approximately at the same frequency. If n specified requirements are involved in Eq. (2.5.21), then the solution per Eq.(2.5.22) may cause an error in the achieved individual specifications by a factor of $n^{1/2}$, at most.

Remember that the three transfer functions $S(s)$, $T_1(s)$ and $T_{un}(s)$ include in their expressions the plant $P(s)$, which is regarded as being known and fixed (no uncertainties). The compensator $G(s)$ is an output of a solution by the optimization process in Eq.(2.5.22), which can be performed by any existing H_∞-norm optimization algorithm, for instance, the *hinfsyn* of μ-Analysis and Synthesis TOOLBOX or the *hinf* of Robust Control TOOLBOX. Both belong to The MATHWORKS Inc.

To summarize, *The basic problem of this design philosophy is to select correctly the weighting functions so that optimization of the performance vector (or matrix in MIMO systems) will lead to a controller G(s) that satisfies in the best way all the system design requirements.*

2.5.5.   The Standard H_∞-Regulator Problem.

The *mixed sensitivity problem* defined in the last section is a special case of the so-called Standard H_∞-Regulator Problem introduced by Doyle (1983). Excellent theoretical treatment on the subject can be found in Kwakernaak (1993) and Skogestad and Postletwaite (1996). In this section, a short explanation of the problem and its generality follow.

The design philosophy of the standard regulator problem is best introduced with the mixed sensitivity problem formulated in the previous section. To formulate the problem, the TDOF canonical feedback structure in Fig.2.1.1 is modified to that in Fig.2.5.2, to which are added the weighting functions W_S, W_1 and W_{un}, as well as those of W_d and W_n which model the disturbance d and the sensor noise n properties. In this context, the weighting functions are chosen to define the design objectives. In the present and future sections, W_d and W_n are assumed without loss of generality to be equal to 1, in order to simplify the writing of the equations.

In the structure of Fig.2.5.2, there exist three newly defined outputs z_1, z_2 and z_3 pertinent to the three inputs r_1, d and n. With the relieving assumption that $W_d = W_n = 1$, the equation of these outputs become:

$$z_1(s) = -S(s)\, W_S(s)\, d(s) \tag{2.5.23a}$$

$$z_2(s) = -G(s)\, S(s)\, W_{un}(s)\, n(s) = -T_{un} W_{un}\, n(s) \tag{2.5.23b}$$

$$z_3(s) = T_1(s)\, W_1(s)\, r_1(s)\; (= T_1 W_1\, r(s) \text{ if } F(s) = 1). \tag{2.5.23c}$$

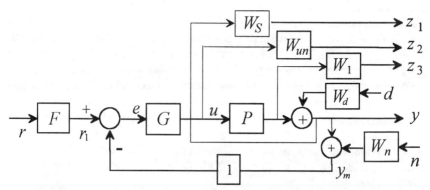

Figure 2.5.2.   Feedback structure of the standard mixed sensitivity regulator problem.

With the adapted canonical system structure in Fig.2.5.2, we can define an input vector

$$\mathbf{w}(s) = \text{col } [d(s), n(s), r_1(s)]$$

and a weighted output vector

$$\mathbf{z}(s) = \text{col } [z_1(s), z_2(s), z_3(s)].$$

The signal vector $\mathbf{z}$ is in fact a system error vector to be minimized as per Eq.(2.5.22). In an ODOF feedback system, Eqs.(2.5.23) can be also derived in terms of one sole input d, n or r_1. If we decide on $w = d$, then,

$$z_1(s) = -S(s) W_S(s) d(s) \tag{2.5.24a}$$

$$z_2(s) = -G(s) S(s) W_{un}(s) d(s) = -T_{un} W_{un} d(s) \tag{2.5.24b}$$

$$z_3(s) = -T_1(s) W_1(s) d(s) \tag{2.5.24c}$$

which are identical to Eqs.(2.5.23), except for the $(-)$ sign in the equation for $z_3(s)$. The signs are of no importance when the norm of a vector is dealt with. With the above definitions, the structure in Fig.2.5.2 can be represented as in Fig.2.5.3, in which a generalized plant $\mathbf{M}(s)$ is defined. The structure in Fig.2.5.3 has a more general interpretation than just the mixed sensitivity problem. It can also deal with the 'robustness' problem treated in Chapter 4. Although the structure in Fig.2.5.3 applies as well to a MIMO control feedback system, in the context of this chapter and Chapter 4, the SISO case is intended.

The generalized plant $\mathbf{M}(s)$ in Fig.2.5.3 can be interpreted as an augmented (generalized) plant in which $\mathbf{w}(s)$ is a vector of external inputs (such as $r(s)$ $d(s)$, $n(s)$ in Fig.2.5.2); $u(s)$ is the control signal at the input to the SISO plant; $\mathbf{z}(s)$ is a vector of weighted external outputs (system errors which define $\mathbf{PV}$ in Eq.(2.5.20)); and e is

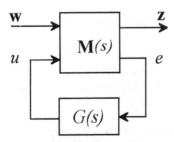

Figure 2.5.3. A canonical structure of the standard H_∞-regulator problem.

the sensed error fed to the controller $G(s)$. (In the MIMO feedback system to be treated in a subsequent chapter, u and e become vectors too.)

Having defined the vector $\mathbf{z}$, whose norm is to be minimized, we can next give an analytical formulation for the augmented plant $\mathbf{M}(s)$ in Fig.2.5.3 in terms of its input and output variables:

$$z_1(s) = W_S(s)[w + P(s)u] \tag{2.5.25a}$$

$$z_2(s) = W_{un}(s)u \tag{2.5.25b}$$

$$z_3(s) = W_1(s)\,P(s)u \tag{2.5.25c}$$

$$e = -w - y = -w - P(s)u. \tag{2.5.25d}$$

Even in the SISO feedback problem, $\mathbf{M}(s)$ is a matrix, so that its inputs and outputs are vectors. We can write for the SISO case

$$\begin{bmatrix} z \\ e \end{bmatrix} = \begin{bmatrix} \mathbf{M}_{11} & \mathbf{M}_{12} \\ M_{21} & M_{22} \end{bmatrix} \begin{bmatrix} w \\ u \end{bmatrix} \tag{2.5.26}$$

in which w and u are scalars, hence,

$$\mathbf{z} = \mathbf{M}_{11}\, w + \mathbf{M}_{12}\, u \tag{2.5.27a}$$

$$e = M_{21}\, w + M_{22}\, u. \tag{2.5.27b}$$

By Eqs.(2.5.25) and Fig.2.5.2, we can find that:

$$\mathbf{M}_{11} = \begin{bmatrix} W_S \\ 0 \\ 0 \end{bmatrix};\ \mathbf{M}_{12} = \begin{bmatrix} W_S P \\ W_{un} \\ W_1 P \end{bmatrix};\ M_{21} = -1;\ M_{22} = -P.$$

The formulation of $\mathbf{M}(s)$ for the MIMO case is treated likewise in Section 8.3.1, where $\mathbf{M}_{21}$ and $\mathbf{M}_{22}$ are also matrices. Finally, we can define the input-output relation in transfer function matrix form

$$\mathbf{z} = \mathbf{T}_{wz}\, \mathbf{w} \tag{2.5.28}$$

$\mathbf{T}_{wz}$ includes the augmented plant $\mathbf{M}(s)$ as well as the controller $G(s)$. The general control problem is then to find the controller $G(s)$ (a transfer function matrix $\mathbf{G}(s)$ in the MIMO case, Chapter 8) which minimizes the H_∞-norm of the transmission from $\mathbf{w}$ to $\mathbf{z}$, Eq.(2.5.22), or, formally,

$$\underset{G(s)}{\text{minimize}} \parallel \mathbf{T}_{wz} \parallel_\infty. \tag{2.5.29}$$

2.5.6.   *Weighting Function Selection*

Selection for the different weighting functions in Eq.(2.5.20) or (2.5.21) is the initial stage in a feedback system design. This is done on the basis of performance specifications defined by the customer. For instance, for a known spectrum of turbulent disturbances on an aircraft, an attenuation factor of the output variable can be specified at different frequencies, thus putting extremal limits on $|S(j\omega)|$. By also fixing its higher corner frequency, we can specify completely $S(j\omega)$, therefore, $W_S(s)$ can be explicitly defined. Moreover, in order to guarantee permitted steady-state errors in following different types of external command inputs, appropriate specifications on $|S(j\omega)|$ have to be prescribed, so that $W_S(s)$ can be accordingly manipulated to its final form. (An additional important requirement on $S(s)$ will be defined in the context of the sensitivity function as defined by Bode, Eq.(2.2.2), when the TDOF uncertain plant feedback system problem will be solved in Chapters 4 and 8). Selection of $W_1(s)$ is based on desired tracking properties of $T_1(j\omega)$, which cannot be achieved independently of $S(j\omega)$ because of the constraining identity $S(j\omega) + T_1(j\omega) = 1$. The designer can find some reasonable way to define a compatible $T_1(s)$ (hence also a compatible $W_1(s)$ that limits the achievable performances of $T_1(s)$ in the frequency-domain). However, the obtained $T_1(s)$ will be an outcome of the H_∞-optimization process. $W_{un}(s)$ can be initially equated to one, unless some special constraints require an appropriate definition for this weighting function. For instance, suppose that the sensor measuring the output of the system is very noisy in a particular frequency range. In this case, $W_{un}(s)$ will be appropriately defined such as to minimize the amplification of the sensor noise at the input u to the plant $P(s)$ in this problematic frequency range.

Practical and formal formulation of weighting functions is attempted in Example 2.5.1.

2.5.7.   *H $_\infty$-Norm Solution of the Mixed Sensitivity Problem*

Solution of the mixed sensitivity problem as mathematically defined by Eq.(2.5.22) can be performed in the frequency-domain or in the state-space frameworks, with two different types of optimizing algorithms. Sophisticated software algorithms are widely described in numerous papers in the literature. Two of them are specially recommended to the reader: Kwakernaak (1990b) for the frequency-domain approach and Doyle et al.(1989) for the state-space approach. For the latter case, software algorithms are formalized in the "μ-Analysis and Synthesis Toolbox" (μ-TOOLS) (Balas et al., 1991). This commercial software package is today extensively used by scientists and engineers in solving the Standard H_∞-Regulator Problem and will be also used in the present book. The theoretical basis for such optimizing algorithms is outlined in Chapter 8.

The solution of the mixed sensitivity control problem by H_∞-norm optimization is next illustrated by Example 2.5.1.

Example 2.5.1.   A mixed sensitivity problem.

The plant transfer function is: $P(s) = 5/[(s + 1)(s + 0.1)]$. The closed-loop system requirements are:

1- Velocity error constant $K_V = 10$.

2- Sensitivity function bandwidth $\omega_{S:-3dB} = 5$rad/sec.

3- $PM > 40^0$ (according to Eq.(2.5.13) this means $|S(j\omega)|_{max} < 1.46 = 3.3$ dB)

4- $|T_1(j\omega)|_{max} < 1.3 = 2.3$ dB.

5- Bandwidth of the unity-feedback $|T_1(j\omega)|$ is to be: $\omega_{-3dB} = 8$rad/sec.

6- Keep sensor white noise amplification $|T_{un}(j\omega)|$ as small as possible.

Solution:

Stage 1. Definition of the sensitivity weighting function: $W_S(s)$.

$S(s)$ is defined from the first three requirements. We next have to find $1/W_S(j\omega)$. Since a finite K_V is necessary and the plant does not contain an integrator, the compensator $G(s)$ must comprise an integrator. Hence,

$$\lim_{s \to 0} L(s) = \frac{K_V}{s}$$

$$\lim_{s \to 0} S(s) = \lim_{s \to 0} \frac{1}{1 + L(s)} = \frac{s}{K_V}$$

This asymptote will cut the 0dB axis at $\omega = 10$ rad/sec $> \omega_{S:-3dB} = 5$rad/sec. To achieve $\omega_{S:-3dB} = 5$rad/sec and $|S(j\omega)|_{max} < 1.46 = 3.3$dB, use the following function

$$S(s) = \frac{s\left(1+\dfrac{s}{a}\right)}{10\left(1+\dfrac{s}{b}\right)^2}$$

where a and b are calculated from the requirements that $|S(j\omega)|_{max} = 1/|W_S(j\omega)|_{max} < 1.46 = 3.3$ dB and $|S(j5)| = 1/|W_S(j5)| = -3$dB $= 0.707$. It is easily found that an appropriate $W_S(s)$ can be:

$1/ W_S(s) = s(1 + s/2.13)/[10(1 + s/5.58)^2]$; $1/ |W_S(j\omega)|$ is shown in Fig.2.5.4.

Stage 2. Definition of the input-output tracking weighting function $W_1(s)$.

$1/W_1(j\omega)$ must be chosen such that the maximum peak value of the unity-feedback transfer function is smaller than 1.3 (=2.3dB). However, at very low frequencies its magnitude should be equal to 1 (0dB). Since we have admitted one integrator in the loop transmission function $L(s)$, the last requirement will be automatically fulfilled even if the only restriction on $|T_1(j\omega)|$ is

$$|T_1(j\omega)| = 1/|W_1(j\omega)| < 1.3 = 2.3\text{db}.$$

Since the plant has two more poles than zeros, and we wish the compensator $G(s)$ to be strictly proper in order to guarantee adequate attenuation of sensor noise at the input to the plant, $L(s)$ must have three more poles than zeros. With this assumption, $T_1(s)$ will have a roll-off rate of -3 at high frequencies (corresponding to a slope of -60 dB/dec). Finally, the form of $T_1(s)$ can be chosen as:

$$T_1(s) = 1.3/[(1 + s/a)(1 + s/b)(1 + s/c)].$$

To achieve also the closed-loop bandwidth requirement of $\omega_{-3dB} = 8$ rad/sec, along with the already mentioned restrictions, it is found that $1/W_1(s) = T_1(s) = 1.3/[(1+ s/6)(1 + s/20)(1 + s/30)]$ is a good choice. $1/|W_1(j\omega)|$ is shown in Fig.2.5.5.

Stage 3. Definition of the control effort weighting function: $1/W_{un}(s)$.

In this example, let us assume that there are no special requirements on $1/W_{un}(s)$, so that we can choose $W_{un}(s) = 1$.

Stage 4. Solution of the H_∞- control design.

The solution was performed using the μ-Tools algorithm *hinfsyn*, and it comes out with a control-law based on output feedback (see Doyle et al. 1989). The program listing is shown in Table 2.5.1. The achieved suboptimal compensator $G(s)$ is:

$$G(s) = \frac{80000\ (s +100)(s^2 + 200s + 100.16)(s + 3)(s + 1)(s + 0.1)}{(s + 6091)(s^2 + 209s + 10972)(s + 91.17)(s + 13.74)(s + 2.13)(s + 0.001)}$$

Stage 5. Evaluation of the solution.

In this context, it is also interesting to solve the same example by classical design procedures using the Nichols and the inverted Nichols charts, together with the usual Bode diagram. A simple compensator was achieved, namely,

$$G(s)_{clas} = 2000(s + 0.1)(s + 1)/[s(s + 20)(s + 50)].$$

(The specified and achieved transfer functions with the H_∞-norm optimization are marked in the resulting plots with the subscript H_∞, namely, $(\_)_{H\infty}$. The subscript *clas* in $(\_)_{clas}$ stands for *classical*.)

$|S(j\omega)|$, $|T_1(j\omega)|$, $|L(j\omega)|$, $\arg L(j\omega)$ and the time responses for both classical and H_∞ solutions are shown in Figs.2.5.4 to 2.5.7. As seen in Figs.2.5.4 and 2.5.5, the defined specifications $1/W_S(j\omega)$ and $1/W_1(j\omega)$ cannot both be perfectly achieved since $T_1(j\omega)$ and $S(j\omega)$ are related, $T_1 + S = 1$. As seen in the figures, the classical solution comes out with higher bandwidths in $|S(j\omega)|$ as well as in $|T_1(j\omega)|$, but, both solutions are quite satisfactory.

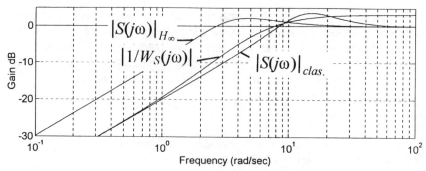

Figure 2.5.4. Sensitivity specifications and resulting
Bode plots for both classical and H_∞ control designs.

The RMS sensor noise amplification from n (white noise) to $u(s)$ was also cal-
culated and found to be equal to $|T_{un}(j\omega)|_{H_\infty}$ (RMS) $= 767.431$. The calculated
sensor noise amplification of the classical design is $|T_{un}(j\omega)|_{clas}$(RMS) $= 181.2$,
which is sensibly lower than that obtained with the H_∞ solution. As shown in
Fig.2.5.7, the reason is that $L(j\omega)_{H_\infty}$ attains at the high frequency range a slope that
is less negative than the slope of $L(j\omega)_{clas}$. Actually, after the H_∞-control solution
is accomplished, it is recommended to fine tune using classical design principles
and to increase the negative slope of $|L(j\omega)|_{H_\infty}$ at high frequencies without deteri-
orating the achieved performances at the operative frequency range. This may
mean adding additional far-off poles with the final objective of decreasing the effect of sensor noise amplification at the input to the plant. This approach is applied
in solving the problems in Chapters 4 and 8.

Fig.2.5.8 shows the output responses $y_{in}(t)_{H_\infty}$ and $y_{in}(t)_{clas}$ to a unit-step command input r_1, and the output responses $y_{dist}(t)_{H_\infty}$ and $y_{dist}(t)_{clas}$ to a unit-step disturbance input d.

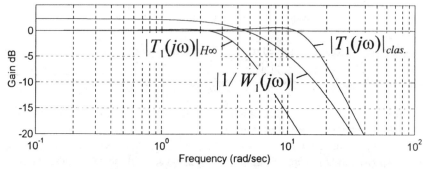

Figure 2.5.5. Bode plots of specifications on $\log |T_1|$ and of the resulting $\log |T_1| = \log |L/(1+L)|$
for both classical and H_∞- control designs.

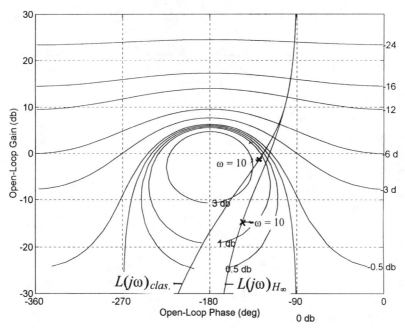

Figure 2.5.6. $L(j\omega)_{clas}$ and $L(j\omega)_{H_\infty}$ on the inverted Nichols chart for both classical and control designs.

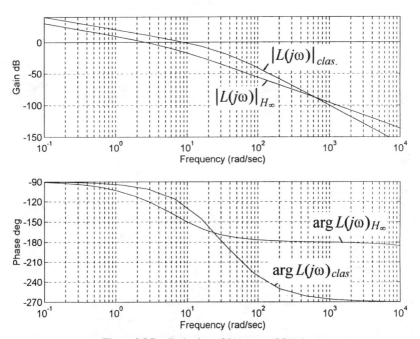

Figure 2.5.7. Bode plots of $L(j\omega)_{clas}$ and $L(j\omega)_{H_\infty}$.

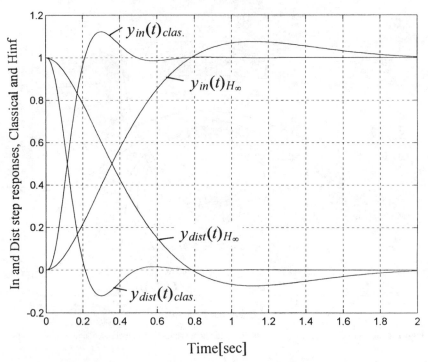

Figure 2.5.8.   Output time responses for reference command and for disturbance input steps.

Remark.   If the prefilter $F(s)$ in Fig.2.5.2 can be physically implemented, the achieved unity-feedback $|T_1(j\omega)|$ can be modified to satisfy a specified input-output tracking specification $|T(j\omega)| = |T_1(j\omega)|\,|F(j\omega)|$, exactly as it was done in the classical Nyquist/Bode oriented design techniques.

2.6.   Classical versus Modern H_∞-Norm Loopshaping.

In the present chapter, feedback control was approached by classical and modern design techniques. In both design paradigms, a control network $G(s)$ was sought to shape the loop transmission function $L(s) = P(s)G(s)$, so that initially specified closed-loop performances are achieved. Some major differences exist between both approaches. In the classical approach, the closed-loop specifications are achieved by directly shaping the loop transmission function $L(j\omega)$ by Nyquist/Bode/Nichols oriented design procedures. With this approach, the design process is very transparent to the designer; by using the Bode plots and the Nichols chart, both open- and closed-loop properties are under the designer's control during the loopshaping process. On the other hand, the modern H_∞-feedback control design procedure consists in defin-

Table 2.5.1.   Matlab program for designing the H$_\infty$-suboptimal controller $G(s)$.

%Hinf solution of Example 2.5.1;%mu251.m; 20 december 1997
%Plant = $G = 5/(s + 0.1)(s + 1)$
%Ws = $10(1 + s/5.58)^2/(s + 0.001)(1 + s/2.13)$
%Wt = $(1 + s/6)(1 + s/20)(1 + s/30)/1.3(1 + s/100)^3$
%Wu = 1
%computation of G, Wt and Ws
ng = [1];dg = [1   1.1   0.1];
G = nd2sys(ng, dg ,5);%plant
nws = 10*[1/5.58^2   2/5.18 1]; dws = [1/2.13   1 + 0.001/2.13   0.001];
Ws = nd2sys(nws, dws, 1.0);
nwt = 213.7*[1 56 900 3600]; dwt = [1 300 3e + 4 1e + 6];
Wt = nd2sys(nwt, dwt, 1/1.3);
Wu = 1;
%end
%preparation of generalized plant P;
systemnames = 'G Wt Wu Ws';
inputvar = '[w(1); u(1)]';
outputvar =' [Wt; Wu; Ws; w - G]';
input_to_G =' [u]';
input_to_Wt =' [G]';
input_to_Wu =' [u]';
input_to_Ws =' [G - u]';
sysoutname =' P';
cleanupsysic =' yes';
sysic;
%end
%start of Hinf algorithm
nmeas = 1; nu = 1; gmn = 0.5; gmx = 20; tol = 0.001;
[khinf,ghinf,gopt] = hinfsyn(P, nmeas, nu, gmn, gmx, tol);
%end
%calculation of suboptimal compensator
[a, b, c, d] = unpck(khinf);
[numg, deng] = ss2tf(a, b, c, d)
roots(numg)
roots(deng)
end

Numerator of compensator $G(s)$:

[0   3.67e + 5   1.15e + 8   1.14e + 10   4.1e + 11   1.4e + 12]

Denominator of compensator $G(s)$:

[1.e0   1.15e + 5   3.54e + 7   3.7e + 9   1.44e + 11   1.0e + 12   1.54e + 12   1.54e + 9]

ing weighting functions for the closed-loop performance specifications, and, by using H_∞ optimization algorithms to obtain the control network $G(s)$. Thus, a large part of the design effort is transferred to the computer. The commercial H_∞-optimization algorithms that are available change iteratively the parameters of the assumed $G(s)$ until a satisfactory solution is obtained. However, if the final outcome is not exactly what the designer expected to obtain, some of the weighting functions can be altered in a logical way so that an ameliorated solution will be achieved.

When SISO feedback systems are designed, comparable solutions from system point of view are obtained with both approaches. However, for the MIMO case, the classical approach is less efficient and also less transparent to the designer, because shaping of any individual loop out of the n loops to be designed, influences the previously obtained feedback properties of the remaining loops. This point will be clarified in Chapter 6, where the MIMO feedback design is treated.

2.7. Summary

Fundamental feedback properties such as the Bode sensitivity equation, the return difference and the invariance of its numerator, asymptotic and internal stability, relative stability etc., are defined and explained in this chapter.

It was shown that design of a SISO feedback system is faced with tradeoffs between contradicting specifications and requirements, such as disturbance attenuation, sensor noise amplification effects, input-output tracking performances, etc. Efficient loopshaping of the loop transmission $L(s)$ is easily performed in the frequency-domain by using design tools such as Bode plots, and Nichols and inverted Nichols charts. The basic difference between the one and the two- degree-of-freedom feedback system was explained as the prelude to the design of uncertain feedback systems. Specifically, it was shown that the design of the prefilter $F(s)$ and the controller $G(s)$ are separable design processes.

Similar results were also obtained by solving the standard H_∞-'modern control' regulator problem in which weighting functions related to the feedback system requirements are first defined. For comparison purposes an illustrative design problem was fully solved with both a H_∞-norm optimization algorithm and with the classical Bode/Nichols design technique.

The standard H_∞-optimal regulator design technique will be used in Chapters 4 and 8 to solve the SISO and MIMO TDOF uncertain feedback problems respectively.

Chapter 3 _____

Practical Topics in the Design of SISO Feedback Systems

3.1. Introduction

This chapter deals with practical aspects in the design of feedback systems. The first step in the design process is to define the specifications and the different requirements of the closed-loop system. In principle, these are given in the time-domain. This is true for such factors as the input-output tracking response, for the disturbance response, for the amplified sensor white noise at the input to the plant, etc. The design proper can be carried out in the s-domain using, for example, the root-locus, or the pole-zero assignment techniques, (Wonham 1967, Brasch and Pearson 1970, D'Azzo and Houpis 1988), or in the frequency-domain, using design techniques developed by Nyquist, Bode, and Nichols. Before this step can be implemented, the time-domain specifications have to be first translated into the s-domain or into the frequency-domain. Of special importance and complexity are the translation of the tracking time response specifications into the frequency-domain. These topics are treated in Sections 3.2 and 3.3.

As indicated in Chapter 2, adequate disturbance rejection is achieved by accomplishing a loop transmission $L(s) = G(s)P(s)$ whose magnitude and bandwidth depend on the characteristics of the disturbance signals, and on their attenuation requirements at the system output. The disturbances are best defined by their spectrum in the frequency-domain. If the plant $P(s)$ is minimum-phase (MP), defined in Section 3.3, then any required bandwidth of $L(j\omega)$ can be achieved, thus providing a complete solution to the disturbance problem.

'Optimality' of $L(j\omega)$ deserves a special attention when the design of feedback systems is performed in the frequency-domain. Its definition depends on the particular characteristics of the plant. Optimality of minimum-phase loop transmission

$L(j\omega)$ is treated in Section 3.4 where the famous Ideal Bode Characteristic is discussed. Unfortunately, if the plant is nonminimum-phase (NMP), defined in Section 3.3, there exist stringent bandwidth limitations which the designer cannot exceed. These are treated in Section 3.5 for plants including RHP zeros.

Section 3.6 deals with plants comprising RHP poles. To achieve stability of such feedback systems, the open-loop transmission must have large bandwidth whose minimum value depends on the location of the unstable poles. In this case, for practical reasons related to sensor noise amplification and also to a potential existence of structural modes in the plant, it is important to achieve the smallest possible bandwidth. In Section 3.6 analytical limitations on minimum achievable bandwidth for such systems are derived.

When the plant contains several RHP poles and zeros, stabilization of the feedback system is not a trivial problem. This subject is treated in Section 3.7 where the Q-parametrization technique (also known as Youla-parametrization) for design of systems comprising an arbitrary number of RHP poles and of zeros is introduced. The basic features of this design technique consist in finding all stabilizing controllers, expressed in parametric form, that can stabilize a given plant, (Youla et al. 1976). Sections 3.8 and 3.9 deal with the problem of obtaining the best feedback benefits for a family of feedback systems comprising both a RHP pole and a RHP zero.

3.2. Frequency and s-Domains to Time-Domain Translations

Most design specifications of feedback control systems are stated in the time-domain. Since many design techniques are performed in the frequency-domain, it is of utmost importance to have reasonably transparent relationships between the time- and the frequency-domains, and vice versa. In this section we deal separately with the time into s-domain and time into frequency-domain translations.

3.2.1. s-Domain to Time-Domain Translation

The dominant pole approach

The loop transmission $L(s)$ may have, in general, a large number of poles and zeros. Consequently, the input-output transfer functions of Eqs.(2.1.1) and (2.1.5), namely,

$$T(s) = \frac{L(s)}{1 + L(s)} \; F(s) = T_1(s)F(s); \; T_1(s) = \frac{L(s)}{1 + L(s)}$$

will consist of a pole-zero pattern having a large number of poles and zeros, as shown in Fig.3.2.1b. If the order of the numerator of $L(s)$ is m, and that of the denominator is n, then $T_1(s)$ will have m zeros and n poles. The prefilter $F(s)$, to be eventually used, can only increase the order of $T(s)$. As an example, for a plant $P(s)$ of order (2)/(4) and a control network $G(s)$ of order (3)/(5), $T_1(s)$ will be of

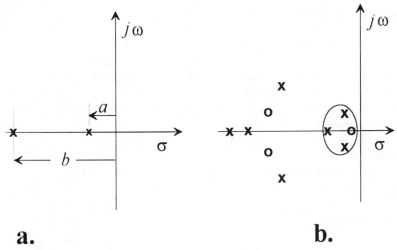

a. **b.**

Figure 3.2.1. Approximation of $T(s)$ by dominant poles and zeros in the s-plane.

an order (5)/(9). With $F(s)$ of an assumed order (1)/(2), the transfer function $T(s)$ will attain the order of (6)/(11). This means that we have to visualize six zeros and eleven poles in the s-plane. It is quite impossible to foretell mentally the time response of a transfer function consisting of so many poles and zeros, unless some simplifications are made. In general, we speak of 'dominant' poles and zeros. This means that we keep the poles and zeros of $T(s)$, which are the closer to the origin in the s-plane, and delete those which are sufficiently distanced from the origin.

The output $y(s)$ of a feedback system can be expressed in the general form

$$y(s) = \frac{N(s)}{D(s)} = \frac{K(s - z_1)(s - z_2)....(s - z_m)}{(s - p_1)(s - p_2).....(s - p_n)} \qquad (3.2.1)$$

To find the time response of $y(s) = T(s)r(s)$ we first have to find the partial-fraction expansion of the above expression, (see D'Azzo and Houpis 1988).

If we suppose that the roots of the denominator are all real and distinct, $p_i \neq p_j$, then there exist n residues $k_1 \, k_2 \ldots k_n$ such that the partial-fraction expansion of $y(s)$ becomes:

$$y(s) = \frac{k_1}{(s - p_1)} + \frac{k_2}{(s - p_2)} + \ldots + \frac{k_k}{(s - p_k)} + \ldots + \frac{k_n}{(s - p_n)} \qquad (3.2.2)$$

The residues k_k are calculated in this special case by the relation:

$$k_k = \lim_{s \to p_k} [(s - p_k)y(s)] \qquad (3.2.3)$$

In term of the calculated residues, the time response of $y(s)$ will be,

$$y(t) = k_1 \, e^{p_1 t} + k_2 e^{p_2 t} + \ldots + k_k e^{p_k t} \cdots + k_n e^{p_n t} \tag{3.2.4}$$

Dominance is a relative notion, which is defined for transfer functions consisting of stable poles, $p_i < 0$, $i = 1, n$. For a pole p_k to be 'dominant' relative to a far-off pole p_n, it is necessary that $|k_k| >> |k_n|$ and that $p_n >> p_k$. In this case, the term $k_n e^{p_n t}$ can be ignored, since this transient response is small in amplitude and dies out quickly relatively to the term $k_k e^{p_k t}$. Thus, the pole p_n can be deleted from the transfer function.

To get a feeling of the notion of 'dominance', let us concentrate on the simple transfer function $T(s) = ab/[(s + a)(s + b)]$ in which $|b| >> |a|$, and whose pole locations are shown in Fig.3.2.1a. The unity-step time response corresponds to $y(s) = T(s)/s$. Thus

$$y(s) = \frac{1}{s} \frac{ab}{(s + a)(s + b)} = \frac{k_1}{s} + \frac{k_2}{s + a} + \frac{k_3}{s + b}$$

where $k_1 = 1$, $k_2 = b/(a - b)$ and $k_3 = -a/(a - b)$. Clearly $|k_2/k_3| = |-b/a|$, which means that the larger the difference between the sizes of the two poles, the larger this ratio will be. The unit-step time response is: $y(t) = (k_1 + k_2 \, e^{-at} + k_3 \, e^{-bt})$. Therefore, if $|a| << |b|$, then $|k_3| << |k_2|$. But since the exponent e^{-bt} decays much faster than the exponent e^{-at}, the term $k_3 \, e^{-bt}$ can be ignored. The time response can then be approximated to $y(t) \cong (k_1 + k_2 \, e^{-at})$, which means that the pole located at $-a$ is the 'dominant pole' of the original $T(s) = ab/[(s + a)(s + b)]$. The latter can, therefore, be simplified to $T(s) = a/(s + a)$ without generating a large error in the time response.

Example 3.2.1. Given $T(s) = 5/[(s + 1)(s + 5)]$, check the feasibility of simplifying it to $T(s) = 1/(s + 1)$, i.e., to a dominant pole located at $s = -1$. $|k_2 / k_3| = 5$ in this example. The time-domain results in Fig.3.2.2 confirm that the 'dominance' of the pole at -1 is justified.

The next example treats a transfer function with a more complicated pole-zero pattern which is shown in Fig.3.2.1b. The dominant poles and zero are encircled.

Example 3.2.2. There is given the transfer function

$$T(s) = \frac{8(s + 1)}{(s + 2) \, (s^2 + 2 \times 0.5 \times 2s + 2^2)} \times$$

$$\frac{120(s^2 + 2 \times 0.9 \times 8s + 8^2)}{(s^2 + 2 \times 0.75 \times 8s + 8^2) \, (s + 10) \, (s + 12)} = T_1 \, (s) \times T_2 \, (s).$$

$T_1(s)$ is the reduced 'dominant' part of the original transfer function and $T_2(s)$ is the remaining part of the original transfer function which includes the far-off poles

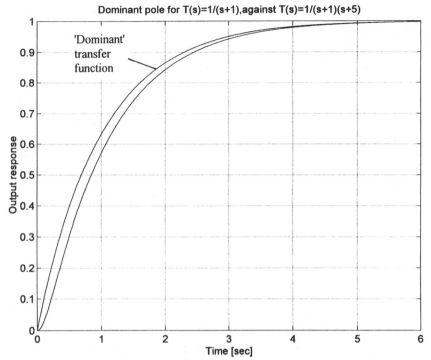

Figure 3.2.2. Step responses of $T(s) = 5/[(s + 1)(s + 5)]$ and of the reduced transfer function $T(s) = 1/(s + 1)$.

and zeros. The resulting unit-step time responses of the original and of the reduced 'dominant' transfer functions are shown in Fig.3.2.3. The time responses shown in the figure consent that the 'pole-zero dominance' approach is acceptable from engineering point of view.

Note that the ignored poles and zeros are distanced from the dominant poles and zeros by a factor of at least five.

Some definitions of a step response

Several important parameters concerning a unit-step time response are next defined in Fig.3.2.4.

t_r-   *rise time* is the time for the response $y(t)$ to increase from 0.1 to 0.9 times its final steady-state value, i.e., $t_r = t_{0.9} - t_{0.1}$.

y_p-   *peak overshoot* is the amplitude of the largest overshoot, generally the first one.

MO-   *maximum overshoot* is the maximum peak value above the final value.

PMO-   *percent maximum overshoot* is the ratio of *MO* to the final value of the time response in percentage.

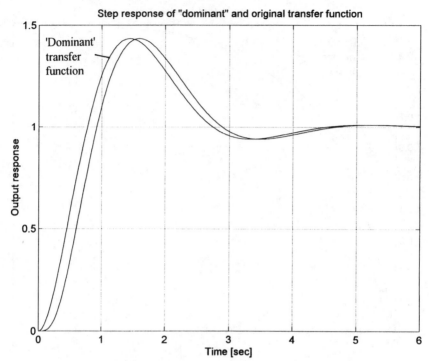

Figure 3.2.3.   Comparison between step time responses of the 'dominant' and of the original transfer functions in Example 3.2.3.

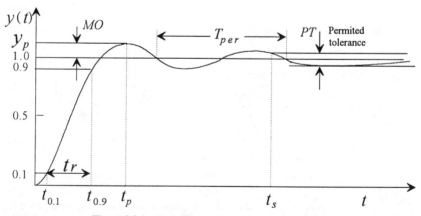

Figure 3.2.4.   Definitions of step response parameters.

t_p- *time to maximum overshoot* is the time required to reach the first overshoot.
PT- *permitted tolerance* is the permitted steady-state offset from the final value.
t_s- *settling time* is the time required for the output response first to enter and then remain within a permitted tolerance.
T_{per}- *time period,* time of one oscillation period.

We can go farther, and try to reduce the number of dominant poles and zeros to only one representative second-order complex pole. This approach is very common because of its effectiveness in simplifying the 'specification stage' in the design of feedback control systems. Use of a simplified dominant transfer function provides an easy way to define the parameters of a desired step time response and also to translate it to the *s*- and to the frequency-domains.

The unit-step time responses of a second-order system for different damping coefficients are shown in Fig.3.2.5.

The damping coefficient completely changes the parameters of a step time response, such as rise time, overshoot, settling time and so on. These parameters can be calculated analytically from the unit-step time response of a complex pole pair of second-order model of $T(s)$:

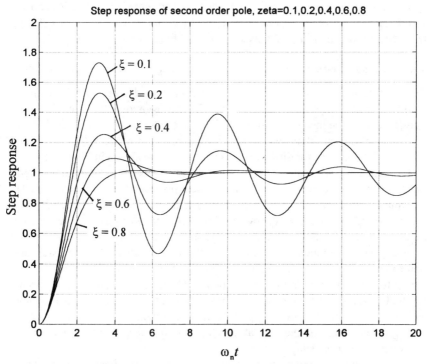

Figure 3.2.5. Unit-step time responses for second-order systems with damping coefficients of $\xi = 0.1, 0.2, 0.4, 0.6,$ and 0.8.

$$y(t) = \mathcal{L}^{-1} \frac{\omega_n^2}{s(s^2 + 2\xi\omega_n s + \omega_n^2)} = 1 + \frac{1}{\sqrt{1-\xi^2}} e^{-\xi\omega_n t} \sin\left(\sqrt{1-\xi^2}\,\omega_n t - \psi\right)$$

(3.2.5)

$$\psi = \tan^{-1} \frac{\sqrt{1-\xi^2}}{-\xi}$$

(3.2.6)

From the above equations, we can calculate some of the step response parameters:

$$t_p = \frac{\pi}{\omega_n\sqrt{1-\xi^2}}\,;\, y_p = 1 + \exp\left(\frac{-\xi\pi}{\sqrt{1-\xi^2}}\right); PMO = 100(y_p - 1); t_s = \frac{4}{\xi\omega_n}$$

(3.2.7)

When the design of the control system is based on s-domain synthesis techniques, such as the root-locus or pole placement methods, the desired closed-loop transfer function $T(s)$ can be specified by a dominant complex pole second-order system. Such a system exhibits the characteristics presented in Eq.(3.2.7), and also additional features such as time period T_{per}, rise time t_r, etc. Some of these parameters are shown in Fig.3.2.6 as a function of the damping coefficient ξ.

3.2.2. Frequency-Domain to Time Domain-Translation: R(ω) to y(t) Translation

When the design is performed in the frequency-domain, the desired time response is to be translated first into the frequency-domain. Moreover, we can translate a transfer function defined in the s-domain into the frequency-domain Bode diagram. For instance, the logarithmic magnitudes versus frequency of second-order complex pole transfer functions for different damping ratios ξ are shown in Fig.C.3.1.

Unfortunately, as we have already seen, a dominant second-order complex pole system is only an approximation of a realistic input-output transfer function. The real transfer function may deviate substantially from that of a second-order complex pole model. Some basic characteristics in the frequency-domain are shown in Fig.3.2.7. These are the *peak value* of $|T(j\omega)|$, the frequency ω_p at which the peak is located and the frequency ω_{-3dB} at which the log magnitude of the transfer function equals -3 dB below $|T(j0)|$. Generally, the peak value of $|T(j\omega)|$ is responsible for the overshooting in the time response. The time to maximum overshoot t_p is found to be proportional to $1/\omega_p$. The rise time of the step time response depends naturally on the bandwidth, ω_{-3dB} of the transfer function. It is shown later that adding poles at high frequencies affects the step time response by generating an equivalent pure time delay.

It is important to emphasize that there are no exact analytical means for translating the magnitude response $|T(j\omega)|$ of a transfer function into its step time

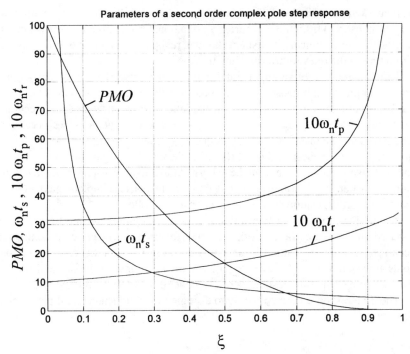

Figure 3.2.6.   Step response parameters of a dominant complex pole second-order system versus the damping coefficients ξ.

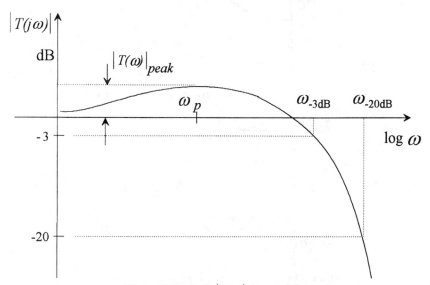

Figure 3.2.7.   Basic $|T(j\omega)|$ characteristics.

response. On the other hand, there are exact analytical relations for evaluating the time response $y(t)$ from the real part $R(\omega)$ of a transfer function. It is shown in this section how to graphically translate a known, real part $R(\omega)$ into the time response pertaining to the relevant transfer function.

Unfortunately, from an engineering point of view, use of $R(\omega)$ for design purposes is impractical, because it can be obtained only by measuring both $|T(j\omega)|$ and arg $T(j\omega)$. In addition, measurement of the latter may be difficult and inaccurate. Moreover, to obtain $R(\omega)$, additional trigonometric computations are necessary, which render the translation from the frequency-domain into the time-domain much more cumbersome. Despite these difficulties, there are some general properties that can be derived in translating from the real part $R(\omega)$ into time response which remain valid also when translation from $|T(j\omega)|$ into time response is implemented. For this reason, a short exposition of $R(\omega)$ to $y(t)$ translation follows.

The proposed graphical translation from frequency-domain into time-domain is based on the assumption that the real part function $R(\omega)$ can be approximated accurately enough by a sum of trapezoids as in Fig.3.2.8. In this case, two trapezoids are used, $R(\omega) \cong R_1(\omega) + R_2(\omega)$. The time response of the original $R(\omega)$ is then the sum of the time responses of each one of the individual trapezoids.

The time response corresponding to a single trapezoid-shaped real part is next derived.

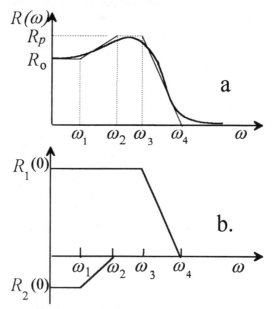

Figure 3.2.8.   Approximated decomposition of $R(\omega)$ into the sum of two trapezoid shaped real parts.

Evaluation of the impulse time response from a real trapezoid standard part

As is well known, the inversion integral of $R(\omega)$ for causal time functions is

$$f(t) = \frac{2}{\pi} \int_0^\infty R(\omega) \cos \omega t \, d\omega \qquad (3.2.8)$$

(See Solodovnikov 1960, Papoulis 1962, or Appendix D).

A trapezoid-shaped real part $R(\omega)$, where ω_2 and ω_1 are the two corner frequencies, is shown in Fig.3.2.9. The impulse time response $g(t)$ of such a real standard part is calculated by Eq.(3.2.8) to be:

$$g(t) = \frac{2R_0}{\pi(\omega_2 - \omega_1)} \frac{(\cos \omega_1 t - \cos \omega_2 t)}{t^2}; \quad R_0 = R(0), t > 0 \qquad (3.2.9)$$

The time function in Eq.(3.2.9) can be normalized by defining $k = \omega_1 / \omega_2$ and $\tau = \omega_2 t$. Eq.(3.2.9) then reduces to:

$$g(t) = g(\frac{\tau}{\omega_2}) = \frac{2R_0\omega_2}{\pi} \frac{(\cos k\tau - \cos \tau)}{(1 - k)\tau^2}; \quad R_0 = R(0), \quad \tau > 0 \qquad (3.2.10)$$

It is important to notice that the time scale is normalized to $\tau = \omega_2 t$, while the amplitude is inversely proportional to ω_2. Finally, the impulse response can be written in a more compact form by defining $\gamma_k(\tau) = [\cos (k\tau) - \cos(\tau)]/[(1-k)\tau^2]$ which has a normalized standard time response, shown in Fig.3.2.10 for different values of k.

Example 3.2.3.　Find the impulse time response of the transfer function whose real part $R(\omega)$ is shown in Fig.3.2.8a and in which $R_p = 1.3$, $R_0 = 1$, $\omega_1 = 1$, $\omega_2 = 3$, $\omega_3 = 4$ and $\omega_4 = 6$ rad/sec.

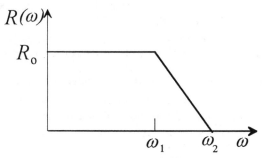

Figure 3.2.9.　Definition of a real trapezoid standard part.

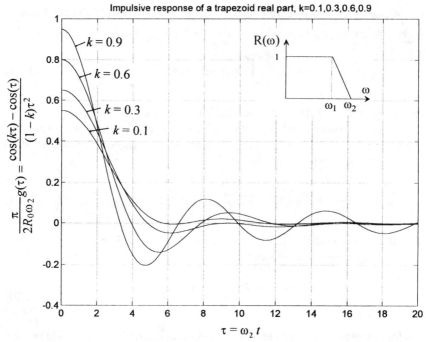

Figure 3.2.10.   Normalized impulse time response for $2R_0 \, \omega_2 / \pi = 1$, and $k = 0.1, 0.3, 0.6$ and 0.9.

Solution: $R(\omega)$ is decomposed into the sum of the real parts $R_1(\omega)$ and $R_2(\omega)$ shown in Fig.3.2.8b, where, $R_1(0) = R_p = 1.3$, $R_2(0) = R_0 - R_p = 1 - 1.3 = -0.3$, $k_1 = \omega_3 / \omega_4 = 4/6 = 0.67$ and $k_2 = \omega_1 / \omega_2 = 0.33$. The approximated time response is calculated by using the graphs in Fig.3.2.10. The parameters of $R_1(\omega)$, which is the first real trapezoid standard part, are: $k_1 = \omega_3 / \omega_4 = 4/6$; the amplitude normalization factor is $2R_p \omega_4 / \pi = 4.96$; and the time scaling is $t = \tau / \omega_4 = \tau/6$. The corresponding impulse response is called $g_1(t)$ in Fig.3.2.11. Next, the impulse response of $R_2(\omega)$ is plotted. For this we use the normalized plot with $k_2 = 0.3$, and scale the time axis by $t = \tau / \omega_2 = \tau / 3$. The normalized amplitude must be multiplied by $2(R_0 - R_p) \omega_2 / \pi = -2 \times 0.3 \times 3/\pi = -0.573$. This time response is called $g_2(t)$. Adding the two responses gives the resulting $g(t) = g_1(t) + g_2(t)$, also shown in Fig.3.2.11. The time responses can be also obtained by direct integration of Eq.(3.2.8).

Evaluation of the unit-step time response from a real trapezoid standard part

The unit-step time response can be calculated by integrating the impulse response of Eq.(3.2.9), or of Eq.(3.2.10) for the normalized case. The outcome for the normalized unit-step time response $h(\tau)$ is given in the following equation, (see also Solodovnikov 1960, Papoulis 1962):

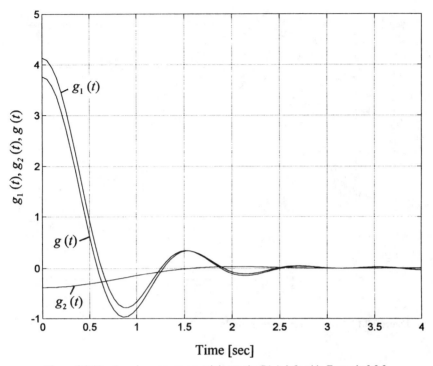

Figure 3.2.11. Impulse response pertaining to the $R(\omega)$ defined in Example 3.2.3.

$$\frac{\pi}{2R_0} h(t) = Si(k\tau) + \frac{1}{1-k}\left[Si(\tau) - Si(k\tau) + \frac{\cos(\tau) - \cos(k\tau)}{\tau}\right] \qquad (3.2.11)$$

where

$$Si(t) \equiv \int_0^t \frac{\sin t}{t}\, dt$$

Normalized unit-step time responses for several k's are shown in Fig.3.2.12.

Example 3.2.4. Find the unit-step response of the system in Example 3.2.3 using the normalized graphs in Fig.3.2.12 for the two real trapezoid parts $R_1(\omega)$ and $R_2(\omega)$ shown in Fig.3.2.8b.

Solution: Applying the same procedure as for Example 3.2.3, we obtain first the step responses $h_1(t)$, $h_2(t)$; finally, we can plot $h(t) = h_1(t) + h_2(t)$, which is also shown in Fig.3.2.13.

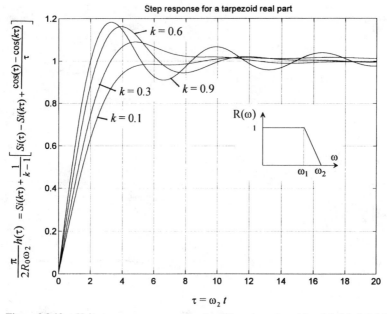

Figure 3.2.12.   Unit-step responses normalized to $2R_0\,\omega_2\,/\pi = 1$, and $k = 0.1, 0.3, 0.6, 0.9$.

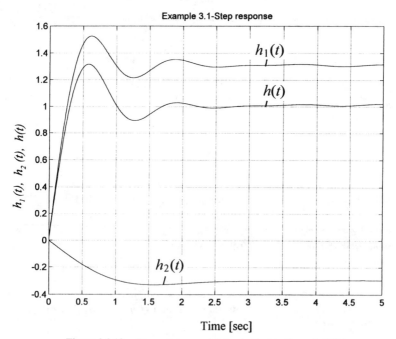

Figure 3.2.13.   Step response pertaining to $R(\omega)$ in Example 3.2.3.

Overshoot of a step time response evaluated from frequency-response characteristic

When the system dynamic is represented by its real part $R(\omega)$, a rough estimation of the overshoot of its step response can be obtained by simple investigation of the plot of $R(\omega)$. In analyzing the step response of a transfer function, we are primary concerned with real parts having the basic features displayed in Figs.3.2.8a and 3.2.9.

In regard to the step response $h(t)$ pertaining to the real trapezoid standard part in Fig.3.2.9, it was shown by Papoulis (1962) that the overshoot is bounded to 18%, i.e.,

$$h_{max}(t) \leq 1.18h(\infty) = 1.18R(0). \tag{3.2.12}$$

If, for example, $R(\omega)$ has the general form presented in Fig.3.2.8a, i.e., it can be decomposed into two real parts such that $R(\omega) = R_1(\omega) - R_2(\omega)$ as in Fig.3.2.8b, then it follows from Eq.(3.2.12) that

$$h_1(t) \leq 1.18 \, R_1(0) = 1.18 \, R_{max}(\omega)$$

hence,

$$h(t) \leq h_1(t) \leq h_1(t)_{max} \leq 1.18R_{max}(\omega) = 1.18R(0) \frac{R_{max}(\omega)}{R(0)}.$$

From the last inequality it follows that

$$h_{max}(t) \leq 1.18h(\infty) \frac{R_{max}(\omega)}{R(0)}. \tag{3.2.13}$$

The above result can be used to correlate the maximum overshoot of the step time response to $|T(j\omega)|_{max}$. Indeed,

$$T(j\omega) = R(\omega) + jX(\omega) = |T(j\omega)|e^{j\phi(\omega)} = |T(j\omega)| \, [\cos \phi(\omega) + j \sin \phi(\omega)] \, . \text{ But,}$$
$R(\omega) = |T(j\omega)|\cos \phi(\omega)$, and since $\cos \phi(0) = 1$, it follows that
$R_{max}(\omega) \leq |T(j\omega)|_{max}$ and $R(0) = |T(j0)|$,

hence,

$$h_{max}(t) \leq 1.18h(\infty) \frac{|T(j\omega)|_{max}}{|T(j0)|} \, . \tag{3.2.14}$$

3.2.3. Frequency-Domain to Time-Domain Translation: $|T(j\omega)|$ to y(t) Translation

Translation from $|T(j\omega)|$ to time-domain is a common practice in engineering. Unfortunately, as already indicated, translation from $|y(j\omega)|$ to $y(t)$ is based mostly on empirical relations from accumulated data and good engineering intuition. The present section presents some approximate relations that help in translating $|T(j\omega)|$ parameters into time-domain parameters.

Time delay due to poles located at high frequencies

The initial value theorem indicates that the time response $y(t)$ near $t = 0$ is closely related to $T(s)$ as s approaches infinity. Existence of poles at high frequencies causes time delay near $t = 0$. To explore this effect, let us have a look on the Bode plot of $|T(j\omega)|$ in Fig.3.2.14 derived from the basic transfer function (marked with $e = 2$ in the figure),

$$T(s) = \frac{1 + s/1.2}{(1 + s/3)(1 + 2 \times 0.5s + s^2)}.$$

Since the excess of poles over zeros in the high frequency range is $e = 2$, the negative slope of its log magnitude versus $\log\omega$ in this range is -40 dB/decade. Next, additional poles are added. Their corner frequencies are located at the frequency at which the log magnitude of the original transfer function is about -20 dB, so that the latter will not be altered noticeably in the frequency range in which $|T(j\omega)| > -20$dB. Additional second-order complex poles, with a natural frequency of $\omega_n = 5.5$ rad/sec and $\xi = 0.65$, are added to the original transfer function. Each additional complex pole increases the excess of poles over zeros by two. The location of the poles and the zeros of the transfer function $T(s)$ does not really matter. The important feature about the magnitude Bode plots of the different transfer functions is that they have approximately the same behavior up to the frequency at which $|T(j\omega)| = -20$ dB. In the frequency range at which $|T(j\omega)| < -20$ dB, the slope becomes more negative, according to the number of excess of poles over zeros of the related transfer functions. Bode plots of $|T(j\omega)|$ for $e = 2, 4, 6, 8$ and 10 are shown in Fig.3.2.14.

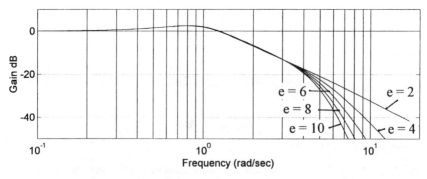

Figure 3.2.14.   Bode plots of $|T(j\omega)|$ for $e = 2, 4, 6, 8$ and 10.

Let $\omega_{0.1}$ be defined as the frequency at which $|T(j\omega)| = 0.1$ ($= -20$ dB), and let $t_{0.1}$ be the time at which the step time response reaches 10% of its final value, (see Sidi 1973). Define

$$A_{0.1} = \omega_{0.1}\, t_{0.1} \tag{3.2.15}$$

The step time responses plotted in Fig.3.2.15 belong to the transfer functions $|T(j\omega)|$'s, whose Bode plots are shown in Fig.3.2.14.

The resulting $A_{0.1}$ obtained from the transfer function magnitudes in Figs.3.2.14 and from the delays in the step responses displayed in Fig.3.2.15 is plotted in Fig.3.2.16 as a function of the excess e of poles over zeros at high frequencies.

Fig.3.2.16 is useful in predicting the equivalent pure time delay caused by the numerous poles of the transfer function located at high frequencies.

Rise time t_r

Another very important parameter of the step time response is the rise time t_r. Different approximations of t_r have been proposed over the past forty years. These are very simplified relations and are not accurate enough. One of them is used for systems with

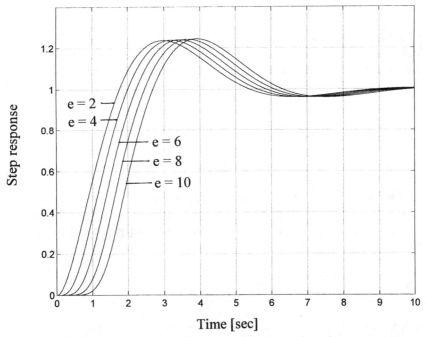

Figure 3.2.15. Step time responses appertaining to the Bode plots of $|T(j\omega)|$ shown in Fig.3.2.14.

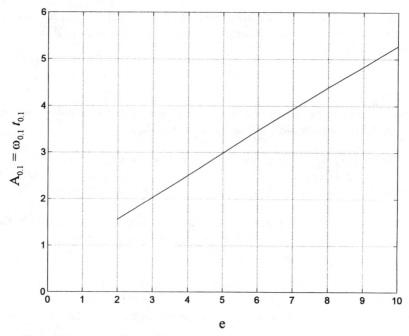

Figure 3.2.16. $A_{0.1}$ as function of e (= excess of poles over zeros at high frequencies).

overshoots smaller than approximately 10%. Define $t_r f_b = k, f_b = \omega_{-3\,dB}/2\pi$, ($\omega_{-3\,dB}$ was already defined as the frequency at which $|T(j\omega)| = -3$dB, with the assumption that $|T(j0)| = 0$ dB). Then, according to Valley and Wallman (1948),

$$0.3 < k < 0.45. \tag{3.2.16}$$

If we define $k_r = t_r \omega_{-3\,dB}$, then

$$1.88 < k_r < 2.83 \tag{3.2.16a}$$

When a large peak value is present in $|T(j\omega)|$ (this also leads to large overshoots in the relevant step response), the above relation does not hold. For such cases, some graphical results for k_r were obtained empirically, based on the transfer function

$$T(s) = \frac{1 + s/zero}{1 + s/3} \frac{1}{s^2 + 2 \times 0.5s + 1} \left[\frac{2^2}{s^2 + 2 \times 0.5 \times 2s + 2^2} \right]^q$$

in which $zero = [0.3 - 7.0]$ and $q = [0 - 4]$. A large number of $|T(j\omega)|$'s and their time responses were generated and analyzed. Fig.3.2.17 shows the extreme

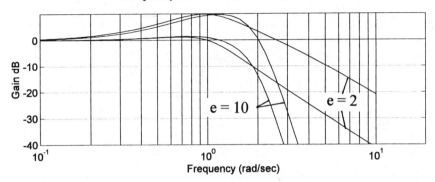

Figure 3.2.17. Extreme $|T(j\omega)|$'s characteristics used in approximating k_r.

Bode plots of $|T(j\omega)|$'s obtained for different q's and $zero$'s. We discern in the figure an excess of poles over zeros of $e = 2$ to $e = 10$ and peak values of 2 to 10 dB. The extreme step time responses for these cases are shown in Fig.3.2.18. Based on the accumulated data from both figures, graph relations were obtained for $k_r = t_r \, \omega_{-3dB}$ versus $|T(j\omega)|_{max}$ for $e = 2, 4, 6, 8$ and 10. These are shown in Fig.3.2.19.

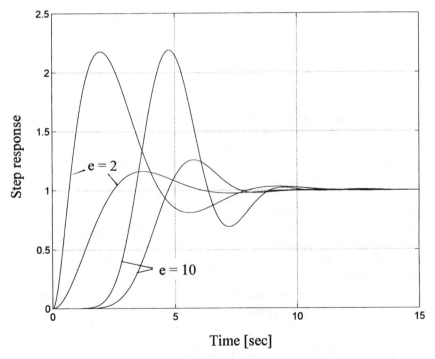

Figure 3.2.18. Step time responses for the transfer functions used in approximating k_r.

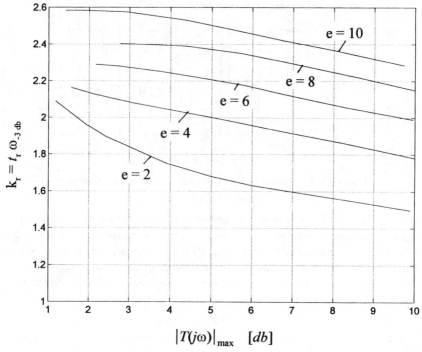

Figure 3.2.19.   Approximated rise time coefficient k_r for different e's.

Additional empirical approximations can be found in the literature, (Sidi 1973, Krishnan and Cruickshanks 1977, Horowitz 1992). However, due to their theoretical and practical limitations, we will not investigate them. Using today's commercial software for control analysis and design, it is easy to perform fast investigations of frequency-domain to time-domain translations, and vice versa, in complex systems.

Finally, a curious translation process from the frequency-domain into the time-domain will be carried out with no other purpose than to illustrate an interesting property intuitively explained. More than twenty five years ago, while investigating frequency to time translations, the author of this book was struck by the qualitative resemblance between the step response and the mirror image about the ordinate axis of $|T(j\omega)|$ versus ω plot in linear frequency scale. Some examples of log magnitudes versus log ω plots of the transfer function

$$T(s) = \frac{1+s}{(1+s/pole)} \frac{1}{1+2\times 0.6s + s^2}$$

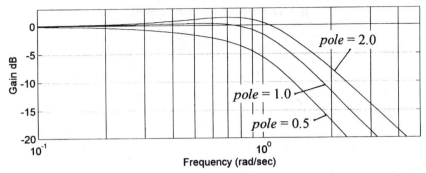

Figure 3.2.20. Bode plot of $T(s) = (s + 1)/[(1 + s/pole)(s^2 + 2 \times 0.6s + 1)]$ for *pole* = 0.5, 1.0, and 2.0.

for *pole* = 0.5, 1.0 and 2.0 are shown in Fig.3.2.20. The exact step responses of these transfer functions are shown in Fig.3.2.21. The plots of $|T(b/\omega)|$ versus b/ω in linear scale are shown in Fig.3.2.22; these are impressively similar to the authentic time responses shown in Fig. 3.2.21 (satisfactory accommodation factors *b* were found empirically to be: *b* = 2 for *pole* = 0.5, and *b* = 2.3 for *pole* = 1.0 and 2.0).

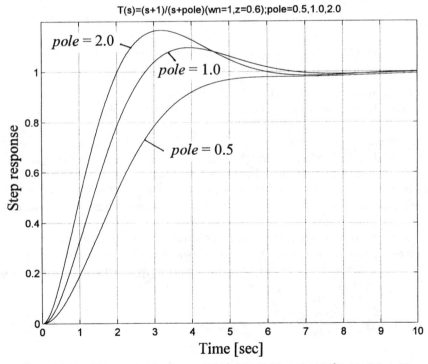

Figure 3.2.21. Unit-step time responses of $T(s) = (s + 1)/[(1 + s/pole)(s^2 + 2 \times 0.6s + 1)]$ for *pole* = 0.5, 1.0 and 2.0.

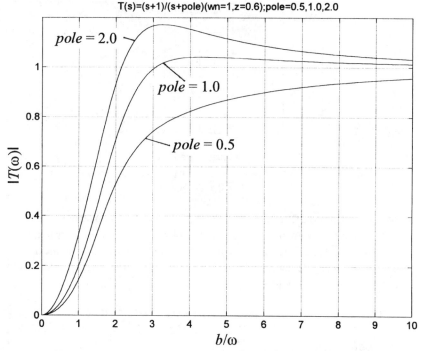

T(s)=(s+1)/(s+pole)(wn=1,z=0.6);pole=0.5,1.0,2.0

Figure 3.2.22. Approximated time responses by $|T(b/\omega)|$ for *pole* = 0.5, 1.0 and 2.0.

3.3.   Input-Output Time-Domain Characteristics
of NMP SISO Feedback Systems

In later sections we will be concerned with NMP plants that considerably compli-
cate the design of feedback control systems. A NMP transfer function is defined
in the literature as a stable transfer function containing at least one RHP zero. As
is later shown in Section 3.5.2, the existence of such RHP zeros limits the achievable feedback system bandwidth, but also generates an inevitable 'pure time delay' in the output time response.

Fig.2.1.1 is a canonical unity-feedback structure of a SISO feedback system.
Let us suppose that the plant $P(s)$ contains a single RHP zero located at $+1/a$. In
this configuration, the input-output transfer function $T(s)$ contains the RHP zero
of the plant in its numerator, namely

$$T(s) = \frac{P(s)G(s)}{1 + P(s)G(s)} \; F(s) = T_{MP}(s) \frac{1 - as}{1 + as} \overset{def}{=} T_{MP}(s)A(s) \qquad (3.3.1)$$

where $T_{MP}(s)$ is minimum-phase and $A(s)$ is an all-pass function that significantly
changes the time domain response of $T_{MP}(s)$, (Sidi 1976). $A(s)$ is a first order Pade

approximation of $e^{-2\,as}$, which, in the time-domain, is an approximation of a pure time delay amounting to $t_{del} \approx 2\,a$ sec. This approximation is accurate enough as long as $1/\,a \geq \omega_{-3dB}$ (See Fig.3.3.1).

The step response $y(t)$ of NMP systems may begin with an undershoot, i.e. $dy(0_+)/dt < 0$. Horowitz and Sidi (1978) showed that if the transfer function $T(s)$ has an odd number of RHP real zeros, then $dy(0_+)/dt < 0$, and the number of zero crossings of $y(t)$ equals the number of RHP zeros of the system's transfer function. When a single RHP zero is present, the amount of undershoot in the step time response depends on the location of this zero relative to the bandwidth frequency ω_{-3dB} of $|T(j\omega)|$. This can be qualitatively explained as follows. Let us suppose that

$$T(s) = T_1(s)\,(1 - a\,s) = T_1(s) - a\,s\,T_1(s), \tag{3.3.2}$$

where $T_1(s)$ is minimum-phase. The step response of $T(s)$ will then be:

$$y(t) = y_1(t) - a\,dy_1(t)/dt \tag{3.3.3}$$

where $y_1(t) = \mathcal{L}^{-1}\,[T_1(s)\,/s]$. It is clear from Eqs.(3.3.2) and (3.3.3) that since $dy_1(t)/dt > 0$ near $t = 0_+$ for a step input, $y(t)$ will be smaller than $y_1(t)$ near $t = 0_+$, and with an undershoot amplitude proportional to a. In fact, when a single NMP zero exists, the negative value of $y(t)$ at $t = 0_+$ follows directly from the initial value theorem. On the other hand, for very large t, $y(t)$ will be positive, which follows from the final value theorem. Hence, there occurs one zero crossing of $y(t)$, as is shown in Fig.3.3.2.

The pure time delay effect for an exemplified transfer function

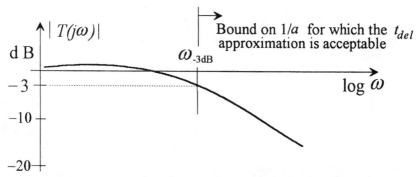

Figure 3.3.1.   An assumed $|T(j\omega)|$ for investigating the influence of a RHP zero on t_{del}.

$$T(s) = \frac{1 + 2s}{(1 + 0.2s)\left(1 + \dfrac{2 \times 0.8s}{1} + \dfrac{s^2}{1^2}\right)} \cdot \frac{1 - as}{1 + as}$$

including a single RHP zero located at $+1/a$ is shown in Fig.3.3.2 (see also Sidi 1976). The time delay of the step time response is quite *linearly related* to a. The undershoot in the step time response increases as the NMP zero located at $1/a$ approaches the bandwidth frequency ω_{-3dB} of the closed-loop transfer function. Note that the undershoot in the step response might become quite large for a RHP zero which is located close to ω_{-3dB}.

To summarize, a detrimental feature in NMP feedback systems is the inevitable existence of time delays and of undershoots in the step response.

Fig.3.3.3 presents $t_{del\,0.1}$, $t_{del\,0.5}$ and $t_{del\,0.9}$ which are the time delays at $0.1y(\infty)$, $0.5y(\infty)$ and $0.9y(\infty)$ respectively as function of $2a$. We note from this figure and from Fig.3.3.4 that the approximation to an ideal delay of $t_{del} = 2a$ sec is more accurate at longer intervals. The explanation for this is that time delay can be approximate by a Pade ratio of polynomials of the form, (Korn and Korn 1968):

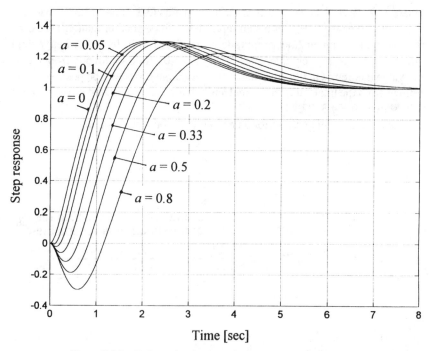

Figure 3.3.2.   Delay and undershoots in the step response caused by a single RHP zero located at $1/a = 0, 0.05, 0.1, 0.2, 0.33, 0.5$ and 1.0.

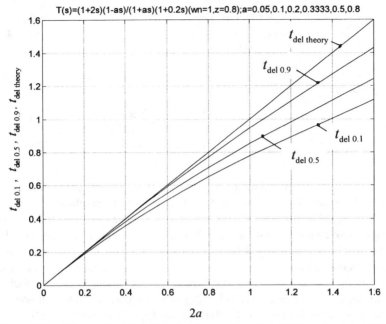

Figure 3.3.3.   Delays at 0.1, 0.5 and 0.9 of $y(\infty)$ caused by a single RHP zero located at $+1/a$.

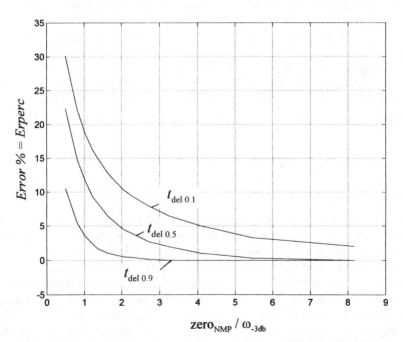

Figure 3.3.4.   Error in $t_{del\,0.1}$, $t_{del\,0.5}$ and $t_{del\,0.9}$ compared to an ideal delay of $t_{del} = 2a$.

$$e^{-2as} \cong \frac{1 - as + \frac{1}{3}(as)^2 - \ldots}{1 + as + \frac{1}{3}(as)^2 + \ldots} \tag{3.3.4}$$

so that

$$T_{MP}(s)e^{-2as} \cong T_{MP}(s)\,\frac{1 - as + \frac{1}{3}(as)^2}{1 + as + \frac{1}{3}(as)^2}. \tag{3.3.5}$$

The accuracy of the approximation depends on the number of terms retained in the above expression. As is well known from Laplace transform relations and the initial and final value theorems, as $t \to 0$, $s \to \infty$; also, as $t \to \infty$, $s \to 0$. From these relations and from Eq.(3.3.4), we conclude that as the time t decreases, the Pade approximation of a pure time delay must include additional higher order terms. On the other hand, when the step response $y(t)$ approaches its final steady- state value, the assumption of $s \to 0$ is more justified, and the representation of the Pade approximation by a dipole $(1 - as)/(1 + as)$ is hence more accurate. It follows that the deviation error from the idealized time delay $t_{del} = 2a$ is smaller at $0.9y(\infty)$ than at $0.1y(\infty)$, as can be observed in Fig.3.3.4. The conclusion is that the a pproximation of a delay by an all-pass transfer function $A(s) = (1 - as)/(1 + as)$ is more justified as $y(t)$ approaches its final steady-state value.

The abscissa variable in Fig.3.3.4 is the value of the RHP zero normalized to the bandwidth ω_{-3dB}; the 'Erperc' is the percentage error of the respective time delay compared to the theoretical delay of $t_{del} = 2a$.

When designing feedback systems with imbedded NMP plants, the inevitable time delay is to be taken into account, and the input-output specifications must be redefined accordingly in order to compensate, at least partially, for this delay.

3.4.   Optimal $L(j\omega)$ for Minimum-Phase Feedback Systems

3.4.1.   Formulation of the Problem

In later sections of this chapter, we will be involved with the problem of achieving the maximum bandwidth of a NMP loop transmission function, and also, the minimum bandwidth of a loop transmission including unstable poles. As an introduction to these important problems, the optimal solution of a minimum-phase loop transmission is first reviewed. Minimum-phase transfer functions $L(s)$ can be regarded as those transfer functions, which, for any given magnitude characteristic $|L(j\omega)|$, are accompanied with the smallest possible arg $L(j\omega)$. See also Section 3.5.

A gross differentiation between *zero type systems* and *higher order* type systems is assumed here. Since in a zero type system, no integrator exists in the loop transmission, in order to achieve a good sensitivity characteristic of the closed-loop, a minimum gain is specified in a prescribed and finite frequency range. Non-zero type systems have at least one integrator in the loop transmission. Thus, the benefits of feedback in the low frequency range are much higher than those for zero type systems. Loop transmissions for both types of systems are sketched conceptually in Fig.3.4.1.

3.4.2. The Ideal Bode Characteristic and its Derivation

The *Ideal Bode Characteristic* (Bode, 1945) was initially formulated to solve the problem of how to design a good communication amplifier in which a specified gain is achieved in a prescribed frequency range with corner frequency ω_0. The principal objective was to decrease the magnitude of $|L(j\omega)|$ as fast as possible in the frequency range $\omega > \omega_0$, subject to prescribed gain and phase margins. The Ideal Bode Characteristic was later used in the design of general feedback control systems, as a guideline to adequately loopshape open-loop transmissions, in which the loop gain decreases as fast as possible in high frequencies (Horowitz 1963).

The Ideal Bode Characteristic (IBC) is an idealization of the specified gain and phase functions displayed in Fig.3.4.1a. It is based on the specifications of $L(j\omega)$ from its real and imaginary parts in different frequency ranges. The basic theory necessary in this section can be found in Bode (1945) and Horowitz (1963). For the readers convenience, some of the important points from the last two references are summarized in Appendix E.

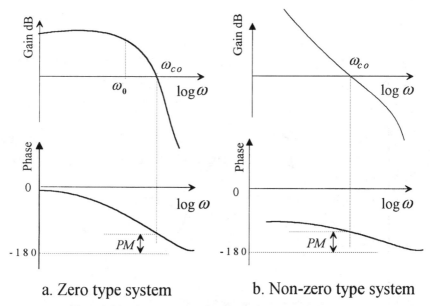

Figure 3.4.1.   Bode diagrams of zero type and non-zero type systems

The IBC transmission function is characterized by the following parameters shown schematically in Fig.3.4.2:

ω_0-   Corner frequency of the useful bandwidth.

GDB-   Gain in dB in the frequency range $\omega < \omega_0$.

β-   The phase margin *PM* is $(1-\beta)\pi$, $0 < \beta < 1$.

GM-   Gain margin

γ- -12γ is the slope at high frequencies in dB/oct, $\gamma > 1$.

The transmission function $L(j\omega)$ is manipulated in the following way: Since $L(j\omega) = |L(j\omega)|e^{j\emptyset(\omega)}$, then $\ln L(j\omega) = \ln |L(j\omega)| + j\emptyset(\omega) = A(\omega) + j B(\omega)$, so that the loop transmission function $L(j\omega)$ can be described by its real and imaginary parts A and B.

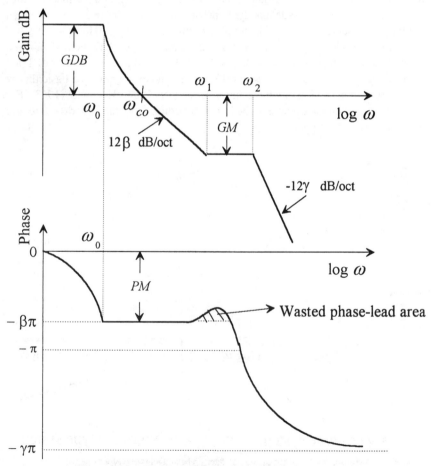

Figure 3.4.2.   Ideal Bode Characteristic and its basic parameters.

The principal stages in deriving the Ideal Bode Characteristic begin with generating a loop transmission function whose gain in the range $\omega < \omega_0$ is *GDB*, and its phase for $\omega > \omega_0$ equals $-\beta\pi$. This provides a specified phase margin *PM* equal to $(1-\beta)\pi$. As shown by Bode, for minimum-phase transmission functions, if the gain $A(\omega)$ in the range $\omega < \omega_0$ is known and the phase $B(\omega)$ in the remaining frequency range $\omega > \omega_0$ is also known, then the complete transmission function is uniquely determined in the entire frequency range. See Appendix E.

Now suppose that the magnitude function reaches the gain margin *GM* at ω_1. From only the magnitude function point of view, a semi-infinite characteristic with a slope of $-12(\gamma - \beta)\pi$ dB/oct can be added at ω_1 in order to achieve the final slope of $-12\gamma\pi$ dB/oct at high frequencies. However, since the addition of the semi-infinite characteristic with negative slope is accompanied by an addition of phase-lag, the phase margin will be violated and its specification will be degraded. In order to prevent the alteration of the phase margin, an intermediate stage is necessary. We add a semi-infinite characteristic with positive slope in a small frequency range $\omega_1 < \omega < \omega_2$ so that some phase-lead is added to the phase function. This compensates for the phase-lag added at ω_2 by the semi-infinite characteristic with the negative slope of $-12(\gamma - \beta)\pi$ dB/oct.

The problem of computing the frequencies ω_1 and ω_2 at which the semi-infinite characteristics are added is now discussed. Since in the frequency range $\omega < \omega_0$ we have specified that $|L(j\omega)| = GDB$[dB], then in this frequency range $A(\omega) = A(0) = \log [10^{GDB/20}]$ (in order to stay in logarithmic units). From Eq.(E.5.2), we find that:

$$B(\omega) = \arg L(j\omega) = -2 \beta \sin^{-1} (\omega/\omega_0), \qquad \omega < \omega_0 \qquad (3.4.1)$$

$$A(\omega) = A(0) - 2\beta \ln\{(\omega/\omega_0) + [(\omega/\omega_0)^2 - 1]^{0.5} \}, \qquad \omega > \omega_0. \qquad (3.4.2)$$

From Eq.(3.4.2) it follows that the decrease in gain at $\omega/\omega_0 = 2^y$ *is*

$$|L(j\omega)| = 12\beta(1 + y) \text{ dB}. \qquad (3.4.3)$$

Computation of ω_1

The above equation can be used to find the location of the frequency ω_1 at which the semi-infinite characteristic with positive slope is to be located. Since the decrease in gain from $|L(j\omega_0)|$ to $|L(j\omega_1)|$ is $\Delta|L(j\omega)|$ (dB) $= GDB + GM$, it follows that

$$y = [(GDB + GM)/12 \beta] - 1 \qquad (3.4.4)$$

since the slope in that region is -12β dB/octave. Finally

$$\omega_1 = \omega_0 2^y. \qquad (3.4.5)$$

Computation of ω_2 (first approach)

The last step is to find the corner frequency ω_2, at which the final semi-infinite gain characteristic should be located. An approximated solution is easily obtained if we assume that the phase-lead added by the semi-infinite characteristic at ω_1 is equal to the amount of negative phase-lag that will be added at ω_0 by the insertion of the semi-infinite characteristic at ω_2. We have assumed that the slope at infinity is -12γ dB/oct. The slope of the semi-infinite characteristics is $-12e$dB/oct in terms of the number of excess e of poles over zeros at infinity. Also, since ω_1 and ω_2 are assumed to be much larger than ω_0, the phase $B(\omega)$ of the semi-infinite characteristic has a linear behavior where $\omega/\omega_0 << 1$. See Fig.E.4.3. Thus

$$\omega_2/\omega_1 = e/\beta. \tag{3.4.6}$$

This concludes the derivation of the Ideal Bode Characteristic for specified *GDB, GM, PM* and *e*.

It is important to remind the reader that the present derivation of the Ideal Bode characteristic is accompanied by a 'wasted phase-lead area', shown in Fig.3.4.2. Moreover, minimization of ω_2 is the primary concern for the Ideal Bode Characteristic. Hence, it is interesting to inquire if there is a way to decrease ω_2 without violating the initially stated specifications. A suggestion for achieving a smaller ω_2 follows.

Computation of ω_2 (second approach)

With the first approach of computing ω_2 it was necessary to locate the semi-infinite characteristic of the final slope so that the produced phase-lag would be canceled at ω_0 by the phase-lead produced by the semi-infinite characteristic with positive slope located at ω_1. Here we suggest locating the semi-infinite characteristic with negative slope at ω_2, so that the phase-lag at ω_{co} (the frequency at which the loop gain is 0 dB) will cancel the phase-lead produced at ω_{co} by the semi-infinite characteristic with positive slope located at ω_1. With this approach, the phase margin will be exactly satisfied. In order to observe the difference between the two solutions, an example will present the two ways of computing ω_2.

Example 3.4.1.   The specifications for the Ideal Bode Characteristic are: $\omega_0 = 1$ rad/sec; log magnitude in the useful frequency range $\omega < \omega_0$ is *GDB* = 40 dB; *PM* = $\pi/4$, (hence $\beta = 0.75$), *GM* = 10 dB; and $e = 4$.

Solution 1: To find ω_1, we use Eq.(3.4.4) for which $y = (40 + 10)/(12 \times 0.75)$-1 = 4.6. Thus $\omega_1 = 23.5$ rad/sec. From Eq.(3.4.5), it follows that $\omega_2 = 4 \times 2^{4.6}/0.75$ = 125 rad/sec. Therefore $\omega_2/\omega_1 = 5.3$. The resulting Ideal Bode Characteristic for $\omega_2 = 125$ rad/sec is shown in Fig.3.4.3.

Solution 2: $\omega_1 = 23.5$ rad/sec as it was found in Solution 1. To find ω_2, we first have to find the added phase-lead at ω_{co}. For this purpose we readily find that ω_{co} = 10.2 rad/sec. Since $\omega_{co} / \omega_1 = 10.2/23.5 = 0.43$, we find from Fig.E.4.3 that ΔPhase = 16° for a semi-infinite constant unity-slope characteristic. Since β = 0.75 was specified, it follows that ΔPhase = $16 \times 2 \times 0.75 = 24°$. Next, we have to find where to locate ω_2 so that the phase-lag contributed at $\omega_{co} = 10.2$ rad/sec by the four far-off poles ($e = 4$) will amount to 24°. Each far-off pole will add $24/4 = 6°$. Use of Fig.E.4.3 shows that $\omega_{co}/\omega_2 = 0.17$. Hence, $\omega_2 = 10.2/0.17$ = 60 rad/sec. The resulting Ideal Bode Characteristic is also shown in Fig.3.4.3. The phase margin specification is exactly satisfied.

It is clear from the nature of the design process that if the ω_2 corner frequency is lowered below 60 rad/sec, the phase margin will be violated. To illustrate this effect, the Ideal Bode Characteristic with $\omega_2 = 40$ rad/sec is also shown in Fig.3.4.3.

The Ideal Bode Characteristic as treated in this section cannot be implemented physically because the semi-infinite and other Bode characteristics cannot be expressed by finite rational polynomials in the *s*-variable. However, the Ideal Bode Characteristic shows clearly what are the minimum crossover frequency ω_{co} and ω_{GM} that can be achieved for specified *GDB, GM, PM* and ω_0. It is very important to notice that any gain bandwidth can be achieved as long as the loop transmission

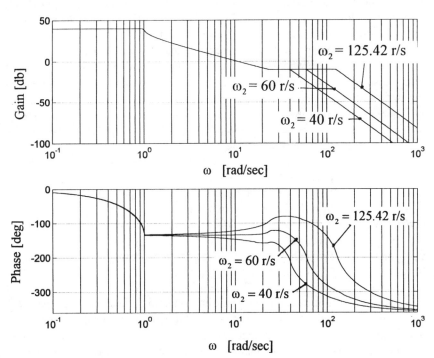

Figure 3.4.3. Ideal Bode Characteristics obtained with $\omega_2 = 40, 60$ and 125 rad/sec.

is minimum-phase. Nevertheless, although increasing of *GDB* will naturally increase the crossover frequency ω_{co}, there is no limit to the achievable magnitude
GDB for any specified frequency band ω_0, while still satisfying the initially set gain
and phase margins. Moreover, the designed Ideal Bode Characteristic remains stable if the gain is decreased by any amount, because the phase-lag in the range $\omega <$
ω_{co} is always smaller than $180°$-*PM*. However, the gain cannot be increased for the
achieved design without decreasing the phase margin.

It will be shown later that if $L(j\omega)$ is allowed to be conditionally stable, more
feedback can be obtained by increasing $|1+L(j\omega)|$ in the low-frequency range.

3.4.3. *Optimization of L(jω) for Conditionally Stable Systems*

Optimization of $L(j\omega)$ should consider increasing the area under the curve of
$|L(j\omega)|$ shown in Fig.3.4.1b in the frequency range $\omega < \omega_{co}$. According to
Eqs.(2.1.1) to (2.1.7), the benefits of feedback will then be increased. (In theory
we are interested in increasing $|1+ L(j\omega)|$, but, since $|1+ L(j\omega)| \approx |L(j\omega)|$ when
$|L(j\omega)| >> 1$, we attempt in practice to increase $|L(j\omega)|$). As was shown by Bode
(1945), (see also Appendix E), the average slope of $|L(j\omega)|$ of minimum-phase
transmission functions is closely proportional to the average argument of $L(j\omega)$.
For unconditionally stable feedback systems, the largest phase-lag of $L(j\omega)$ must
be less than $-\pi$ rad. Therefore, the negative slope of $|L(j\omega)|$ can be at most -40
dB/dec in the low-frequency range where $|L(j\omega)| > 0$ dB. Hence, if the slope is to
become more negative, the loop transmission function $L(j\omega)$ must become conditionally stable, with a phase-lag more negative than $-\pi$ rad in the low frequency
range, and with the drawbacks of conditional stability. A rough sketch of such a
loop transmission function is shown in Fig.3.4.4. Its basic characteristics are as
follows:

-mπ/2-	Phase-lag as $\omega \to 0$, pointing to the existence of *m* poles in the loop transmission at the origin.
-eπ/2-	Phase-lag as $\omega \to \infty$, pointing to the existence of an excess *e* of poles over zeros at infinity.
PM-	$PM = (1\text{-}\beta)\pi$-Phase margin.
ω_{co}-	Specified crossover frequency.
GMH, GML-	Specified *high* and *low* gain margins, above and below 0 dB re-spectively.
ω_{GMH} and ω_{GML}-	Frequencies at *GMH* and *GML* respectively.
$|T(j\omega)|_{max}$-	Maximum unity-feedback peak value.

To handle such optimal gain and phase characteristics, the finite-line phase segment shown in Fig.E.4.6 can be used, as we did beforehand for the design of an
Ideal Bode Characteristic. It is attractive to use for this purpose the finite-line phase
segments, and also the constant phase characteristic .(Bode 1945, Horowitz 1963
and Appendix E). But, instead of using these theoretical characteristics, we will

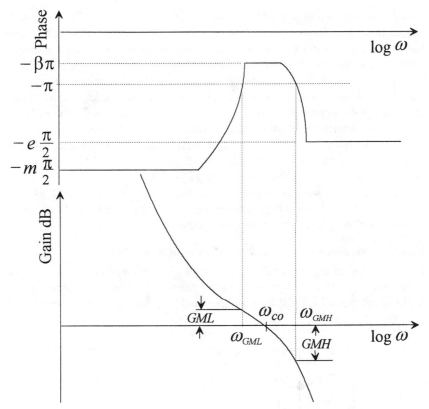

Figure 3.4.4. A conditionally stable loop transmission function.

design a conditionally stable loop transmission with Bode plots of physically realizable real and complex poles and zeros. Use of the Nichols chart offers insights
into an additional very important specification, namely, the maximum peak value
of $|T| = |L/(1 + L)|$.

Example 3.4.2. Design an optimal conditionally stable system with the following specifications: $m = 3$, $e = 3$, $PM = 40°$, $\omega_{co} = 2$ rad/sec, $GML = 10$ dB, GMH
$= 10$ dB, $|T(j\omega)|_{max} = 3$ dB.

Solution: The design consists of three principal steps.
Step 1. Choosing an initial loop transmission consisting of one integrator and a
gain of $k = 2$ to fit the $\omega_{co} = 2$ rad/sec specification.
Step 2. A second-order complex pole is added, so that the excess of three far-off
poles over zeros is assured ($e = 3$), together with the specified $\omega_{co} \approx 2$ rad/sec,
$PM = 40°$ and $GMH = 10$ dB. A simple cut-and-try procedure leads to the choice
of the complex pole $25/(s^2 + 6s + 25)$.

Step 3. The first two steps procured a loop transmission that satisfies the specifications in the high frequency range $\omega > 2$ rad/sec. We are now left with the problem of adding 2 additional integrators at the origin, so that the specification $m = 3$ will be also satisfied. In order to prevent the addition of appreciable phase-lag in the frequency region in which *PM, GM* and ω_{co} are already satisfied, each one of the additional integrators must be accompanied by a low frequency zero located at z. This will prevent the added phase-lag by $(s + z)/s$ from decreasing the achieved phase margin specification. The values z of the zeros are accommodated to satisfy also the *GML* specification. In this example, $z = 0.3$ was calculated, for which the gain k had to be slightly decreased to $k = 1.8$ in order not to spoil the achieved specifications in the previous stages.

The emerging $L(j\omega)$'s in each one of the design stages are shown in Figs.3.4.5 and 3.4.6, from which it is clearly seen that the initially stated specifications are satisfied, including the unity-feedback gain limitation of $+3$dB.

Benefits of feedback and the number of integrators at s = 0

Clearly, by increasing the number of integrators, a larger magnitude $|L(j\omega)|$ is obtained in the low frequency range. This is equivalent to improving the benefits of feedback. Figs.3.4.7 and 3.4.8 show three loop transmissions with the same high

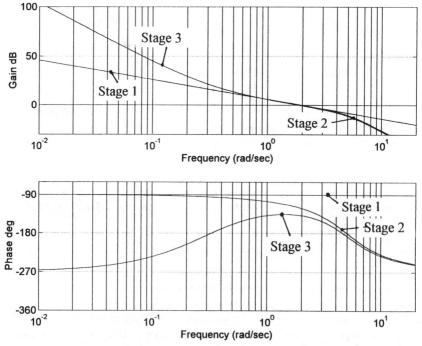

Figure 3.4.5.   Design steps on the Bode diagram.

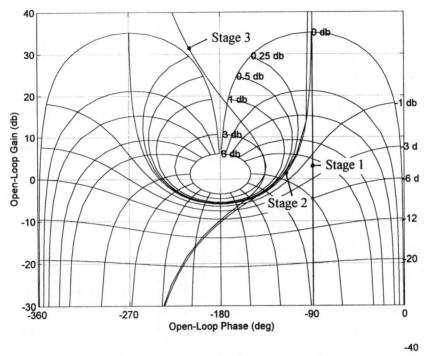

Figure 3.4.6.   Design steps on the Nichols chart.

frequency behavior but with a different number of integrators, namely, 2, 3 and 4. These loop transmissions are:

$$L_1(s) = \frac{2(s + 0.2)}{s^2} \frac{25}{s^2 + 2 \times 0.65 \times 5s + 5^2}$$

$$L_2(s) = \frac{1.8(s + 0.3)^2}{s^3} \frac{25}{s^2 + 2 \times 0.75 \times 5s + 5^2}$$

$$L_3(s) = \frac{2.2(s + 0.18)^3}{s^4} \frac{25}{s^2 + 2 \times 0.75 \times 5s + 5^2}.$$

The second transmission loop $L_2(j\omega)$ is the solution of Example 3.4.2.

As we see in Figs.3.4.7, the logarithmic magnitude versus $\log\omega$ of the three loop transmissions are quite identical in the frequency range $\omega > 0.5$ rad/sec, but they differ appreciably at frequencies below $\omega = 0.3$ rad/sec. This points to a progressive amelioration of 'benefits of feedback' as the number of integrators located at the origin is increased.

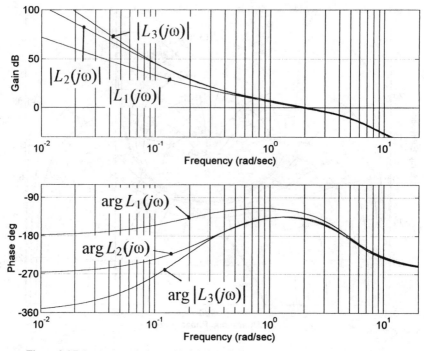

Figure 3.4.7. Loop transmissions with 2,3 and 4 integrators at $s = 0$ on the Bode diagram.

Optimization of the open-loop transmission function.

Optimization of the loop transmission from the point of view of the benefits of feedback will be reconsidered in another context. Meanwhile, note that $L_2(j\omega)$ and $L_3(j\omega)$ are tangential to the 3 dB unity-feedback constant gain contour. This means that in this frequency range, the loop transmission achieves the maximum permitted and available phase-lag. We shall show later that this condition is necessary in order to optimize the loop transmission.

3.5. Limitations on $L(j\omega)$ Including RHP Poles or Zeros

It was shown in Section 3.4 that large bandwidths can be obtained in feedback systems in which the plant is minimum-phase. This enables us to achieve any desired low sensitivity function S_p^T to plant uncertainties, together with good external disturbance rejection. Nonetheless, due to practical reasons, such as inherent sensor noise amplification, the practicing engineer is forced to limit the gain bandwidth of the controlled system (Horowitz 1963, Horowitz and Sidi 1972, Sidi 1976). Nevertheless, there is a large class of physical plants, the such as above-mentioned nonminimum-phase plants, for which the loop transmission bandwidth that can be achieved is **theoretically limited,** implying inherent limitations to the benefits of

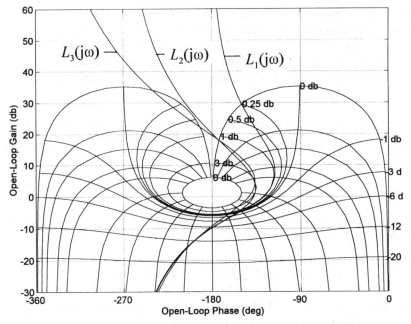

Figure 3.4.8. Loop transmissions with 2, 3 and 4 integrators at $s = 0$ on the Nichols chart.

feedback. This class of plants is characterized by the nonminimum-phase phenomenon caused by RHP zeros, pure time delays or the sampling process. RHP poles, on the contrary, put **theoretical limitations** on the minimum achievable bandwidth of the feedback controlled system.

Since the remainder of this chapter deals with plants including RHP poles and zeros, it is instructive to point out some special properties of such plants.

RHP zeros

A NMP transfer function was defined as a transfer function that contains at least one RHP zero. for instance,

$L_{NMP}(s) = L_1(s)(s - a)$, with $L_1(s)$-minimum-phase. Rewrite this equation as follows:

$$L_{NMP}(s) = L_1(s)(s - a) = L_1(s)(s + a)\frac{s - a}{s + a} = L_{MP}(s)\frac{s - a}{s + a} \qquad (3.5.1)$$

where $L_1(s)(s + a) = L_{MP}(s)$ is the minimum-phase counterpart of $L_{NMP}(s) = L_1(s)(s - a)$.

From Eq.(3.5.1), it is clear that $|L_{NMP}(j\omega)| = |L_{MP}(j\omega)|$, but

$$\arg[L_{NMP}(j\omega)] = \arg[L_{MP}(j\omega)] - 2\tan^{-1}(\omega/a). \qquad (3.5.2)$$

This implies that the phase-lag of a NMP system is always larger than that of its minimum-phase counterpart, particularly at the high frequencies. From here stems the name *nonminimum-phase*. This annoying property is responsible for limitations on the maximum crossover frequency ω_{co} that can be achieved. As a result, the achievable benefits of feedback with such systems is limited.

RHP poles

To get a feeling of an important property of unstable transfer functions, let $L(s) = L_1(s) /(s-a)$, where $L_1(s)$ is minimum-phase and stable.

$$L(s) = \frac{L_1(s)}{s-a} = \frac{L_1(s)}{s+a}\frac{s+a}{s-a} = L_2(s)\frac{s+a}{s-a}. \tag{3.5.3}$$

$L_2(s)$ is the stable transfer function counterpart of $L(s)$, and it is clear again that $|L(j\omega)| = |L_2(j\omega)|$, but,

$$\arg[L(j\omega)] = \arg[L_2(j\omega)] - \pi + 2\tan^{-1}(\omega/a) \tag{3.5.4}$$

The above equation implies that the phase-lag of an unstable system is always larger than that of its stable counterpart, especially at the low frequencies. As $\omega \to 0$, the additional phase-lag attains $-180°$ for a single unstable pole. As a result, the specified phase margin can be achieved at comparatively high frequencies, where the additional phase-lag becomes less harmful. With such systems, there are limitations on the minimum crossover frequency ω_{co} that can be achieved. The constrained large gain bandwidth is generally accompanied with the effect of a highly amplified sensor noise at the input to the plant.

The remaining part of this chapter is dedicated to the analysis of plants with RHP poles and/or zeros, with the aim of finding the limitations of attainable feedback benefits for such systems.

3.5.1.   Limitations on the Sensitivity Function $S(j\omega)$ for Feedback Systems with RHP Poles

It is well-known that for any minimum-phase open-loop rational transfer function in which the number of poles exceeds at least by two the number of zeros, the following integral relation exists, (Bode 1945, Horowitz 1963,)

$$\int_0^\infty \ln|S(j\omega)|\, d\omega = 0. \tag{3.5.5}$$

The above equality can also be expressed as

$$\int_0^\infty \ln|1 + L(j\omega)|\, d\omega = 0. \tag{3.5.6}$$

This equation means that in most practical minimum-phase systems the net feedback area (in decibels-radians/sec units) is zero. Sensitivity reduction area, where $|S(j\omega)| < 1$, is concentrated preferably in the low frequency range where sensitivity specifications are to be satisfied. The positive area of ln $|S(j\omega)|$ in the integral in Eq.(3.5.5) is spread in the higher frequency range, where no sensitivity reduction is required. However, when the plant is unstable, NMP, or both, Eqs.(3.5.5) and (3.5.6) do not hold anymore. Moreover, in unstable -NMP systems, the sensitivity function is alternately positive or negative, according to the relative locations of the RHP poles and zeros. There may very well be situations in which it becomes impossible to achieve a negative sensitivity area (in dB) in a specified frequency range, (Horowitz 1979, Leithead and O'Reilly 1991.) Freudenberg and Looze (1985, 1987) have shown that if unstable poles exist in the plant transfer function, then for practical systems in which the number of poles exceeds at least by two the number of zeros,

$$\int_0^\infty \log |S(j\omega)| d\omega = \pi \sum_{i=1}^{Np} Re[p_i] \qquad (3.5.7)$$

where N_p is the number of RHP poles which are located at p_i.

According to this result, the existence of RHP poles increases the positive part of the sensitivity integral. However, no conclusions can be deduced on the gain bandwidth limitations to practical systems, because the loop transmission $L(j\omega)$ can be manipulated so that the positive part of the integral of $\log|S(j\omega)|$ can be located in the high frequency range where the design specifications are more relaxed.

Let us look at the following example, in which the sensitivity function of an unstable-NMP $L_1(s)$ is compared with another loop transmission $L_2(s)$, in which all the RHP poles and zeros of $L_1(s)$ are relocated symmetrically in the LHP. (Both unity-feedback systems are stable).

$$L_1(s) = \frac{1}{1.89} \frac{(s - 0.2)}{s} \frac{(s/3 - 1)}{(s/12 - 1)(s/120 - 1)(s/1000 + 1)^2}$$

$$L_2(s) = \frac{1}{1.89} \frac{(s + 0.2)}{s} \frac{(s/3 + 1)}{(s/12 + 1)(s/120 + 1)(s/1000 + 1)^2}$$

$L_1(j\omega)$ and $L_2(j\omega)$ are shown in Fig.3.5.1, while $|S_1(j\omega)|$ and $|S_2(j\omega)|$ are shown in Fig.3.5.2.

We see in Fig.3.5.2 that the existence of RHP poles augments drastically the positive part of the sensitivity function. As a result, the frequency band in which feedback benefits are achieved is considerably reduced by a factor of roughly 300/0.1=3000, in this case.

Numerous weighted integral relations are reported in the literature; unfortunately, they have no real capability to help the practicing engineer in the design stage. They

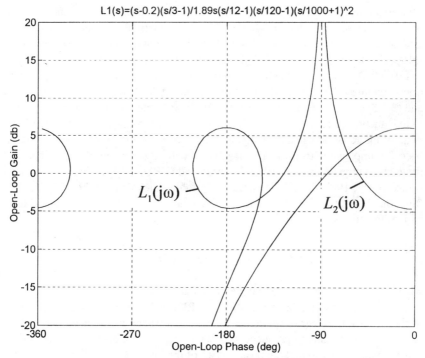

Figure 3.5.1. $L_1(j\omega)$ and $L_2(j\omega)$ on the Nichols chart

rather show qualitatively the limitations on the sensitivity function. Some less general, but more practical results can be obtained for real specific problems.

3.5.2.   Bandwidth Limitations due to RHP Zeros, Maximum Achievable ω_{co}

This section deals with limitations on the maximum achievable bandwidth in SISO feedback systems due to the existence of RHP zeros in the plant. The limits will

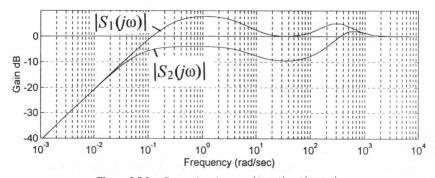

Figure 3.5.2.   Comparison between $|S_1(j\omega)|$ and $|S_2(j\omega)|$.

be approximated by an analytical relation that allows a quick evaluation of the maximum crossover frequency ω_{co} that can be achieved for such feedback systems, (Sidi 1997b).

Formulation of the problem

We shall be concerned with the non-zero-type loop transmission shown schematically in Fig.3.4.1b. It is clear from this figure that high loop gains are achievable below the crossover frequency. Thus, the basic limitation of a NMP loop transmission function will be the **maximal** crossover frequency ω_{co} that can be achieved. The benefits of feedback are, consequently, directly related to the maximal attainable ω_{co}.

Computation of relationships between gain margin, phase margin and ω_{co}

Let us make the following assumptions:

Assumption 1-The minimum-phase part of the loop transmission function can be approximated in the vicinity of the crossover frequency ω_{co} and above it by $L_{MP}(s)$ $= k/s^{2\alpha}, 0 < \alpha < 1$. With no loss of generality, we can assume that this holds for a sufficiently wide frequency range around ω_{co}. On the basis of this assumption, arg $L(j\omega)_{MP} \approx -\alpha\pi$ in the range $\omega \geq \omega_{co}$ (see Bode 1945 and also Appendix E.)

Assumption 2.-The all-pass function $A(s) = (a - s)/(a + s)$ relevant to the RHP zero located at a adds a phase-lag of $-2 \tan^{-1} (\omega/a)$ to the argument of $L_{MP}(s)$. As a result, the overall phase-lag of $L(s) = L_{MP}(s) (a - s)/(a + s)$ amounts to

$$\arg L(j\omega) = \arg L_{MP}(j\omega) + \arg [(a - s)/(a + s)] = -\alpha\pi - 2 \tan^{-1}(\omega/a).$$

Assumption 3.-The phase-lag added by the all-pass function $A(s)$ increases gradually to $-\pi$ rad at high frequencies. As a result, for any $\alpha > 0$, the overall phase-lag of $L(j\omega)$ must attain the value of $-\pi$ rad at a finite frequency $\omega < \infty$. This frequency was previously denoted by ω_{GM}, at which arg $L(j\omega_{GM}) = -\pi$, and where the gain margin is GM (see Fig.3.5.3.)

Assumption 4.-The *PM* is defined as $PM = (1-\beta)\pi$, see Fig.3.5.3.

With the above assumptions and notations, our problem now is to find the relationships between the maximum ω_{co} that can be achieved, and the specified gain and phase margins, (namely, *GM* and *PM*), in a loop transmission that includes a single RHP zero located at $+a$.

The argument of $L(j\omega)$ at ω_{co} is:

$$-\alpha\pi -2 \tan^{-1} (\omega_{co}/a) = -\beta\pi = -\pi + PM,$$

therefore

$$\frac{\omega_{co}}{a} = \tan \frac{(1 - \alpha)\pi - PM}{2} = \cot \frac{\alpha\pi + PM}{2} \qquad (3.5.8)$$

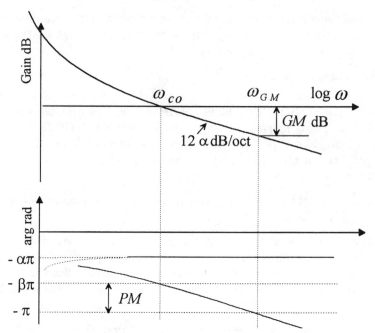

Figure 3.5.3. Definition of ω_{co}, ω_{GM}, *GM*, *PM* and α.

Similarly, we can find ω_{GM} in terms of α and a,

$$\frac{\omega_{GM}}{a} = \tan \frac{(1 - \alpha)\pi}{2} = \cot \frac{\alpha\pi}{2} \qquad (3.5.9)$$

Therefore

$$GM = \left[\frac{\omega_{GM}}{\omega_{co}}\right]^{2\alpha} = \left[\frac{\tan \dfrac{\alpha\pi + PM}{2}}{\tan \dfrac{\alpha\pi}{2}}\right]^{2\alpha} \qquad (3.5.10)$$

For any given *GM* and *PM*, α can be calculated from Eq.(3.5.10). Inserting the calculated α into Eq.(3.5.8) yields the maximum achievable crossover frequency normalized to *a*: $\omega_{aco} = \omega_{co}/a$. Analytical closed form solution of the above transcendental equations becomes unrealistic. Hence, these equations were solved numerically. The resulting graphs of the maximum achievable crossover frequency $\omega_{aco} = \omega_{co}/a$ as functions of *GM* and *PM* are shown in Fig.3.5.4, in which *PM* is a parameter.

In the practical design of $L(s)$, the results in Fig.3.5.4 might not be exactly achieved due to the realistic behavior of $L(j\omega)$ in the frequency range $\omega > \omega_{GM}$,

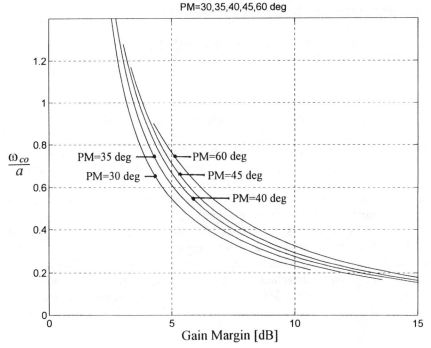

Figure 3.5.4. ω_{co}/a as function of *GM* in dB with *PM* in degrees as parameter.

where $|L(j\omega)|$ is ultimately reaching a slope more negative than -12α dB/oct. This violates assumption 1, but the results are still very useful in foreseeing the approximate maximum achievable ω_{co}.

The resulting graphs in Fig.3.5.4 can be expressed in the following analytical form:

$$\frac{\omega_{co}}{a} = \frac{k_1\,(PM) + k_3}{GM + k_2\,(PM) + k_4} \qquad (3.5.11)$$

Using the graphical results in Fig.3.5.4, the following approximation was achieved for k_1, k_2, k_3 and k_4,

$$\frac{\omega_{co}}{a} = \frac{0.02PM[\text{deg}] + 1.6}{GM[dB] - 0.026PM[\text{deg}] - 0.24} \qquad (3.5.12)$$

where *PM* is in degrees and *GM* is in dB. Eq.(3.5.12) is a good expression for the graphic results in Fig.3.5.4 in the range $PM = 30°$ to $45°$ and $GM = 4$ to 12db, as can be checked by direct substitution of *GM* and *PM* in the equation.

These results are now illustrated by the example below.

Example 3.5.1.   Design a loop transmission $L(s)$ with maximum achievable ω_{co}, if the plant transfer function is

$$P(s) = (s - 3)/[s(s + 8)].$$

Repeat the designs for adequate $L(s)$'s with one and two integrators at $s = 0$.

Solution: By conventional loopshaping procedures, the following loop transmission functions, $L_1(s) = -2.5(s - 3)(s + 0.5)/[s(s + 8)(s + 0.1)]$ and $L_2(s) = -2.5(s - 3)(s + 0.4)/[s^2(s + 8)]$, were obtained with one and two integrators respectively at the origin. Their frequency responses are shown in Figs.3.5.5 (the Nichols chart) and 3.5.6 (the Bode diagram).

The Bode plots show that for both $L_1(s)$ and $L_2(s)$, $GM[dB] \cong 10$ dB, $PM \cong 45°$ and $\omega_{co} = 1.0$ rad/sec. For these parameters, the theoretically achievable crossover frequency (according to Fig.3.5.4) is $\omega_{co} = 0.9$ rad/sec. The difference between the theoretically achievable, and the practically achieved crossover frequencies, as we thought would occur, is caused by the additional far-off poles that

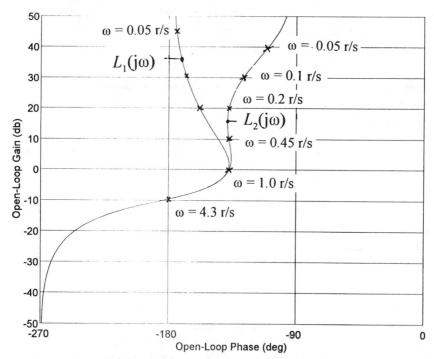

Figure 3.5.5. $L_1(j\omega)$ and $L_2(j\omega)$ on the Nichols chart.

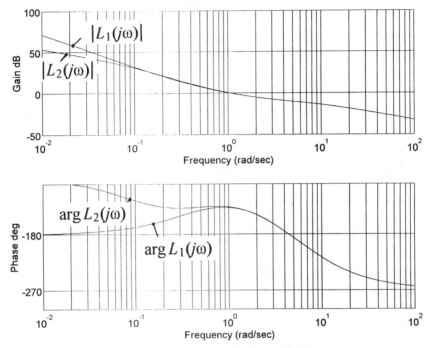

Figure 3.5.6.   Bode plots of $L_1(j\omega)$ and $L_2(j\omega)$.

have been added to both loop transmissions. These poles make the loop transmissions approach the final slope of three integrators as $\omega \to \infty$. The integral (in decibels-radians per second units) of the feedback area $\int |1 + L_2(j\omega)| \, d\omega$ in the range $\omega < \omega_{co}$ is higher than that fo $L_1(j\omega)$ due to the additional integrator at the origin. Thus, improvement of the sensitivity function $S(j\omega) = 1/[1 + L(j\omega)]$ is achieved. More integrators can be added in order to increase the magnitude of the loop transmission function in the frequency range $\omega < \omega_{co}$, while keeping ω_{co} at its nominally achieved location. However, the benefits of feedback cannot be improved at frequencies beyond ω_{co} (about 0.9 rad/sec in this case!).

Existence of additional RHP zeros can only aggravate the situation. When more than one RHP zeros are present in the plant, they can be approximated as an equivalent single RHP zero.

3.5.3. Equivalent NMP Zero Approximation to Multiple NMP Zeros (Sidi and Yaniv 1999).

Suppose that the plant contains m RHP zeros. Each one can be displayed as an all-pass transfer function. When all the RHP zeros are considered, an overall all-pass function is obtained, namely,

$$A(s) = \frac{(s - z_1)}{(s + z_1)} \frac{(s - z_2)}{(s + z_2)} \cdots\cdots \frac{(s - z_m)}{(s + z_m)}. \tag{3.5.13}$$

The argument, due to all the RHP zeros and to all the LHP poles of $A(s)$ at a frequency ω, amounts to

$$\arg[A(s)]_{s=j\omega} = m\pi - 2 \sum_{i=1}^{m} \tan^{-1} (\omega/z_i) \tag{3.5.14}$$

But, since the smallest RHP zero, let us say z_1, is the crucial because of stability considerations, the following approximation holds in the frequency range $\omega < z_1$:

$$\tan^{-1} (\omega/z_i) \approx \omega/z_i \tag{3.5.15}$$

so that Eq.(3.5.14) can be modified to

$$\arg[A(s)]_{s=j\omega} \approx m\pi - 2 \sum_{i=1}^{m} (\omega/z_i) = m\pi - 2\omega \sum_{i=1}^{m} (1/z_i) = m\pi - 2\omega/z_{eq}. \tag{3.5.16}$$

From the above equation we can define an approximate expression for an equivalent RHP z_{eq},

$$1/z_{eq} = \sum_{i=1}^{m} 1/z_i \tag{3.5.17}$$

The approximation of the argument in Eq.(3.5.16) is very definitely poor in the high frequency range. But, this is not a bothersome reality because the relative stability is defined in the vicinity of the crossover frequency ω_{co} where the approximation is satisfactory. Hence, with the equivalent RHP zero located at z_{eq}, we can analyze the feedback limitations as per the results in Fig.3.5.4 and Eq.(3.5.12).

An example will illustrate the usefulness of the 'equivalent RHP zero' in finding the feedback limitations from the graphs in Fig.3.5.4.

Example 3.5.2.   Suppose that the plant comprises two RHP zeros located at $z_1 = 3$ and $z_2 = 6$ rad/sec. By loopshaping, obtain the loop transmission function with the maximum achievable ω_{co} and with a prescribed phase margin of $PM = 45°$.

Solution: We find first the equivalent RHP z_{eq} by use of Eq.(3.5.17), namely, $z_{eq} = 2$. From Fig.3.5.4, we find that $\omega_{co}/a = 0.305$, thus, the approximated maximal $\omega_{co} = 2 \times 0.305 = 0.61$. Two loop transmission functions were designed, $L_1(s)$ comprising the equivalent NMP zero, and $L_2(s)$ comprising the two original NMP zeros, namely,

$$L_1(s) = \frac{-2.35(s - 2)(s + 0.4)}{s(s + 0.1)(s + 8)}; \quad L_2(s) = \frac{3.8(s - 3)(s - 6)(s + 0.35)}{s(s + 0.1)(s + 8)(s + 15)}.$$

$L_1(j\omega)$ and $L_2(j\omega)$ are plotted in Fig.3.5.7. The obtained crossover frequency is ω_{co} = 0.65 for both transmission functions, which is quite close to the estimated maximum value of 0.61. As previously indicated, the differences in behavior of both transfer functions at high frequencies are quite pronounced. Nevertheless, this does not defy the conclusions about the maximum obtainable crossover frequency.

To summarize, the RHP zeros limit the open-loop bandwidth when output feedback is used. This is accompanied by all the compulsory drawbacks, such as limited capabilities in attenuating effects due to external disturbances and to plant uncertainty. (To remind the reader, a second, and no less detrimental feature of NMP plants is that a time delay in the step response of the closed-loop transfer function is introduced with an inevitable undershoot, as discussed in Section 3.3).

Remark. Sampled-data linear feedback systems exhibit NMP characteristics when analyzed in the w-domain. The w transform is defined as $w = (z - 1)/(z + 1)$, where z is the Z transform variable. Actually, when a continuous transfer function is sampled and transformed to the w-domain, a RHP zero emerges, whose value decreases as the sampling frequency is reduced (see Saucedo and Schiring 1968). Consequently, the maximum achievable crossover frequency of the sampled-data loop transmission function is limited by the value of the sampling frequency (see Sidi 1976, and Section 4.7).

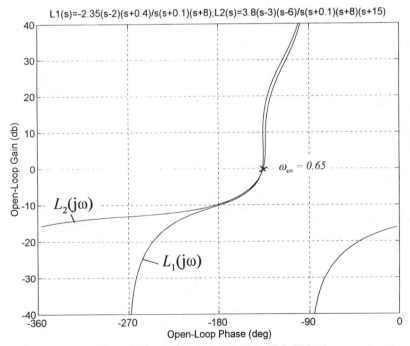

Figure 3.5.7. $L_1(j\omega)$ and $L_2(j\omega)$ on the Nichols chart.

3.6   Limitations on Unstable $L(j\omega)$-Minimal Achievable ω_{co}

3.6.1   Introduction

The existence of RHP poles causes the loop transmission function to acquire 'NMP' features because of the increased phase-lag at low frequencies as expressed by Eq.(3.5.4). The phase-lag generated by a single, unstable pole located at $\omega = +a$ is $-\pi + \text{tang}^{-1}(\omega/a)$. This phase starts at $-180°$ and increases progressively towards $-90°$ at high frequencies. The effect on the achievable loop transmission, caused by the additional phase-lag in the low frequency range, is totally different than that caused by RHP zeros; a RHP pole puts a lower limit on the achievable ω_{co}. Since at $\omega = 0$ the open-loop phase is $-180°$, it is clear that the magnitude of $L(j\omega)$ cannot be decreased at will. A low-frequency gain margin (*GML*) must be provided. In reality, there are no physical systems in which the plant, together with the control network, have an excess of poles over zeros smaller than two at high frequencies. Moreover, in order to minimize sensor noise amplification, far-off poles will be added, so that, the loop transmission tends to have at least three more poles than zeros at high frequencies, with the impact that $L(j\omega)$ must cross the $-180°$ axis in the Nichols chart. Therefore, the usual gain margin *GM* will become evident and finite. With these practical assumptions, the control problem is well defined: find a relationship between achievable phase and gain margins, and a minimal ω_{co}, as a function of the location of a single unstable pole.

3.6.2   Functional Relationships

Basic characteristics of an unstable loop transmission function are shown in Fig.3.6.1.

To obtain the stated relationship, consider the loop transmission function (Sidi,1997(b))

$$L(s) = \frac{k}{\left(\frac{s}{a}-1\right)\left(\frac{s^2}{\omega_n^2} + \frac{2\xi}{\omega_n}s+1\right)} \tag{3.6.1}$$

Let us define the normalized Laplace variable $s_a = s/a$, and also the normalized frequencies $\omega_a = \omega/a$, $\omega_{aco} = \omega_{co}/a$ and $\omega_n = \gamma a$. With these definitions, $L(s)$ of Eq.(3.6.1) becomes

$$L(s_a) = \frac{k}{(s_a - 1)\left(\frac{s_a^2}{\gamma^2} + \frac{2\xi s_a}{\gamma} + 1\right)} \tag{3.6.2}$$

At very low frequencies, arg $L(j\omega_a) \to -\pi$, hence, at $s_a = 0$, $k = L(j0) = GML$

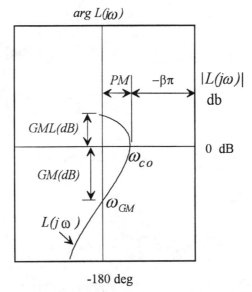

Figure 3.6.1. Basic characteristics of an unstable loop transmission on the Nichols chart

(the low frequency gain margin). The gain and phase of $L(j\omega_a)$ can be written in terms of *GML*, γ and ξ as follows

$$|L(j\omega_a)| = \frac{k\gamma^2}{\sqrt{1 + \omega_a^2}\sqrt{\left(\gamma^2 - \omega_a^2\right)^2 + \left(2\,\xi\,\gamma\omega_a\right)^2}} \tag{3.6.3}$$

$$\arg L(j\omega_a) = -\pi + \tan^{-1}\left(\frac{\omega}{a}\right) - \tan^{-1}\left(\frac{2\xi\omega_n\omega}{\omega_n^2 - \omega^2}\right)$$

$$= -\pi + \tan^{-1}(\omega_a) - \tan^{-1}\left(\frac{2\,\xi\,\gamma\omega_a}{\gamma^2 - \omega_a^2}\right) \tag{3.6.4}$$

Eqs.(3.6.3) and (3.6.4) can be used to find the phase margin *PM*, the crossover normalized frequency ω_{aco} and the usual gain margin normalized frequency ω_{aGM}. Next, let us write the relationship between the *GML*, the normalized crossover frequency ω_{aco} and γ. By Eq.(3.6.3)

$$|L(j\omega_{aco})| = \frac{GML\,\gamma^2}{\sqrt{1 + \omega_{aco}^2}\sqrt{\left(\gamma^2 - \omega_{aco}^2\right)^2 + \left(2\,\xi\,\gamma\omega_{aco}\right)^2}} = 1$$

thus

$$GML = \sqrt{1+\omega_{aco}^2} \, \sqrt{\left(1 - \frac{\omega_{aco}^2}{\gamma^2}\right)^2 + \left(\frac{2\,\xi\,\omega_{aco}}{\gamma}\right)^2} \qquad (3.6.5)$$

In order to calculate the usual high frequency gain margin *GM*, we have to find first the frequency ω_{aGM} at which the phase of $L(j\omega_a)$ is $-\pi$ (and $|L(j\omega_{aGM})| < 1$). Use Eq.(3.6.4) to obtain

$$-\pi + \tan^{-1}(\omega_{aGM}) - \tan^{-1}\left(\frac{2\,\xi\,\gamma\,\omega_{aGM}}{\gamma^2 - \omega_{aGM}^2}\right) = -\pi$$

from which it follows that

$$\omega_{aGM} = \frac{2\,\xi\,\gamma\,\omega_{aGM}}{\gamma^2 - \omega_{aGM}^2} = \sqrt{\gamma^2 - 2\xi\gamma} \qquad (3.6.6)$$

To find the gain margin *GM*, substitute $\omega_a = \omega_{aGM}$ in Eq.(3.6.3), so that:

$$GM = \frac{\gamma\,GML}{\left(1 + \gamma^2 - 2\xi\gamma\right)2\xi}. \qquad (3.6.7)$$

Next, a relation for the phase margin *PM* is to be found. The phase margin was defined previously as follows (Fig.3.6.1): at ω_{aco} the phase is $-\pi\beta$. Hence the *PM* equals $PM = (1-\beta)\pi$. From Eq.(3.6.4) we can write for a given *PM* at ω_{aco} :

$$\arg L(j\omega_{aco}) = -\beta\pi = -\pi + PM = -\pi + \tan^{-1}(\omega_{aco}) - \tan^{-1}\left[\frac{2\xi\gamma\omega_{aco}}{\gamma^2 - \omega_{aco}^2}\right]$$

hence

$$\tan^{-1}\left[\frac{2\xi\gamma\omega_{aco}}{\gamma^2 - \omega_{aco}^2}\right] = \tan^{-1}(\omega_{aco}) - PM. \qquad (3.6.8)$$

Therefore

$$\left[\frac{2\xi\gamma\omega_{aco}}{\gamma^2 - \omega_{aco}^2}\right] = \frac{\omega_{aco} - \tan(PM)}{1 + \omega_{aco}\tan(PM)}. \qquad (3.6.9)$$

Finally, by use of Eqs.(3.6.5) to (3.6.9), we can get a set of graphical relationships between γ, *PM*, ω_{aco}, *GML*[dB] and *GM*[dB] for different ξ's . To accomplish that, we first differentiate Eq.(3.6.4) in order to obtain the minimum argument of $L(s_a)$, which happens to be at $\omega_a = \omega_{aco}$. Having found ω_{aco} as function of γ and ξ, we obtain the *PM* from Eq.(3.6.8). *GML* is found from Eq.(3.6.5), and so on. These relations are shown in Fig.3.6.2 for $\xi = 0.5$.

The graphs on the figure clearly show the maximum *PM* for a given γ, and the minimum ω_{aco} that can be achieved for each case. Fig.3.6.3 shows the resulting loop transmissions on the Nichols chart for $\gamma = 3.65, 5.3 , 8.3, 14.5, 33$ and 1000, with respective phase margins of $30°, 40°, 50°, 60°, 70°$ and $80°$.

The analytical derivations of the results shown in Figs.3.6.2 and 3.6.3 are based on the assumption that $\xi = 0.5$, which is reasonable in practical designs of loop transmission functions. Similar graphical results can be obtained for other values of ξ. Results obtained with $\xi = 0.4$ and 0.6 demonstrated that no significant differences in the obtained graphical results in Fig.3.6.2 were perceived. To summarize, the graphs in Fig.3.6.2 give a satisfactory approximation to the smallest ω_{co} that can be achieved for a given unstable pole, and for specified phase and gain margins.

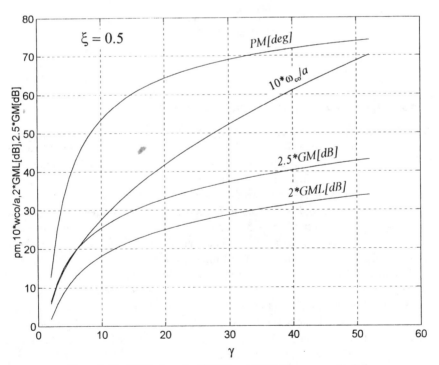

Figure 3.6.2. *PM*[deg], ω_{co}/a, *GM*[dB] and *GML*[dB] versus γ, $\xi = 0.5$.

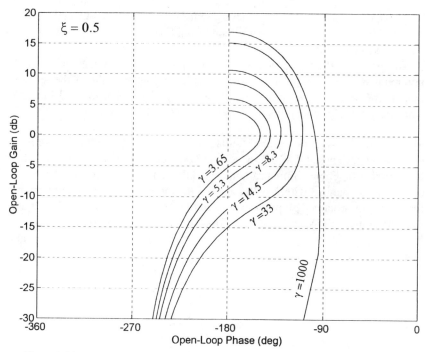

Figure 3.6.3.   Realization of the loop transmission functions for different γ's and ξ = 0.5.

3.6.3.   *Application of the Results in Practical Problems.*

In any practical feedback control problem, we are interested in reducing ω_n (γ in this case) as much as possible, in order to minimize the RMS noise amplification from n to u in Fig.2.1.1. The results in Fig.3.6.2 can be used to find what the constraints will be on a loop transmission function containing an unstable pole. For instance, let us suppose that we dictate $PM = 40°$. The smallest γ with which this PM can be achieved is γ = 5.3 in Fig.3.6.2. This choice ascertains also that $\omega_{co}/a = 1.8$. For the chosen γ = 5.3, and $PM = 40°$, we also find that $GML[dB] = 5.8$ dB and that GM [dB]= 7.2 dB. These results are confirmed in the Nichols chart of Fig.3.6.3 which shows the resulting $L(j\omega_a)$ by Eq.(3.6.2) for different γ's.

Practical loop transmission functions will be more complicated than the assumed forms in Eqs.(3.6.1) and (3.6.2), since they will contain a large number of poles and zeros in addition to the unstable pole. Nonetheless, optimal shaping of the loop transmission function in the frequency domain will possess the basic characteristics shown in Figs.3.6.1 and 3.6.3, for which the results in Fig.3.6.2 hold. Here again additional integrators can be added at $s = 0$ in order to increase the magnitude of the loop transmission in the frequency range $\omega < \omega_{co}$, while still keeping ω_{co} in its nominally achieved location.

In case that more than one RHP poles are involved in the plant transfer function, an equivalent RHP pole can be approximated, as we did in Section 3.5.3 for multiple RHP zeros.

3.6.4. Equivalent RHP Pole Approximation to Several RHP Poles,
Sidi and Yaniv 1999

Suppose that the plant comprises m RHP poles. Each one is displayed as an inverted all-pass transfer function. The expression for the inverted overall all-pass transfer function considering all the RHP poles takes the form

$$M(s) = \frac{(s + p_1)}{(s - p_1)} \frac{(s + p_2)}{(s - p_2)} \cdots \cdots \frac{(s + p_m)}{(s - p_m)}. \tag{3.6.10}$$

The argument, due to all RHP poles and to all LHP zeros of $M(s)$ at a frequency ω, amounts to

$$\arg[M(j\omega)] = -m\pi + 2 \sum_{i=1}^{m} \cot^{-1}(p_i/\omega) \tag{3.6.11}$$

But, since the largest RHP pole, let us say p_1, is the crucial one for stability, the following approximation holds in the frequency range $\omega > p_1$:

$$\cot^{-1}(p_i/\omega) \approx p_i/\omega \tag{3.6.12}$$

and Eq.(3.6.11) takes the approximate form

$$\arg[M(j\omega)] = -m\pi + 2 \sum_{i=1}^{m} (p_i/\omega) = -m\pi + 2(p_{eq}/\omega). \tag{3.6.13}$$

Finally, we can define an approximate expression for an equivalent RHP p_{eq}, namely,

$$p_{eq} = \sum_{i=1}^{m} p_i \tag{3.6.14}$$

The approximation of the argument in Eq.(3.6.13) is certainly poor at the low frequency range. But, this is not a bothersome reality because the relative stability is defined in the vicinity of the crossover frequency ω_{co} where the approximation is satisfactory. Hence, with the equivalent RHP pole located at p_{eq}, we can analyze the feedback limitations as per the results in Fig.3.6.2. The following example illustrates the usefulness of the equivalent unstable pole p_{eq} approximation.

Example 3.6.1.   Suppose that the plant comprises two RHP poles located at $p_1 = 1$ and at $p_2 = 3$. Design a loop transmission function with a minimum ω_{co} and with a prescribed phase margin of $PM = 40°$.

Solution: First, from Eq.(3.6.14) it follows that the equivalent RHP pole is located at $p_{eq} = 4$, and from Fig.3.6.2, it follows that $\omega_{co}/a = 1.85$, so that $\omega_{co} = 7.4$. Two loop transmission functions were designed; $L_1(s)$ comprising the equivalent RHP pole, and $L_2(s)$ comprising the two original unstable poles of the plant, namely:

$$L_1(s) = \frac{8}{(s-4)(s^2/21.2^2+s/21.2+1)}$$

and

$$L_2(s) = \frac{16(s+2.2)(s+5)}{(s-1)(s-3)(s^2/20^2+1.6s/20+1)(s+15)}.$$

$L_1(j\omega)$ and $L_2(j\omega)$ are shown in Fig.3.6.4. We find that $\omega_{co} = 7.8$ for $L_1(j\omega)$ and $\omega_{co} = 7.5$ for $L_2(j\omega)$, both quite close to the theoretical limit predicted by the re-

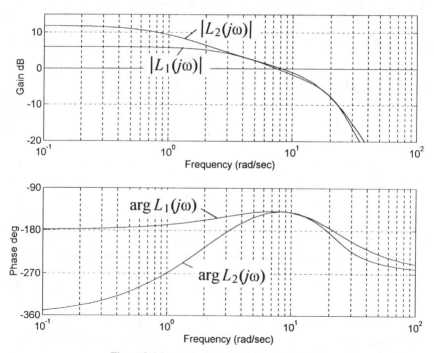

Figure 3.6.4.   Bode plot of $L_1(j\omega)$ and of $L_2(j\omega)$.

sults in Fig.3.6.2. However, we see also that, as expected, $L_1(j\omega)$ and $L_2(j\omega)$ differ quite seriously in the low frequency range.

3.7. Stabilization

3.7.1. Introduction

Until now, we have been dealing with different design techniques and problems generally associated with minimum-phase plants, or with plants containing several RHP zeros **or** poles (but not both of them simultaneously). Limitations on achievable crossover frequencies related to specified gain and phase margins were obtained analytically for this quite common class of plants. However, stabilization of feedback control systems, in which RHP poles and zeros are included simultaneously in the plant transfer function, is not a straightforward problem. A practical question that arises is whether a stabilizing controller can be always found in a feedback structure with an imbedded plant that includes an arbitrary number of right-half-plane poles and zeros. The answer is positive, and a design procedure for stabilizing such plants will be introduced.

Guillemin suggested in the late 1940s how to determine the open-loop transfer function from the defined closed-loop transfer function (Truxal, 1955). Analytical treatment of this problem can already be found in the late 1950s (Newton at al. 1957). Pioneer works in systematic analytic derivations of stabilizing controllers for both SISO and MIMO feedback systems can be found in Youla, Bongiorno and Lu (1974), Youla, Bongiorno and Jabr (1976), Youla, Jabr and Bongiorno (1976), Bongiorno and Youla (1977). Additional basic treatment of the subject can be found in Desoer et al. (1980), Vidyasagar (1985), Morari and Zafiriou (1989), Doyle, Francis and Tannenbaum (1992). The suggested design techniques for stabilizing such unfriendly unstable-NMP plants are based on parametrization of an assumed controller, and in finding its parameters. In general, a stable plant can be always stabilized with a stable compensator. This is not true for plants containing RHP poles and zeros.

3.7.2. Strongly Stabilizable Plants.

In the feedback control structure of Fig.2.1.1, it is assumed that if the plant contains hidden modes, these are asymptotically stable. A *strongly stabilizable* plant is a plant that can be stabilized with a stable compensator. An important theorem related to such control feedback systems, proven in Youla et al. (1974), follows.

Theorem 3.7.1 Consider a plant $P(s)$, (with possibly hidden modes that can only be asymptotically stable), containing l *distinct real zeros* in the RHP, $\sigma_1, \sigma_2, \ldots,$ σ_l, and let the total number of *real poles* of $P(s)$ to the right of σ_i, each counted according to its multiplicity, be denoted by v_i, $i = 1, 2, \ldots, l$. Then the plant is *strongly stabilizable* if and only if the integers v_i, $i = 1, 2, \ldots, l$ are either *all even* or *all odd*.

In most practical systems, the number of poles is larger than the number of zeros, (the plant is strictly proper, $P(\infty) = 0$). Since the number of real poles of $P(s)$ to the right of $+\infty$ is zero, an even integer, the following important corollary was also proven.

Corollary 3.7.1 A plant, (with possibly hidden modes that can only be asymptotically stable), which is strictly proper, $P(\infty) = 0$, is strongly stabilizable if, and only if, every *real* zero of $P(s)$ in the RHP lies to the left of an *even* number of *real* poles of $P(s)$, the latter counted according to their multiplicity. The corollary is very important because it helps the designer to clarify for himself why the achieved stabilizing compensator is unstable for a feedback control system including a NMP-unstable plant (Sections 3.9.2 and 3.9.3). For plants comprising a relatively small number of RHP poles and zeros, it is sometimes clear from root-locus method rules if unstable poles are necessary for stabilizing the feedback system. But, for more elaborated unstable-NMP plants, the necessity of RHP poles for stabilization is not always evident.

Systematic design procedures are presented in the next two sections for stabilizing a feedback structure with an imbedded plant including an arbitrary number of RHP poles and zeros.

3.7.3. *Parametrization of the Stabilizing Controller: Stable Plant*

Here we assume that the plant transfer function $P(s)$ is stable and that all control networks $G(s)$ in Fig.2.1.1, for which the feedback system is internally stable, are parametrized. The parameters of controllers are chosen so that certain design features are achieved. The idea behind the following theorem 3.7.2 originates in Newton et al. (1957). The proof can be found in Doyle et al.(1992).

Theorem 3.7.2   Assume that $P(s)$ is a stable transfer function. The set of all $G(s)$s for which the feedback system in Fig.2.1.1 is internally stable is given by

$G(s)$: $= Q(s)/[1-P(s)Q(s)]$; $Q(s)$ is a stable transfer function.

In this theorem $Q(s)$ is defined as

$$Q(s): = G/[1 + GP] \qquad (3.7.1)$$

which is the transfer function from r to u, with $F(s) = 1$; we also find that $T_{un}(s)$ $= -Q(s)$ by Eq.(2.1.4). For internal stability, $Q(s)$ must be a stable transfer function. To apply the above theorem to any practical problem, all we have to do is to choose the desired transfer function $u(s)/r_1(s) = Q(s)$ in Fig.2.1.1, complying with design specifications. The control network $G(s)$ is then automatically obtained from Eq.(3.7.1), namely,

$$G(s) = Q(s)/[1-P(s)Q(s)].$$ (3.7.2)

In choosing $Q(s)$ and its special features, and knowing $P(s)$, care must be taken to assure that $G(s)$ will be asymptotically stable and a proper transfer function, (preferably strictly proper in order to decrease sufficiently the sensor noise amplification, see Section 2.4.1). An example will emphasize some problems in using this technique.

Example 3.7.1. Suppose that $P(s) = 1/[(s+0.5)(s+1)]$. Parametrize a control network $G(s)$ to stabilize the feedback system. Let us try

$$Q(s) = k/(s+a).$$ (3.7.3)

By Eq.(3.7.2) we obtain

$$G(s) = \frac{k(s + 0.5)(s + 1)}{s^3 + (1.5 + a)s^2 + (0.5 + 1.5a)s + a0.5 - k}.$$ (3.7.4)

The achieved transfer function is strictly proper. However, if $k > 0.5a$, the compensator $G(s)$ is unstable, which puts a first constraint on the chosen $Q(s)$ if $G(s)$ is to be stable. Moreover, even if $k < 0.5a$, for a compensator to be stable, the polynomial of the denominator of $G(s)$ must only have stable roots.

Remark 1. This purely systematic way of designing the controller has its deficiencies. First, for an arbitrarily chosen transfer function $Q(s) = -T_{un}(s)$, the control network $G(s)$ may turn out to be unstable. This is unreasonable, and practically unacceptable by control designers when dealing with stable plant feedback systems. This situation is never encountered when stable plant feedback systems are designed in the frequency-domain by using Nyquist/Bode-oriented design techniques. Moreover, a synthetic choice of $Q(s)$ does not automatically take care of additional, important design parameters, such as phase and gain margins, crossover frequency, etc.

***Example 3.7.1*-continued** Suppose that from sensor noise amplification at the plant input, or from steady-state error coefficient considerations, we decide to choose $a = 5$. In order to find a stable compensator $G(s)$, we can fix $k = 2 < 0.5a$. With this choice of the parameters of $Q(s)$, $G(s)$ becomes

$$G_1(s) = \frac{2(s + 0.5)(s + 1)}{(s + 4.8825)(s + 1.5515)(s + 0.066)}.$$

Next, suppose that k is increased to 5 in order to ameliorate some feedback system performances. With this choice of k, the compensator becomes

$$G_2(s) = \frac{5(s + 1)(s + 0.5)}{(s + 4.6739)(s + 2.0829)(s - 0.2568)}$$

which is an unstable compensator. $L_1(j\omega)$ and $L_2(j\omega)$ for both designs are shown on the Nichols chart in Fig.3.7.1.

Notice that $L_2(j\omega) = G_2(j\omega)P(j\omega)$ becomes conditionally stable as expected, because of the existence of an unstable pole in the loop transmission function.

Remark 2. The parameters of the parametrized $Q(s)$ can be fixed so that adequate error coefficients are achieved, if needed. For instance, if $Q(s)$ is chosen to have the form presented in Eq.(3.7.3) and if we put $k = 0.5a$, then $G(s)$ in Eq.(3.7.4)

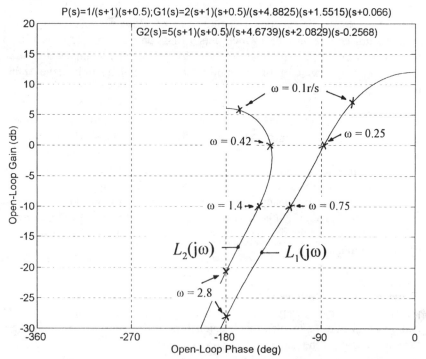

Figure 3.7.1. $L_1(j\omega) = G_1(j\omega) P(j\omega)$ and $L_2(j\omega) = G_2(j\omega) P(j\omega)$ on the Nichols chart.

will comprise one integrator at the origin. With the assumed plant in Example 3.7.1, the loop transmission $L(s)$ will also contain one integrator, which assures a zero steady-state error for a step input $r(t) = U(t)$, and a finite steady-state error for a velocity input $r(t) = R_v\, t\, U(t)$ (See Appendix G.)

3.7.4. Parametrization of the Stabilizing Controller: Unstable Plant

In this section, the plant is assumed to be unstable, or more generally, it may also include RHP zeros. Numerous design techniques provide straightforward procedures for stabilizing stable plant feedback systems. Stabilization and loopshaping in the frequency-domain based on the Nyquist criterion lead easily to internal stabilization of the feedback system with the simple theoretical constraint of no encirclements of the stability critical point $[-1, j0]$. However, when the plant contains an appreciable number of RHP poles and zeros, stabilization by use of Nyquist-oriented design techniques is not any more an obvious and straightforward procedure. The reason is the need to satisfy the due number of encirclements of the critical point in the complex plane. A more systematic algebraic approach is needed to stabilize an unstable plant feedback system. Once again, a parametrized stabilizing controller will be sought.

Coprime factorization

Coprime factorization is an essential element in the parametrization of the stabilizing controller. Let us introduce the symbol $\mathscr{S}$ for the family of all stable, proper real-rational functions. It is a well-known fact that transfer functions are generally defined as a ratio of polynomials, for instance $P(s) = N(s)/D(s)$, where $N(s)$ and $D(s)$ may comprise roots in the RHP. Thus, they may be not in the family $\mathscr{S}$ of stable rational functions. When parametrization of the stabilizing controller for an unstable-NMP plant $P(s)$ is studied, it is easier and preferable to work with stable transfer functions. This means that instead of working with polynomials $N(s)$ and $D(s)$ which may include RHP roots, we can rearrange these polynomials to be in $\mathscr{S}$ as stable transfer functions. The two newly defined transfer functions $N(s)$ and $D(s)$ are *coprime* if two additional transfer functions $X(s)$ and $Y(s)$ can be found in $\mathscr{S}$ that satisfy the equation

$$N(s)X(s) + D(s)Y(s) = 1, \tag{3.7.5}$$

known as the Bezout identity.
If this equation holds, $N(s)$ and $D(s)$ can have no common zeros in the RHP, nor at $s = \infty$. Let us suppose that

$$P(s) = N(s)/D(s) = 1/(s-2).$$

To render $N(s)$ and $D(s)$ coprime and in $\mathscr{S}$, we can arrange them in the following way,

$$N(s) = 1/(s + 1)^m ; \quad D(s) = (s - 2)/(s + 1)^m$$

with m an integer equaling the higher degree of $N(s)$ and $D(s)$, in order that these functions will not have a common zero at $s = \infty$. If so, we can define

$$N(s) = 1/(s + 1) ; \quad D(s) = (s - 2)/(s + 1).$$

Now, let us suppose that we know how to find $X(s)$ and $Y(s)$ so as to satisfy the identity in Eq.(3.7.5). Then, we can proceed to find a procedure to parametrize a controller stabilizing the general plant $P(s)$.

Parametrization of the stabilizing controller

This part follows closely Desoer et al.(1980) and Doyle et al.(1992).
The following lemma is necessary for the proof of the Theorem 3.7.3 that follows the lemma.

Lemma 3.7.1.   Let $G(s) = N_G / D_G$ be a coprime factorization over $\mathscr{S}$. Then the feedback system is internally stable iff

$$1/(N N_G + D D_G) \in \mathscr{S}.$$

Theorem 3.7.3 is stated next:

Theorem 3.7.3.   The set of all $G(s)$'s for which the feedback system is internally stable equals

$$G := \left\{ \frac{X + DQ}{Y - NQ}; Q \in \mathscr{S} \right\}. \tag{3.7.6}$$

The proof of this theorem is based on the Bezout identity of Eq.(3.7.5) and on Lemma 3.7.1. Different variations of the proof can be found, for instance, in Youla et al. (1976), or Desoer et al. (1980). It is important to notice that coprime factorization and related theorems can be expressed also in state-space formulation. (For example, see Net et al. 1984).

   The example below illustrates the use of Theorem 3.7.3 which provides a systematic way for stabilizing an unstable-NMP plant.

Example 3.7.2.   Suppose that $P(s)=(s - 3)/[(s - 1)(s - 2)(s + 5)]$. Find a compensator to stabilize the feedback system in which is imbedded the plant $P(s)$.

Solution: A possible coprime factorization of $P(s)$ is

$$N_P(s) = (s-3)/(s+1)^3 ; D_P(s) = (s-1)(s-2)(s+5)/(s+1)^3.$$

$G(s) = N_G(s)/D_G(s)$ is the stabilizing compensator that must be of the form, (See Appendix F),

$$N_G(s) = (as^2 + bs + c)/(s + q)^2 \; ; \; D_G(s) = (ds^2 + es + f)/(s + q)^2.$$

Since there is no reason why q cannot be chosen equal to 1, let us choose $q = 1$. We are then left with the problem of calculating the compensator parameters a, b, c, d, e, and f by satisfying the Bezout identity in Eq.(3.7.5), namely:

$$\frac{(s - 3)}{(s + 1)^3} \frac{(as^2 + bs + c)}{(s + 1)^2} + \frac{(s - 1)(s - 2)(s + 5)}{(s + 1)^3} \frac{(ds^2 + es + f)}{(s + 1)^2} = 1.$$

To achieve the design, the unknown coefficients of the emerging polynomial in the numerator are equated to those of the emerging polynomial in the denominator which are known, because the closed-loop poles have been a priori fixed. We find that $a = -29$; $b = -140$; $c = 153$; $d = 1$; $e = 3$; $f = 46$, hence, according to the last theorem,

$$G(s) = \frac{N_G(s)}{D_G(s)} = \frac{-29s^2 - 140s + 153}{s^2 + 3s + 46} = -29 \frac{(s + 5.746)(s - 0.918)}{(s + 1.5)^2 + 6.614^2}.$$

The input-output transfer function of the unity-feedback system with the prefilter $F(s) = 1$ becomes

$$T(s) = \frac{y(s)}{r(s)} = -29 \frac{(s + 5.746)(s - 3)(s - 0.918)}{(s + 1)^5}.$$

Since there are no pole-zero cancellations between $P(s)$ and $G(s)$, the system is internally stable as expected.

3.8. A Design Procedure for Maximizing Gain and Phase Margins of a Class of Unstable-NMP Plants

3.8.1. Formulation of the Problem

It is well known that feedback systems with plants including several unstable poles and NMP zeros may have inherently very poor performances and sensitivity properties. Note that in feedback systems with such imbedded plants, more than one ω_{co} may exist, thus obtaining loop transmissions in which the log magnitude is alternately positive and negative in different frequency ranges (Midelton, 1991; Horowitz, 1992). With such plants, the designer is generally quite satisfied from an engineering point of view if he succeeds in obtaining a stable closed-loop system with fairly acceptable design performances. However, he is never sure that he has obtained the best possible solution. The basic pole-zero pattern in the s-complex plane for such system is important. In fact, different plant structures may lead to quite complex pole-zero patterns of the stabilizing compensator. Numerous works deal with the synthesis problem of such systems, with the basic task of finding an adequate compensator, preferably an asymptotically stable one (see Section 3.7.2). It is important to have a systematic procedure for changing the parameters of the stabilizing compensator until the best feedback performances are achieved.

Bongiorno and Youla (1977) prove that any unstable-NMP plant $P(s)$ in which the hidden modes (if they do exist) are asymptotically stable, can be stabilized with a control network of the form assumed in Eq.(3.7.6). In this equation, $N(s)$, $D(s)$, $X(s)$ and $Y(s)$ are determined by the plant $P(s)$, and $Q(s)$ is any chosen rational function free of finite poles in the RHP or on the imaginary axis. The parameters of $Q(s)$ are used to meet certain performance specifications. The poles of $Q(s)$ are the closed-loop poles of the feedback system, freely chosen by the designer.

In order to introduce the difficulties with such design procedures, let us refer to a solved example taken from Bongiorno and Youla (1977).

Example 3.8.1.   Suppose that $P(s) = (s-1)/[s(s-2)]$. A stabilizing network $G_1(s)$ is to be designed so that a velocity error coefficient of $K_v = 10$ is to be achieved.

The following compensator, (designed by Bongiorno and Youla ©1977 IEEE,)

$$G_1(s) = (218s^3 + 3938s^2 - 2200s - 1000)/(s^3 - 185s^2 - 3759s - 50),$$

adequately stabilizes the closed-loop system. The behavior of the loop transmission function on the Nichols chart is shown in Fig.3.8.1 as $L_1(j\omega)$. For this special case, it is important to discern the very small gain and phase margins of the achieved design. Actually, an improvement might be possible by changing the parameters of $G_1(s)$. But, due to the large number of such parameters, (seven in this case), it is extremely difficult to foresee what parameters will improve significantly the design. When the same problem is solved by the systematic approach presented in this section, much larger gain and phase margins are obtained with the following designed controller (see also Appendix F),

$$G_2(s) = 140 \times 143(s-0.1)(1+100s)/(s-100)(1+14300s).$$

The loop transmission $L_2(j\omega)$ obtained by using $G_2(s)$ is also shown in Figure 3.8.1.

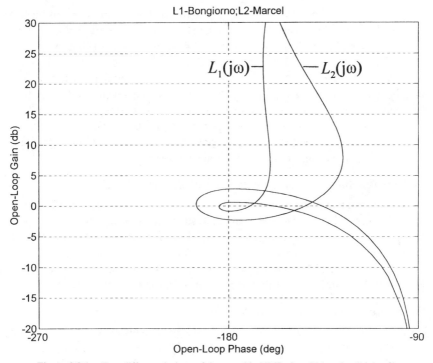

Figure 3.8.1.   Two different designs of the unstable-NMP plant $P(s) = (s-1)/s(s-2)$.

The question to be answered is what are the best closed-loop performances that can be achieved for an arbitrary unstable-NMP plant. There seems to be no analytical answer to that question, although qualitative analysis can be found in the technical literature (Horowitz and Liaou 1984 and Leithead and O'Reilly 1991). Nonetheless, a design procedure will be presented that enables to achieve the best feedback performances for a simplified class of unstable-NMP plants, defined later in Section 3.9.

3.8.2.   Basic Stages in the Proposed Design Procedure.

The principal design stages are :

1-Discard temporarily the LHP poles and zeros out of the plant.

Partition the plant $P(s)$ as follows,

$$P(s) = P(s)_{MP} \, P(s)_{NMP.}$$

Generally, unstable-NMP plants contain also a large number of LHP poles and zeros. These are allocated to the minimum-phase part of the plant, namely, to $P(s)_{MP}$. This part of the plant can be generally neglected in the initial design stages;

$P(s)_{MP}$ will be reincorporated in a later stage to the final optimum loop transmission function. The remaining plant $P(s)_{NMP}$ contains the problematic RHP poles and zeros of the original plant. This reduced plant is thus constrained to contain only the RHP poles and zeros for which inherent design limitations exist. If $P(s)_{NMP}$ happens to be improper, some additional LHP poles of the plant are left in it, so that the simplified plant $P(s)_{NMP}$ remains proper or strictly proper. A compensator $G_1(s)$ is then designed to obtain an optimal loop transmission $L_1(s) = G_1(s)P(s)_{NMP}$. In the final Stage 4 of this design procedure, the temporarily neglected LHP poles and zeros of $P(s)_{MP}$ will be reincorporated adequately back into the achieved optimal $L_1(s)$ in order to obtain the final and complete loop transmission function.

2-Obtain the controller structure that can stabilize the plant.

Use any known technique to stabilize the problematic plant $P(s)_{NMP}$ that contains the RHP poles and zeros. The RHP pole-zero structure of $P(s)_{NMP}$ will show where the poles and zeros of the compensator $G_1(s)$ have to be located relative to the plant's RHP poles and zeros in order to ascertain stabilization, (Youla et.al. 1974 and Theorem 3.7.1). The number of free parameters of the stabilizing controller depends on the complexity of the reduced NMP-unstable plant (Appendix F).

3-Optimize the loop transmission function.

The performances of a closed-loop feedback system, namely its sensitivity function $S(s)$ and its complementary sensitivity function $T_1(s)$, are well defined by the loop transmission function $L_1(j\omega)=G_1(j\omega)P_{NMP}(j\omega)$ displayed normally on Bode plots and on the Nichols chart. Gain bandwidths, crossover frequencies, phase and gain margins are readily detected on these diagrams. In this stage, maximization of gain and phase margins, and crossover frequencies is performed according to design specifications by adequately changing the parameters of the compensator $G_1(s)$. However, in order to perform an efficient design, it is first necessary to find out what are the limitations on these basic system specifications due to the RHP poles and zeros of the constrained plant. These are presented in Sections 3.5 and 3.6 for plants containing RHP poles or RHP zeros, but not both simultaneously. (The objective of Section 3.9 is to find the achievable performances and limitations for loop transmission functions comprising an unstable-NMP dipole. It is also of interest to obtain generalized relationships between phase and gain margins, and the crossover frequencies which limit the obtainable system bandwidths).

4-Incorporation of $P_{MP}(s)$ back into the final $L(s)$.

To compensate for the neglected $P(s)_{MP}$ in the first design stage, a second compensator is provided which is basically equal to $G_2(s) = 1/ P(s)_{MP}$. If $P(s)_{MP}$ happens to be strictly proper, then $G_2(s)$ will consist of more zeros than poles, and will not be physically realizable. Hence, we have to add to it a sufficient number of far-off poles to render it proper or strictly proper. These additional poles, located sufficiently faraway from the problematic RHP poles and zeros, will have little effect on the previously achieved 'optimum' design properties in stage 3 . Finally,

$$L(s) = L_1(s)G_2(s)P(s)_{MP} = G_1(s)P(s)_{NMP} G_2(s)P(s)_{MP}$$
$$= G_1(s)G_2(s)P(s) = G(s)P(s)$$

and the designed compensator comes to be $G(s) = G_1(s)G_2(s)$.

Example 3.8.1-continuation. The above principal design stages are exemplified in obtaining the resulting $L_2(j\omega)$ shown in Fig.3.8.1 for the plant $P(s) = (s - 1)/[s(s - 2)]$ treated in Example 3.8.1.

Design stage 1.

The given plant which is already in its simplified form, contains only the RHP poles and zeros. The integrator is left for explanatory reasons. (For a more efficient design process, the integrator will be removed in the next section. It will be shown that better 'optimal' results are attained if the integrator is not included in the reduced plant $P(s)_{NMP}$, but added to the loop transmission at a later stage). For this explanation, we retain the original form of $P(s)$, namely, $P(s)_{NMP} = (s - 1)/[s(s - 2)]$

Design stage 2.

Suppose we wish to assign three poles to the closed-loop system, for instance, $D(s) = (s + p_1)(s + p_2)^2$. According to Appendix F, the simplest stabilizing controller that can be used for this purpose is expressed in the parametric form

$$G(s) = (as + b)/(s + c)$$

which contains 3 free parameters. To find a, b and c, we can use any known pole placement technique. The closed-loop poles are the roots of the numerator's polynomial of the return difference, namely, of

$$1 + G(s)P_{NMP}(s) = 1 + \frac{(s - 1)}{s(s - 2)} \frac{as + b}{s + c}$$
$$= \frac{s^3 + s^2(a + c - 2) + s(b - a - 2c) - b}{s(s - 2)(s + c)}.$$

Assume that we choose the closed-loop poles to be $(s + 2)$ and $(s + 4)^2$, then the denominator of the closed-loop transfer function will be $D(s) = (s + 2)(s + 4)^2 = s^3 + 10s^2 + 32s + 32$. By equating the coefficients of the numerator of $1 + G(s)P(s)$ to those of $D(s)$, we get $a = 88$, $b = -32$, $c = -76$. The importance of these values is that they show the pole-zero pattern of the controller that stabilize $P(s)_{NMP}$, namely, a RHP zero located at $+32/88 = +0.3636$ which precedes the NMP zero of the plant, and a RHP pole located at $+76$, which is placed to the right side of the unstable pole of the plant. The resulting pole-zero pattern of the compensator conforms with the fact that for a stable closed-loop system, the number of RHP poles to the right of each RHP zero of the loop transmission $L(s) = G(s)P_{NMP}(s)$ must be an even number, (Bongiorno and Youla 1977, Leithead W. and O'Reilly J. 1991).

Design stage 3.

The obtained $L_2(j\omega)$ is shown on the Nichols chart in Fig.3.8.1, with the gain and phase margins clearly perceived. These margins are ameliorated by slightly relocating the RHP pole and zero of the controller. Although some cut-and-try procedure seems to be necessary, it is intuitively clear that decreasing the value of the zero and increasing the value of the pole of the compensator should increase the gain and phase margins until the best $L(j\omega)$ is achieved. Finally, $a = 140$; $b = -14$; $c = -100$ are chosen and the resulting compensator comes to be

$$G_2(s)=140(s-0.1)/(s-100).$$

Design stage 4.

In the present example, this design stage is not applicable because $P_{MP}(s) \equiv 1$. However, with this compensator, the achieved $K_v = 0.07$ is much smaller than 10, as initially specified. To obtain $K_v = 10$, a standard lag-lead network with gain of 143 at $s \to 0$ is used, such as $143(1+\tau s)/(1+143\tau s)$. τ is fixed so that no more than $3°$ phase-lag is added to $L_2(j\omega)$ at $\omega_{co} = 0.1$ rad/sec. The final compensator is then

$$G_2(s)=140\times 143(s-0.1)(1+100s)/[(s-100)(1+14300s)].$$

The resulting $L_2(j\omega)$ is shown in Fig.3.8.1.

The cut-and-try procedure in Stage 3 for the plant in Example 3.8.1 can be completely avoided if the integrator is also discarded temporarily from the simplified plant P_{NMP}. Moreover, a true optimal solution can be achieved with additional tradeoffs between gain and phase margins, crossover frequencies, and the sensor noise amplification. This is shown in the next sections 3.9.2 and 3.9.3.

3.9. Limitations on Feedback Systems Including an Unstable-NMP Plant

Optimization of the loop transmission function $L(s)$ for the general problem of feedback systems in which the plant contains numerous unstable poles and RHP zeros does not seem to be feasible. Hence, optimization of the loop transmission in the proposed design procedure of Section 3.8.2 will be performed for the simpler plant containing one unstable pole preceding one RHP zero, or vice versa. First, we have to find global limits on ω_{co}, and gain and phase margins as a function of the ratio of the RHP pole and zero distances from the origin. Next, based on tradeoffs between the obtained theoretical limitations, we can design the 'best achievable' loop transmission function.

The analysis will be carried out independently for plants in which the unstable pole precedes the RHP zero, and next, for cases where the RHP zero precedes the unstable pole. These specific problems are analyzed in numerous papers, (some of them are referenced in the introduction), but, to the author's knowledge, no explicitly formulated feedback system limitations related to such plants can be found in the literature.

Hopefully, using the same idea presented here, general system limitations can be found for plants with more complex RHP pole-zero patterns.

3.9.1.   Reformulation of the Design Problem

The design problem to be solved can be reformulated as follows:

A-Given a plant comprising one unstable pole and one NMP-zero, derive the crossover frequency ω_{co}, and phase and gain margin limitations as functions of the ratio between the pole and the zero distances from the origin.

B-Based on tradeoffs between the obtained limitations in A, design the best achievable loop transmission function.

C-Increase the benefits of feedback by adding to the optimized loop transmission function one or more integrators at $s = 0$ without significantly deteriorating the achieved performances in B.

In the next two subsections, we calculate global limits on achievable feedback performances due to the existing RHP zero and unstable pole in the plant. These limits are expressed in a similar way as in Section 3.6. Analytical results will be found to allow a quick evaluation of the maximal crossover frequency and of the gain and phase margins that can be achieved. The results are presented in graphical form allowing a quick insight into tradeoffs between the feedback system parameters.

3.9.2.   Plant with an Unstable Pole Preceding a RHP Zero.

Let us adopt the following form for the transfer function of the plant

$$P(s) = P_1(s) \times k_1 \frac{(s/b - 1)}{(s/a - 1)}; \ a < b \tag{3.9.1}$$

where $P_1(s)$ is a stable minimum-phase transfer function. The loop transmission function to be designed is $L(s) = G(s) P(s)$. In order to ascertain internal stability when stabilizing the system, no RHP zeros and poles of the plant should be canceled by the controller $G(s)$. However, as already mentioned, LHP zeros and poles of the plant can be ignored in the initial design stage of the controller, and relocated later in the optimized loop transmission with no harmful effects. Thus, the basic $P(s)$ to be dealt with can be simplified to $P(s) = k_1(s/b-1)/(s/a-1)$. Also, in order to preclude high, if not infinite sensor noise amplification at the input to the plant, the compensator $G(s)$ must include at least one more pole than zeros. Consequently, $L(s)$ will also include at least one more pole than zeros at the high frequency range. According to Corollary 3.7.1, in order to achieve asymptotically stability for this defined unstable and NMP plant, an asymptotically stable compensator can be used, for instance,

$$G(s) = k_2/(s/c + 1).$$

Here k_2 and c are two free parameters of the controller, necessary and sufficient to stabilize the closed-loop feedback system. With these assumptions, the simplest form of the loop transmission function becomes (with $K = k_1 k_2$)

$$L(s) = K(s/b-1)/[(s/a-1)(s/c+1)] \; ; \quad a < b \qquad (3.9.2)$$

The behavior of $L(s)$ in the Nichols chart has the basic characteristics shown in Fig.3.9.1.

   The goal is to find for a known ratio b/a the limitations on phase, gain margins, and the crossover frequency as a function of the location of the compensator pole in $G(s) = k_2/(s/c+1)$. (A more complicated compensator $G(s)$, as well as the initially discarded far-off LHP poles and zeros, can only deteriorate the optimum achievable phase and gain margins). As seen in Fig. 3.9.1, due to the unstable pole, two gain margins are to be defined. The first one is called *Gain Margin Low* (*GML*) while the second one is the usual (high frequency) *Gain Margin* (*GM*) at ω_{GM}. The frequencies, poles and zero will be normalized to the unstable pole location at $+a$. Define $\beta = b/a$, $\gamma = c/a$. The Laplace variable s is also normalized to the location of the unstable pole, $s_a = s/a$. With these definitions, the results to be obtained are not dependent on the location of the RHP pole and zero, but only on the ratio $\beta = b/a$. For a given plant (a, b, and hence also the ratio β, are fixed), *GML*(dB),

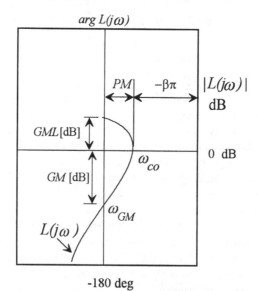

Figure 3.9.1.   Basic characteristics of $L(s) = K(s/b-1)/[(s/a-1)(s/c+1)]$

GM(dB), PM(deg), and the normalized ω_{aco} and ω_{aGM} will depend on γ, one of the two free parameters of the controller. The calculation of these parameters follow:

$$L(s_a) = K(s_a/\beta - 1) / [(s_a - 1)(s_a/\gamma + 1)] \qquad (3.9.3)$$

From Eq.(3.9.3) we find that

$$GML = |L(j0)| = K = k_1 k_2 \qquad (3.9.4)$$

(k_2 is the second free parameter of the controller). Hence

$$|L(j\omega_a)| = GML\, \frac{\gamma}{\beta}\, \frac{\sqrt{\omega_a^2 + \beta^2}}{\sqrt{(\omega_a^2 + 1)(\omega_a^2 + \gamma^2)}} \qquad (3.9.5)$$

and

$$\arg L(j\omega_a) = \pi - \tan^{-1}(\omega_a/\beta) - \tan^{-1}(\omega_a/\gamma) - [\pi - \tan^{-1}(\omega_a)]$$

$$= \tan^{-1}(\omega_a) - \tan^{-1}(\omega_a/\beta) - \tan^{-1}(\omega_a/\gamma) \qquad (3.9.6)$$

Using trigonometric relations, it is easily found that

$$\tan\{\arg[L(j\omega_a)]\} = \frac{\omega_a[\beta\gamma - \omega_a^2 - \omega_a(\beta + \gamma)]}{\beta\gamma - \omega_a^2 + \omega_a^2(\beta + \gamma)} \qquad (3.9.7)$$

By differentiating Eq.(3.9.7), and equating the resulting equation to zero, we can find the normalized crossover frequency ω_{aco} at which the argument of $L(j\omega_a)$ is maximal. Namely,

$$\frac{1}{\omega_a^2 + 1} - \frac{\beta}{\omega_a^2 + \beta^2} - \frac{\gamma}{\omega_a^2 + \gamma^2} = 0. \qquad (3.9.8)$$

From Eq.(3.9.8) it follows that:

$$\omega_{aco}^4(1 - \beta - \gamma) + \omega_{aco}^2(\beta^2 + \gamma^2 - \beta\gamma^2 - \beta^2\gamma - \beta - \gamma)$$
$$+ \beta\gamma(\beta\gamma - \beta - \gamma) = 0, \qquad (3.9.9)$$

which is an explicit relation for the crossover frequency ω_{aco} as function of β, (known and fixed) and the free parameter γ.

To find ω_{aGM}, we use Eq.(3.9.6) with $\arg[L(j\omega_{aGM})] = -\pi$. To find GM, we use Eq.(3.9.5) with $\omega_a = \omega_{aGM}$. To find GML use Eq.(3.9.5) with $\omega_a = \omega_{aco}$ and also the relation $|L(j\omega_{aco})| = 1$. The results for $\beta = 4$, and $\gamma = 0$–100 are displayed in Fig.3.9.2. First, it is important to realize from the graphs in this figure that with

$\beta = b/a = 4$, the maximal obtainable phase margin is about $PM = 36$ deg ($\gamma = 100$). Moving the compensator pole farther away by increasing γ will not help much, but will adversely increase the effect of amplified sensor noise at the plant input. The graphs in the figure also show that the maximal achievable gain margins are: $GM(dB) = 6.1dB$ and $GML(dB) = 5.8dB$. Also, it is seen that ω_{aco} cannot exceed the value of 1.95.

The graphical results in the figure allow tradeoffs in designing the loop transmission $L(s)$, but they also show what are the best design specifications that can be achieved for a given unstable and NMP plant with known RHP zero-pole locations. The normalized to $a^{0.5}$ graphical result of $|T_{un}|$ (RMS)/$a^{0.5}$ is also displayed in the figure in order to allow as well tradeoffs in terms of the sensor noise amplification at the input to the plant ($u/n = T_{un}$ in Fig.2.1.1).

The following Example 3.9.1 illustrates the use of the graphical results in Fig.3.9.2.

Example 3.9.1. $k_1 = 0.5$; $a = 3$; $b = 12$, hence $\beta = 4$, for which the graphical results in Fig.3.9.2 apply.

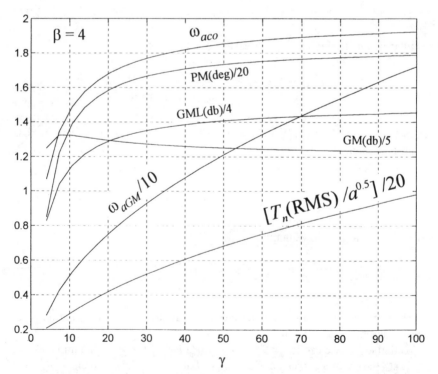

Figure 3.9.2. *PM*[deg], ω_{co}/a, *GM*[dB], *GML*[dB] and $|T_{un}|$(RMS)/$a^{0.5}$ versus γ, $\beta = 4$.

Design tradeoffs: Suppose that a $PM = 34°$ is mandatory. This specification can be achieved with $\gamma = 40$, or $c = 3 \times 40 = 120$, leading to

$$L_1(s) = -1.89(s/12 - 1)/[(s/3 - 1)(s/120 + 1)].$$

The sensor noise amplification $u/n = 20.9$ (in RMS units). If this level of amplified sensor noise is not acceptable because of exaggerated control effort, we have to decrease γ. Let us try $\gamma = 14$, or $c = 3 \times 14 = 42$. The following argumentation is used in finding k_2: for the chosen $\gamma = 14$ we find on the same Fig.3.9.2 that $GML = 1.75$, hence, $k_2 = GML/k_1 = 1.75/0.5 = 3.52$. Finally,

$$L_2(s) = -1.75(s/12 - 1)/[(s/3 - 1)(s/42 + 1)]$$

for which choice $PM = 30°$, only 4° less than the obtained phase margin with the initially chosen compensator pole location at $c = 120$. We find that the noise amplification is reduced to $u/n = 12.12$(RMS). Both $L_1(j\omega)$ and $L_2(j\omega)$ are shown on the Nichols chart of Fig.3.9.3. They exhibit the same basic behavior as that of $L(j\omega)$ in Fig.3.9.1.

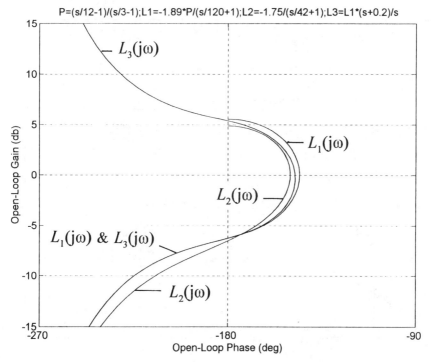

Figure 3.9.3. $L_1(j\omega)$ and $L_2(j\omega)$ of Example 3.9.1 and also $L_3(j\omega) = L_1(j\omega) \times (j\omega + 0.2)/j\omega$ on the Nichols chart.

Achievable specifications: With this given plant, (and a fairly high $\gamma = 100$) the best achievable specifications are approximately: $\omega_{co} = 1.9 \times 3 = 5.7$ rad/sec, phase margin $PM = 1.77 \times 20 = 35.5$ deg, $GML(\mathrm{dB}) = 5.7$ dB, $GM(\mathrm{dB}) = 6.1$ dB.

For the convenience of the reader, the resulting limitations on $GML(\mathrm{dB})$, $GM(\mathrm{dB})$, PM (deg), ω_{aco}, ω_{aGM} and $|T_{un}|(\mathrm{RMS})/a^{0.5}$ for $\beta = 20$ are also shown in Fig.3.9.4. Additional graphs can be prepared for any β, according to the specific problem.

An important feature in feedback control systems is to obtain a good sensitivity function $S(j\omega) = 1/[1 + L(j\omega)]$, which means, high loop transmission magnitudes below the crossover frequency ω_{co}. To achieve that, we can add one or more integrators at $s = 0$, but without decreasing noticeably the already achieved gain and phase margins. For instance, an integrator is added to $L_1(s)$ in Example 3.9.1 with a compatible zero that prevents alteration of the already achieved relative stability specifications. The resulting $L_3(j\omega)$ is also displayed in Fig.3.9.3, where

$$L_3(s) = L_1(s)(s + 0.2)/s$$

The difference between $L_1(j\omega)$ and $L_3(j\omega)$ is in the behavior at frequencies below ω_{co}. The integral of the magnitude (in decibels-radians per second units) of the

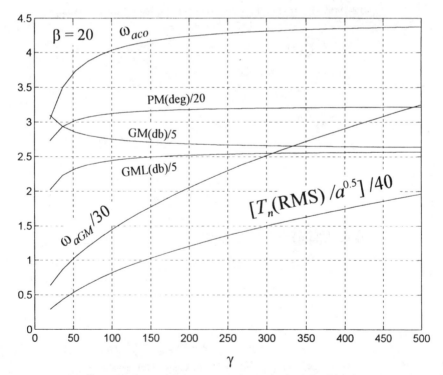

Figure 3.9.4. $PM[\mathrm{deg}]$, ω_{co}/a, $GM[\mathrm{dB}]$, $GML[\mathrm{dB}]$ and $|T_{un}|$ $(\mathrm{RMS})/a^{0.5}$ versus γ, $\beta = 20$.

feedback area $\int |1 + L_3(j\omega)| d\omega$ in the range $\omega < \omega_{co}$ is higher than that for $L_1(j\omega)$ due to the additional integrator. Thus, improvement of the sensitivity function $S(j\omega) = 1/[1 + L(j\omega)]$ is achieved. Many more integrators can be inserted at $s = 0$ in order to increase the magnitude of the loop transmission in the frequency range $\omega < \omega_{co}$, while still keeping unaltered the achieved ω_{co} and also the appropriate phase and gain margins. In summary, ω_{co} is limited as per the graphical results in Figs.3.9.2 and 3.9.4, and *it cannot be increased at will*.

It is interesting to have a simple way of foreseeing what are the best achievable specifications as function of $\beta = b/a$ without trying to save on sensor noise amplification, which means that we can choose $\gamma >> \beta$, for instance, choose $\gamma = 1000$. The results are shown in Fig.3.9.5. They show clearly what maximal crossover frequency and gain and phase margins can be achieved in a loop transmission function in which the location of the RHP pole and zero are known.

Graphical results similar to those in Figs.3.9.2 and 3.9.4 for any β of interest can be obtained by running the MATLAB M-file program listed in Table 3.9.1.

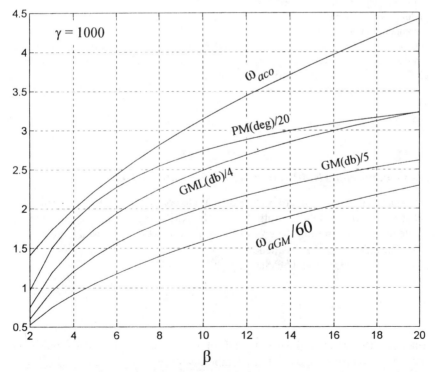

Figure 3.9.5. *PM*[deg], ω_{co}/a, *GM*[dB], *GML*[dB] and ω_{aGM} versus β, $\gamma = 1000$.

Table 3.9.1.   Matlab M-File program for obtaining
graphical results in Figs.3.9.2 and 3.9.4.

%pozem.m 21 April 1997
%one nst pole at wa + one NMP zero at wa*beta + one pole at wa*gama
global beta
gama = linspace(beta, 25 * beta, 300
for i = 1:30
%computation of wac0 (ω_{aco} *in the text*)
sq(i) = gama(i)^4 * (beta − 1)^2 + 2 * gama(i)^3 * (beta^3 + beta^2 − beta − 1) + ...
gama(i)^2 * beta^4 + 2 * beta^3 − 6 * beta^2 + 2 * beta + 1) + ...
gama(i) * 2(−beta^4 − beta^3 + beta^2 + beta) + beta^2 * beta − 1)^2;
sqr(i) = sqrt(sq(i));
wacosq(i) = (−gama(i)^2 * (1 − beta) + gama(i) * (1 + beta^2) − beta^2 + beta −
  sqr(i))/ ...
(2 * (− beta − gama(i) + 1));
waco(i) = sqrt(wacosq(i));
arg(i) = (−pi + atan(waco(i)) − atan(waco(i)/beta) − atan(waco(i)/gama(i))) * 180/pi;
pm(i) = 180 + arg(i);
%computation of GML
gml(i) = beta * sqrt((1+waco(i)^2) * (gama(i)^2 + waco(i)^2))/ ...
(gama(i) * sqrt(waco(i)^2 + beta^2));
gmldb(i) = 20 * log10(gml(i));
%computation of wagm
wagmsq(i) = (1 − 1/beta − 1/gama(i)) * beta * gama(i);wagm(i) = sqrt(wagmsq(i));
%computation of gmdb
gm(i) = gml(i) * gama(i) * sqrt(wagm(i)^2 + beta^2)/ ...
(beta * sqrt((wagm(i)^2 + 1) * (wagm(i)^2 + gama(i)^2)));gmdb(i) = 20 * log10(gm(i));
end
end

3.9.3   Plant with a NMP Zero Preceding an Unstable Pole

This pole-zero plant structure is more difficult to control than the previous one, because there exists a natural contradiction: the NMP-zero, which precedes the unstable pole, tends to limit the crossover frequency, while the unstable pole tends
to increase the crossover frequency.
In this case Eq.(3.9.1) will be changed to

$$P(s) = P_1(s) \times k_1 \frac{(s/a − 1)}{(s/b − 1)}; \quad a < b. \tag{3.9.10}$$

Since the RHP plant zero lies to the left of an odd number of unstable poles, the
stabilizing compensator cannot be asymptotically stable (Theorem 3.7.1). Therefore, its simplest form can be chosen to be

$$G(s) = k_2/(s/c - 1),$$

Similarly to Eq.(3.9.3), we have

$$L(s_a) = K(s_a - 1)/[(s_a/\beta - 1)(s_a/\gamma - 1)] \tag{3.9.11}$$

The general behavior of this loop transmission function on the Nichols chart is shown in Fig.3.9.6. Note that for this structure of the plant, there exist two crossover frequencies, two phase margins, and two gain margins.
Analysis of this system is similar to that performed in Section (3.9.2).

$$|L(j\omega_a)| = GML \frac{\beta\gamma\sqrt{\omega_a^2 + 1}}{\sqrt{(\omega_a^2 + \beta^2)(\omega_a^2 + \gamma^2)}} \tag{3.9.12}$$

$$\arg L(j\omega_a) = [\pi - \tan^{-1}(\omega_a)] - [\pi - \tan^{-1}(\omega_a/\beta)] - [\pi - \tan^{-1}(\omega_a/\gamma)]$$
$$= -\tan^{-1}(\omega_a) + \tan^{-1}(\omega_a/\beta) + \tan^{-1}(\omega_a/\gamma) - \pi \tag{3.9.13}$$

After we take the derivative of Eq.(3.9.13) and equate the resulting equation to zero, we find an explicit equation for the normalized crossover frequencies ω_{aco1} and ω_{aco2}.

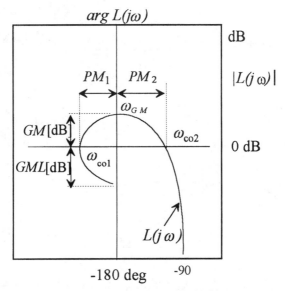

Figure 3.9.6. Basic characteristics of $L(s) = K(s_a - 1)/[(s/b - 1)(s/c - 1)]$

$$\omega^4_{aco} (\beta + \gamma - 1) + \omega^2_{aco} (\beta\gamma^2 + \beta + \gamma\beta^2 + \gamma - \beta^2 - \gamma^2) \qquad (3.9.14)$$
$$+ \beta\gamma(\gamma + \beta - \beta\gamma) = 0$$

The resulting ω_{aco}'s, and phase and gain margins for $\gamma = 0$–100 are shown in Fig.3.9.7 for $\beta = 4$, and in Fig 3.9.8 for $\beta = 20$. The sensor noise amplification curve $|T_{un}|(RMS) = u/n$ used for design tradeoff purposes is also shown in these figures.

Additional graphs can be prepared for any β, according to the specific problem. An example of how to use these graphical results follows.

Example 3.9.2. $k_1 = 0.5$; $a = 3$; $b = 12$. In this case $\beta = 4$, for which the results in Fig.3.9.7 apply.

Design tradeoffs: Suppose that a $PM_1 = 34°$ deg is mandatory. This specification can be achieved with $\gamma = 40$, or $c = 3 \times 40 = 120$. For these parameters, the loop transmission is

$$L_1(s) = +(1/1.89)(s/3 - 1)/[(s/12 - 1)(s/120 - 1)].$$

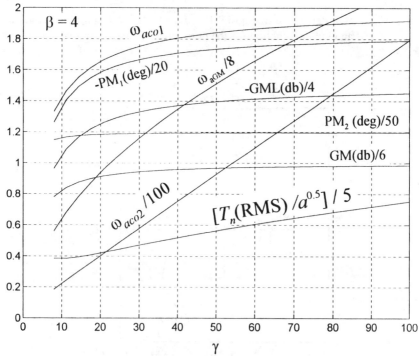

Figure 3.9.7. ω_{co1}/a, PM_1[deg], ω_{co2}/a, PM_2[deg], GM[dB], GML[dB] and $|T_{un}|(RMS)/a^{0.5}$ versus γ, $\beta = 4$.

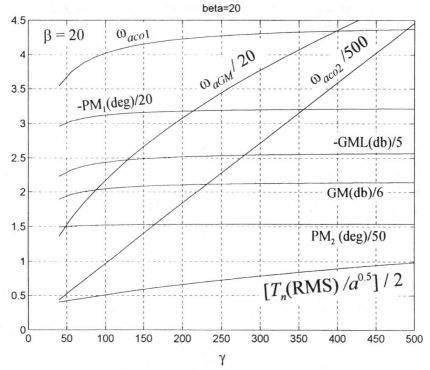

beta=20

Figure 3.9.8. ω_{co1}/a, PM_1[deg], ω_{co2}/a, PM_2[deg], GM[dB], GML[dB] and $|T_{un}|$ (RMS)$/a^{0.5}$ versus γ, $\beta = 20$.

The sensor noise amplification at the plant input is $u/n = 4.48$ (in RMS units). If this level of amplification is unacceptable, we have to decrease γ. Let us try $\gamma = 14$, or $c = 3 \times 14 = 42$. For these parameters, the loop transmission is

$$L_2(s) = (1/1.75)(s/3 - 1)/[(s/12 - 1)(s/42 - 1)].$$

With the above loop transmission function $PM_1 = 30°$, only 4° less than with the initially chosen compensator pole location at $c = 120$. We find that the noise amplification is reduced to $u/n = 3.4$ (in RMS units). Both $L_1(j\omega)$ and $L_2(j\omega)$ are shown in Figs.3.9.9 and 3.9.10.

Here again, the sensitivity function $S(j\omega) = 1/[1+L(j\omega)]$ can be improved at low frequencies by introducing to the loop transmission function one (or more) integrators at $s = 0$, for instance,

$$L_3(s) = L_1(s) \times (s - 0.2)/s$$

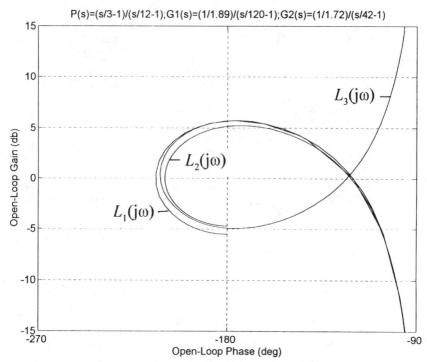

$P(s)=(s/3-1)/(s/12-1);G1(s)=(1/1.89)/(s/120-1);G2(s)=(1/1.72)/(s/42-1)$

Figure 3.9.9. $L_1(j\omega)$ and $L_2(j\omega)$ of Example 1 and also
$L_3(j\omega) = L_1(j\omega) \times (j\omega-0.2)/j\omega$ on the Nichols chart.

(From root-locus method rules, the added compensating zero must be in the RHP. See also Example 3.9.1. Its location is fixed by the usual tradeoff in the frequency-domain between a minimum deterioration of PM_1 and the increase of the frequency $\omega_1 = 0.15$ rad/sec in Fig.3.9.10, below which the magnitude in dB of the loop transmission function becomes positive, with the aim of ameliorating the sensitivity function in that frequency range). The resulting $L_3(j\omega)$ is also shown in Figs.3.9.9 and 3.9.10. For well known reasons, with plants including several RHP poles and zeros, the magnitude of the loop transmission (in dB units) is alternately positive or negative in different frequency ranges (Horowitz 1979, Leithead and O'Reilly 1991). In our case, for $\omega < \omega_1 = 0.15$ rad/sec, the magnitude increases indefinitely as $s \to 0$, thus increasing the benefits of feedback in the low frequency range. However, the benefits of feedback are very limited in the frequency range $\omega_{co1} < \omega < \omega_{co2}$ as per the results in Figs.3.9.9 and 3.9.10.

Achievable specifications: With this assumed plant, (and a fairly high $\gamma = 100$) the best achievable specifications are: $\omega_{co1} = 1.9 \times 3 = 5.7$ rad/sec, $PM_1 = 1.77 \times 20 = 35.5$ deg, $GML(dB) = 5.7$ dB, $GM(dB) = 5.8$ dB, $PM_2 = 1.2 \times 50 = 60°$.

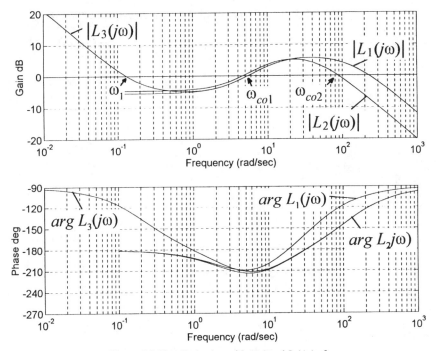

Figure 3.9.10. Bode plots of $L_1(j\omega)$ and $L_2(j\omega)$ of
Example 3.9.2 and $L_3(j\omega) = L_1(j\omega) \times (j\omega - 0.2)/j\omega$.

Far-off poles: The achieved optimal $L_3(s)$ in this example has an excess of poles over zeros equals to one, $e = 1$ (see also Fig.3.9.11). In real feedback systems, for reasons already mentioned several times in the book, e should be at least equal to two or to three. Let us decide on $e = 3$, and then locate two far-off poles at $s = -1000$. The new and final loop transmission becomes

$$L_4(s) = L_3(s)/(1+s/1000)^2$$

which is also shown in Fig.3.9.11.

Remark. Stability considerations show that the critical point in the Nichols chart [0db, $-180°$] is encircled twice (2 open-loop RHP poles) in the correct direction (clockwise in the Nichols chart!). $L_4(j\omega)$ coincides with $L_3(j\omega)$ in the low frequency range, but tends to $-270°$ at high frequencies. $L_1(j\omega)$ of Example 3.9.2 (no integrator at the low frequencies) is also shown in the figure. As is discerned in this figure, the addition of the far-off poles has little effect on PM_1 , but has diminished PM_2 by close to 25°. Note that $L_4(j\omega)$ crosses the $-180°$ vertical axis three times.

Here again it is of interest to have a simple way of foreseeing the best achievable specifications as function of $\beta = b/a$ without trying to save on bandwidth,

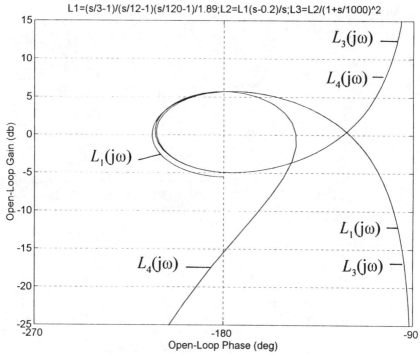

Figure 3.9.11. Addition of far-off poles to $L_3(s)$:
$L_4(j\omega) = L_3(j\omega)/(1 + j\omega/1000)^2$ on the Nichols chart.

which means, for $\gamma \gg \beta$, for instance, choose $\gamma = 1000$. The results are shown in Fig.3.9.12. Some of them, the crossover frequencies for example, are normalized to the location of the RHP zero. They show clearly what maximal crossover frequencies, gain and phase margins can be achieved with a loop transmission function in which the location of the RHP pole and zero are a priori known.

3.10.   Summary.

In this chapter we considered practical topics in the design of SISO feedback systems, such as ways of translating system functions from the frequency-domain into the time-domain, and vice versa. We also discussed the formulation and achievement of optimal loop transmissions for MP, NMP and unstable plants. For the last two plant classes, there exist stringent limitations on achievable bandwidths. These were stated and illustrated with solved examples.

Conditions for internal stability of feedback systems are stated and illustrated for plants that can be unstable and NMP. Procedures for the stabilization of such

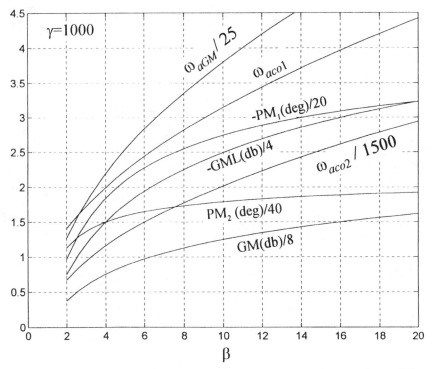

Figure 3.9.12. ω_{co1}/a, PM_1[deg], ω_{co2}/a, PM_2[deg], GM[dB] and GML[dB] versus β, $\gamma = 1000$.

plants based on Q-parametrization principles are described and illustrated with design examples.

The existence of a NMP zero in the plant of the physical system has two basic effects. The first one is a rigid limitation on the achievable gain bandwidth of the loop transmission function. This leads to limitation of the benefits of feedback with respect to sensitivity to disturbances and to uncertainty of plant parameters. The second effect is the undershoot that always exists in the step time response. The existence of an unstable pole has the effect of imposing a lower bound on the achievable open-loop crossover frequency ω_{co}, which is related to the required phase and gain margins. The effect of additional unstable poles and NMP zeros is also analyzed. The existence of both a single RHP zero and a single RHP pole aggravates the situation and causes the appearance of two crossover frequencies whose locations are fixed by the values of the RHP pole and zero. The results shown in this chapter allow tradeoffs between maximal gain and phase margins, and the crossover frequency of the loop transmission function.

Chapter 4 _____

Synthesis of SISO LTI Uncertain Feedback Systems

4.1 Introduction

In the previous chapters we considered feedback systems in which the parameters of the plant $P(s)$ were assumed to be fixed and known. Unfortunately, these parameters are always uncertain to some extent. For small uncertainties, the analytical results of the previous chapters hold, and the treated design techniques remain unchanged. Bode (1945) was the first to explore the design of uncertain plant feedback systems in communication amplifiers, by the sensitivity function $S_P^T = \dfrac{dT/T}{dP/P} = \dfrac{1}{1 + L(s)}$. This equation is inadequate for dealing with finite and large plant uncertainty. Horowitz (1963) suggested using, $S_P^T = \dfrac{\Delta T/T}{\Delta P/P}$, which describes sufficiently well the sensitivity of feedback systems to large, but finite plant uncertainties (See Section 4.2).

The expression 'uncertain plant' does not forcefully mean 'unknown plant'. It rather means that the plant's transfer function has parameters whose values lie within known limits. In this context we have to mention the notions of 'structured' and of 'unstructured' uncertain plant models. The former are related to plants with a fairly known dynamical structure, so that they can be modeled by ordinary differential equations. They stand in contrast to the latter class of 'unstructured' plant models treated in Section 4.8, for which no conventional mathematical modeling is feasible.

This chapter deals with quantitative design of feedback systems around highly uncertain plants. The meaning of 'quantitative' is that the uncertainties of the plant are known 'quantitatively', and that the aim of the design is to achieve 'quantitatively' defined system performances. From here stems the name QFT-'Quantitative Feedback Theory'. The 'classical' design approaches presented in Sections

4.2 to 4.7 use the Nichols chart as the design medium on which the uncertain plant is displayed in the form of 'templates', whose patterns and sizes represent the plant uncertainty at different frequencies. When the 'modern' H_∞-control design technique is adopted, the uncertain plant is represented as a disc-shaped template displayed on the complex plane. Both classical and modern H_∞-norm design philosophies for highly uncertain plants are explained and illustrated in detail.

First, we consider the design of feedback systems in which a minimum-phase plant is imbedded. For this class of plants, any specified sensitivity reduction to given plant uncertainty can be achieved, Section 4.3. Section 4.4 treats the same problem for unstable plants.

Section 4.5 deals with the design of uncertain feedback systems with a NMP plant. For this class of plants, since there are fundamental limitations on the achievable open-loop bandwidth (Section 3.5.2), the situation is strongly aggravated when plant uncertainty is present. For such design problems, it may not be possible to achieve initially set system specifications. This drawback can be circumvented by relaxing the initially specified tracking sensitivity performances to a level that allows completion of the design. Because they exhibit NMP properties, similar limitations exist in designing sampled-data uncertain feedback systems. Section 4.7 is concerned with sampled-data uncertain feedback systems.

The classical design approach for solving the uncertain plant feedback problem exploits frequency-domain oriented design techniques performed basically on the Nichols chart. Section 4.8 treats the standard H_∞-regulator problem (Section 2.5), which is also a powerful tool for solving the TDOF uncertain plant feedback problem. Extensive use is made here of H_∞-norm optimization algorithms.

The design techniques treated in this chapter cover SISO uncertain feedback systems which are frequently fundamental to the design of MIMO uncertain feedback systems treated in later chapters.

The peculiarities of the classical QFT frequency-domain design technique presented in this chapter derive from the fact that it uses visual means which allow a close and a transparent insight into the tradeoffs between different open-loop and closed-loop properties. In order to understand the simplicity and the advantageous features of the techniques explained hereafter, it is recommended that the reader solves some examples without the help of existing, commercial software. Once sufficient experience and deeper understanding of the techniques by hand design calculations has been obtained, then one can take advantage of computerized tools in automatic control (such as the Matlab QFT-toolbox for the frequency oriented design techniques, and the μ–Analysis and Synthesis, or the LMI-toolboxes for the H_∞-control design).

4.2 Statement of the Uncertain Plant Feedback Problem

The TDOF feedback system with which we are dealing is schematically represented in Fig.4.2.1. It is mathematically described by Eqs.(2.1.1) to (2.1.7).

The problem here is how to design the controller G and the prefilter F such that

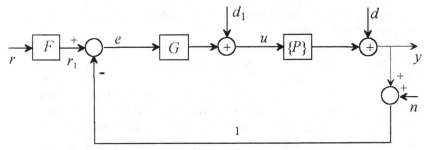

Figure 4.2.1. A canonical uncertain TDOF unity-feedbacksystem.

for a given set of plants $\{P\}$: (i) the closed-loop is stable (robust stability) and its sensitivity to known uncertainties of the plant is within given specifications (robust performance); and (ii), for a given set of bounded disturbances $\{d\}$, and/or $\{d_1\}$, the plant output is bounded according to given specifications:

1-The plant $P(s)$ can be any member of a given set of plants denoted by $\{P(s)\}$.

2-There are given two time functions $B_U(t)$, $B_L(t)$ and a command input $r(t)$ (for example a step) that specify the output tolerances on $y\,(t)$ in the form: for all $P \in \{P\}$,

$$B_L(t) \le y(t) \le B_U(t) \tag{4.2.1}$$

Exemplified bounds B_L and B_U are shown in Fig.4.2.2a.

3-There are given time functions $D_U\,(t)$, $D_L\,(t)$ and $D_{U1}\,(t)$, $D_{L1}\,(t)$ that specify the output tolerances of y to external disturbances in the form: for all $P \in \{P\}$ and all $d \in \{d\}$ and/or $d_1 \in \{d_1\}$

$$D_L(t) \le y(t) \le D_U(t) \quad \text{and/or} \quad D_{L1}(t) \le y(t) \le D_{U1}(t) \tag{4.2.2}$$

Exemplified bounds D_L and D_U are shown in Fig.4.2.2b.

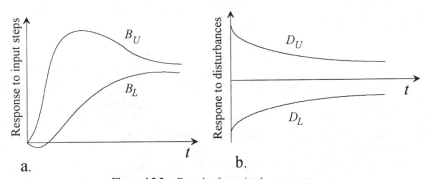

Figure 4.2.2. Bounds of permitted responses to
a: a step command input, and **b:** to disturbance inputs.

4-An optimization criterion is given to guide the designer to a preferred solution out of all possible solutions.

5-Design a controller $G(s)$ and a prefilter $F(s)$ such that for all plants $P \in \{P\}$, the system is stable and Eqs.(4.2.1) and (4.2.2) are satisfied for a command step input $r(t)$ and for all disturbances $d \in \{d\}$ or $d_1 \in \{d_1\}$,

The design technique presented in this chapter is in the frequency-domain, so that the closed-loop time-domain tolerances are translated first into the frequency-domain in the following forms: (from now on the magnitudes of transfer functions and their bounds in the frequency-domain will be given in decibel (dB) units, unless otherwise stated)

Tracking specifications

Two functions $B_U(\omega)$, $B_L(\omega)$ are given that specify the output specifications of the transfer function magnitude $|T(j\omega)|$ in the form: for all $P \in \{P\}$

$$B_L(\omega) \leq |T(j\omega)| \leq B_U(\omega) \tag{4.2.3}$$

Disturbance rejection specifications

Function $D(\omega)$ and $D_1(\omega)$ specify the output specifications of $|T_d(j\omega)|$ or of $|T_{d1}(j\omega)|$ respectively, in the form: for all $P \in \{P\}$ and all $d \in \{d\}$ and/or $d_1 \in \{d_1\}$ of disturbances introduced in d or d_1

$$|T_d(j\omega)| \leq D(\omega) \text{ and also } |T_{d1}(j\omega)| \leq D_1(\omega). \tag{4.2.4}$$

Note that in order to simplify the notation, the same letters are used to represent the time and the frequency-domain specifications. The variables ω or t are added where needed to avoid confusion.

Peaking in the disturbance rejection transfer function gains

Closed-loop transfer functions that are too underdamped are avoided by specifying two numbers β and γ, such that

$$|T_1(j\omega)| \leq \beta \text{ and } |T_d(j\omega)| \leq \gamma; \forall P \in \{P\}. \tag{4.2.5}$$

Plants may be minimum-phase, nonminimum-phase, stable or unstable; they may include time delays; they can vary in time slowly, and they may be imbedded in a continuous or in a sampled-data feedback system. A single design technique for all these type of plants does not exist. The following plant categories will be considered in this chapter:

Category I-All plants in $\{P\}$ are minimum-phase (no RHP poles and zeros). In such cases a solution exists for any given specifications, provided that the gain sign of all plants in $\{P\}$ is fixed.

Category II-The plants in $\{P\}$ may have RHP poles but not RHP zeros. In this case, too, a solution for any given specifications exists provided the gain sign of all plants in $\{P\}$ is fixed. In this category, the bandwidth of the loop transmission function tends to be large because of the existence of RHP poles, as explained in Section 3.6.

Category III-The plants in $\{P\}$ are stable but have RHP zeros and/or pure time delay. A solution exists provided the specifications are not too stringent. The loop transmission bandwidth is forced to be low (see Section 3.5.1).

Category IV-The set $\{P\}$ is embedded in a sampled-data feedback system. The design technique is similar to that for category III dealing with NMP plants.

We shall first describe the design technique for minimum-phase uncertain plants using the classical Bode/Nichols approach. The technique is in the frequency-domain, graphical in nature, and constitutes the basis for the design of the remaining categories.

4.3   A Design Technique for Minimum-Phase LTI Uncertain Plants (Category I)

In this category, any plant in the set $\{P\}$ is minimum-phase and the gain sign of all plants is the same. The 'design to performance' technique is a 7-step procedure given below. A detailed description of each step is presented. The major steps of this design technique are mainly performed on the Nichols chart.

Step 1. Translation of the time-domain tolerances into frequency-domain tolerances.

Step 2. Preparation of templates for the uncertain plant at a discrete number of frequencies which are chosen according to the uncertain plant properties and also according to the input-output tracking frequency-domain specifications.

Step 3. Derivation of 'bounds' on the loop transmission $L(j\omega)$ in the Nichols chart, whose graphical features are influenced by the plant's uncertainty templates, and by all the frequency-domain specifications such as β, γ, $B_U(\omega)$, $B_L(\omega)$, $D_U(\omega)$, $D_L(\omega)$, etc.

Step 4. Design of a nominal $L_n(j\omega)$ that satisfies the bounds derived in step 3 in an optimal way.

Step 5. Derivation of $G(s)$ from the designed $L_n(s)$ in step 4.

Step 6: Design of the prefilter $F(s)$ to achieve the closed-loop tracking specifications.

Step 7. Evaluation of the design and refinement of the solution if necessary. This may include addition of bounds for some newly chosen problematic frequencies and, consequently, modification of $G(s)$ and $F(s)$ might be inevitable.

4.3.1.   Step 1: Translation of Time-Domain into Frequency-Domain Tolerances

Since the design procedure is in the frequency-domain, the time-domain tolerances must be translated into frequency-domain tolerances. A typical translation is shown in Fig.4.3.1 where time-domain tolerances of the closed-loop step responses are translated into frequency-domain tolerances of $|T(j\omega)|$. The translation process can be executed in the s-plane or directly in the frequency-domain by one or more of the techniques treated in Chapter 3.

Direct time-domain into frequency-domain translation

Using the results of Section 3.2.3, time-domain specifications with their tolerances can be directly translated into a very good approximation in the frequency-domain, as in Fig. 4.3.1.

Time-domain into frequency-domain translation via the s-domain

It is common to define the time-domain tolerances by the step response tolerances of a complex pole pair of a second-order model of $T(s)$, as explained in Section 3.2.1. For instance, these complex poles may be allocated in an acceptable region in the s-plane, as in Fig.4.3.2a. A large number of second-order complex poles belonging to this region are translated into the frequency-domain, as shown in Fig.4.3.2b, by the plain curves. The extreme $|T(j\omega)|$'s cases are candidates for the upper and the lower specification bounds. Note that the extreme cases remain parallel at the high frequencies with a finite magnitude tolerance in dB. But, it is very important to broaden the permissible range of $|T(j\omega)|$ in Fig.4.3.2b as much as possible for this clearly permits design by an $L(j\omega)$ of smaller bandwidth. To broaden the permissible range of $|T(j\omega)|$, one may proceed by trial-and-error, trying $|T(j\omega)|$ functions which progressively decrease faster, as functions of frequency, until the time-response specifications are intolerably violated. Similarly, one tries $|T(j\omega)|$ functions which progressively decrease more slowly, until again the time-domain specifications are intolerably violated. The upper and the lower bounds $B_L(\omega)$ and $B_U(\omega)$ are finally set for the permitted $|T(j\omega)|$'s. They are represented by the

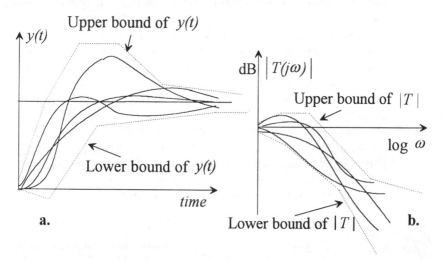

Figure 4.3.1.   (a)-Time-domain tolerances and (b)-Frequency-domain tolerances.

dashed curves in the figure. With these modified bounds, no sensitivity specifications are defined in the high frequency range $\omega > \omega_a$ (Fig.4.3.2b).

We emphasized in Chapter 3 that translation from $|T(j\omega)|$ into time-domain, and vice versa, is only an approximation. Hence, with both of the above mentioned time into frequency- domain translation alternatives, we have to check by simulation the consistency between the specified time response tolerances and their translation to a family of acceptable $|T(j\omega)|$'s. It is important to avoid continuation of the design process if the translation is not satisfactory. If necessary, $B_U(\omega)$ and $B_L(\omega)$ are redefined.

4.3.2. Step 2: Preparation of Templates for the Uncertain Plant

Although the plant is generally described by its transfer function $P(s)$, we are interested in its behavior in the frequency-domain, namely, in $P(j\omega)$. We perform this translation when creating the plant templates for a determined number of plants in the set $P \in \{P(s)\}$. In some real problems, it may occur that a linear analytical model of the plant $P(s)$ is not sufficiently known. However, there exists the possibility that $P(j\omega)$ can be directly obtained by physical measurements. If this is the case, it is assumed that measured data on $\{P(j\omega)\}$ are accumulated for a sufficiently large number of relevant frequencies and plant elements in the set $\{P(j\omega)\}$.

The sensitivity problem of the input-output tracking specifications for uncertain plants is best solved on the Nichols chart. The uncertain set $\{P(j\omega)\}$ will be expressed on this chart as *templates* created by all plants in the set and for different frequencies. The frequencies for which the templates are to be formed depend on the specifications of $|T(j\omega)|$ as shown in Fig.4.3.2b, and also on the plant set properties. The templates at two different frequencies are shown in Fig.4.3.3. These templates are prepared for the set $\{P\}$ defined by the transfer function

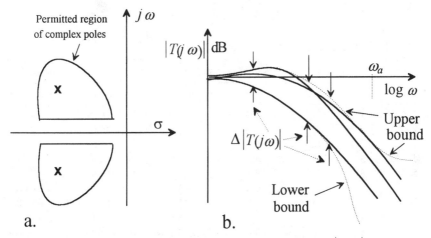

Figure 4.3.2. Translation of second-order complex poles tolerances into $|T(j\omega)|$ tolerances.

$$P(s) = ka/(s + a); \quad k = [1-5], a = [1 - 10] \tag{4.3.1}$$

Each template can be prepared and presented graphically on the Nichols chart at a given frequency by a sufficient number of chosen plant elements. From Eq.(4.3.1), we can calculate $P(j\omega)$ at different frequencies over the range of plant parameters. For instance, let us create templates at $\omega = 1$ and at $\omega = 20$ rad/sec. The magnitude of $P(j\omega)$ in dB and its phase in degrees are calculated at these frequencies for a dense enough set of plants. Nine cases are picked and presented in Table 4.3.1. We are now ready to create the templates at these frequencies.

Using the data in Table 4.3.1, we can locate the set $\{P(j\omega)\}$ for different cases and frequencies on the Nichols chart. $(\ln L(j\omega) = \ln|L| + j \arg L$, the ordinate is in dB and the abscissa is in degrees). To create the template at $\omega = 1$ rad/sec for instance, we use the data accumulated in Table 4.3.1, and we locate the relevant plant cases at this frequency on the Nichols chart shown in Fig.4.3.3. The subscript in the plant designation denotes the plant case number. For example $P_1(j1) = [-3\text{dB}; -45°]$ is located on the Nichols chart according to the Cartesian coordinates which are the log magnitude and phase axes of the loop transmission function L, and is designated by the number (1), $P_3(j1)$ is located at 0dB and $-5.7°$, etc. $P_4(j1)$, $P_6(j1)$, $P_7(j1)$ and $P_9(j1)$ are similarly located on the same chart. The template at $\omega = 1$ rad/sec is obtained by joining the extreme points and forming the closed contour shown in Fig.4.3.3. Using the same procedure, templates at additional frequencies can be prepared. (See for example the template at $\omega = 20$ rad/sec, also shown in the figure). The designation of the case number is needed in step 6 of the design process. When one plant case is chosen as *nominal* and is denoted by P_n, the same nominal plant case must be used for all templates. The designer should choose carefully the finite set of plant cases so that the closed contour obtained with them includes all possible and extreme plant uncertainties.

Table 4.3.1. Plants values at $\omega = 1$ and 20 rad/sec

Case	k	a	$\omega = 1$ rad/sec		$\omega = 20$ rad/sec	
			$\|G\|$dB	Phase deg	$\|G\|$dB	Phase deg
1	1	1	−3.0	−45.0	−26.0	−87.0
2	1	2	−1.0	−26.6	−20.0	−84.3
3	1	10	−0.0	−5.7	−7.0	−63.4
4	3	1	6.5	−45.0	−16.5	−87.1
5	3	2	8.5	−26.6	−10.5	−84.3
6	3	10	9.4	−5.7	2.5	−63.4
7	5	1	10.9	−45.0	−12.0	−87.4
8	5	2	13.1	−26.6	−6.1	−84.3
9	5	10	13.6	−5.7	7.0	−63.0

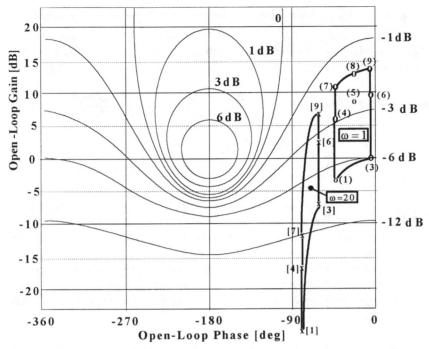

Figure 4.3.3. Templates of $P(s) = k/(s+a)$ at $\omega = 1$ and 20 rad/sec, with $k \in [1-5]$, $a \in [1-5]$.

4.3.3. Step 3: Derivation of Bounds on the Loop Transmission $L_n(j\omega)$ in the Nichols Chart

Feedback system design in the frequency-domain consists of adequately shaping the nominal loop transmission $L_n(j\omega) = GP_n$. Suppose that by using the control network $G(s)$, a loop transmission $L_n(j\omega)$ has been designed which satisfies the specifications for some arbitrarily chosen nominal plant $P_n(j\omega)$. It is clear that if the plant parameters change appreciably from the nominal, the loop transmission with the same $G(s)$ will be altered. There is also the possibility that the closed-loop transfer function for the newly chosen plant condition might become unstable. *The task of the design technique presented here consists in finding control networks $G(s)$ and $F(s)$ that will satisfy the closed-loop design specifications for all plants in the set $P \in \{P\}$.* For example, all the $|T(j\omega)|$'s should lie inside the specified bounds in Fig.4.3.2b.

In fact, all system specifications will be satisfied for all plants in the set $\{P\}$ by designing a compatible nominal loop transmission function $L_n(s) = G(s)P_n(s)$. Permitted bounds on $L_n(j\omega)$ are most easily obtained on the Nichols chart (Horowitz and Sidi 1972). The next section presents a graphical technique for drawing up these bounds which guarantee input-output tracking specifications, sufficient disturbance rejection, and maximum permitted peaking in $|T_1|$ and $|S|$.

Bounds on $L_n(j\omega)$ for satisfying (input-output) tracking sensitivity specifications

The templates of $P(j\omega)$ are manipulated on the Nichols chart to find the position of $L_n(j\omega)$ which satisfies the specifications of Fig.4.3.2b on $\log |T(j\omega)|$. As there is no ignorance of $F(s)$ and of $G(s)$, it is sufficient to satisfy the following relation:

$$\Delta \log| T(j\omega)| \overset{def}{=} \max_{P\in\{P\}} \log \left| \frac{L(j\omega)F(j\omega)}{1 + L(j\omega)} \right| - \min_{P\in\{P\}} \log \left| \frac{L(j\omega)F(j\omega)}{1 + L(j\omega)} \right|$$

$$= \Delta \log\left| \frac{L(j\omega)}{1 + L(j\omega)} \right| = \Delta \log|T_1(j\omega)| \qquad (4.3.2)$$

where the notation Δ stands for the range of change of the function following the sign, and T_1 denotes the unity-feedback transfer function. The graphical solution of the last equality is a continuous curve on the Nichols chart. It is named the *bound* on $L_n(j\omega)$ at the frequency ω. (It splits the logarithmic complex plane into two regions. If $L_n(j\omega)$ lies in one of them, the closed-loop specifications are satisfied; if $L_n(j\omega)$ does lie in the 2nd region, then the closed-loop specifications may not be satisfied). The obtained bounds on $L_n(j\omega)$ at each frequency depend on both the permitted closed-loop tolerances $\Delta|T(j\omega)|$, as well as on the uncertainty characters of the plant template at that frequency.

To show how we obtain these bounds, a specific frequency ω is chosen and the template for that frequency is prepared and lied on the Nichols chart, as in Fig.4.3.4. First, we select one of the plants (it does not matter which one) to be the 'nominal plant' $P_n(j\omega)$. For the present presentation, we choose $P_1(j\omega)$ as the nominal plant. It is very important to note that since $\ln L = \ln G + \ln P$, the pattern of the template outlined by the different plant cases may be translated (but not rotated) on the Nichols chart. The amount of translation is given by the value of $G(j\omega)$. In other words, we can move the template up and down by $|G(j\omega)|$ dB along the open-loop log magnitude vertical axis, or move it to the left and to the right by $\arg G(j\omega)$ along the open-loop phase horizontal axis (no rotation of the template!). With these observations, we can now use the template to derive the bound that defines the region on the Nichols chart such that if $L_n(j\omega) = G(j\omega)P_n(j\omega)$ is in this region, the closed-loop satisfies the inequality

$$\Delta\log |T(j\omega)| \leq B_U(\omega)\text{-}B_L(\omega). \qquad (4.3.3)$$

for the entire plant set $\{P(j\omega)\}$.

As an example, suppose that the tracking specifications at $\omega = 1$ are such that

$$\Delta\log |T(j1)| \leq B_U(1)\text{-}B_L(1) = 2 \text{ dB}.$$

(Since according to Eq.(4.3.2) $\Delta\log|T(j\omega)| = \Delta\log|T_1(j\omega)|$, we can simplify the notation in this explanation by referring to $|T_i(j\omega)|$ as the unity-feedback magnitude for plant case i).

The template for $\omega = 1$ is a bold solid line contour, shown in Fig.4.3.4. Some of the plant cases are also marked. Now suppose that we wish to find the location of the bound at the open-loop vertical line of $-135°$. Position the nominal plant location of $P_1(j1)$ on the vertical line of $-135°$, and at -7.5 dB for instance. Since contours of constant $|T_1| = |L/(1+L)|$ are available on the Nichols chart in Fig.4.3.4, we find that $|T_1(j1)| = -6$db, $|T_4(j1)| = +3$dB, $|T_7(j1)| = +2.9$dB, $|T_9(j1)| = -0.3$db and $|T_3(j1)| = -5.8$dB. Hence, $\Delta|T(j1)| = +3 -(-6) = 9$dB. But the specifications at $\omega = 1$ rad/sec dictates $\Delta\log|T(j1)| = 2$dB only. This means that the initially tried location for case 1 in Fig.4.3.4 is not a successful choice; the template must be elevated by $G(j1)$ until $\Delta\log|T(j1)| = 2$dB at most. Suppose next that $G(j1)$ shifts the template by locating case 1 at [9.5dB, $-135°$] as shown in the figure. This new location for the nominal plant case 1 satisfies the sensitivity specification $\Delta\log|T(j1)| \leq 2$dB, because $|T_1(j1)| = +1.9$dB, $|T_3(j1)| = -0.1$dB, $|T_7(j1)| = +0.7$dB, $|T_9(j1)| = 0$dB, so that finally $\Delta\log|T(j1)| = 2$ dB at most. Hence, the location [+ 9dB, $-135°$] becomes a point of the bound on $L_n(j1)$ on the Nichols chart, satisfying $\Delta\log|T(j1)| = 2$dB. Note that increasing $|G(j1)|$ will guarantee that $\Delta\log|T(j1)| < 2$ dB, but decreasing it, will not.

The same manipulation of the template at $\omega = 1$ may be repeated along a newly chosen vertical line, and a corresponding new minimum of $|L_1(j1)|$ can be found. For instance, to find the bound on $L(j1)$ along the $-45°$ vertical line, we locate case 1 at [+8dB, $-45°$], which satisfies the a priori specification $\Delta\log|T(j1)| = 2$dB. This process can be repeated for a sufficient number of points, for instance each $5°$ of open-loop phase, until a continuous curve of the bound on $L_n(j1)$ is accomplished. This is the solid bold curve shown in Fig.4.3.4. This bound insures that if the loop transmission $L_n(j\omega)$ at $\omega = 1$ is located on the Nichols chart anywhere above or on the bound, $\Delta|T(j1)|$ for all plants in the set $\{P(j1)\}$ will not be greater than 2dB, thus satisfying the $|T(j1)|$ sensitivity specification.

The entire process is naturally repeated at other frequencies. Theoretically, bounds are to be drawn for an infinite number of frequencies, but this is unrealistic and also unnecessary. A practical set of derived bounds is shown in Fig.4.3.6.

Remember also that it does not matter which case was chosen as the nominal plant $P_n(j\omega)$. This is an important property of the design technique. The attained bounds depend on that choice, but the outcome $G(s)$ does not.

Bounds on $L_n(j\omega)$ for satisfying disturbance rejection specifications

The system response to command inputs $r(t)$ is not the only response function of interest. There are, in most systems, also disturbances to be considered. It is necessary, of course, to design $L(s)$ so that the disturbances are properly attenuated for all plants in the set $\{P(s)\}$. Bounds on $L_n(j\omega)$ for satisfying closed-loop specifications of the form

$$|T_d| = \left|\frac{1}{1+GP}\right| \leq D(\omega); \forall P \in \{P\} \tag{4.3.4}$$

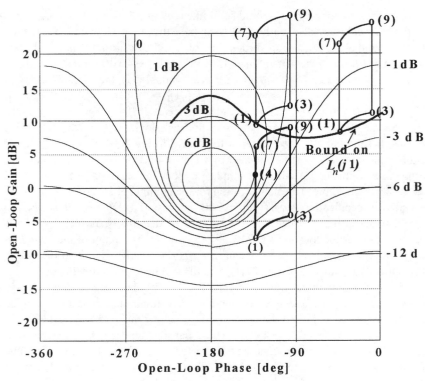

Figure 4.3.4.   Template of $\{P(j1)\}$ and resulting bounds on $L_n(j1)$ on the Nichols chart.

can be easily drawn by using the contours of constant $|1/(1+L)| = |S|$ belonging to the inverted Nichols chart. These are the dotted contours in Fig.4.3.5, whose constant gains are marked inside dotted frames.

When the output-disturbance problem is treated, we usually have to consider separately the low, the high and the very high frequency ranges.

Low frequency range: Generally there is a low frequency range, $\omega < \omega_0$, in which disturbance rejection is mandatory. In this range, $L(j\omega)$ for all plants must be located above the appropriate contour of constant $|S| = D(\omega)$. The bounds must be drawn for the nominal plant case with which the input-output tracking specification bounds on $L_n(j\omega)$ were obtained in the previous design step. A template for the set of uncertain plants is shown in the upper part of Fig.4.3.5. The nominal plant is marked by 'o'.

Suppose that at the frequency ω_1 appertaining to the template, the disturbance rejection specification is $|T_d(j\omega_1)| \leq -6\text{dB}$. In this case, we locate the template so that it barely touches the contour of constant $|S| = |1/(1+L)| = -6\text{dB}$ from above. In this figure, the nominal case $L_n(j\omega_1)$ is located at $[11\text{dB}; -125°]$. We repeat this process for additional open-loop phase vertical lines on the Nichols chart, for example every 5°, until we obtain the continuous contour $B_d(\omega_1)$. Note that this bound extends from $-360°$ to $0°$. Hence, if $L_n(j\omega_1)$ lies above this bound, the $|T_d(j\omega_1)|$ specifications for all $P(s)$ in $\{P(s)\}$ are satisfied, that is

$$|T_d(j\omega_1)| = \left|\frac{1}{1 + L(j\omega_1)}\right| \leq -6 \text{ dB}; \forall P \in \{P\}.$$

High frequency range: Sooner or later there will be a frequency range $\omega \geq \omega_0$ in which no disturbance rejection is required. In this range, we are interested in avoiding large peaks in $|T_d(j\omega)|$, in order to prevent underdamped, closed-loop complex poles. The procedure for obtaining a bound that guarantees $|T_d(j\omega_2)|_{max} \equiv \gamma \leq 3$ dB is now explained.

The template at ω_2 touches from outside the contour of constant $|S| = 3$dB in Fig.4.3.5. The template is shifted down without being rotated. At the same time, it is kept constantly adjacent to the contour of constant $|S| = 3$dB. The position of the nominal plant in the template draws the continuous bound B_2 on the Nichols chart. Consequently, if $L_n(j\omega_2)$ stays outside the created bound B_2, no plant case of the template will lie inside the closed contour of constant $|S| = 3$dB, thus guaranteeing $|T_d(j\omega_2)|_{max} < 3$dB.

Very high frequency range: As $\omega \to \infty$ the plant template approaches a vertical line, whose length depends on the range of the plant parameters. For example, if $P(s) = ak/(s+a)$, then as $s \to \infty$, $P(s) \to ak/s$, the template's width reduces to zero, while its length amounts to $20 \log(ak)_{max}$-$20 \log(ak)_{min}$. This property characterizes all sets of plants that in high frequencies degenerate to $P(s) = k/s^e$, where e is the excess of poles over zeros. In fact, at high frequencies above some ω_h, the templates will resemble this at $\omega = \omega_h$, shown in the figure, as a straight line. We can find the disturbance bound of $|T_d(j\omega)|$ for that template too, in the same way we did at $\omega = \omega_2$. The resulting bound is called *the high frequency bound* and is denoted by B_h in Fig.4.3.5.

The procedure explained here holds for disturbance d, but not for disturbance d_1 shown in Fig.4.2.1. This drawback can be remedied by converting d_1 to an equivalent disturbance $d = P(j\omega)d_1$ introduced at the plant output. However, since this disturbance depends on $P(j\omega)$, it follows that the above process for calculating and drawing disturbance bounds for d_1 can be applied using worse case plant choice.

Bounds on $L_n(j\omega)$ for satisfying maximum peaking in $|T_1(j\omega)|$

Bounds on $L_n(j\omega)$ to satisfy the unity-feedback $|T_1(j\omega)|_{max} < \beta$ constraint must be also added on the Nichols chart. The meaning of these bounds is that the templates at different frequencies should not cross the unity-feedback constant gain contours of permissible β (in dB) in the Nichols chart. The process in drawing

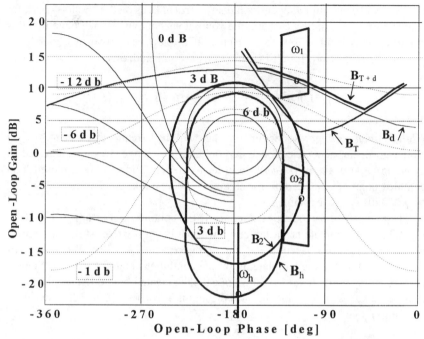

Figure 4.3.5.   Inverted Nichols chart for creating bounds on $L(j\omega)$ for disturbance rejection.

these bounds is basically identical to that explained in deriving the bounds for $|T_d(j\omega)|_{max} < \gamma$, except that contours of constant $|T_1(j\omega)| = \beta$ are now considered.

Combined bounds for tracking and disturbance rejection specifications

Until now, we have found separately the bounds for satisfying the tracking and the disturbance rejection specifications at several given frequencies. To obtain the combined bounds on $L_n(j\omega)$, we have to find their intersection. For instance, Fig.4.3.5 shows the bound on $L_n(j\omega_1)$ for input-output tracking specifications, marked as B_T, and the bound B_d for disturbance rejection specifications. Since $L(j\omega_1)$ must lie above both bounds, a combined bound, marked in the figure as B_{T+d}, is formed. The combined bound includes the sections of the higher gains of each one of the individual bounds B_T and B_d.

This completes the process of deriving bounds on $L_n(j\omega)$ at different frequencies so that all the open and closed-loop specifications of the feedback control system are satisfied. When these bounds are drawn, they look conceptually as in Fig.4.3.6.

The bounds obtained in this chapter by hand calculations can be drawn with an acceptable degree of accuracy by plotting the templates on a transparent piece of paper, where the nominal plant case has been marked. The transparent template is then shifted on the Nichols chart until the relevant bound is formed by the location of the marked nominal plant case. The entire process might be quite time consuming, but it is very much recommended for newcomers to exercise this design technique by hand calculations. After acquiring sufficient practical experience, one can use the Matlab QFT-toolbox (Chait and Yaniv 1993), for creating quickly and automatically templates and accurate bounds of all kinds.

4.3.4. Step 4: Design of L(s) to Satisfy the Specification Bounds

In the step 3, a set of bounds was drawn on the Nichols chart. The property of a bound is that if $L_n(j\omega) = G(j\omega)P_n(j\omega)$ is located in the permitted region defined by its bounds at each ω, then, the input-output tracking, the disturbance and the peaking specifications are guaranteed for all plants in the set $\{P(s)\}$. After the derivation of bounds on $L_n(j\omega)$ at a sufficient number of frequencies is completed, we proceed to shape a nominal loop transmission function that satisfies all the bounds. By definition

$$L_n(j\omega) = G(j\omega)P_n(j\omega), \tag{4.3.5}$$

hence,

$$\ln L_n = \ln G + \ln P_n = \ln |G| + \ln|P_n| + j[\arg(P_n) + \arg(G)]. \tag{4.3.6}$$

Thus, the templates at different frequencies can be shifted, but not rotated, on the Nichols chart, by adding to them the necessary gain and phase that the control network $G(j\omega)$ can provide. This is exactly the shaping process of $L_n(j\omega)$, which must satisfy the bounds at all frequencies. (The optimal way for doing this will be defined later).

Practically, there are two distinct ways to obtain a $L_n(j\omega)$: (i) An optimal $L_n(j\omega)$ can be obtained by first plotting on the Nichols chart the nominal plant $P_n(j\omega)$ for which the bounds were prepared. Then, using classical loopshaping techniques, which consist in adding poles, zeros, lead-lag and other control networks, a $L_n(j\omega)$ is obtained which satisfies the bounds at all frequencies.(See Eq.(4.3.6)). (ii) An optimum $L_n(j\omega)$ is shaped on the Nichols chart for the existing bounds, and the control network is derived from the relation $G(s) = L_n(s)/P_n(s)$.

Practical loopshaping of a satisfactory $L_n(j\omega)$ can be performed by using the Matlab QFT-toolbox in real time mode. With the real time facilities existing in this toolbox, $L_n(j\omega)$ is designed on the Nichols chart, which explicitly shows the bounds, by adding, in an iterating mode, standard compensating networks.

There exist many controllers $G(s)$ for which $L(j\omega)$ satisfies the bounds. Nevertheless, practical considerations based on saving bandwidth leads to the following definition of an optimal $L(j\omega)$ and to guidelines for how to come close to it.

Definition and properties of optimal L(jω)

An optimal designed $L(j\omega)$ is such that it satisfies all system specifications and which, under certain constraints, decreases as rapidly as possible with frequency. There is no limit on the latter if e, defined as the excess of poles over zeros of $L(s)$, is allowed to be infinite. In practice, e must be finite, so that the constraint of a fixed e must be added. The problem is to determine that $L(j\omega)$, which satisfies the bounds and which is at some very large ω, **as small as possible**. This means that, as $L(s) \to k/s^e$, the optimal $L(s)$ satisfies all the bounds with the minimum k.
$\underset{s\to\infty}{}$

Intuition and practice lead to the conjecture that the optimum $L(j\omega)$ with maximum permissible phase-lag of $-(90e)°$ has the properties shown in Fig.4.3.6. Up to some frequency defined by the active frequency range in which system specifications are to be satisfied, it lies on the appropriate bound at each ω. For $\omega \geq \omega_x \cong \omega_h$ up to some ω_A it lies on the bottom 'U' of B_h as shown. At ω_A the phase jumps abruptly from $-\theta_A$ to $-(90e)°$. Hence, $|L(j\omega_A)|$ goes to infinity on the vertical line $\theta = -\theta_A$ and returns along the vertical line $\theta = -(90e)°$. In practice, in order to work with control networks having reasonably high damping, a more practical $L(j\omega)$, without the abrupt jump, should be preferred. This $L(j\omega)$ is shown in the figure by the dotted line. In the region $\omega_x \leq \omega \leq \omega_y$, $L(j\omega)$ lies on the high frequency B_h bound as defined in Fig.4.3.6, then goes softly to a phase of $-(90e)°$. Moreover, beyond ω_y, $L(j\omega)$ is not allowed to possess a phase-lag larger than $-(90e)°$.

It can be shown that under certain conditions an optimum $L(j\omega)$ lies on the bounds at all frequencies (Horowitz and Sidi 1972; Horowitz 1973). The defined optimal $L(j\omega)$ tends to decrease the gain of $|L(j\omega)|$ to minimum in the high frequency range. But this was also a necessary condition for $L(j\omega)$ to minimize the sensor noise amplification, as discussed in Section 2.4.1.

Based on the above definition of the optimal loop transmission $L(j\omega)$, some conclusions of practical importance follow:

1. In general, sensor noise is concentrated at high frequencies. Thus, most of the sensor noise is amplified at the plant input u by the gain $|T_{un}| = |G/(1+GP)|$. At high frequencies, $|L| = |GP| << 1$. Therefore, $u_n \approx -G(j\omega)n$, where u_n is the effect of the amplified noise n at the input to the plant. A lower gain controller (i.e, with a smaller $|G(j\omega)|$) will diminish the noise effect at the plant input, thus avoiding its saturation.

2. A lower bandwidth solution demands less control effort, thus saving energy and increasing the actuator life time.

3. In deriving the optimal $L_n(j\omega)$, the designer tends to shape the loop transmission so that $L_n(j\omega)$ will lie at least at one frequency as low as possible on its relevant bound. This practical approach will lead to the desired low bandwidth solution.

4. Note that in the frequency range $\omega_x \leq \omega \leq \omega_y$, the boundary B_h has a constant phase-lag. As a result, $L_n(j\omega)$ can be approximated in this range by alternating poles and zeros compensating networks.

4.3.5.   Step 5: Derivation of the Control Network G(s)

Once $L_n(j\omega)$ has been derived, $G(s)$ is easily obtained from the relation

$$G(s) = L_n(s) / P_n(s) \qquad (4.3.7)$$

4.3.6.   Step 6: Design of the Prefilter F(s) to Achieve $|T(j\omega)|$ tracking specifications

The designed controller $G(s)$ guarantees that for all plants in $\{P\}$, and with no uncertainties in G and F,

$$\Delta|T(j\omega)| = \max_{\{P\}}\left|\frac{GPF}{1+GP}\right| - \min_{\{P\}}\left|\frac{GPF}{1+GP}\right| \le B_U(\omega) - B_L(\omega). \qquad (4.3.8)$$

The tracking specifications are defined for all plants in $\{P\}$ by the constraints

$$B_L(\omega) \le \min_{\{P\}}\left|\frac{GPF}{1+GP}\right| < \max_{\{P\}}\left|\frac{GPF}{1+GP}\right| \le B_U(\omega) \qquad (4.3.9)$$

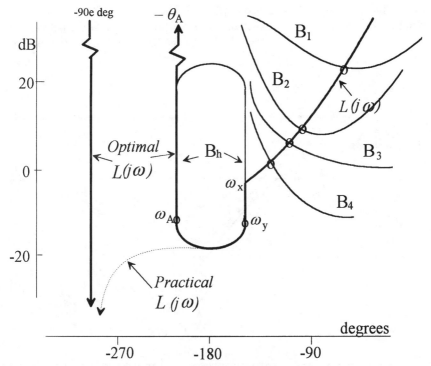

Figure 4.3.6.   Definition of optimum and practical $L(j\omega)$ on the Nichols chart.

For example, the difference between the maximum and the minimum magnitudes in dB of the dashed curves in Fig.4.3.7 belonging to $|T_1|$ is smaller than, or equal to the difference between the Bode plots of the admissible B_U and B_L bounds belonging to $|T|$. These bounds are named *Upper* and *Lower Bounds*. Thus Eq.(4.3.8) is satisfied, but not Eq.(4.3.9). (Note that $|T_1(j\omega)|$ for all plants can be graphically obtained from the Nichols chart displaying $L_n(j\omega)$ and the plant templates, or by straightforward numerical computation). The task of the prefilter $F(s)$ is to shift the Bode plots of the obtained $|T_1(j\omega)|$'s for all plant conditions to lie within the Bode plots of B_U and B_L. This can be done by classical loopshaping with $F(j\omega)$. This assigns to the designer the second-degree-of-freedom.

The dotted parts of the lower and upper specified bounds of $|T(j\omega)|$ below -20dB deviate from the original specifications obtained in Section 4.3.1 by the dominant complex pole second-order model of $T(s)$ in the permitted region of Fig.4.3.2a. We noted in this connection that the extreme $|T(j\omega)|$ cases remain parallel at the high frequencies with a finite magnitude tolerance in dB. With this initial choice, the specified bounds at high frequencies are too narrow. Thus, in order to guarantee these unnecessarily tough tracking specifications, the bounds on $L_n(j\omega)$ in the Nichols chart will never degenerate to that of B_h in Fig.4.3.6. This is the reason for the modification of the upper and of the lower permitted bounds in Fig.4.3.2 at the higher frequencies, so that no tracking sensitivity specifications are to be satisfied beyond ω_a. The level of -20dB is chosen arbitrarily. But we know from experience (see Section 3.2.3) that the behavior of $|T(j\omega)|$ below -20dB can be neglected when the basic features of the time re-

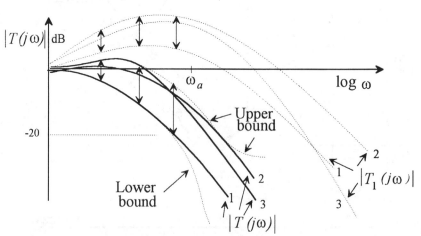

Figure 4.3.7. $|T_1(j\omega)|$'s for different plant cases, and the corrected $|T(j\omega)|$'s by the prefilter $F(j\omega)$

sponse are considered, as long as the output signal energy is mainly located at low frequencies.

4.3.7. Step 7: Evaluation of the design.

Simulation in the time-domain, as well as in the frequency-domain, is necessary in order to check satisfaction of the initially defined system specifications. The design process guarantees that the frequency-domain specifications are satisfied for all frequencies and plants in $\{P(s)\}$. However, time-domain simulations are mandatory for the following reasons:

1. If the original specifications are given in the time-domain, their translation into the frequency-domain is an approximation only, in the sense that there is not an exact translation between these two domains. It is important, therefore, to check if the achieved time-domain responses conform with the original system time-response specifications.

2. In order to achieve a practical controller, its bandwidth must be sufficiently low. This can be obtained by easing the tracking specifications at high frequencies. This will not generally impact appreciably on the tracking and the disturbance time-domain responses. (For a quantitative discussion see Chapter 3). But still, it is important to check the price paid in quality of the time-domain responses for that saving in bandwidth.

3. The harmful effect of the sensor noise and also of plant resonance existing in the high frequency range can be decreased by adding far-off poles to the controller. (Of course this should be done carefully). The disadvantage of adding such poles is that they introduce effective delays in the closed-loop input-output time response, the amount of which can be predicted and finally checked by simulation. (See Chapter 3, Section 3.2.3).

As one can easily see from the above arguments, time-domain simulation is an important step in evaluating the achieved performances of the feedback system in order to decide if a second design iteration is necessary.

Remark 1. It is important to point out that the complexity of the plant transfer function does not make any difference to the simplicity of the explained design procedure. The examples to be solved in this chapter are based on low-order plants in order to ease the presentation of the solution. In real physical feedback systems, with much more complicated plant structures, the simplicity and the efficiency of the presented solutions are preserved.

Remark 2. In prior Nyquist-oriented and root-locus design techniques for solving the uncertain feedback systems, pairing of a nominal $T_n(s)$ and a nominal plant $P_n(s)$ was necessary for achieving a good solution in relation to sensor noise amplification, not an easy task. (Horowitz 1963, Horowitz 1969 and Olson and Horowitz 1970). The design technique explained here eliminates entirely the necessity for pairing (Horowitz and Sidi 1972).

4.3.8   Main Example.

The following example displays in detail the different steps of the presented design procedure.

Example 4.3.1.   The TDOF feedback system to be implemented is described schematically in Fig.4.2.1. The uncertain plant set $\{P\}$ is

$$P(s) = \frac{k}{(s + a)(s + b)}; \quad k \in [1-10], a \in [1-5], b \in [0.2-1].$$

The closed-loop specifications are in both the time-and the frequency-domains. The time-domain specifications related to the step response $y(t)$ are $1.5 < t_r < 2.5$. The maximum overshoot is to be less than 20%. The frequency-domain specifications are: (i) The unity-feedback constraint of $|T_1(j\omega)|_{max} = \beta < 3\text{dB}$ guarantees that sensor noise cannot be amplified by more than 3dB as measured at the plant output, Eq.(2.1.7). (ii) The transfer function magnitude $|T_d(j\omega)|$ for disturbances introduced at d in fig.4.2.1 satisfies $|T_d(j\omega)|_{max} = |S(j\omega)|_{max} = \gamma < 3\text{dB}$. Note that these frequency-domain specifications guarantee also that the loop transmission $L = GP$ for all plant cases and at all frequencies is located distantly enough from the stability critical point [0dB, $-180°$]. The β and γ constraints, being smaller than 3dB, guarantee a phase margin of 45°, and also a gain margin of 11dB, see Section 2.5.2.

Step 1. Translation of time-domain into frequency-domain specifications.

The first step in the design is to translate the time-domain tolerances into frequency-domain tolerances. A model $T(s)$ consisting of a dominant second-order complex pole pair that satisfies the time-domain specifications is used for that purpose. Use is made of Fig.3.2.6. For the overshoot to be less than 20%, we find that $\xi > 0.45$ is necessary. Also, $\xi < 0.8$ is chosen in order to guarantee a small step response overshoot, so that the steady-state value is crossed close to the specified rise time. In accordance with these parameters, we choose $0.45 < \xi < 0.8$. Next, in order to convert the specifications on the rise time t_r into the frequency-domain, the graph of $10\omega_n t_r$ in the same figure is used in order to obtain the permitted region of ξ versus ω_n, shown in Fig.4.3.8.

Translation of the acceptable range of complex pole pair of second-order model of $T(s)$ into the frequency responses $|T(j\omega)|$ is shown in Fig.4.3.9. The allowed $\Delta|T(j\omega)|$ at several frequencies is obtained from this figure, and is summarized in Table 4.3.2.

As mentioned previously, hard specifications in high frequencies cost a lot in excessive bandwidth. However, in general, they have a negligible effect on the system step-time response. Therefore, it is essential to ease the specifications in the frequency range where $|T(j\omega)| < -20\text{dB}$. As a result, these specifications are modified in Fig.4.3.9 in order to allow a larger amount of acceptable $\Delta|T(j\omega)|$. In

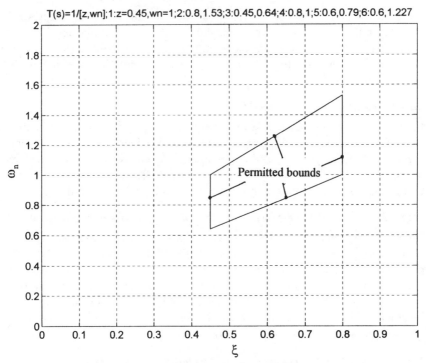

Figure 4.3.8. Permitted region of ω_n versus ξ for specified t_r and maximum overshoot.

the range $\omega > 2$ rad/sec, the lower bound is decreased by adding a pole located at $\omega = 1.5$ rad/sec. In the range $\omega > 6$ rad/sec, the upper bound is increased by adding a zero located $\omega = 3.3$ rad/sec. The newly specified upper and lower bounds are approximated to

$$T_{upper}(s) = \frac{(1 + s/0.25)(1 + s)(1 + s/3.333)}{(1 + s/0.5)^2 (1 + s/20)\left(1 + \dfrac{2 \times 0.6}{1.3} s + \dfrac{s^2}{1.3^2}\right)}.$$

$$T_{lower}(s) = \frac{1}{(1 + s/1.5)\left(1 + \dfrac{2 \times 0.65}{0.75} s + \dfrac{s^2}{0.75^2}\right)}.$$

Table 4.3.2. Permissible $\Delta|T(j\omega)|$ at several substantial frequencies

ω rad/sec	0.2	0.3	0.5	0.7	1.0	1.5	2.0	3.0	5.0	10.0	20.0
$\Delta|T(j\omega)|$dB	0.6	1.2	3.0	4.0	7.0	11.0	14.0	24.0	—	—	—

The modified permitted bounds in the frequency-domain are shown in Fig.4.3.9. The step time responses shown in Fig.4.3.10 pertain to the transfer functions whose magnitude Bode plots are shown in Fig.4.3.9. The obtained step response bounds are shown in the Fig.4.3.10. They ought to comply with the initially set time specifications.

Step 2. Preparation of plant templates

In this step plant templates at several frequencies are prepared on the Nichols chart. The chosen frequencies depend on the specified bounds of $|T(j\omega)|$ shown in Fig.4.3.9. Accordingly, the resulting bounds on $L(j\omega)$ will be found at the frequencies $\omega = 0.2, 0.3, 0.5, 0.7, 1.0, 1.5, 2, 3, 5, 10, 20$ rad/sec, which are in the useful frequency range. Plant templates at some of them are shown in Fig.4.3.11.

Step 3. Derivation of bounds on the loop transmission $L_n(j\omega)$ in the Nichols chart

Bounds for the following 3 types of specifications are drawn on the Nichols chart: (i) Bounds for satisfying $\Delta|T(j\omega)|$ at $\omega = 0.2, 0.3, 0.5, 0.7, 1.0, 1.5, 2.0, 3.0$ rad/sec; (ii) Bounds for satisfying $|T_1(j\omega)|_{max} < 3$dB at the same frequencies; and (iii) bounds for satisfying $|T_d(j\omega)|_{max} < 3$dB at the above frequencies, but also at some additional higher frequencies, namely, at $\omega = 5.0, 10.0, 20.0$ rad/sec. The intersection of all of these bounds are shown in Fig.4.3.12. The nominal case used in preparing these bounds is $P_n(s) = P_{15}(s) = 10/[(s+1)(s+3)]$.

Step 4. Loopshaping of $L_n(j\omega)$ to satisfy its bounds

Loopshaping of $L_n(j\omega) = GP_n$, based on the derived bounds in the previous step, is performed in the Nichols chart. $L_n(j\omega)$ should be located above the bounds at $\omega = 0.2, 0.3, 0.5, 0.7, 1.0, 1.5, 2, 3$ rad/sec and outside the closed bounds at $\omega = 5, 10, 20$ rad/sec. Moreover, $L_n(j\omega)$ is close to optimal if it lies on the bounds at each frequency and if its magnitude at the high frequencies is as low as possible.

The designed $L_n(j\omega)$ shown in Fig.4.3.12 lies on the bounds at low frequencies, i.e., at the range $\omega < 5$ rad/sec. $L_n(j\omega)$ satisfies the disturbance specifications in the

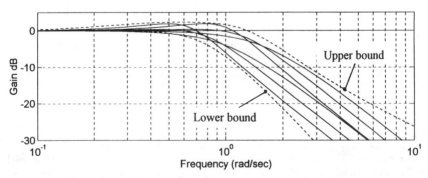

Figure 4.3.9. Bounds on $|T(j\omega)|$ for the specified step time responses.

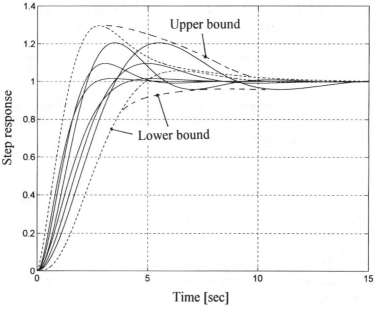

Figure 4.3.10.   Permitted bounds on time responses based on the acceptable ω_n and ξ.

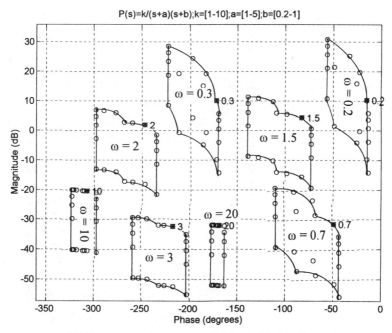

Figure 4.3.11.   Plant templates at ω = 0.2, 0.3, 0.7, 1.5, 2, 3, 10, 20 rad/sec

high frequency range $\omega > \omega_h = 5$ rad/sec, but does not lie on the high frequency bounds at $\omega = 5, 10, 20$ rad/sec. This is due to the existence of large distances between the bounds. For instance, the bound at $\omega = 3$ rad/sec, which is the highest frequency for which sensitivity specifications are to be satisfied, is very distant from the bounds at $\omega = 5, 10$ and 20 rad/sec. Consequently, manipulation of $L_n(j\omega)$, to force it to lie on all of them, necessitates a very complicated control network $G(s)$. In order to avoid a too complicated controller, we are inclined to accept a $L_n(j\omega)$ that does not lie on the bounds at all frequencies. The transfer function of the designed practical loop transmission shown in Fig.4.3.12 is quite simple:

$$L_n(s) = \frac{13.73}{s} \frac{1 + s/1.678}{1 + s/2.38} \frac{80^2}{s^2 + 2\times0.6\times80s + 80^2}.$$

Nonetheless, this solution is quite close to an optimal one as defined in Section 4.3.4. The loop transmissions for all plant cases in $\{P(s)\}$ are shown in Fig.4.3.13.

Step 5. Derivation of the control network G(s)

As already mentioned, there are two ways to derive the control network $G(s)$. We have chosen here the technique of first loopshaping a compatible loop transmis-

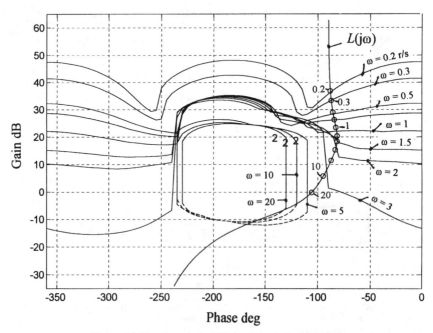

Figure 4.3.12.   Bounds on $L_n(j\omega)$ and the designed $L_n(j\omega)$.

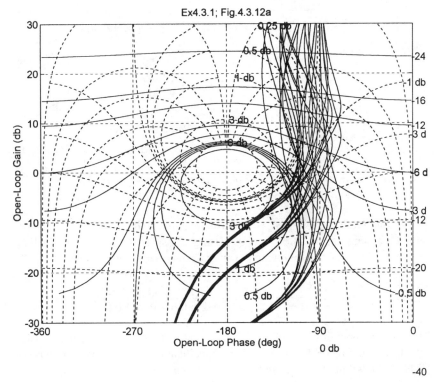

Figure 4.3.13. $L(j\omega)$'s for all plants in $\{P(s)\}$ on the combined Nichols & inverted Nichols charts.

sion $L_n(j\omega)$ that satisfies the bounds. Since these are derived with the chosen nominal plant Case 15 whose transfer function is

$$P_n(s) = P_{15}(s) = 10/(s^2 + 4s + 3),$$

it follows that

$$G(s) = \frac{L_n(s)}{P_n(s)} = \frac{1.373}{s} \frac{1 + s/1.678}{1 + s/2.38} \frac{(s^2 + 4s + 3)80^2}{s^2 + 2\times0.6\times 80s + 80^2}.$$

Step 6. Design of the prefilter F(s) to achieve the tracking specifications

The final step consists in designing the prefilter $F(s)$ to satisfy the input-output tracking specifications of $T(s)$. The controller $G(s)$ guarantees that $\Delta|T_1(j\omega)| \le B_U - B_L$. The task of the prefilter $F(s)$ is to guarantee that also $B_L \le |T_1(j\omega)F(j\omega)| \le B_U$. Once $G(s)$ is known, the unity-feedback $|T_1(j\omega)|$'s are computed for all the plants in the set $\{P(s)\}$. Bode plots of all $|T_1(j\omega)|$'s are shown in Fig.4.3.14, together with the specific permissible bounds.

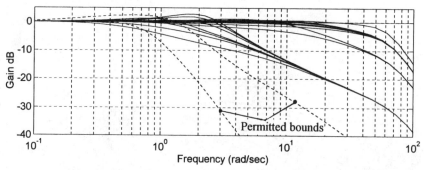

Figure 4.3.14. $|T_1(j\omega)|$'s and the permissible bounds on $|T(j\omega)|$.

The second DOF, namely $F(s)$, is now used to shift all the $|T_1(j\omega)|$'s into the permitted tracking specification bounds. Using classical frequency-domain loop-shaping techniques, the following $F(s)$ was designed for that purpose,

$$F(s) = \frac{0.7}{s+0.7} \frac{3}{s+3} \frac{s^2 + 2 \times 1 \times 0.8s + 0.8^2}{s^2 + 2 \times 0.6 \times 0.8s + 0.8^2}.$$

The transfer functions $|T(j\omega)|$'s for all the plant in $\{P(s)\}$ were calculated. These are shown in Fig.4.3.15. The tracking specifications are satisfied because all $|T(j\omega)|$'s lie within the upper and the lower permitted bounds B_U and B_L.

Step 7. Evaluation of the design

Finally, we can evaluate the achieved design in the time-domain. The step time responses for all plants in the set $\{P(s)\}$ are shown in Fig.4.3.16. They all lie within the permitted bounds, also shown, and no design modification is necessary.

It is necessary to point out that in the solved main example, the plant is minimum-phase and stable. In this case, any time-domain specifications could be set and achieved for all uncertainties in the plant parameters. By easing the time-domain

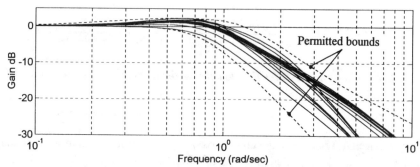

Figure 4.3.15. $|T(j\omega)| = |F(j\omega)T_1(j\omega)|$ for all plant cases in the set $\{P(s)\}$.

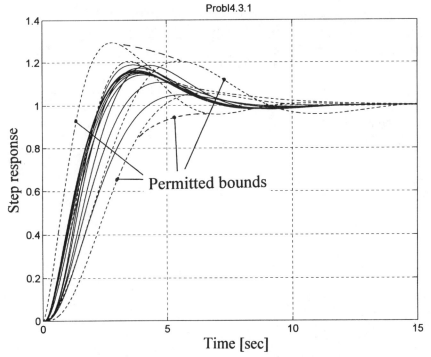

Figure 4.3.16.   Step responses of the achieved design (solid lines)
and of the specifications (dotted lines)

specifications close to $t = 0$, smaller magnitudes of the loop transmission $L(j\omega)$ can be obtained at high frequencies, thus preventing excessively high sensor noise amplification, as explained in Section 2.4.

The Matlab M-files program for solving the main example 4.3.8, using the QFT-toolbox, are documented in Tables 4.3.1 and 4.3.2. Table 4.3.1 is the M-file for creating the matrix of polynomial coefficients pertaining to all the plant cases. Table 4.3.2 is the M-file for obtaining the bounds on $L_n(j\omega)$ at the relevant frequencies and for designing the optimal $L_n(j\omega)$.

4.4   Design Technique for Unstable Uncertain Plants (Category II)

We have seen in Section 3.6 that for unstable plant feedback systems, there is a range of frequencies in which the magnitude of the loop transmission must be larger than 0dB (conditionally stable systems). This range depends on the location of the unstable poles. Unfortunately, the minimum achievable bandwidth of $L(j\omega)$ may emerge as much larger than the bandwidth needed to satisfy the closed-loop sensitivity specifications.

Table 4.3.1. M-file for preparing the matrix of
polynomial coefficients for all the plant cases

```
%plpr4_3_8.m Example 4.3.8.
%P(s) = k/(s + a)(s + b); k = [1 − 10]; a = [1 − 5];b=[0.2 − 1];
c = 1;
%
a = 1; b = 0.2;
for k = linspace(1,10,5)
        nump(c,:) = k;
        dnp(c,:) = [1, a + b, a * b];
c = c + 1
end
%
a = 1; b = 0.5;
for k = linspace(1, 10, 2)
        nump(c,:) = k;
        dnp(c,:) = [1, a + b, a * b];
c = c + 1
end
%
a = 3; b = 0.2;
for k = linspace(1, 10, 2)
        nump(c,:) = k;
        dnp(c,:) = [1, a + b, a * b];
c = c + 1
end
%
a = 3; b = 0.5;
for k = linspace(1, 10, 2)
        nump(c,:) = k;
        dnp(c,:) = [1, a + b, a * b];
c = c + 1
end
%
a = 3; b = 1;
for k = linspace(1, 10, 2)
        nump(c,:) = k;
        dnp(c,:) = [1, a + b, a * b];
c = c + 1
end
%
a = 5; b = 1;
for k = linspace(1, 10, 5)
        nump(c,:) = k;
        dnp(c,:) = [1, a + b, a * b];
c = c + 1
end
```

Table 4.3.2. M-file for obtaining the boundaries on $L_n(j\omega)$ and also the optimal $L_n(j\omega)$.

```
%prob4_3_8.m; Example 4.3.8
w = [0.2, 0.3, 0.5, 0.7, 1, 1.5, 2, 3, 5, 10, 20];
p = freqcp(nump, denp, w);
nompt = 15;
figure(1); plottmpl(w, w, p, nompt);
%
ws1 = [1.41, 1.41, 1.41, 1.41, 1.41, 1.41, 1.41, 1.41, 1.41, 1.41, 1.41];
bnd1 = sisobnds(1, w, w, ws1, p, 0, nompt);
bd1 = bnd1 (:, 1:8);
figure(6);plotbnds(bd1);
ws2 = [1.41, 1.41, 1.41, 1.41, 1.41, 1.41, 1.41, 1.41, 1.41, 1.41, 1.41];
bnd2 = sisobnds(2, w, w, ws2, p, 0, nompt);
bd2 = bnd2(:, 9:11);
ws7 = [1.07, 1.14, 1.4, 1.6, 2.24, 3.55, 5.0, 15.8, 50, 50, 50;1,1,1,1,1,1,1,1,1,1,1];
bnd7 = sisobnds(7, w, w, ws7, p, 0, nompt);
bd7 = bnd7(: , 1:8);
%addition of 3 dbs closed-loop bound;
bd77 = grpbnds(bd1, bd7);
bd777 = sectbnds(bd77);
bnd = grpbnds(bd777, bd2);
figure(2); plotbnds(bnd);
%loopshaping;
nump0 = [1]; denp0 = [1];
w = logspace(−2, 2.5, 100);
lpshape(w, bnd, nump0, denp0, 0, numg0, deng0)
end
```

The design technique for uncertain unstable plants is exactly the same as that for uncertain minimum-phase plants. We shall show what the difficulties are in such cases by using: (i) an uncertain plant that includes stable, but also unstable poles and (ii) a control network $G(s)$ that stabilizes the uncertain plant feedback system and which emerges with a loop transmission $L(j\omega)$ that satisfies the specification bounds.

The problem considered here is designing the flight control system of a modern aircraft. The longitudinal transfer function for elevator displacement is:

$$\frac{\theta(s)}{\delta_e(s)} = \frac{k(1+s\,\tau_{phu})(1+s\,\tau_{sho})}{\left[\left(\frac{s}{\omega_{phu}}\right)^2 + \frac{2\,\xi_{phu}}{\omega_{phu}}s+1\right]\left[\left(\frac{s}{\omega_{sho}}\right)^2 + \frac{2\,\xi_{sho}}{\omega_{sho}}s+1\right]}$$

where θ is the pitch angle in the longitudinal plane and δ_e is the elevator displacement. The longitudinal dynamics for nearly all aircraft in most flight conditions can be represented by two characteristic modes, a long-period oscillation called the 'phugoid mode', and a short-period oscillation called the 'short-period mode', characterized by ω_{phu}, ξ_{phu}, ω_{sho} and ξ_{sho} respectively. The plant parameters depend on flight conditions, which are the altitude and the Mach number (McRuer et al. 1973, Blakelock 1991). Actually, the phugoid and the short period second-order complex poles are quite distanced from each other in the s-plane. Generally, the ratio between the short period and the phugoid oscillatory frequencies lies in the range of 10 to 20. As a result, when the fast maneuvering modes of the aircraft are considered, the phugoid dynamics can be omitted. The transfer function to be used in the design stage of the flight control can then be approximated by the short-period dynamics only, which is

$$\frac{\theta(s)}{\delta_e(s)} = \frac{k(1 + s\,\tau_{sho})}{s\left[\left(\frac{s}{\omega_{sho}}\right)^2 + \frac{2\,\xi_{sho}s}{\omega_{sho}} + 1\right]} \, .$$

In order to achieve high maneuverability, modern aircraft are designed so that the airframe dynamics verges on instability, or may even be unstable under some flight conditions. The task of the automatic control system is to stabilize the aircraft under all flight conditions (robust stability), and to satisfy tracking performances (robust performance) within the operational flight envelope.

Example 4.4.1.   Design a pitch orientational control system of a military aircraft whose short-period dynamics at different flight conditions are given in Fig. 4.4.4. The input-output tracking dynamics $T(s)$ should be basically approximated to a second-order complex pole, whose acceptable parameters in the s-plane are shown in Fig.4.4.1. The usual specifications for maximum closed-loop peaking are: $|T_d(j\omega)|_{max} < 4$dB, and also $|T_1(j\omega)|_{max} < 4$dB. For tutorial simplicity, we shall assume that τ_{sho} is very small, thus the zero of the short period can be deleted from the transfer function. (In a real flight control system, τ_{sho} is also dependent on flight conditions and is a part of the uncertainty of the plant. Its omission here does not change in any way the generality and the simplicity of the design technique). The design process is now described step-by-step.

Step 1. Translation of time-domain specifications into frequency-domain specifications

The tracking specifications $T(s)$ are modeled by a second-order complex pole whose acceptable range in the s-plane is shown in Fig.4.4.1, where the upper half s-plane is only displayed.

Fig.4.4.2 shows the magnitude Bode plots for several $T(s)$'s modeled by second-order complex poles located in the acceptable specification range of

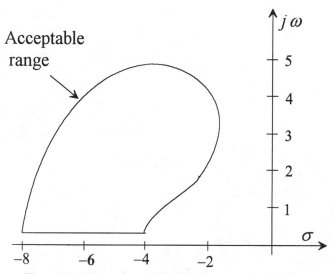

Figure 4.4.1.   Range of acceptable closed-loop second-order poles.

Fig.4.4.1. These plots define the tracking specifications in the frequency-domain

$$|T_{lower}(j\omega)| \le |T(j\omega)| \le |T_{upper}(j\omega)|.$$

The upper and lower bounds of $|T(j\omega)|$ in Fig.4.4.2 are approximated by the transfer functions

$$T_{upper}(s) = \frac{1.28(s + 2.2)(s + 16.36)(s + 30)}{(s + 6)^2(s^2 + 2 \times 0.9 \times 6.2s + 6.2^2)}$$

and

$$T_{lower}(s) = \frac{122.5}{(s + 10)(s^2 + 2 \times 0.9 \times 3.5s + 3.5^2)}.$$

From Fig.4.4.2 We find that the permitted changes $\Delta|T(j\omega)|$ at several meaningful frequencies are as summarized in Table 4.4.1

The time-domain tolerances in Fig.4.4.3 are obtained by plotting the step time responses for some of the second-order complex pole model of $T(s)$ in the acceptable range in Fig.4.4.1, together with the step time responses of the limiting transfer functions $T_{upper}(s)$ and $T_{lower}(s)$.

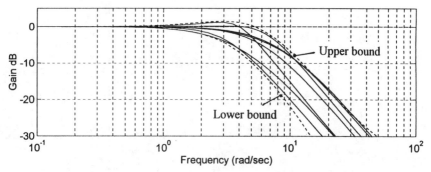

Figure 4.4.2.   Tracking specification bounds in the frequency-domain corresponding to closed-loop second-order poles in the acceptable range shown in Fig.4.4.1.

Step 2. Preparation of templates

The assumed plant model is:

$$P(s) = \frac{k}{s\left[\left(\frac{s}{\omega_n}\right)^2 + \frac{2\xi s}{\omega_n} + 1\right]}$$

where ω_n and ξ are dictated by the second-order complex pole locations of $P(s)$ in the s-plane, as shown in Fig.4.4.4.

We are now ready to prepare the plant templates at several frequencies. The chosen frequencies must be in the useful tracking dynamics frequency range, and up to three times that range. (Explicitly it depends on the uncertainty properties of the plant, and also on the tracking specifications at high frequencies). The useful range is up to about $\omega = 15$ rad/sec, as Fig.4.4.2 shows. Therefore, the frequencies for drawing bounds on $L_n(j\omega)$ are chosen to be at $\omega = 0.5, 1, 2, 3, 4, 5, 7, 10, 15, 20, 50$ rad/sec. The templates at these frequencies are shown in Figs.4.4.5 and 4.4.6. Note that the templates at the low frequency range can be as wide as 360° in the Nichols chart.

Step 3. Derivation of bounds on the loop transmission $L_n(j\omega)$ in the Nichols chart

The techniques presented in Section 4.3.3 are used for derivation of the bounds on $L_n(j\omega)$. Bounds to satisfy the specifications of $\Delta|T(j\omega)|$ as given in Table 4.4.1 were first obtained. These are shown in Fig.4.4.7. Bounds to satisfy the peaking

Table 4.4.1. Permitted changes in $\Delta|T(j\omega)|$

ω	0.5	1	2	3	4	5	7	10	15	20	50
$\Delta|T(j\omega)|$dB	0.35	1	3.2	7.6	9	11	12.5	17.5	25	—	—

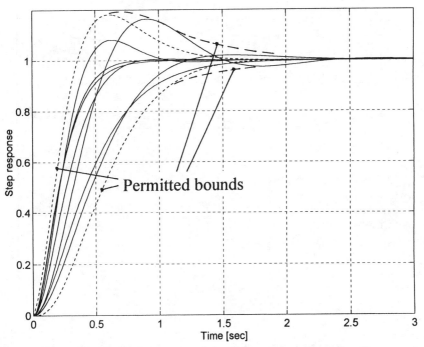

Figure 4.4.3. Time-domain tolerances on unit-step response corresponding to closed-loop second-order poles in acceptable range shown in Fig.4.4.1.

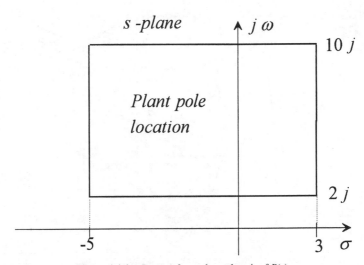

Figure 4.4.4. Range of complex pole pair of *P(s)*.

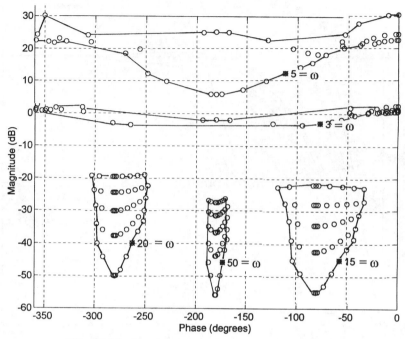

Figure 4.4.5.   Plant templates at various substantial frequencies.

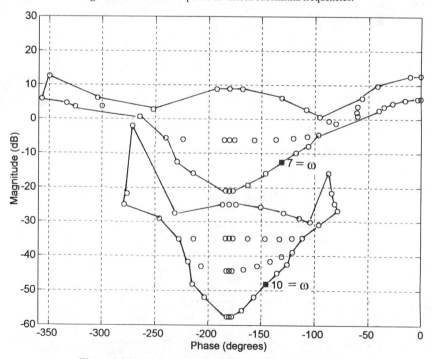

Figure 4.4.6.   Plant templates at some intermediate frequencies.

specifications $|T_d(j\omega)|_{max} < 4\text{dB}$ and $|T_1(j\omega)|_{max} < 4\text{dB}$ were next derived. The intersections of all these bounds are shown in Fig.4.4.8.

For the unstable plant problem at hand, due to the special features of some of the templates having a width of close to $360°$, the bounds on the Nichols chart have some peculiar and unpleasant features. Fig.4.4.7 shows bounds at $\omega = 0.5, 3, 4$ and 5 rad/sec which are essential in satisfying tracking sensitivity specifications of $|T(j\omega)|$. In the region in the Nichols chart (arg $L(j\omega) > -180°$) where $L_n(j\omega)$ will be manipulated and finally located, we see that the bound at $\omega = 5$ rad/sec is more elevated in magnitude than the bounds at $\omega = 3$, and 4 rad/sec. Since $|L_n(j\omega)|$ is most likely a decreasing function of ω, the bounds at these frequencies will be satisfied if the bound at $\omega = 5$ rad/sec is satisfied. Thus there is no need to consider them. For similar reasons, bounds at $\omega = 1$ and 2 rad/sec do not appear in Fig.4.4.8.

Step 4. Design of the loop transmission $L_n(s)$ to satisfy the bounds

Loopshaping of $L_n(j\omega)$ that satisfies the bounds prepared in Step 3 is performed next. As already noted, properties of optimal $L_n(j\omega)$ are that $L_n(j\omega)$ lies on the bounds, or, at least, as near as possible to them at each frequency, and that it achieves the lowest attainable magnitude at high frequencies. Unfortunately, due

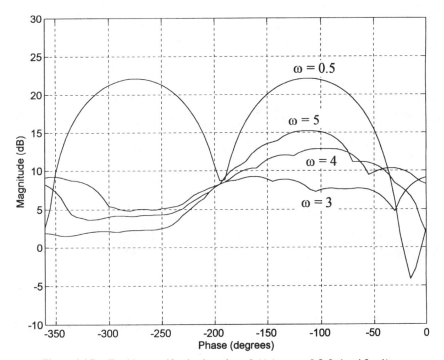

Figure 4.4.7. Tracking specification bounds on $L_n(j\omega)$ at $\omega = 0.5, 3, 4$ and 5 rad/sec.

to unfavorable mutual location of the bounds, $L_n(j\omega)$ does not lie on all bounds at the respective frequencies, although it satisfies them. Due to the special nature of the present problem, the bound at $\omega = 10$ rad/sec is quite distanced from the higher frequency bounds at $\omega = 15, 20, 50$ rad/sec. Manipulating $L_n(j\omega)$ to lie on all bounds would necessitate a substantially complicated control network $G(s)$. Instead, we achieved a nominal loop transmission pertaining to the nominal plant (case 3) which does not lie on all the bounds, but is simple and sufficiently close to optimal:

$$L_n(s) = L_3(s) = \frac{10}{s} \frac{1+s/3.264}{1+s/15} \frac{1+s/150.1}{1+s/32.64} \frac{1}{1+\frac{2\times0.5s}{700}+\left(\frac{s}{700}\right)^2}.$$

$L_n(j\omega)$ is shown in Fig.4.4.8.

The nominal loop transmission function $L_3(j\omega)$ is again shown in Fig.4.4.9, together with the loop transmissions pertaining to additional plant cases. Since the $L(j\omega)$'s of unstable plant cases are conditionally stable, this dictates a minimum lower bound on the crossover frequency ω_{co} (see section 3.6.2). Note especially

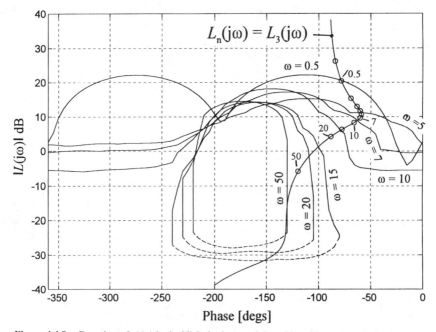

Figure 4.4.8.   Bounds on $L_n(j\omega)$ in the Nichols chart, and the achieved loop transmission $L_3(j\omega)$.

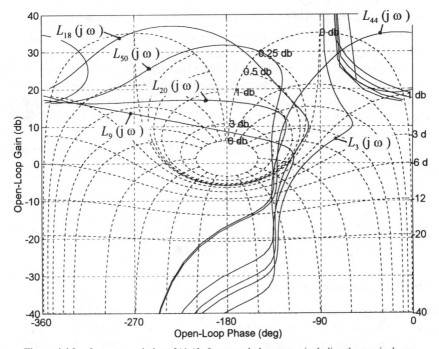

Figure 4.4.9. Loop transmissions $L(j\omega)$'s for several plant cases, including the nominal case.

$L_9(j\omega)$, whose upper low frequency gain margin (*GML*) is small, but satisfactory since it satisfies the $\beta < 4$ dB performance constraint.

Step 5. Derivation of the control network G(s)

In step 3 of this design process, we have chosen the technique of deriving first a nominal loop transmission which satisfies the bounds. Since a $L_n(j\omega)$ was derived for the chosen plant case 3 as nominal, $G(s) = L_3(s) / P_3(s)$, where

$$P_3(s) = \frac{3.606^2}{s^2 + 2 \times 0.83s + 3.606^2},$$

and finally

$$G(s) = \frac{L_3}{P_3} = \frac{10}{s} \frac{1 + s/3.264}{1 + s/15} \frac{1 + s/150.1}{1 + s/32.64} \frac{1 + \dfrac{2 \times 0.83s}{3.606} + \left(\dfrac{s}{3.606}\right)^2}{1 + \dfrac{2 \times 0.5s}{700} + \left(\dfrac{s}{700}\right)^2}.$$

Note that $G(s)$ is strictly proper so that the sensor noise reaching the input to the plant is not over amplified.

Step 6. Design the prefilter F(s) to achieve the tracking specifications

The final step is to design the prefilter $F(s)$, so that the tracking specifications are satisfied. Once $G(s)$ is known, we can calculate the unity-feedback magnitudes $|T_1(j\omega)|$'s of all plants in the set $\{P(s)\}$. Their Bode plots are shown in Fig.4.4.10. Note that most $|T_1(j\omega)|$'s lie outside the permitted bounds of the tracking specifications. This is not surprising, because so far the design only guarantees that change in $|T_1(j\omega)|$ is no larger than the maximum permitted change in $|T(j\omega)|$, shown in the same figure.

The designed prefilter $F(s)$ that shifts all $|T_1(j\omega)|$s into the permissible bounds of $|T(j\omega)|$ in Fig.4.4.11 is:

$$F(s) = \frac{1 + s/50}{(1 + s/5)(1 + s/10)} \frac{s^2 + 6.5s + 9}{s^2 + 6s + 9}$$

Step 7. Evaluation of the design

Finally, we can evaluate the achieved design in the frequency and the time domains. Fig. 4.4.9 shows that all $L(j\omega)$ satisfy the β and γ specified constraints (which also guarantee acceptable gain and phase margins for all plant elements in $\{P(s)\}$ as per Section 2.5.2). The permitted step-response bounds are shown in Fig.4.4.12 by the dotted lines. The unit-step responses for all plants are shown in the same figure. Most of them lie well within the permitted bounds, except for slight discrepancies for two plant cases. After all, it should be remembered that frequency into time translations are inexact, and this can lead to these small anomalies in the resulting time responses. Slight additional manipulation of $L_n(j\omega)$ by

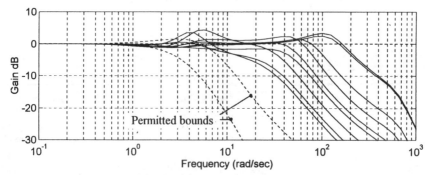

Figure 4.4.10. Simulated $|T_1(j\omega)|$s (solid lines) and the tracking specification bounds of $|T(j\omega)|$ (dashed lines)

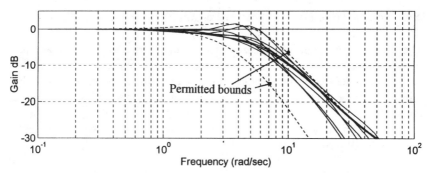

Figure 4.4.11.   Simulated $|T(j\omega)| = |F(j\omega)|\,|T_1(j\omega)|$ for all plants in the set $\{P(s)\}$, and the tracking permitted bounds of $|T(j\omega)|$ (dashed lines).

the compensator $G(s)$, and also of the prefilter $F(s)$, can help to bring all step responses completely within the permitted bounds.

To summarize, the frequency and the time-domain specifications are practically achieved, but with a comparatively large bandwidth because of the instability of the plant.

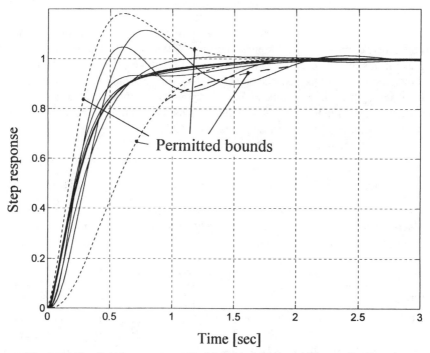

Figure 4.4.12.   Step time responses $y(t)$ of the achieved design and the permitted bounds.

4.5.   Design Technique for NMP Uncertain Plants (Category III.a)

The drawback of a plant which includes RHP zeros is that its phase-lag as a function of frequency decreases faster than that of a minimum-phase plant with the same magnitude frequency response. In fact, the crossover frequency of a non-minimum-phase loop transmission is limited, as explained and discussed in Section 3.5.2.

Some preliminary facts and definitions are in order when the uncertain plant contains NMP zeros or pure time delays. Let

$$L(s) = L_A(s)(1 - ds) = L_A(s)(1 + ds)\frac{(1-ds)}{(1+ds)} = L_{MP}(s)\frac{(1-ds)}{(1+ds)} = L_{MP}(s)A(s) \quad (4.5.1)$$

where $L_{MP}(s)$ is a minimum phase transfer function, and $A(s) = (1 - ds)/(1 + ds)$ is an all-pass function. Clearly

$$|L(j\omega)| = |L_{MP}(j\omega)|; \quad \arg L(j\omega) = \arg L_{MP}(j\omega) + \arg A(j\omega) \quad (4.5.2)$$

where

$$\arg A(j\omega) = -2 \tan^{-1}(\omega d) \quad (4.5.3)$$

The extra phase-lag due to $A(j\omega)$ is close to zero at very low frequencies, but monotonously decreases toward a phase-lag of $-180°$ as $\omega \to \infty$. This phase-lag very much limits the achievable bandwidth that can be obtained for NMP plants. The direct implication of the last statement is that possibly no solution exists for a given feedback problem in which the plant is uncertain and includes a RHP zero.

Steps 3 and, 4 in the design technique described in Section 4.3 have to be modified slightly for NMP uncertain plants (Sidi 1976). The necessary modification becomes clear with the following example. Let the set $\{P\}$ be defined as

$$P(s) = \frac{k}{s}\frac{1-ds}{1+bs}; \quad 0.3 \le k \le 1, \quad 0.3 \le b \le 1, \quad 0.05 \le d \le 0.1$$

The parameters of some of the plant cases are assigned in Table 4.5.1.

Table 4.5.1. Some plant cases for the plant set $\{P\}$.

Case	1	2	3	4	5	6	7	8	7'
k	1	3.0	1.0	3.0	1.0	3.0	1.0	3.0	1.0
b	0.3	0.3	1.0	1.0	0.3	0.3	1.0	1.0	1.0
d	0.05	0.05	0.05	0.05	0.1	0.1	0.1	0.1	−0.1

Cases 1 to 8 belong to NMP plant cases. Case 7' in the table does not belong to the plant, but is introduced in order to modify steps 3 and 4 of the general feedback design technique for NMP uncertain plants. Case 7' belongs to the minimum-phase part of the plant partition in Eq.(4.5.1).

Templates at the frequencies $\omega = 1, 6, 50$ rad/sec are shown in Fig. 4.5.1. The points numbered 1, 2, 3, 4, 5, 6, 7, 8 belong to the NMP plant cases 1 to 8. The points numbered 1', 2', 3', 4', 5', 6', 7', 8' are the minimum-phase counterparts of the NMP cases in the plant partition in Eq.(4.5.1). The points belonging to the actual NMP plant are located to the left of the minimum-phase plant cases, the difference in phase-lag being equal to the phase contributed by the all-pass function $A(s) = (1 - ds)/(1 + ds)$ at $s = j\omega$. The magnitude remains the same for both the minimum-phase and for the nonminimum-phase plant cases, because $|A(j\omega)| = 1$.

Bounds on $L(j\omega)$ in the Nichols chart for NMP systems
(Step 3 of the general design technique).

Bounds on $L_n(j\omega)$ can be obtained directly with a NMP plant as nominal (Horowitz and Sidi 1978). In this case, the nominal NMP plant transfer function is drawn on the Nichols chart and manipulated by the control network $G(j\omega)$ un-

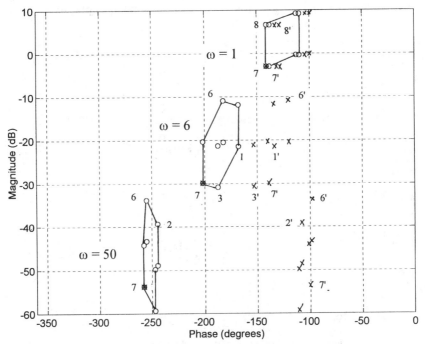

Figure 4.5.1. Templates of the NMP plant at $\omega = 1, 6, 50$ rad/sec, and the minimum-phase counterpart of some of the plant cases.

til the nominal $L_n(j\omega) = P_n(j\omega)G(j\omega)$ that satisfies the bounds is achieved. However, it is easier to design a minimum-phase optimal $L_n(j\omega)$ that lies on its bounds,
because the Bode fundamental relations, which pertain to minimum-phase transmission functions, can be directly applied in this design stage (Sidi 1976). This is
the natural way to obtain an optimal $L_n(j\omega)$, as was explained in Section 4.3.3 (see
also Fig.4.3.6). This means also that we ought to draw the bounds on $L_n(j\omega)$ on
the basis of the NMP part of the templates, but, by choosing any one of the
minimum-phase extra cases (marked by dash signs (')) as the nominal plant case.

To illustrate the procedure, we choose the minimum-phase case 7' to be the
nominal one, and we draw the bounds at $\omega = 6$ and 50 rad/sec for the following
requirements:

$$\Delta|T(j6)| \leq 10\text{dB}; \quad |T_1(j6)|_{max} \leq \beta = 3\text{dB},$$

$$|T_d(j6)|_{max} \leq \gamma = 3\text{dB}; \quad |T_d(j50)|_{max} \leq \gamma = 3\text{dB}.$$

The resulting bounds are shown in Fig.4.5.2 and are marked B_{6MP} for the bound
at $\omega = 6$ rad/sec, and $B_{50\,MP}$ for the bound at $\omega = 50$ rad/sec. Both have been obtained with 7' as the nominal minimum-phase plant. The figure also shows $B_{6\,NMP}$,
which is obtained for the NMP part of the template, but, with the NMP plant case
7 as nominal. Due to the phase difference between the nominal plant cases 7' and

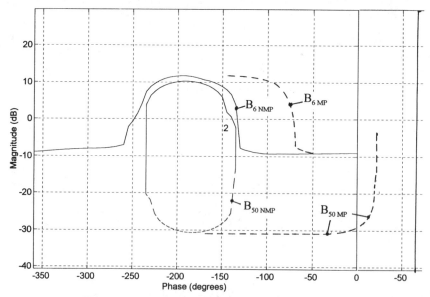

Figure 4.5.2. Bounds on MP and NMP loop transmissions at
$\omega = 6$ and 50 rad/sec, obtained respectively with plants 7' and 7 as nominal.

7, the bound B_{6MP} at $\omega = 6$ is moved to the right of the bound B_{6NMP} by the amount of phase-lag difference contributed by the all-pass function at $\omega = 6$. This fact by itself, although it leads to an inevitable loss in phase-lead, does not prevent the design completion.

The vertical part of the NMP bound $B_{50\,NMP}$ is also moved to the right by an amount equal to the phase difference between the MP and the NMP nominal plant cases 7' and 7 at $\omega = 50$ rad/sec. However, the bound $B_{50\,MP}$ at $\omega = 50$ rad/sec lies partially in the region where the phase is **positive** on the Nichols chart. This fact prevents the completion of the design of $L_n(j\omega)$, as is shown next.

Using Bode phase-gain relations (see Appendix E), it can be seen that there exists no $L(j\omega)$ for which $L(j6)$ lies on the -9.5dB horizontal part of the bound $B_{6\,MP}$ and $L(j50)$ lies below the horizontal part of the bound B_{50MP}. This is explained as follows. From the gain-phase relation corresponding to a constant-slope attenuation characteristic, we know that (by Eq.(E.4.4) and Fig. E.4.2) for an average phase-lag of $-90°$, the attenuation slope will be about -20dB/decade. consequently, $L(j50)$ can lie about 16.7 dB below $L(j6)$. Next, suppose that $L(j6)$ is located at $[-9.5$ dB; $-60°]$, then $L(j50)$ will be located at $[-25.6$dB; $-120°]$, only 16.7 dB below $L(j6)$. However, the vertical distance between the horizontal parts of B_{6MP} and that of B_{50MP} is more than 22dB. Thus, crossing the vertical distance between B_{6MP} and B_{50MP} is impossible in this case, and **no practical $L(j\omega)$ can be found to satisfy these bounds** (see also the explanation in Step 4 of the next example).

Example 4.5.1. The plant and its uncertainties are defined as follows:

$$P(s) = k(1-d\,s)/[s(1+b\,s)]; \quad k = [1-3], b = [0.3-1], d = [0.05-0.1]$$

The tracking specifications are defined in Fig.4.4.2. β and γ are specified to be equal to 3dB at all frequencies, so that the following constraints are to be satisfied:

$$|T_d(j\omega)|_{max} \leq 3\text{dB}; |T_1(j\omega)|_{max} \leq 3\text{dB}$$

Solution: The design process should follow the seven steps defined in Section 4.3.1. Since we are interested in this problem as a means of emphasizing some special features in the design of uncertain NMP control feedback systems, we shall stress important details in some of the design steps, and abbreviate explanations of design steps that have been treated at length in the solution of Examples 4.3.1 and 4.4.1.

Step 1. Translation of time-domain tolerances into frequency-domain tolerances- 1st trial design

We use the translation stage in Example 4.4.1. The permitted $\Delta|T(j\omega)|$ at several frequencies are obtained from Fig.4.4.2. These are summarized in Table 4.5.2.

Table 4.5.2. Permitted changes in $|T(j\omega)|$

ω rad/sec	1	2	4	6	10	20	50	100
Δ $\|T(j\omega)\|$db	1	3	7	10	14	—	—	—

Step 2. Preparation of templates

The plant cases to be used in this design example are defined in Table 4.5.1. Templates for the plant set $\{P(s)\}$ based on these cases are prepared at frequencies at which $\Delta|T(j\omega)|$ is specified in Table 4.5.2. These are shown in Fig.4.5.3. The cases of the NMP plant are marked by 'o'. The MP counterpart of case 7 is marked by 'x' and is numbered as 7' on each one of the templates. Case 7' is chosen to be the nominal case in obtaining the bounds on $L_n(j\omega)$ in the next design step

Step 3. Derivation of bounds on $L_n(j\omega)$ on the Nichols chart -1st trial design

As already explained, $L_n(j\omega)$ will be designed as minimum-phase. In this design example, the bounds on $L_n(j\omega)$ were prepared with the QFT-toolbox by using case 7' as the nominal plant. These bounds are displayed in Fig.4.5.4.

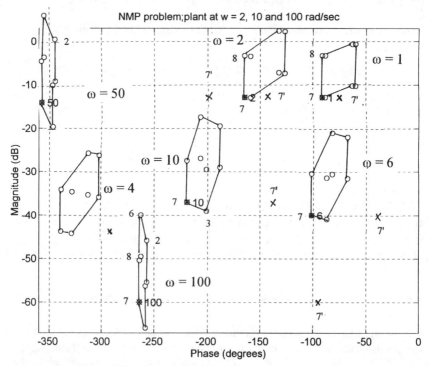

Figure 4.5.3. Plant templates at various substantial frequencies.

Step 4. Derivation of the loop transmission function $L_n(j\omega)$-1st trial design

This is the most important and critical stage of the present problem. It emphasizes the difficulties encountered with NMP plant feedback systems. The bounds in Fig.4.5.4 are such that there can be no practical solution of $L_n(j\omega)$ unless some relaxation in the tracking specifications is attempted. The reason for this is explained as follows: Suppose that an initial $L_n(j\omega)$ has been designed so that $L_n(j10)$ lies on the bound B_{10}. From point of view of the slope of $|L_n(j\omega)|$ in this region, the best choice is to have $L_n(j10)$ located at $[-11\text{dB}; -40°]$, which is on the respective bound and approximately at its maximum phase-lag and minimum gain. Next, $L_n(j\omega)$ is to be manipulated so that $L_n(j20)$ will lie on the vertical part of the bound B_{20}, and as low as possible in gain, or below its horizontal part. If we assume an average phase-lag of $-25°$ in the frequency range $\omega = 10$ to 20 rad/sec, then this average phase-lag is accompanied with an average slope in gain of $-6 \times 25/90\text{dB/octave} = -1.67\text{dB/octave}$. Thus, $L_n(j20)$ will be located at a magnitude lower by about 1.67db than that of $L_n(j10)$ on the vertical part of the bound B_{20}, namely, at $L_n(j20) = [-12.7\text{dB}; -10°]$. This is clearly not a satisfactory solution, because with such a low phase-lag at $\omega = 20$ rad/sed, we cannot decrease sufficiently the gain. Now let us try to attain the B_{20} bound at its lowest level of -31dB. For this to happen, let us suppose that we can ensure in the frequency range $10 < \omega < 20$ rad/sec an average phase-lag of $-120°$. We can then achieve an average slope of $-6 \times 120/90 = -8\text{dB/octave}$. This means that we can achieve $|L_n(j20)| \approx (-12.7 -8)\text{dB} = -20.7\text{dB}$. This is also not a satisfactory solution

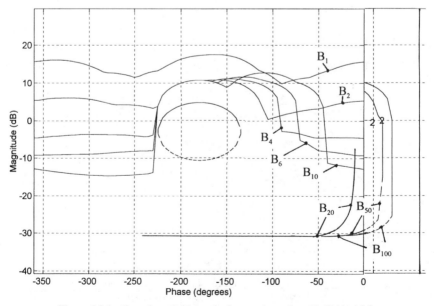

Figure 4.5.4. Bounds on $L_n(j\omega)$ at the frequencies assigned in Table 4.5.2.

since $L_n(j20)$ cannot reach the bound B_{20} at its minimum level of -31dB. $L_n(j20)$ will consequently remain in the forbidden region.

To summarize, the permitted regions of $L_n(j\omega)$ at $\omega = 50$ and at 100 rad/sec are below the horizontal parts of the permitted bounds, which are located at a level of -31dB, or to the right of their respective vertical parts on the Nichols chart, where the argument is positive. Under these conditions, there is no way to locate $L_n(j\omega)$ in the range $\omega > 20$ rad/sec in the permitted region on the Nichols chart. The final conclusion is that there is no solution to this problem. In other words, there exists no practical $L(j\omega)$ that satisfies the bounds. The only way to circumvent this difficulty is to relax the tracking specifications at all frequencies, and try a 2nd trial design.

Step 1. Translation of time into frequency-domain specifications-2nd trial design.

We shall now enlarge the range of acceptable closed-loop second-order poles of $T(s)$. The specified acceptable range in Fig.4.4.1 is enlarged to that shown in Fig.4.5.5. When translating these new specifications in the s-plane to permissible new boundaries in the frequency-domain, the limitting transfer function $T_{lower}(s)$ (which is the same as in Example 4.4.1) changes to

$$T_{lower}(s) = \frac{20}{(s + 5)(s^2 + 2 \times 0.9 \times 2s + 2^2)}$$

while $T_{upper}(s)$ remains the same as in the 1st trial design. The new tracking specifications in the frequency-domain will then be as in Fig.4.5.6.

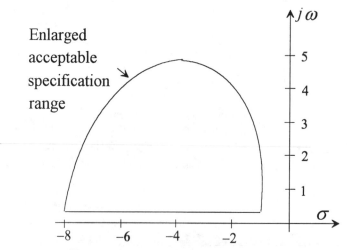

Figure 4.5.5. Enlarged range of acceptable closed-loop second-order poles for the second trial design.

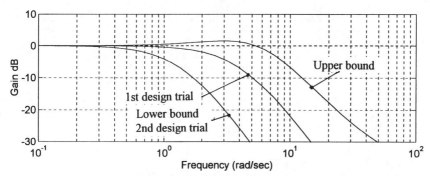

Figure 4.5.6. New tracking specification bounds of $|T(j\omega)|$ for the 2nd trial design.

The new time-domain permitted bounds are shown in Fig.4.5.7. They are based on the new *s*-plane tracking specifications shown in Fig.4.5.5. From Fig.4.5.6 we can derive the new permitted $\Delta|T(j\omega)|$ for the 2nd trial design. They are shown in Table 4.5.3

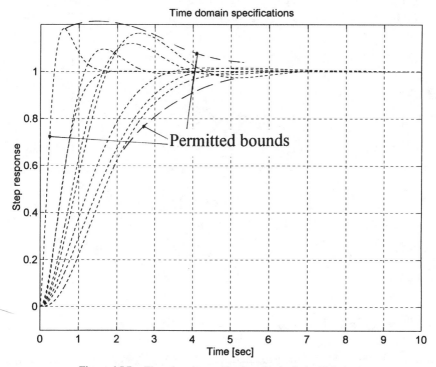

Figure 4.5.7. Time-domain specifications for the 2nd trial design.

Table 4.5.3. $\Delta|T(j\omega)|$ for the 2nd trial design

ω	0.5	1	2	3	4	5	7	10	15	20	50
$\Delta|T(j\omega)|$dB	0.35	1	3.2	7.6	9	11	12.5	17.5	—	—	—

The specifications of β and γ are relaxed to

$$|T_1(j\omega)|_{max} \le \beta = 6\text{dB}; \quad |T_d(j\omega)|_{max} \le \gamma = 6\text{dB}.$$

Step 2. Preparation of templates.
This step was achieved in the previous first trial design.

Step 3. Derivation of bounds on $L_n(j\omega)$ on the Nichols chart-2nd trial design
As already explained, the designed loop transmission function will be minimum-phase, so that we use again case 7' as the nominal plant case in finding the bounds on $L_n(j\omega)$. The new bounds are prepared with the QFT-toolbox. They are shown in Fig.4.5.8.

Step 4. Derivation of the loop transmission function $L_n(j\omega)$-2nd trial design
$L_n(j\omega)$ which satisfies the new bounds of the 2nd trial design exists, it is shown in Fig. 4.5.8. It seems that there is no practical way to further decrease the magnitude of $L_n(j\omega)$ without upsetting the bounds at the low frequencies: $L_n(j1)$ is located on

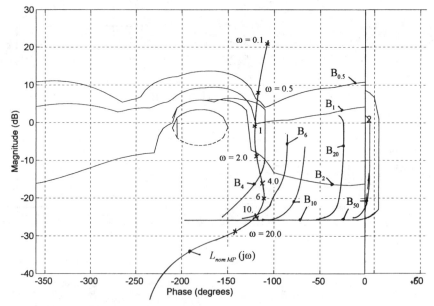

Figure 4.5.8.   Bounds on $L_{nom\ MP}$ at ω = 0.5, 1, 2, 4, 6, 10, 20, 50, 100 rad/sec for the 2nd trial design.

the lowest admissible level of the bound B_1. On the other hand, $L_n(j10)$ lies on the horizontal part of B_{10}. This means that the relaxation of the bounds in Figs.4.5.5 and 4.5.6 for the 2nd trial design barely suffice to permit a successful design of $L_n(j\omega)$. The $L(j\omega)$'s for different plants cases are shown in Fig. 4.5.9. They all satisfy the permitted specifications of $|T_1(j\omega)|_{max} < 6$dB and $|T_d(j\omega)|_{max} < 6$dB. The specifications of $\Delta|T(j\omega)|$ are also satisfied, since $L_n(j\omega)$ lies at all frequencies on the permitted bounds or above them. The achieved minimum-phase nominal loop transmission is:

$$L_n(s) = \frac{1.656}{s} \frac{1+s/1.73}{1+s/0.58} \frac{30^2}{s^2+2\times0.4\times30s+30^2}.$$

Step 5. Derivation of the controller $G(s)$ from $L_n(j\omega)$-2nd trial design
In step 4 we have chosen the technique of deriving a minimum-phase loop transmission $L_n(j\omega)$ that satisfies its bounds. Since the bounds were derived for plant case 7', and knowing

$$P_{nMP}(s) = P_{7'}(s) = (0.1s + 1)/(s + 1),$$

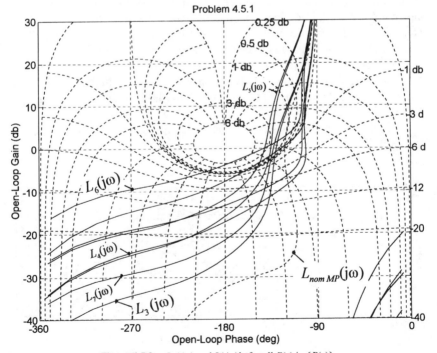

Figure 4.5.9. $L_n(j\omega)$ and $L(j\omega)$'s for all $P(s)$ in $\{P(s)\}$

we find that

$$G(s) = \frac{L_n}{P_{7'}} = \frac{1.656 \times 30^2}{s^2 + 2 \times 0.4 \times 30s + 30^2} \frac{1 + s/1.73}{1 + s/0.5774} \frac{s+1}{0.1s+1}.$$

Step 6. Design of the prefilter F(s)-2nd trial design

The final step is to design the prefilter $F(s)$ which is necessary for satisfying the input-output tracking specifications. The magnitudes of $|T_1(j\omega)|$ for different plants are shown in Fig.4.5.10. They all lie outside the permitted bounds, which was expected.

The following filter

$$F(s) = \frac{2}{s+2} \frac{s+0.8}{s+0.8/1.6} \frac{s+0.8}{s+0.8 \times 1.6}$$

was designed to shift all $|T_1(j\omega)|$s within the modified specification bounds of $|T(j\omega)|$. The latter are also shown in Fig.4.5.11.

Step 7. Evaluation of the design.

Fig. 4.5.9 shows that adequate phase and gain margins are obtained by satisfying the β and γ specifications. The step-time responses of the 2nd trial design are shown in Fig.4.5.12. They show that the time-domain specifications are satisfied, except for small discrepancies for some plants in $\{P(s)\}$. Additional manipulation of the filter $F(s)$ can improve the step time responses if necessary.

It is important to notice that the design technique for plants containing more than one NMP zero remains exactly the same. The only difference will be discerned in Eq.(4.5.1), which will contain additional all-pass functions pertaining to the additional RHP zeros.

Example 4.5.1 accentuates clearly the difficulties encountered with NMP uncertain feedback systems.

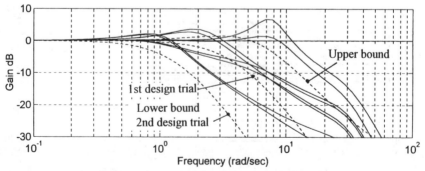

Figure 4.5.10.   Unity-feedback $|T_1(j\omega)|$s for several plants in $\{P(s)\}$.

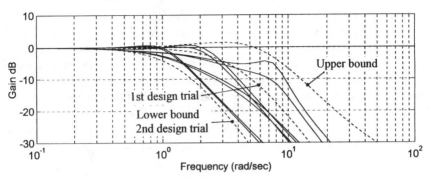

Figure 4.5.11. $|T(j\omega)| = |T_1(j\omega)| |F(j\omega)|$ for all plant cases of the 2nd trial design.

The plant in this example is simple, but the design process remains exactly the same for real problems with much more complex NMP transfer functions. In any case, the burden of computing more complicated, realistic, transfer functions falls upon to the computer software.

Nonminimum-phase effects can be discerned in many aircraft and missile applications. The transfer function $\theta(s)/\delta_e(s)$ for elevator displacement to the angular

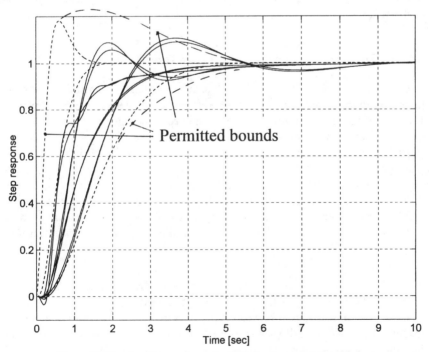

Figure 4.5.12.   Step time responses for the 2nd and successful trial design

motion in the pitch plane of an aircraft was presented in Section 4.4. Generally, this transfer function is minimum-phase. On the other hand, if the transfer function $u(s)/\delta_e(s)$ of the forward velocity increment to elevator displacement is observed, the phugoid and the short period dynamics in the denominator remain the same as in $\theta(s)/\delta_e(s)$, but the numerator acquires a nonminimum-phase zero. The same is true for the transfer function $a_z(s)/\delta_e(s)$ of vertical acceleration a_z to elevator displacement δ_e of aircraft or missiles.

Just to get an idea of the arising difficulties with such plants, let us have a look at the short period transfer function of a military aircraft (or of a missile) which is:

$$\frac{a_z(s)}{\delta_e(s)} = \frac{-46(s+4.6)(s-4.6)}{s^2 + 2 \times 0.12 \times 2.6s + 2.6^2}.$$

This second-order transfer function consists of a complex pole pair with natural frequency of 2.6 rad/sec, and a damping coefficient of 0.12. Since the NMP zero is located not far from the complex pole, its effect may be quite harmful when trying to achieve a sufficiently large crossover frequency. In addition, the plant parameters of the airframe may also change appreciably with altitude and Mach number. Here we are faced with a real, unfriendly feedback system control problem that can be solved with the design technique explained in this section (see Benshabat and Chait, 1993).

4.6   Design Technique for Plants with Pure Time Delays (Category III.b)

The procedure for designing feedback systems in which the uncertain plant contains pure time delays follows exactly the same design steps as for NMP plants. Practically, each minimum-phase bound is moved to the right in the Nichols chart by a phase amounting to ωt_d radians for a pure time delay of t_d sec. The design steps remain exactly identical to those explained in Section 4.5. In practice, the plant may contain NMP zeros together with pure time delays. The design technique presented in Section 4.5 still remains applicable.

Real feedback systems with pure time delays can be encountered, for instance in the chemical industry. Take as an example, a reactor process whose production rate, which is a function of catalyst addition, is modeled by a simplified transfer function of the form $P(s) = \dfrac{Ke^{-st_d}}{(s+a)^2}$, where all the parameters are generally uncertain. In such feedback systems, t_d can be of the order of several to tens of minutes, and a, of the order of 1/500 rad/sec. Both, however, have large uncertainties.

Large pure time delays also exist in control systems dealing with heat transfer; feedback control design of such systems must follow the procedure explained in Section 4.5.

Finally, one of the most elementary models related to human operators can be represented as a transfer function of the form $P(s) = \dfrac{Ke^{-st_d}}{1+s\tau}$, with uncertainties in K, τ and t_d. When designing a feedback system in which a human operator is part of the loop, this model becomes a part of the system plant.

4.7   Design Technique for Sampled-Data Feedback Systems with LTI Uncertain Plants (Category IV)

4.7.1.   *Design of Sampled-data Feedback Systems in the Frequency-domain*

This section deals with the design of uncertain sampled-data feedback systems (Sidi 1977). The design procedure is the same as that for NMP plants. The reason for this approach is that when performing the analysis and design of sampled-data systems in the frequency-domain, using the bilinear transformation $w = (z-1)/(z+1)$, then the loop transmission function $L(w)$ in the *w-domain* generally contains a NMP zero located at $w = 1$ (Saucedo and Schiring 1968). If this is the case, the design of the sampled-data feedback system follows exactly the same procedure used in the design of continuous feedback systems containing a NMP plant.

It is now necessary to point out some facts about common design techniques in the frequency-domain for sampled-data feedback systems, (Saucedo and Schiring 1968, Kuo 1980, Franklin and Powell 1990, Houpis and lamont 1992).

A sampled-data transfer function $P^*(s)$ can be expressed in three different domains: the *s-domain* (ω-*domain*), the *z-domain* and the *w-domain*. The basic equation of the sampling process is

$$P^*(s) = \frac{1}{T_s} \sum_{-\infty}^{\infty} P(s + jn\omega_s) + \frac{1}{2} p(0_+) \tag{4.7.1}$$

which relates the continuous plant $P(s)$ to its sampled-data form $P^*(s)$. In the above equation ω_s is the sampling frequency; $T_s = 2\pi/\omega_s$ is the sampling period; and $p(0_+)$ is the impulse time response of $P(s)$ at $t = 0_+$. However, the following transformations are also commonly used. (Saucedo and Schiring 1968):

$$\mathscr{L}[P^*(s)] = P(z); \quad P(w) = P[z=(1+w)/(1-w)] \tag{4.7.2}$$

and, for $s = j\omega$

$$\mathscr{L}[P^*(s)|_{s=j\omega}] = \mathscr{L}[P^*(j\omega)] = P(z = e^{j\omega T_s}) \tag{4.7.3}$$

Note that in Eq.(4.7.2) $z = e^{sT_s}$, and $w = (z-1)/(z+1)$. Explicitly, since $z = e^{j\omega T_s}$, it follows that w is a complex expression, because

$$w = \frac{z-1}{z+1} = \frac{e^{j\omega T_s} - 1}{e^{j\omega T_s} + 1} = \frac{e^{j\omega T_s/2} - e^{-j\omega T_s/2}}{e^{j\omega T_s/2} + e^{-j\omega T_s/2}} = \tanh \frac{j\omega T_s}{2} = j \tan \frac{\omega T_s}{2} = u + jv$$

From the above equation, it follows that

$$v = \tan(\pi\omega/\omega_s) = \tan(\omega T_s/2); \quad u = 0. \tag{4.7.4}$$

This means that there is an exact equivalence of the sampled transfer function $P^*(j\omega)$ in the z and w domains. If the magnitudes and phase versus frequency are compared for $P^*(j\omega)$; $P(z = e^{j\omega T_s})$ and $P(w = j\tan(\omega T_s/2))$, perfect agreement is observed. This result is expected since both the z-plane and the w-plane are conformal mappings and have equivalent points. Based on Eq.(4.7.4) and Fig.4.7.1, we can define for our purposes

$$T(j\omega) = \frac{y(j\omega)}{r^*(j\omega)} = \frac{F^*(j\omega)G^*(j\omega)}{1 + G^*(j\omega)P^*(j\omega)} P(j\omega) \tag{4.7.5a}$$

or

$$T = \frac{y(s)}{r^*(s)} = \frac{F(z)G(z)}{1 + G(z)P(z)} P(s) = \frac{F(w)G(w)}{1 + G(w)P(w)} P(s). \tag{4.7.5b}$$

Eq.(4.7.5b) is not consistent from a mathematical point of view, since w, s and z are three different, independent variables in the same equation. However, it is correct if w and z are interpreted as per Eqs.(4.7.3) and (4.7.4).

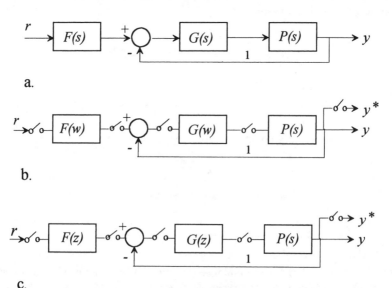

a.

b.

c.

Figure 4.7.1.   A two-degree-of-freedom canonical sampled-data feedback system configuration.

Design in the w-domain is a common practice in sampled-data systems because it follows almost exactly the Bode/Nichols frequency-domain techniques of continuous feedback systems.

It is well-known that if the continuous transfer function $P(s)$ is of an order higher than one, and $P(s)$ does not contain pure time delays, then $P(w)$ shall include one NMP zero located at $w = 1$. This is summarized in the following theorem.

Theorem 4.7.1. Given a transfer function $P(s)$ that does not contain pure time delays, and for which the excess of poles over zeros is $e > 1$, then $P(w)$ contains a NMP zero located at $w = 1$.

Proof: Since it is assumed that $e > 1$, the initial value theorem gives

$$\lim_{s\to\infty} sP(s) = \lim_{t\to 0} p(t) = 0, \tag{4.7.6}$$

thus,

$$\lim_{k\to 0} p(kt) = \lim_{z\to\infty} P(z) = \lim_{z\to\infty} \frac{a_1 z^m + a_2 z^{m-1} + \ldots + a_{m+1}}{b_1 z^n + b_2 z^{n-1} + \ldots + b_{n+1}} = 0 \tag{4.7.7}$$

which implies $n > m$ and $b_1 \neq 0$. Now, by using the definition $z = (1 + w)/(1 - w)$, it follows that

$$P(z) = \frac{a_1 z^m + a_2 z^{m-1} + \ldots + a_{m+1}}{b_1 z^n + b_2 z^{n-1} + \ldots + b_{n+1}}$$

$$= \frac{a_1 \left(\dfrac{1+w}{1-w}\right)^m + a_2 \left(\dfrac{1+w}{1-w}\right)^{m-1} + \ldots + a_{m+1}}{b_1 \left(\dfrac{1+w}{1-w}\right)^n + b_2 \left(\dfrac{1+w}{1-w}\right)^{n-1} + \ldots + b_{n+1}} \tag{4.7.8}$$

and consequently, $P(w)$ contains the factor $(1-w)^{n-m}$ in its numerator. Since $P(s)$ does not contain a pure time delay, neither does $P(z)$. Thus, $n-m$ must be less than 2, so that $n-m = 1$. From Eq.(4.7.8) it follows that $P(w)$ must contain a RHP zero located at $w = 1$ ◇.

It is worth mentioning that if the excess of poles over zeros of $P(s)$ is $e = 1$, then $P(w)$ will not include the NMP zero located at $w = 1$. However, in most practical physical systems, the number of excess of poles over zeros of $L(s)$ is $e > 1$, so that the NMP zero at $w = 1$ generally exists. This RHP zero limits the bandwidth of sampled-data feedback system, exactly in the same way it did in Section 3.5 for NMP continuous feedback systems.

It is instructive to realize that the NMP nature of sampled-data feedback systems is not explicitly exhibited in the sampled-data s and z-domains. When designing in the latter two domains, the practicing engineer is confronted with the uncomfortable feeling that he cannot always achieve the desired specifications and wonders whether a better solution could not be found to his problem. A lot of wasted design time could be saved if the designers were aware of the inevitable NMP zero located at $w = 1$, with all the detrimental implications. The plant transfer function $P(w)$ may contain additional NMP zeros due to plant dynamics.

4.7.2.   Time into Frequency-Domain Translation for Sampled-Data Systems

Time into frequency-domain translation is essential in the design technique presented here. The form of the usually used transfer function $T^*(s) = y^*(s)/r^*(s)$ is very convenient for analysis, but, the latter is not the input-output transfer function we are really interested in. The true output of interest is $y(s)$, not $y^*(s)$ (see Fig.4.7.1b). The reason is that the output of interest in a physical dynamical system is continuous, although there is sampling inside the feedback loop. Hence, in the feedback structure of Fig.4.7.1b, the design specifications should be set for

$$\frac{y(s)}{r^*(s)} = \frac{F^*(s)G^*(s)P(s)}{1+G^*(s)P^*(s)} = \frac{F^*(s)G^*(s)P^*(s)}{1+G^*(s)P^*(s)}\frac{P(s)}{P^*(s)}. \tag{4.7.9}$$

The following question is of interest: If we have two systems, one continuous as in Fig.4.7.1a and the other is sampled as in Fig.4.7.1b, and both have exactly the same Fourier transforms $y(j\omega)$, what can we expect from their respective time responses $y_1(t)$ and $y_2(t)$? According to the uniqueness of the Fourier transform (Goldberg, 1970), we can expect that if $y_1(j\omega) = y_2(j\omega)$, then $y_1(t) = y_2(t)$. Although this is a qualitative argument, it is very effective for signals whose bandwidths are sufficiently lower than the sampling frequency ω_s.

In practice it will be very difficult to design a sampled-data feedback system with a continuous output $|y(j\omega)|$ exactly equal to the output of a continuous feedback system for the same input. The discrepancy will be especially pronounced at integer multiples of $\omega_s/2$ ($\omega = n\omega_s/2$, n is an integer). However, at these frequencies, the magnitude $|T(j\omega)|$ of the sampled-data system must be already reasonably attenuated because of stability considerations (Horowitz 1963). On the other hand, two systems having the same frequency responses $|T(j\omega)|$ at almost all frequencies, but differing at the frequency range in which their respective gains are reasonably small, will exhibit very similar step time responses (Sidi 1977 and Section 3.2.3). In this respect, $G(s)$, $F(s)$, $G(w)$ and $F(w)$ of Fig.4.7.1 were designed so that $|T|$ for both continuous and sampled-data systems were almost identical in the significant frequency range. Two examples are shown in Fig.4.7.2a,b, the solid lines belonging to signals of the continuous system, namely cases 1 and 2 in Fig.4.7.2. The dotted lines belong to signals of the sampled-data system, cases 1' and 2'. The digital control signal at the input to the plant for cases 2' is also shown in Fig.4.7.2b.

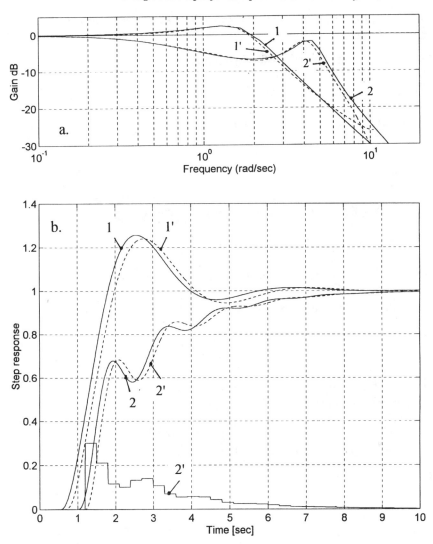

Figure 4.7.2.   Two $|T^*(j\omega)|$'s, two $|T(j\omega)|$'s and their respective step responses.

To summarize, the simulated results show that in designing sampled-data feed-back systems, the translation from the time-domain into the frequency-domain can follow, with very good approximation, the techniques already discussed in Chapter 3 and in the present chapter for continuous systems. Consequently, there is an advantage in performing the design in the *w*-domain in which Nyquist/Bode/Nichols design techniques can be directly implemented.

4.7.3.   Synthesis Technique for Sampled-Data Feedback Systems with Uncertain Plants

The input-output tracking sensitivity problem for the sampled-data case can be solved in a way that is similar to what we did for the continuous case. This is because, for the feedback structure shown in Figs.4.7.1b,c, we find that

$$T = \frac{y}{r*} = F* \frac{G*P}{1+G*P*} = F* \frac{G*P*}{1+G*P*} \frac{P}{P*}$$ (4.7.10)

and therefore

$$\Delta\log|T| = \max_{P\in\{P\}} \log\left|\frac{P}{P*}\frac{P*G*F*}{1+G*P*}\right| - \min_{P\in\{P\}} \log\left|\frac{P}{P*}\frac{P*G*F*}{1+G*P*}\right|$$

$$\leq \max_{P\in\{P\}} \log\left|\frac{P*G*F*}{1+G*P*}\right| - \min_{P\in\{P\}} \log\left|\frac{P*G*F*}{1+G*P*}\right| + \max_{P\in\{P\}} \log\left|\frac{P}{P*}\right| - \min_{P\in\{P\}} \log\left|\frac{P}{P*}\right|.$$

From the equation it follows that

$$\Delta\log|T| \leq \Delta \log\left|\frac{G*P*}{1+G*P*}\right| + \Delta \log\left|\frac{P}{P*}\right|$$ (4.7.11)

Eq.(4.7.11) is similar to Eq.(4.3.2) except for the additional term $\Delta\log|P/P*|$. The design technique in Section 4.5 is based on the fact that $\Delta\log|T(j\omega)|$ is given a priori at different frequencies. Since $P(j\omega)$ and $P*(j\omega)$ are also known a priori, we can incorporate $\Delta\log|P(j\omega)/P*(j\omega)|$ into $\Delta\log|T(j\omega)|$ so that the following expression is well-defined and quantitatively known:

$$\Delta \log|T_{new}(j\omega)| = \Delta\log|T(j\omega)| - \Delta \log\left|\frac{P(j\omega)}{P*(j\omega)}\right|$$ (4.7.12)

The nominally defined permitted tolerances of $|T(j\omega)|$ will then be decreased according to the known expression $\Delta\log|P(j\omega)/P*(j\omega)|$, i.e, $B_U - B_L$ will be replaced by $B_U - B_L - \Delta\log|P(j\omega)/P*(j\omega)|$. Thus, the tracking sensitivity specification $B_U - B_L$ of $|T(j\omega)|$ will be satisfied if $G*$ is designed such that

$$\Delta \log|T_{new}(j\omega)| = \Delta \log\left|\frac{G*P*}{1+G*P*}\right|$$

(4.7.13)

$$= \Delta \log\left|\frac{L*(j\omega)}{1+L*(j\omega)}\right| \leq B_U(\omega) - B_L(\omega) - \Delta \log\left|\frac{P(j\omega)}{P*(j\omega)}\right|$$

In order to simplify the notation, 'T' will stand for 'T_{new}' from now on. The design will be performed in the w-domain, so that in terms of the frequency $v = \tan(\pi\omega/\omega_s)$,

$$\Delta \log|T(jv)| = \Delta \log\left|\frac{G(jv)P(jv)}{1 + G(jv)P(jv)}\right| = \Delta \log\left|\frac{L(jv)}{1 + L(jv)}\right| \qquad (4.7.14)$$

which is identical to Eq.(4.3.2). Therefore, the design technique explained in Section 4.5 for solving the continuous NMP feedback systems can be applied directly to solve the sampled-data uncertain feedback system problem. Although we could end here this section, nonetheless, some peculiarities emerge in the solution process because the design steps are carried out in three different domains, s, z and w. We consequently feel that a complete design illustration as presented in Example 4.7.1 might still be helpful to a deeper understanding of the design procedure.

Example 4.7.1
1. The uncertain plant set is defined as

$$P(s) = k\omega_0^2/[s(s^2 + 2\xi\omega_0 s + \omega_0^2]; \quad 1 < \omega_0 < 2, \; 0.4 < \xi < 0.9.$$

2. Figs.4.7.6 and 4.7.7 show the permitted bounds in the frequency-domain of the input-output transfer function $T = y/r*$. Fig. 4.5.12 shows the relevant time-domain boundaries within which the step responses for all plants in the above set should lie.
3. The sampling frequency is relatively low compared to the required closed-loop dynamics of the feedback system, namely, $\omega_s = 20$ rad/sec, $T_s = 0.3142$ sec.
4. The plant is preceded by a zero-order-hold.
5. Specification of maximum permitted peak values compels the constraints $|T_1(jv)|_{max} < \beta = 4\text{dB}$ and $|T_d|_{max} < \gamma = 4\text{dB}$.

Solution: Follow the usual design steps which were exemplified with the solution of the NMP continuous uncertain feedback system problem. Due to the NMP nature of the sampled-data loop transmission, the bounds on $L_n(jv)$ will be found on the basis of a minimum-phase nominal plant.

Step 1. Translation of time-domain tolerances into frequency-domain tolerances.

After the s to ω-domain translation stage is completed, we can find from the obtained Fig.4.7.7 the permitted $\Delta|T(j\omega)| \equiv \Delta|T(jv)|$ at several frequencies in the useful frequency range. These are summarized in Table 4.7.1. Since the design will be performed in the w-domain, the specifications of $\Delta|T(jv)|$ will be used.

Table 4.7.1. Specifications on $|T(j\omega)| \equiv |T(jv)|$

ω rad/sec	0.5	1	1.5	2	3	4	5	7	8
v	0.08	0.16	0.24	0.32	0.51	0.73	1	1.96	3
$\Delta |T(jv)|$dB	1.2	4.0	7.0	10.0	18.0	24.0	30.0	50.0	50

Step 2. Preparation of templates

We now have to prepare templates of the uncertain plant at frequencies for which the tolerances $\Delta|T(jv)|$ are given in Table 4.7.1. $P(s)$ is transformed to $P(w)$ from the continuous s-domain to the sampled-data w-domain by the following sequence of transformations, $P(s) \to P(z) \to P(w)$, where $P(w)$ is a polynomial transfer function whose numerator and denominator are of the same order, hence

$$P(w) = \frac{n_1 w^2 + n_2 w + n_3}{d_1 w^2 + d_2 w + d_3}$$

The polynomial coefficients for some cases are given in Table 4.7.2, in which the nominal case 7 is the MP part of case 5. Plant templates prepared at the relevant frequencies in Table 4.7.1 are shown in Fig.4.7.3.

The nominal case (case 7), which is the minimum-phase counterpart of case 5, is shown to the right of each NMP plant template. The NMP zero is located naturally at $w = 1$. Fig.4.7.3 shows the phase-lag between the NMP plants and its MP part which increases with frequency until it reaches 180° as $v \to \infty$ (or equivalently as $\omega \to \omega_s /2$).

Step 3. Derivation of bounds on the loop transmission $L_n(jv)$ in the Nichols chart

As already explained, since the designed loop transmission function comes to be minimum-phase, we use case 7 as the nominal plant case when deriving the bounds. The obtained bounds on $L_n(jv)$ are shown in Fig.4.7.4.

Table 4.7.2. Plant cases and their polynomial coefficients in the w-domain

case	ω_n	ξ_n	n_1	n_2	n_3	d_1	d_2	d_3
1	1.0	0.4	−0.27	0	0.27	3.4	0.44	0.09
2	2.0	0.4	−0.92	0	0.92	2.91	0.79	0.3
3	1.0	0.6	−0.26	0	0.26	3.29	0.63	0.08
4	2.0	0.6	−0.83	0	0.83	2.67	1.06	0.27
5	1.0	0.9	−0.24	0	0.24	3.06	0.86	0.07
6	2.0	0.9	−0.71	0	0.71	2.42	1.35	0.23
7 (Nom, MP)	1.0	0.9	0.24	0.47	0.24	3.06	0.86	0.07

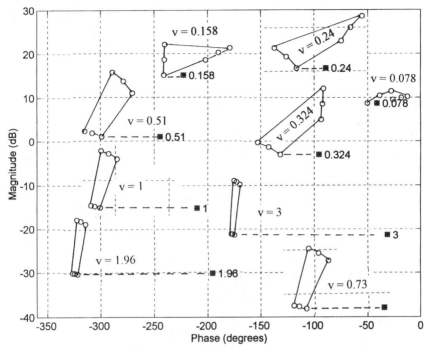

Figure 4.7.3.   Plant templates at $v = 0.078, 0.158, 0.24, 0.324, 0.51, 0.73, 1, 1.96, 3.0$.

Step 4. Design of $L_n(jv)$ to satisfy its bounds

This is the most important and critical step in the solution of the present problem. It emphasizes the difficulties encountered with sampled-data uncertain
feedback systems. The bounds in Fig.4.7.4 are such that a $L_n(jv)$ can be *barely*
achieved. This means that for more stringent $\Delta|T(jv)|$ tolerances no solution ex-
ists. The obtained minimum-phase $L_n(jv)$ is also shown in Fig.4.7.4. It is important to note that $L(j0.24)$ lies practically on the bound $B_{0.24}$, while $L_n(j0.32)$
and $L_n(j0.51)$ lie to the right of the bounds $B_{0.32}$ and $B_{0.51}$ respectively. This indicates that there is a waste in phase-angle capabilities, and that consequently
there is a potential to ameliorate $L_n(jv)$. On the other hand, $L_n(j0.73)$ and $L_n(j1.0)$
lie slightly inside the permitted bounds $B_{0.73}$ and $B_{1.0}$ respectively, indicating
that more phase-lead is to be procured at these frequencies. By adding an additional *lag-lead-lead-lag* control network, (see Appendix C, Section C.5), the
wasted phase-lead in the region $v = 0.32 - 0.51$ can be transferred to the frequency region $v = 0.73-1.0$ where some phase-lead is to be procured. This
stage was omitted here in order to remain with a simpler control network $G(w)$.
The last consideration suggests that, practically, this is the best $L(w)$ that can be
achieved.

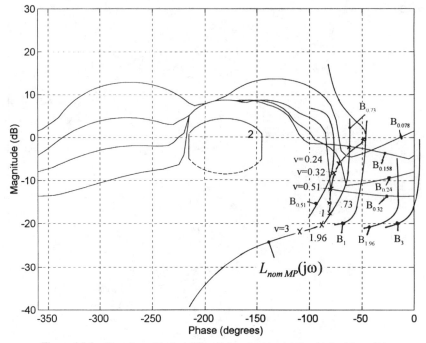

Figure 4.7.4.   Bounds on $L(jv)$ at different frequencies, and the obtained $L_{n\,MP}(jv)$

Step 5. Derivation of the controller G(z) from $L_{n\,MP}$ (jv)

$L(w)$ was manipulated in the present solution by first plotting $P_n(jv)$ on the Nichols chart and then adding the usual compensating networks until a $L_n(jv)$ satisfying its bounds was achieved. With this approach in designing $L_n(jv)$, these networks add to the overall control compensator $G(w)$,

$$G(w) = \frac{4.34}{w}\ \frac{25}{w^2 + 2\times 0.5\times 5w + 5^2}\ \frac{w+0.21}{w+0.4284}\ \frac{w+0.02625}{w+3.430}\ \frac{w+0.3837}{w+0.652}$$

Since the compensator $G(w)$ is to be implemented with a microprocessor, it must be transformed to $G(z)$ by the inverse transformation $w = (z-1)/(z+1)$, which gives

$G(z) =$

$$4.348\ \frac{z+1}{z-1}\ \frac{25z^2 + 50z + 25}{31z^2 + 48z + 21}\ \frac{1.21z - 0.79}{1.4284z - 0.5716}\ \frac{1.026z - 0.974}{4.43z + 2.43}\ \frac{1.384z - 0.6163}{1.65z - 0.348}\ .$$

Using this control network, some $L(jv)$'s for different plants were computed. These are shown on the Nichols chart in Fig.4.7.5. $L_{nMP}(jv)$ (minimum-phase) is

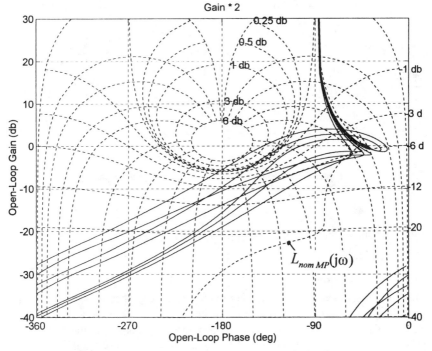

Figure 4.7.5. $L(jv)$ for different plants, $L_{n\,MP}(jv)$ is also shown.

also displayed. The sampled-data $L(jv)$'s (which are NMP) are moved to the left of the minimum-phase $L_{nMP}(jv)$ by an amount equal to the phase-lag generated by the all-pass function $(1-w)/(1+w)$, as explained in Section 4.5.

Step 6. Design the prefilter $F(z)$ to achieve the tracking specifications

The final step is the design of the prefilter $F(z)$ necessary to satisfy the input-output tracking specifications. The unity-feedback $|T_1(j\omega)|$ plots for different plant cases are shown in Fig.4.7.6. Most of them lie outside the permitted bounds, especially at the low frequencies.

All $|T_1(j\omega)|$'s are to be shifted within the permitted upper and lower bounds in Fig.4.7.6. The following prefilter was designed for that purpose:

$$F(w) = \frac{w+0.1666}{w+0.0472}\ \frac{w+0.01346}{w+0.0472}\ \frac{w^2 + 2\times0.3\times0.61w+0.61^2}{w^2 + 2\times0.6\times0.61w+0.61^2}.$$

The digital compensator to be physically implemented becomes in the z-domain

$$F(z) = \frac{1.1666z-0.833}{1.0472z-0.953}\ \frac{1.01346z-0.9865}{1.0472z-0.953}\ \frac{1.738z^2 - 1.256z+1.0062}{2.1z^2 - 1.2562z+0.642}.$$

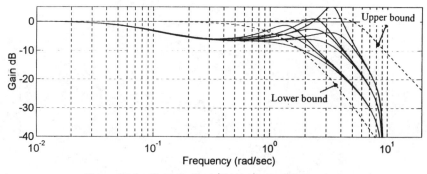

Figure 4.7.6.   Unity-feedback $|T_1^*(j\omega)|$'s for different plants

Fig. 4.7.7 shows the resulting Bode plots of $y(j\omega)/r^*(j\omega)$. They lie well within the permissible bounds.

Step 7. Evaluation of the design.

Step time responses are shown in Fig.4.7.8. Practically, they all satisfy the time-domain specifications, except for small discrepancies at some plant cases. A slight ringing is perceived in one of the time responses. This is due to the fact that the relevant $L(jv)$ to this case in Fig.4.7.5 is adjacent to the unity-feedback constant gain contour of 6dB.

A word of caution is appropriate: The designer has to calculate the coefficients of the digital compensators $G(z)$ and $F(z)$ with the due accuracy for discrete systems.

It is of interest to mention that the QFT design technique can be also used for nonlinear uncertain plants (Horowitz 1976, Horowitz, Sidi and Erickson 1984, and Yaniv 1991.

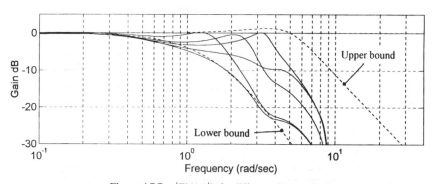

Figure 4.7.7. $|T^*(j\omega)|$'s for different plants cases

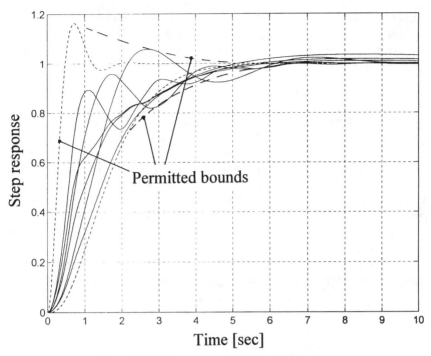

Figure 4.7.8.   Step responses for different plant cases.

4.8   Design of Continuous LTI Uncertain Feedback Systems by H_∞ -Norm Optimization

4.8.1.   Introduction

H_∞-control design was introduced in Chapter 2. In this section, the same H_∞ -control design technique will be used to solve the uncertain plant feedback problem, as defined and solved in previous sections by a classical, Bode/Nichols design technique.

The 'classical' and the 'modern H_∞' design philosophies seem very different in nature, but in fact, there is much in common between both design paradigms. This point will be clarified in this section, as well as in Chapter 8, where the design of MIMO uncertain feedback systems is treated.

When feedback control design with H_∞ -norm optimization is approached, the uncertainties of the plant are represented on the complex plane in the form of disk-shaped templates with radii dependent on the level of uncertainty at each frequency. The design objectives are to obtain a controller that will keep the system stable for all possible plants in the defined set $\{P(s)\}$, and to satisfy specified design specifications. In this context, the two basic issues of 'robust stability' and 'robust performance' will be treated in this section. The primary objective of this section is to solve the SISO TDOF uncertain feedback problem by using H_∞ -norm optimization algorithms. Once again, analysis and synthesis of the feedback control system is based on defining the uncertain plant and the system requirements *in the frequency domain framework*.

4.8.2. Robust Stability.

The notion of *robust stability* can be defined as follows: The system is stable for the nominal plant and also for all the plants in the set $\{P(s)\}$.

To get a feeling of the 'robust stability' notion, let us consider Fig.4.8.1 which shows the nominal loop transmission $L_n(j\omega)$, pertaining to the nominal plant $P_n(j\omega)$. When the nominal plant is perturbed to any member $P(j\omega)$ in the uncertain set $\{P(j\omega)\}$, the nominal loop transmission $L_n(j\omega) = G(j\omega)P_n(j\omega)$ is modified to $L(j\omega) = G(j\omega)P(j\omega)$. This is also shown in the figure.

Suppose that $L_n(j\omega)$ does not contain unstable poles. In this case, the closed-loop will be stable if $L_n(j\omega)$ does not encircle the stability critical point $[-1+j0]$. The vector a denotes the difference between the nominal and the perturbed loop transmissions, namely, $a = L(j\omega) - L_n(j\omega)$. The vector b is defined as $b = -1 - L_n(j\omega)$. As long as the magnitude of a is smaller than that of b, the perturbed loop transmission $L(j\omega)$ will not encircle the critical point $[-1 + j0]$, and the perturbed feedback system will remain stable, as Fig.4.8.1 shows. In other words, stability is guaranteed if (see Doyle et al.1992 and Kwakernaak 1993),

$$|L(j\omega) - L_n(j\omega)| < |1 + L_n(j\omega)|; \text{ for all real } \omega \qquad (4.8.1)$$

which is equivalent to the following inequality:

$$\frac{|L(j\omega) - L_n(j\omega)|}{|L_n(j\omega)|} \frac{|L_n(j\omega)|}{|1 + L_n(j\omega)|} < 1, \quad \forall\omega. \qquad (4.8.2)$$

By use of Eqs.(2.1.5) and (2.1.8), we can write for the nominal plant

$$T_{1n}(s) = \frac{L_n(s)}{1 + L_n(s)} = 1 - S_n(s) \qquad (4.8.3)$$

where $S_n(s)$ is the sensitivity function of the nominal plant $P_n(s)$. From Eqs.(4.8.2) and (4.8.3) it follows that

$$\frac{|L(j\omega) - L_n(j\omega)|}{|L_n(j\omega)|} |T_{1n}(j\omega)| < 1; \quad \forall\omega \qquad (4.8.4)$$

which indicates that if the inequality of Eq.(4.8.4) is satisfied, the perturbed closed-loop system remains stable. If this condition holds for all the per-

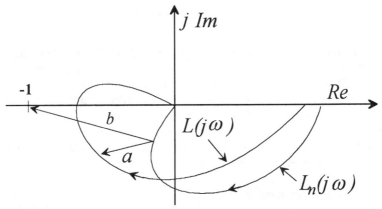

Figure 4.8.1.   Stability under perturbation of the plant, adapted
from Kwakernaak (1993) by permission of Pergamon Press.

turbed plants in the set $\{P(s)\}$, the system is said to be *robust*. Since the compensator $G(s)$ is supposed to be fixed and certain, the relative changes of the term

$\dfrac{|L(j\omega) - L_n(j\omega)|}{|L_n(j\omega)|}$ appearing on the left side of Eq.(4.8.4) express the perturba-

tions in $L(j\omega)$ due to uncertainties of the plant. If the plant uncertainty is explicitly known as a function of frequency, then the relative changes above can be calculated at each frequency and their limits can be expressed by a rational function
$W(s)$ in the following form:

$$\frac{|L(j\omega)-L_n(j\omega)|}{|L_n(j\omega)|} = \frac{|P(j\omega)-P_n(j\omega)|}{|P_n(j\omega)|} \le |W(j\omega)| ; \quad \forall \omega \qquad (4.8.5)$$

With this definition of $W(j\omega)$ and the inequality relation in Eq.(4.8.4), Eq.(4.8.5)
can be given its final form (after multiplying both sides by $|T_{1n}(j\omega)|$):

$$\frac{|L(j\omega)-L_n(j\omega)|}{|L_n(j\omega)|} |T_{1n}(j\omega)| < |W(j\omega)T_{1n}(j\omega)| \qquad (4.8.6)$$

But if

$$|W(j\omega)T_{1n}(j\omega)| < 1; \quad \forall \omega \qquad (4.8.7)$$

then it follows by Eq.(4.8.4) that the closed-loop system remains stable for all per-
turbations of the plant bounded as in Eq.(4.8.5). In terms of the H_∞-norm symbolism, Eq.(4.8.7) can be rewritten as follows:

$$\|W(j\omega)T_{1n}(j\omega)\|_\infty < 1; \quad \forall \omega \tag{4.8.8}$$

In the beginning of this discussion, it was assumed that the nominal loop transmission function is stable and that no encirclements of the critical point occur. The same results are obtained if the nominal loop transmission function contains unstable poles; the nominal closed-loop system is stable; and the perturbed loop transmission include the same number of unstable poles.

For an efficient use of Eq.(4.8.8) in practical feedback problems, it is important to develop plant models by which the uncertainties are simply and adequately expressed in the frequency-domain.

4.8.3. Plant Uncertainty Modeling.

The way in which the uncertain plant template is created is strongly influenced by the framework in which the design of the feedback system is performed; in Section 4.3.2 the plant template was generated in the Nichols chart. The process of modeling the uncertain plant in this section was simple, easy and unique. However, when H_∞ -control design is approached, different ways to model the uncertain plant are needed, depending on the kind of uncertainty we are faced with and on the closed-loop system objectives to be achieved, such as robust stability, robust performance, etc. Several uncertainty plant models are discussed in length in Weinmann (1991), Doyle et al. (1992), Skogestad and Postletwaite (1996).

In the analysis and design of feedback problems involved with uncertain plants, three basic categories of uncertainties may be distinguished:

1. Modelled dynamics uncertainty:

In this category, the physical structure of the plant is comparatively well-known. This means that the transfer function of the plant is obtained by taking the Laplace transform of a set of well-defined differential equations representing the dynamics of the plant. The obtained transfer function has a known structure with a defined number of parameters which may be exactly known. Possibly, as in most real physical systems, these parameters may be bounded between their maximum and minimum values, which, hopefully, are known to the designer. A representative example in this category is the transfer function of a military aircraft whose parameters change enormously under flight conditions (altitude and Mach number).

2. Unmodelled dynamics uncertainty.

Contrary to the previous category, the dynamics equations of the plant are not sufficiently known to allow a structured transfer function to be obtained with well-defined parameters whose uncertainty bounds are known. For instance, when dealing with airframe dynamics, structural modes with unpredictable dynamics may appear in high frequencies. Their influence on the total uncertainty of the plant can still be taken into account, by defining the unpredictable dynamics as a perturbation of the form $\|\Delta(j\omega)\|_\infty \le 1$ with uncertainty in all directions in the complex plane, but multiplied by a normalizing weighting function $W(j\omega)$. Here we are faced with a disc-shaped uncertainty, which is, by definition, more conservative than the uncertainty of the physical plant really is. This is the 'template' counterpart of the classical design paradigm, treated in Section 4.3.2.

3. *Lumped plant uncertainty.*

This is a more general modeling, including both parametric and unmodelled dynamic uncertainty elements. These are combined into a single lumped perturbation of a chosen structure. Returning once more to the aircraft plant model, the basic dynamics, which are in the low frequency range, about less than 20 rad/sec, can be parametrically modeled by writing the differential equations of the plant dynamics. The parameters can be validated next in wind tunnels and finally in flight tests. However, at higher frequencies, there still remain uncertainties due to unknown or to neglected dynamics, pure time delays, poorly defined high frequency structural modes and so on. These uncertainties are very complex, possibly unrealistic for parametric modeling. The primary difficulty with unmodelled dynamics is in the unpredictable phase-lag of the plant at high frequencies. Fortunately, the exemplified models in this section take care of this difficulty by simple mathematical modeling. Here, again, the disc-shaped uncertainty might be more conservative than the plant uncertainty really is.

Multiplicative uncertainty model.

A simple and practical model of an uncertain plant is shown in Fig.4.8.2. In this figure the model is *multiplicative* in the sense that the 'uncertainty' part of the perturbed plant $P(s)$ multiplies the nominal plant $P_n(s)$, namely,

$$P(s) = P_n(s)[1 + W_{MP}(s)\Delta_{MP}(s)]; \ \Delta_{MP}(j\omega) \le 1, \forall \omega \qquad (4.8.9)$$

(The subscript $(\_)_{MP}$ stands for *M*ultiplicative *P*erturbation).

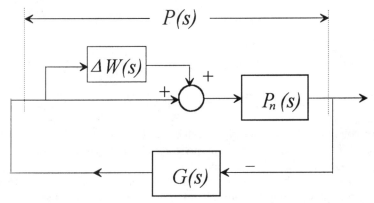

Figure 4.8.2. Feedback system with multiplicative uncertainty model of the plant, (adapted from Skogestad and Postlethwaite (1996), by permission of John Wiley & Sons).

Sometimes the functions $W_{MP}(s)$ and $\Delta_{MP}(s)$ can be found directly, as in the following example.

Example 4.8.1.   The plant is any transfer function $P(s) = kP_o(s)$ with a bounded gain k within the limits $k_{min} < k < k_{max}$.

Solution: Choose Δ to be a real scalar such that $|\Delta| \leq 1$, in other words, $-1 \leq \Delta \leq 1$, and also choose the nominal plant to be $P_n(s) = k_n P_o(s)$; $k_n = (k_{max} + k_{min}) / 2$. Next define $k_a = (k_{max} - k_{min})/(k_{max} + k_{min})$. With these choices and definitions, we can model the uncertain plant in the following way:

$$P(s) = P_n(s) [1 + W_{MP}(s)\Delta(s)] = k_n P_o(s)[1 + k_a\Delta]$$

where $W_{MP}(s) = k_a$ and $|\Delta| \leq 1$, or, $-1 \leq \Delta \leq 1$. It is easily found that the entire set of uncertain plant parameters is covered by inserting in the above equation, values of Δ bounded within the limits $\Delta = \pm 1$.

A real plant model is generally more complex and direct algebraic modeling is very difficult to perform. In the context of H_∞-control analysis and design, we can use Eq.(4.8.9) to model the uncertain plant in the much more useful frequency-domain in the following way. Eq.(4.8.9) can be rewritten as

$$\frac{P(j\omega)-P_n(j\omega)}{P_n(j\omega)} = W_{MP}(j\omega)\Delta_{MP}(j\omega); \quad |\Delta_{MP}(j\omega)| \leq 1 \qquad (4.8.10)$$

$W_{MP}(j\omega)$ in the above equation is a kind of normalizing weighting function which allows limiting the value of $|\Delta_{MP}(j\omega)|$ to unity. We can calculate the maximum value of the left side in Eq.(4.8.10) for the entire uncertain set $\{P(j\omega)\}$, and for all frequencies. Let us call this value $\delta_{MP}(\omega)$, namely,

$$\delta_{MP}(\omega) = \max_{\{P(j\omega)\}} \left| \frac{P(j\omega) - P_n(j\omega)}{P_n(j\omega)} \right|. \qquad (4.8.11)$$

Together with Eq.(4.8.10), this leads to

$$|W_{MP}(j\omega)| \geq \delta_{MP}(\omega); \quad \forall\omega. \qquad (4.8.12)$$

Very complicated uncertain plants can be modeled by use of Eqs.(4.8.11) and (4.8.12). Finally, $W_{MP}(s)$ can be approximated from $|W_{MP}(j\omega)|$. $W_{MP}(s)$ is generally chosen to be stable and minimum phase.

The next example clarifies some important points and shows a way to model a dynamic plant using the multiplicative uncertainty model in the frequency-domain.

Example 4.8.2.   The uncertain plant is defined by

$$P(s) = k/[(s + a)(s + b)]; \ k = [1 - 10], \ a = [1 - 5], \ b = [20 - 30]$$

Find the weighting function $W_{MP}(s)$ in Eq.(4.8.9) that models the uncertainty of the plant.

Solution: To carry the procedure line streamed by Eqs.(4.8.11) and (4.8.12), a nominal plant is to be chosen. This is one of the principal drawbacks in the H_∞ -control design paradigm, because the choice of the nominal plant case strongly influences the optimality of the achieved design. (This problem does not exist within the classical design technique treated in Section 4.3. Read Remark 2 at the end of Section 4.3.7). More will be said in a later section concerning the choice of the nominal plant. Meanwhile, let us choose the nominal plant parameters by intuitively fixing them as equal to the average values of their uncertain parameters, namely $k_n = 5.5$, $a_n = 3$, and $b_n = 25$. With this choice, the nominal plant becomes $P_n(s) = 5.5/[(s+3)(s+25)]$.

Bode plots of $|P(j\omega)/P_n(j\omega) - 1|$ for extreme values of the parameters k, a and b are shown in Fig.4.8.3. Based on the resulting plots, it is easy to obtain the

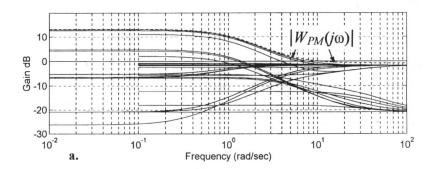

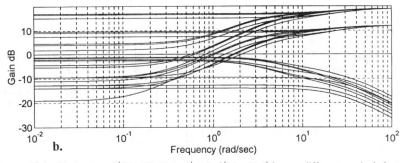

Figure 4.8.3.   Bode plots of $|P(j\omega)/P_n(j\omega) - 1|$ and of $|W_{MP}(j\omega)|$ for two different nominal plants, **a.** $P_n(s) = 5.5/[(s+3)(s+25)]$; **b.** $P_n(s) = 1/[(s+1)(s+20)]$

envelope $\delta(\omega)$, from which it is not difficult to approximate $W_{MP}(s)$. The weighting function $W_{MP}(s)=0.91(s+5)/(s+1)$, whose magnitude versus frequency plot is shown in Fig.4.8.3, approximates adequately $\delta(\omega)$ for all ω. It is important to notice that when different plants are chosen for nominal, $\delta(\omega)$ may increase drastically, thus enlarging the radii of the uncertainty disk-shaped templates at different frequencies. For example, when the nominal plant was chosen to be $P_n(s) = 1/[(s+1)(s+20)]$, it was found that $\delta(\omega) \approx 8$; $\forall\ \omega$, with the consequence that it could be approximated by $W_{MP}(s) \approx 8$. With a different choice of the nominal plant, for instance $P_n(s) = 5.5/[(s+3)(s+25)]$, it turns out that $\delta(\omega) \approx 5$ for frequencies in the range $\omega < 1$ rad/sec, and $\delta(\omega) \approx 1$ in the range $\omega > 5$ rad/sec. This is a significant amelioration, and of special importance when we seek the optimizing controller in the next sections. Note also that the overall changes in $|P(j\omega)/P_n(j\omega)-1|$ at high frequencies are about 20 dB for case **a**, in Fig.4.8.3, while they amount to about 43 dB for the second choice of nominal plant, case **b** in the same figure. This might become an important factor when we come to treat the TDOF uncertain feedback problem in Section 4.8.6.

Inverse multiplicative uncertainty model

The inverse multiplicative uncertainty model version is shown in Fig.4.8.4. In this case

$$P(s) = P_n(s)[1 + W_{IMP}(s)\Delta_{IMP}(s)]^{-1}; \Delta_{IMP}(j\omega) \leq 1, \forall\omega \qquad (4.8.13)$$

where the subscript $(\_)_{IMP}$ stands fo *I*nverse *M*ultiplicative *P*erturbation.

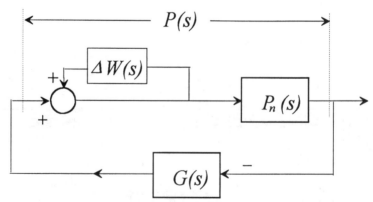

Figure 4.8.4. Feedback system with Inverse multiplicative uncertainty model of the plant, (adapted from Skogestad and Postlethwaite (1996), by permission of John Wiley & Sons).

Additive uncertainty model

In this case, an additive complex perturbation is added around the nominal plant $P_n(s)$

$$P(s) = P_n(s) + W_{AP}(s)\Delta_{AP}(s); \; |\Delta_{AP}(j\omega)| \leq 1, \quad \forall \omega \qquad (4.8.14)$$

(The subscript $(\_)_{AP}$ stands for *Additive Perturbation*). This uncertainty model is represented in Fig.4.8.5 below.

$\Delta_{AP}(j\omega)$ generates a disk with a radius equal to or smaller than 1. Hence, $P(j\omega)$ in Eq.(4.8.14) represents at each frequency a disk-shaped template of radius $|W_{AP}(j\omega)|$ centered at $P_n(j\omega)$. Here again we can approximate the weighting function $W_{AP}(s)$ by using the procedure used in Example 4.8.1, with the only difference that Eq.(48.11) must be changed to

$$\delta_{AP}(\omega) = \max_{\{P(j\omega)\}} |P(j\omega) - P_n(j\omega)|. \qquad (4.8.15)$$

Inverse additive uncertainty model

In this case, there is a negative feedback of uncertainty around the nominal plant (see Fig. 4.8.5a).

The perturbed plant becomes:

$$P(s) = P_n(s)[1 + \Delta_{IAP} W_{IAP}(s) P_n(s)]^{-1} \qquad (4.8.16)$$

(The subscript $(\_)_{IAP}$ stands for *Inverse Additive Perturbation*).

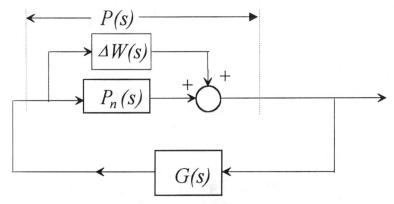

Figure 4.8.5.   Feedback system with additive uncertainty model, (adapted from Skogestad and Postlethwaite (1996), by permission of John Wiley & Sons).

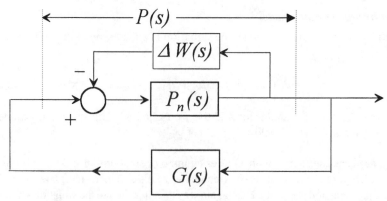

Figure 4.8.5.   Feedback system with inverse additive uncertainty model, (adapted from Skogestad and Postlethwaite (1996), by permission of John Wiley & Sons).

With this model, it is also easy to treat unstable plants. The following example shows how the weighted function $W_{IAP}(s)$ can be calculated analytically for certain plant structures.

Example 4.8.3.   Let us suppose that the uncertain plant is given by:

$$P(s) = K/(s+a); a = [-3 \text{ to} +2], K=1.$$

Find an inverse additive uncertainty model for this uncertain plant.

Solution: By use of Eq.(4.8.16) we find that

$$P(s) = 1/[s+a+\Delta_{IAP}W_{IAP}].$$

Use a constant weighting function, $W_{IAP}(s) = C$. In order to find the nominal a and C, we just write two simple equations: $a + C = -3$; $a - C = 2$, from which we get $a = -0.5$; $C = -2.5$. Hence, the model for the uncertain plant becomes $P(s) = 1/[s -0.5 + 2.5 \Delta_{IAP}]$; $\|\Delta_{IAP}\|_\infty \leq 1$. With this model, the entire range of a is accomplished by changing Δ_{IAP} within its fully allotted range.

Unfortunately, with more complicated plant structures, the parametric modeling might be very difficult to implement, if not impossible, as the following example shows.

Example 4.8.4.   As given, there is an uncertain plant of the form:

$$P(s) = K/(s^2 +as+b), a = [1-5], b = [5-15], K=1.$$

Find an expression of the form $P(s) = P_n(s)[1 + \Delta_{IAP} W_{IAP}(s) P_n(s)]^{-1}$ for the uncertain plant.

Solution: A real Δ_{IAP} can be used, $-1 \le \Delta_{IAP} \le 1$. If we next choose the parameters of the nominal plant case to be the average values of a and b, we get $P_n(s) = 1/(s^2+3s+10)$. It is then easily found that $W_{IAP}(s) = 2s + 5$ is the needed weighting transfer function, because, with this choice, $P(s) =$

$$\frac{1}{(s^2+3s+10)\left[1+\Delta_{IAP}(2s+5)\dfrac{1}{s^2+3s+10}\right]} = \frac{1}{(s^2+3s+10)+\Delta_{IAP}(2s+5)}.$$

Finally, we see that for the extreme values of Δ_{IAP} which are ±1, the extreme perturbed plant parameters become

$$P(s) = \frac{1}{s^2+s(3\pm2)+(10\pm5)}$$

However, not all combinations of a and b are modeled with the above expression.

In the first stage of the feedback system design, based on the uncertain plant parameters, we have to find an approximation of the weighting function $W_-(s)$ for the chosen uncertainty model. Needless to say, the best design solution will be obtained if the nominal plant is chosen such that $|W_-(j\omega)|$ is as low as possible at all frequencies, contributing to uncertainty disk-shaped templates of minimum radii. This objective is not always easy to achieve.

The next step is to find conditions under which the closed-loop feedback system remains stable for all plants in the uncertain set $\{P(s)\}$. These conditions depend naturally on the chosen uncertainty model.

4.8.4. Robust stability for Different Kinds of Uncertainty Plant Models.

The robust stability problem was introduced in Section 4.8.2 in the complex plane by showing the plots of both the nominal $L_n(j\omega)$ and the perturbed $L(j\omega)$ transmission functions (see Fig.4.8.1). The robust stability condition for the uncertainty modeling in Section 4.8.2 was summarized in Eq. (4.8.8). The uncertainty model described by Eq.(4.8.5) comes to be the multiplicative uncertainty plant modeling treated in the previous section 4.8.3. Therefore, we can restate the robust stability condition for the multiplicative uncertainty plant model in the following theorem:

Theorem 4.8.1: For the *multiplicative uncertainty* model of $P(s)$ the compensator $G(s)$ provides robust stability iff

$$\|W_{MP}(s)T_{1n}(s)\|_\infty < 1 \; ; \quad (T_{1n}(s) \text{ is stable}). \tag{4.8.17}$$

Proof: Sufficiency was outlined in detail in Section 4.8.2. For a full proof, see Doyle et al.(1992). The result of the above theorem is equivalent to the practical engineering condition

$$|T_{1n}(j\omega)| < \frac{1}{|W_{IMP}(j\omega)|}; \quad \forall \omega \qquad (4.8.18)$$

The meaning of the last equation is as follows. Suppose that a limiting weighting function $|W_{MP}(j\omega)|$ has been obtained for the uncertain plant. The feedback system for the nominal case is to be designed as stable and such that the inequality of Eq.(4.8.18) is satisfied. Then, the feedback system remains stable for all plants in the set $\{P(s)\}$. The stability condition in Eq.(4.8.17), (or in Eq.(4.8.18)) is very general and also applies for unstable plants, but with the restriction that the nominal unstable plant and the remaining plants in the plant set $\{P(s)\}$ contain the same number of unstable poles. This is necessary because, for stabilization of the nominal unstable plant, the loop transmission must encircle the stability critical point $[-1+j0]$ $N=-p$ times. As a result, the same number of encirclements must be assured for all the plants in the set $\{P(s)\}$.

Robust stability theorems for other uncertainty models are given without proof.

Theorem 4.8.2.   For the *inverse multiplicative uncertainty* model of $P(s)$, the compensator $G(s)$ provides robust stability iff

$$\|W_{IMP}S_n(s)\|_\infty < 1 ; \quad (S_n(s) \text{ is stable}). \qquad (4.8.19)$$

The result of the above theorem is equivalent to the practical engineering condition

$$|S_n(j\omega)| < \frac{1}{W_{IMP}(j\omega)}; \quad \forall \omega. \qquad (4.8.20)$$

Theorem 4.8.3.   For the *additive uncertainty* model of $P(s)$, the compensator $G(s)$ provides robust stability iff

$$\|W_{AP}G(s)S_n(s)\|_\infty < 1 ; (S_n(s) \text{ is stable}). \qquad (4.8.21)$$

The result of the above theorem is equivalent to the practical engineering condition

$$|G(j\omega)S_n(j\omega)| < \frac{1}{W_{AP}(j\omega)}; \quad \forall \omega \qquad (4.8.22)$$

Theorem 4.8.4.   For the *inverse additive uncertainty* model of $P(s)$, the compensator $G(s)$ provides robust stability iff

$$\|W_{IAP}(s)P_n(s)S_n(s)\|_\infty < 1 ; \quad (S_{1n}(s) \text{ is stable}). \qquad (4.8.23)$$

The result of the above theorem is equivalent to the practical engineering condition

$$|P_n(j\omega)S_n(j\omega)| < \frac{1}{W_{IAP}(j\omega)}; \quad \forall\omega \qquad (4.8.24)$$

An example of how to use these results may be helpful here.

Example 4.8.5. There is given a plant with the uncertainties defined in example 4.8.2. Find a compensator $G(s)$ that provides stability for all plants in the uncertain set $\{P(s)\}$. Use the multiplicative uncertainty plant model in solving this example.

Solution: Use of Eq.(4.8.18) will provide the stabilizing compensator. In the first stage, let us manipulate $L_n(s)$ so that the obtained $|T_{1n}(j\omega)|$ is as close as possible to $1/|W_{MP}(j\omega)|$. It was found in Example 4.8.2 that $W_{MP}(s) = 0.91(s+ 5)/(s+ 1)$. In order to arrive at a practical nominal unity-feedback transfer function $T_{1n}(s)$, let us choose

$$T_{1n}(s) = 100(s+1)/[(s+5)(s+100)].$$

Then,

$$L_n(s)=T_{1n}(s)/[T_{1n}(s)-1] = 100(s+1)/(s^2+5s+400)= G(s)P_n(s)$$

From this equation we find that

$$G(s) = \frac{100(s+1)(s+3)(s+25)}{5.5(s^2 +5s+400)}.$$

However, this compensator is not physically realizable (more zeros than poles) and we have to add two far-off poles, located for example at $s = -1000$. We get finally

$$G(s) = \frac{10^8(s+1)(s+3)(s+25)}{5.5(s^2 +5s+400)(s+1000)^2}.$$

$|T_{1n}(j\omega)|$ and $1/|W_{MP}(j\omega)|$ are displayed in Fig.4.8.6.

It is seen that in the frequency range $\omega > 100$ rad/sec, $|T_{1n}(j\omega)|$ does not follow exactly $1/|W_{MP}(j\omega)|$. But this is a physical necessity since the roll-off rate of $|T_{1n}(j\omega)|$ must be at least -1. In a practical, physical system, the far-off poles can be located closer to the origin without significant alteration of the achieved relative stability. When the nominal loop transmission function $L_n(j\omega)$ is displayed in the complex plane and when circles with radii equal to $|L(j\omega)W_{MP}(j\omega)|$ are superimposed with their centers located on $L_n(j\omega)$ at the appropriate frequencies (for instance at ω $=10$, 15 and 50 r/s), it is perceived that these circles do no encircle the stability critical point $[-1, j0]$. But they are very close to it. This means that the stability margins are very low (see Fig.4.8.7). From an engineering viewpoint, such a situ-

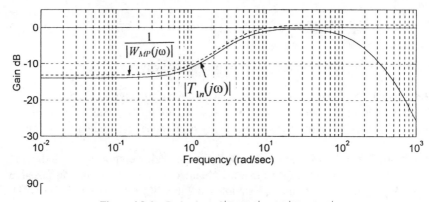

Figure 4.8.6.   Bode plots of $|T_{1n}(j\omega)|$ and $1/|W_{MP}(j\omega)|$.

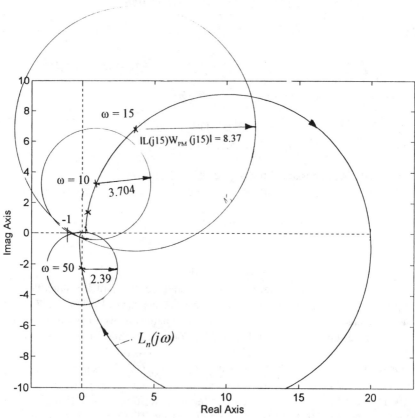

Figure 4.8.7.   Nominal $L_n(j\omega)$ and disk-shaped plant uncertainties with radii equal to $|L_n(j\omega) W_{MP}(j\omega)|$ at $\omega = 10$, 15 and 50 rad/sec.

ation is unacceptable, and it compels us to define and develop the 'robust performance' requirement, which is treated in the next section.

We must not forget that the disk-shaped template of the uncertain plant may be a very conservative choice when all the plant uncertainties are taken into account. The reason is that, actually, only a small part of the disk is filled with perturbed $L(j\omega)$'s due to parametric uncertainties. This is seen in Fig.4.8.8 in which $L(j\omega)$'s for all extreme parameters of this example are plotted. They are all quite distanced from the stability critical point. On the other hand, if unstructured uncertainty is admitted in the form of frequency dependent $|\Delta(j\omega)| < 1$, then the disk-shaped plant uncertainty is plainly justified, as observed in Fig.4.8.7.

4.8.5. Robust Performance.

Achieving robust stability is a most important feature in feedback system design, but not a sufficient one. The system must provide additional quantitative performances as defined by the customer. The problem of 'design to specifications' was treated in previous chapters and sections. When robust stability is achieved, there might be plant conditions for which the usual stability margins are very poor. The standard H_∞-regulator problem was defined and treated in some length in Section 2.5. Then the mixed sensitivity problem was solved, with the objective

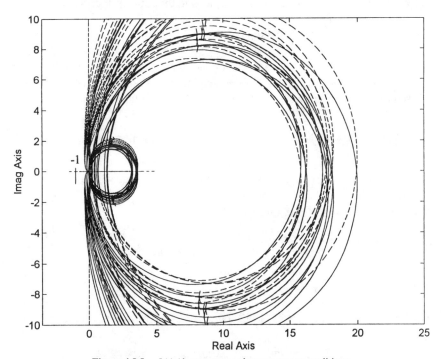

Figure 4.8.8. $L(j\omega)$'s at extreme plant parameter conditions.

of satisfying the nominal performance condition in Eq.(2.5.16), namely, $\|W_S(j\omega)S(j\omega)\|_\infty < 1$. As explained in Sections 2.5.2 to 2.5.4, definition of an adequate sensitivity transfer function $S(s)$ is related to required sufficient gain and phase margins and additional desired performances such as steady-state error coefficients, maximum peak values of $|S(j\omega)|$, etc. (It is advised to reread Section 2.5.4 treating the 'mixed sensitivity problem'). Since we are concerned here with an uncertain plant set $\{P(s)\}$, the next objective should be to guarantee not only internal stability, but also satisfaction of the sensitivity and other performances for all plants in the uncertain set $\{P(s)\}$. To summarize, both Eqs.(2.5.15) and (4.8.17) are to be satisfied in a way to be defined next.

Finally, the notion of *robust performance* can be defined as follows: The system satisfies performance specifications for the nominal plant and also for all the plants in the set $\{P(s)\}$. The robust performance conditions can be derived graphically or algebraically, as in Doyle et al (1992) or Skogestad and Postlethwaite (1996).

1. Algebraic derivation.

Robust performance requires that the weighted sensitivity inequality in Eq.(2.5.15) be satisfied for all plant conditions in the set $\{P\}$, that is

$$\max_{\{P\}} |Ws(j\omega)S(j\omega)| < 1; \quad \forall\omega. \tag{4.8.25}$$

The sensitivity function for any plant condition, in terms of the nominal loop transmission function $L_n(j\omega)$ and of the weighting function $W_{MP}(j\omega)$, can be expressed in the following way for the multiplicative uncertainty plant model:

$$S(j\omega) = [1 + L(j\omega)]^{-1} = 1/[1 + L_n(j\omega) + L_n(j\omega)\, W_{MP}(j\omega)\Delta_{MP}(j\omega)]$$

The supremum for $S(j\omega)$ in the last equation is obtained when we choose $\Delta_{MP}(j\omega) = -1$.

Multiplying both sides by $W_S(j\omega)$ we get

$$
\begin{aligned}
\max_{\{P\}} |W_S(j\omega)S(j\omega)| &= \frac{|W_S(j\omega)|}{|1 + L_n(j\omega)| - |W_{MP}(j\omega)L_n(j\omega)|} \\
&= \frac{|W_S(j\omega)S_n(j\omega)|}{1 - |W_{MP}(j\omega)T_{1n}(j\omega)|}
\end{aligned}
\tag{4.8.26}
$$

which together with Eq.(4.8.25) leads to the robust performance condition

$$\max_{\{P\}} \left[|W_S(j\omega)S(j\omega)| + |W_{MP}(j\omega)T_{1n}(j\omega)| \right] < 1; \quad \forall\omega. \tag{4.8.27}$$

This condition is stated in the following theorem:

Theorem 4.8.4:   A necessary and sufficient condition for robust performance is

$$\| \,|W_S S| + |W_{MP} T_{1\,n}| \,\|_\infty < 1 \qquad (4.8.28)$$

2 Graphical derivation

It is instructive to derive Eq.(4.8.28) graphically. Eq.(4.8.25) can be rewritten as

$$|W_S(j\omega)| < |1+L(j\omega)|; \,\forall\omega, \quad \forall\,\{P\} \qquad (4.8.29)$$

The last equation is illustrated graphically in Fig.4.8.9. For robust performance to be attained it is necessary that for all plants in $\{P\}$, $L(j\omega) = L_n(j\omega) + W_{MP}(j\omega)$ $L_n(j\omega)$ stay outside the disk of radius $|W_S(j\omega)|$ centered at $[-1+j0]$. Since $L(j\omega)$ lies at each frequency inside the disk with radius $W_{MP}(j\omega)L_n(j\omega)$ centered on $L_n(j\omega)$, the two disks are not allowed to overlap if the robust performance condition is to be satisfied. This leads to the inequality

$$|W_S(j\omega)| + |W_{MP}(j\omega)\,L_n(j\omega)| < |1+L_n(j\omega)| \qquad (4.8.30)$$

After dividing both sides of the last equation by $|1+L_n(j\omega)|$, we get Eq.(4.8.27).

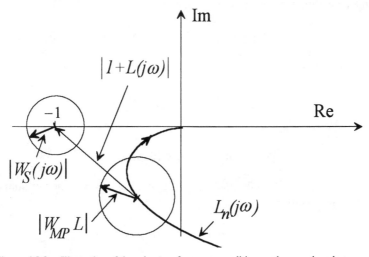

Figure 4.8.9.   Illustration of the robust performance condition on the complex plane, (adapted from Skogestad and Postlethwaite (1996), by permission of John Wiley & Sons).

To summarize, the robust performance problem can be interpreted as the mixed sensitivity problem treated in Section 2.5.4, but with the addition of the newly defined weighting function $W_{MP}(s)$. The frequency dependent $W_{MP}(j\omega)$ is related to the uncertainties of the parameters of the plant set $\{P(s)\}$, structured or unstructured. The last design stage consists in solving optimally an H_∞ − norm of the form displayed in Eq.(2.5.21), or even in Eq.(4.8.27). Optimization for robust performance using Eq.(4.8.27) is closely related to optimizing a mixed sensitivity Euclidean vector norm (as in Eq.(2.5.21)), namely,

$$\left\| \begin{matrix} W_S S_n \\ W_{MP} T_{1n} \end{matrix} \right\|_\infty = \max_\omega \sqrt{|W_S S_n|^2 + |W_{MP} T_{1n}|^2} < 1. \tag{4.8.31}$$

Robust performance conditions for different uncertainty plant models, such as the additive, the inverse multiplicative or the inverse additive, can be found in Doyle et al.(1992).

In addition, there are some constraints on the selected weighting functions $W_{MP}(s)$ and $W_S(s)$ that must be satisfied so that the obtained solution will guarantee robust performance for the entire uncertain set $\{P(s)\}$.

Algebraic design constraint

A necessary condition exists for robust performance related to the weighting functions $W_{MP}(s)$ and $W_S(s)$, namely,

$$\min \{|W_{MP}(j\omega)|, |W_S(j\omega)|\} < 1; \quad \forall \omega \tag{4.8.32}$$

The proof is elementary and based on the identity $T_1(s) + S(s) = 1$ which holds for all plant conditions in the set $\{P(s)\}$. The proof can be found in Doyle et al.(1992),

$$|W_S| = |W_S(S + T_1)| \le |W_S S| + |W_S T_1|.$$

If we admit that

$$|W_S| \le |W_{MP}|; \quad \forall \omega$$

then

$$|W_S| = |W_S(S + T_1)| \le |W_S S| + |W_{MP} T_1|$$

which by Eq.(4.8.27) implies $|W_S| < 1$. Eq.(4.8.32) can be validated in the same way for the condition

$$|W_{MP}| \le |W_S|; \quad \forall \omega.$$

The practical conclusion is that either $|W_S| < 1$ or $|W_{MP}| < 1$ must hold at each frequency.

Additional analytic constraints exist when the plant transfer function includes RHP poles and zeros.

Design for robust performance specifications

Solution to problems for robust performance can be achieved by use of any available H_∞-norm optimization algorithms, for instance, *hinfsyn* in μ-Tools, or *hinfric* in LMI-Tools, both belonging to MATLAB. A design example follows.

Example 4.8.6. This example is a continuation of Example 4.8.5 with the difference that a sensitivity weighting function is also defined in order to satisfy stability performances similar to those in Example 2.5.1, namely,

$$W_S(s) = \frac{10(1 + s/5.58)^2}{s(1 + s/2.13)}.$$

Here again $P(s) = k/[(s + a)(s + b)]; k = [1 - 10], a = [1 - 5],$ and $b = [20 - 30]$

Solution: Suppose that $W_{MP}(s) = 0.91(s+5)/(s+1)$ is to be used (as in Example 4.8.5) for the uncertain plant $\{P(s)\}$ defined in Example 4.8.2. $|W_S(j\omega)| > 1$ in a part of the entire frequency range (Fig.2.5.4); however, as is seen in Fig.4.8.3, $|W_{MP}(j\omega)| > 0$ dB $= 1$, $\forall\omega$. These two inequalities contradict the constraint in Eq.(4.8.32). Hence, the robust performance problem is not solvable with the choice of the nominal plant $P_n(s)=5.5/[(s+3)(s+25)]$. Using a different choice of nominal plant shows that when we adopt $P_n(s) = 10/[(s+1)(s+20)]$ as the nominal plant, then the limiting weighting function is $|W_{MP}(j\omega)| = 0.91 < 1$, $\forall\omega$ and the problem becomes solvable, since, with this choice of $P_n(s)$, Eq.(4.8.32) is satisfied.

The H_∞-norm optimization algorithm used for solving the present example is *hinfreq*. The listing of the Matlab program is given in Table 4.8.1. The transfer function of the obtained controller is

$$G(s) = \frac{(s + 20)(s + 3.237)(s + 1)}{(s + 2.13)(s + 0.001)(s^2 + 286.4s + 40823.9)}.$$

The resulting loop transmission functions for extreme plant conditions are shown on the inverted Nichols chart in Fig.4.8.10 (see Section 2.3.3 and Fig.2.3.4). Bode plots of $|S(j\omega)|$'s are shown in Fig.4.8.11. Bode plots of $|T_1(j\omega)|$'s are shown in Fig.4.8.12.

Some practical conclusions and remarks based on the graphical results of the obtained solution, follow:

1− The existing gain and phase margins are very conservative, more than 30dB and 70 degrees respectively. There is a local waste of phase-lag that can be used to decrease the magnitude of the loop transmissions at high frequencies, thus, achieving a better attenuation of sensor noise at the input to the plant (see Sections

Table 4.8.1. Matlab program for designing the H_∞ controller

```
%lmi484.m 17 January 1998
%Ws = 10(1 + s/5.58)/\2/(1 + s/0.001)(1 + s/2.13);
%Wpm = 0.91(s + 5)/(s + 1),not compatible because }Wpm} >1 for all w!!
%use Wpm = 0.8, derived for the nominal plant Pn = 10/(s + 1)(s + 20);
%computation of Wpm and Ws in system model form;
nws = 10*[1/5.58/\2 2/5.58 1] ;dws = [1/2.13 1 + 0.01/2.13 0.001];
ws = ltisys('tf', nws, dws);
nwpm = 0.9*[1];dwpm = [1];wpm = ltisys('tf', nwpm, dwpm)
%end of computation of Wpm , Ws and g0( nominal plant);
np = 10;dp = [1 21 20];g0 = ltisys('tf',np,dp);
Paug = sconnect('r(1)', 'Ws;Wpm','K:e = r-G0','G0:K', g0,'Ws:e', ws,'Wpm:G0',wpm);
%Paug = smult(P, sdiag(ws,wpm,1)) in another possibility to derive Paug;
[gopt,k] = hinfric(Paug,[1 1],300,1 , 1e−5);
[numglmi, denglmi] = ltitf(k);
% resulting controller
numglmi
denglmi
end
%numerator polynomial of controller
numglmi =
0  2.4541e4  5.9479e5  2.159e6  1.5887e6
%denominator polynomial of controller
denglmi =
1.0  2.8857e2  4.143e4  8.699e4  8.695e1
%roots on numerator of controller
roots(numglmi)
−20
−3.2369
−1.0
%roots of denominator of controller
rooots(denglmi)
−1.4322e2 + 1.4252e2i
−1.4322e2−1.4252e2i
−2.13
−0.001
```

2.4.1 and 2.4.3). Here we are confronted with an example of how classical design principles can be useful in ameliorating the control solution obtained by H_∞-norm optimization.

2− The maximum peak value of the sensitivity transfer function magnitude for all plant conditions is smaller than 0.5 dB, although specifications for $|S(j\omega)|_{max} < 3$ dB were defined.

3− The resulting plots in Fig.4.8.12 show that there is no sensed peaking in

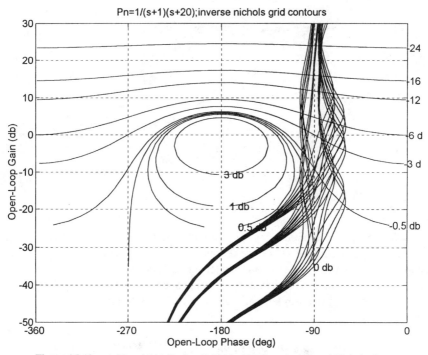

Figure 4.8.10.   Achieved $L(j\omega)$'s for all $P(s)$ in $\{P(s)\}$ on the inverted Nichols chart.

$|T_1(j\omega)|$, while a slight peaking of 1 to 2 dB might be preferable as far as the step time response is concerned. The feedback system structure for this solved problem is, in fact, a ODOF unity-feedback structure. For such a system, no constraints and specifications can be defined and achieved exactly for several input-output transfer functions, because only one control compensator can be used in the H_∞-control design process. The bandwidths of all $|T_1(j\omega)|$'s extent between $\omega_{-3dB} =$

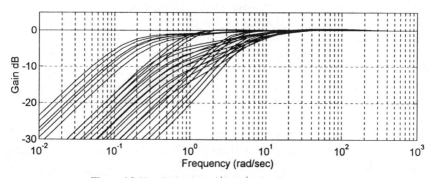

Figure 4.8.11.   Bode plots of $|S(j\omega)|$'s for all $P(s)$ in $\{P(s)\}$

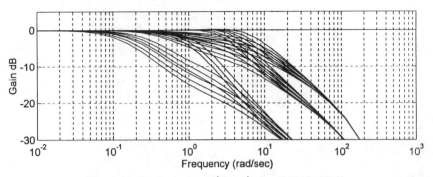

Figure 4.8.12. Bode plots of $|T_1(j\omega)|$'s for all $P(s)$ in $\{P(s)\}$

0.1 and 8 rad/sec. This frequency range might be excessively large, and not fitted to the defined specifications of the feedback problem. There is no way, at this stage, to control these closed-loop transfer function characteristics. The next task will be to control defined input-output tracking specifications by using the second degree-of-freedom in a similar way we proceeded with the QFT design technique in Section 4.3.

4.8.6. H_∞-Optimization Implied in the Design of TDOF Uncertain Feedback Systems

In Sections 4.1 to 4.7 solution of the TDOF uncertain feedback problem was our primary concern In these sections, quantitative specifications on $|T(j\omega)|$ were defined and ultimately achieved using classical design approaches.

The present section 4.8.6 deals with our primary task of solving the TDOF uncertain feedback problem by using a H_∞-optimization design technique (Sidi 1999). Robust performance specifications were achieved in the last Example 4.8.5, but in a very general form. The ODOF unity-feedback $|T_1(j\omega)|$'s for most plant cases are all well behaved in Fig.4.8.12. However, they do not satisfy quantitative performance specifications. In reality, we want all the tracking frequency-domain responses well within defined upper and lower bounds, as in Fig.4.3.9 and Example 4.3.1. Clearly, the frequency-domain responses in Fig.4.8.12 are outside these bounds. Use of the prefilter $F(s)$ in a TDOF feedback system structure, as in Fig.2.1.1 (or Fig.4.8.13 below), cannot help shift the responses in Fig.4.8.12 within the permitted upper and lower bounds shown in Fig.4.3.9, because the changes $\Delta|T_1(j\omega)|$ in Fig.4.8.12 are larger than the allowed $\Delta|T(j\omega)|$ in Fig. 4.3.9 at the relevant frequencies.

A design procedure for a TDOF uncertain feedback system using H_∞-optimization algorithms will be next derived. The basic design philosophy is quite similar to that explained in Section 4.2, namely, the classical QFT design approach. It includes two principal stages:

Stage 1: Obtain input-output tracking quantitative sensitivity specifications defined in the form of **maximal permitted changes** $\Delta|T(j\omega)|$, Eq.(4.3.3). Use any H_∞-optimization algorithm to solve the standard mixed sensitivity regulator problem for achieving these defined robust performance specifications. The first degree-of-freedom is used in this stage and the inner-loop controller $G(s)$ is obtained.

Stage 2: Use the prefilter $F(s)$ (the second degree-of-freedom) to shift the unity-feedback functions $|T_1(j\omega)|$'s obtained in Stage 1 within the permitted bounds, Eq.(4.2.3).

The powerful H_∞-optimal control design technique used in Stage 1 is complemented here with classical design principles in Stage 2.

For the reader's convenience, Fig.2.5.2 is reproduced with small alterations in Fig.4.8.13.

Stage 1 consists in designing for robust performance specifications by adequately defining the sensitivity weighting function $W_S(s)$, so that specifications on a permitted amount of $\Delta|T_1(j\omega)|$ are satisfied for $\forall\ \omega$, and for the entire set $\{P(s)\}$. We shall see that when the H_∞-optimal control design is performed for the TDOF uncertain problem, definition of $W_S(s)$ alone is insufficient, because the control effort weighting function $W_{un}(s)$ also influences the design results. The latter function is in the end used for fine tuning. This design stage is next discussed.

We return to the initial definition of the sensitivity function $S(s)$ which is, according to Bode (1945),

$$S_P^T = \frac{\partial T/T}{\partial P/P} = \frac{d\ln(T)}{d\ln(P)} = \frac{1}{1 + G(s)P(s)} = \frac{1}{1 + L(s)}. \tag{4.8.33}$$

$P(s)$ in the above equation belongs to the uncertain plant set $\{P(s)\}$, and $G(s)$ is fixed. (To simplify the notation, from here on we will use $S(s)$ instead of S_P^T).

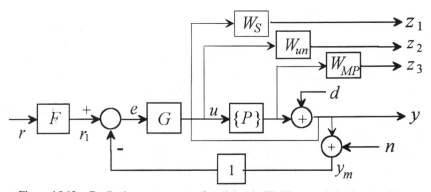

Figure 4.8.13. Feedback system structure for solving the TDOF uncertain feedback problem.

Bode in his basic theorem stated the meaning of this equation: *The variation in the final gain characteristic in dB, per dB changes in the gain of P, is reduced by feedback in the ratio* $1 + L(s) : 1$.

The above equation which is exact for infinitesimal changes only, can also be used for finite changes. Horowitz (1963) suggested rewriting it as follows:

$$S_P^T = \frac{\Delta T/T_f}{\Delta P/P_f} = \frac{1}{1 + L(s)} \tag{4.8.34}$$

where $\Delta T = T_f - T_0$ and $\Delta P = P_f - P_0$, T_f and T_0 are the final and the initial unity-feedback transfer functions respectively and where P_f and P_0 are the nominal and the perturbed plants respectively.

Remark. Should Eq.(4.8.34) be defined slightly differently, such as

$S_P^T = \dfrac{\Delta T/T_0}{\Delta P/P_0} = \dfrac{1}{1+L(s)}$, then, for the same ΔT and ΔP, the value of the resulting

S_P^T will be different. Hence, care must be taken when Eq.(4.8.34) is used for large uncertainties.

Two approaches are presented here to modify the initially defined weighting function $W_S(s)$, so that input-output *sensitivity specifications* due to uncertainties of the plant are also satisfied.

1st approach. When designing to keep the magnitude of $|T(j\omega)|$ within specified tolerances, we may be interested in using the following version of the sensitivity equation

$$|S(j\omega)| = \frac{|\Delta T/T|}{|\Delta P/P|} = \left|\frac{1}{1+L(j\omega)}\right| \tag{4.8.35}$$

We had to choose a nominal plant $P_n(s)$ out of $\{P(s)\}$ in the design for robust performance. The same nominal plant ought to be used in finding the maximum changes $|\Delta P/P_n|_{max}$, for all ω, and for all $P(s)$ in $\{P\}$. But we also have to define the maximum permitted changes $|\Delta T/T_n|_{max}$, $\forall \omega$. $|S(j\omega)|$ can be then completely specified. This enables us to approximate the sensitivity weighting function $W_S(s)$ which will be used when designing for robust performance, as in Example 4.8.5. This stage should come out with a feedback solution for which the changes $\Delta|T_1 (j\omega)|$ will be no larger than the maximum specified tolerances.

However, before reaching the H_∞-optimization stage, we do not know what $|T_n(j\omega)|$ is. Therefore, the maximum relative changes $|\Delta T/T_n|$ cannot be defined a priori, although ΔT is initially specified. Consequently, the sensitivity function $S(s)$ cannot be exactly specified before the design stage is completed. As a result, we must make some conservative assumptions in order to achieve a design that satisfies (or even initially oversatisfies) the tracking sensitivity specifications. In order to obtain a conservative $S_n(s)$, it is suggested to assume a nominal $T_n(s)$ so that $\Delta T/T_n$ will be minimal for all ω. This will lead to a conservative choice of $W_S(s)$ in the sense that the control design will emerge with $\Delta|T_1(j\omega)|$ smaller than as per the specified tolerances.

When the multiplicative uncertainty plant modeling is attempted, the maximal relative changes of the plant are calculated by Eq.(4.8.11). In this way, the term $|\Delta P/P_n|_{max}$ can be calculated for use in Eq.(4.8.35) when defining $|S(j\omega)|$.

Unfortunately, due to the above mentioned practical difficulties encountered when implementing the suggested 1st approach, it seems to be preferable to use a second approach based on Eq.(4.8.33).

2nd approach. With this method, the logarithmic version of Eq.(4.8.33) is used, namely,

$$|S(j\omega)| = max \, \Delta|T(j\omega)|(\text{dB}) \, / \, max \, \Delta|P(j\omega)|(\text{dB}) \qquad (4.8.36)$$

in which $max\Delta|T(j\omega)|$ are the maximal permitted changes of $\Delta|T(j\omega)|$ in dB as per Eq.(4.3.3) and Fig.4.3.2b. Similarly, $max \, \Delta|P(j\omega)|$ are the maximal changes of the logarithmic magnitude of the uncertain plant, as in Fig.4.8.14. Once the nominal sensitivity function $|S_n(j\omega)|$ is so derived, $W_S(s)$ can be approximated for use in the H_∞-norm optimization stage. In selecting $|S_n(j\omega)|$, this 2nd approach seems to be more efficient and practical, although initially more conservative.

Fortunately, it does not really matter which approach we choose in defining $|S_n(j\omega)|$, since its accuracy characteristics are not very important for two reasons. First, both approaches are not exact because the basic sensitivity equation is only correct for infinitesimal plant changes. This is not our case. Second, when the H_∞-control design is performed, the achieved nominal $|S_n(j\omega)|$ will not exactly follow the selected $1/|W_S(j\omega)|$ since the H_∞ optimization algorithms minimize an Euclidean vector norm. Consequently, none of the elements of the mixed sensitivity vector in Eq.(2.5.20) can be satisfied individually with an equality sign such as $|S_n(j\omega)W_S(j\omega)| = 1$. Some tradeoff between the different weighting functions is **anyway** necessary for completing the design. It is suggested to use the control effort weighting function $W_{un}(s)$ as a 'tuning parameter' in the design process. The idea is to iterate with different $W_{un}(s)$ until Eq.(4.3.3) is exactly satisfied by a few frequencies in the useful frequency range. Up to two to three design iterations are usually more than sufficient.

The selection of $W_S(s)$ is based on the resulting $|S(j\omega)|$ obtained by Eq.(4.8.35) or Eq.(4.8.36). $W_{un}(s)$ is chosen arbitrarily for the first design iteration. We proceed then to the next design step which consists in obtaining the optimal compensator $G(s)$ by one of the known algorithms that solve the H_∞-control problem. In this first trial design, we use a low gain $|W_{un}(j\omega)|$. This is equivalent to accepting large effort signals at the input to the plant due to command and to disturbance inputs, and also to sensor noise. With this assumptions, the H_∞-control solution will tend to have very high gain $|L(j\omega)|$, but, also a very low gain $|S(j\omega)|$ at useful frequencies. Thus, an overdesign is achieved even if the nominal sensitivity function $|S_n(j\omega)|$ is correctly defined. With this initial solution, draw the Bode plots of $|T_1(j\omega)|$'s for $\forall P(s)$ in $\{P\}$ and check if $\Delta|T_1(j\omega)|$ is smaller than the permitted tolerances of $|T(j\omega)|$. If so, increase $|W_{un}(j\omega)|$ which will lead to an H_∞-control solution with smaller magnitudes of $|L(j\omega)|$, and, consequently, larger magnitudes of $|S_n(j\omega)|$. In other words, with reduced sensitivity qualities of the unity-feedback transfer function $T_1(s)$. Check again for the maximal changes $\Delta|T_1(j\omega)|$ and iterate the choice of $W_{un}(s)$ until these changes comply with the specified tolerances of $|T(j\omega)|$. This completes the first design stage.

In the second design stage, the prefilter $F(s)$ is designed so that all $|T_1(j\omega)|$'s are shifted within the permitted bounds of $|T(j\omega)| = |F(j\omega)T_1(j\omega)|$ (see Step 6 in Section 4.3). Generally, no more than two to three design iterations with different $|W_{un}(j\omega)|$ are necessary, as will be demonstrated in Example 4.8.7. The different steps of the design process using the H_∞-control design for solving the TDOF uncertain plant feedback system problem are next summarized:

Stage 1:

Step 1. Translation of the time-domain tolerances into frequency-domain tolerances. See Section 3.2.

Step 2. Choice of a nominal plant and of the uncertainty plant weighting function $W_{MP}(s)$ for robust stability. See sections 4.8.3 , 4.8.4 and Example 4.8.2.

Step 3. Derivation of the sensitivity weighting function $W_S(s)$, based on Eq.(4.8.35) or (4.8.36). See also Section 4.8.5- *design for robust performance specifications,* and Example 4.8.6. Choose a low-gain $W_{un}(s)$ weighting function.

Step 4. Check for satisfaction of Eq.(4.8.32).

Step 5. Run the H_∞-norm optimization program. Use, for instance, *hinfsyn* of the μ-Analysis and Synthesis Toolbox or *hinflmi, hinfric* of the LMI Toolbox.

Step 6. With the obtained suboptimal controller $G(s)$, calculate $|T_1(j\omega)|$ for all plants in $\{P(s)\}$. If the maximal changes in $|T_1(j\omega)|$ are exactly satisfied at some frequencies according to the specified upper and lower bounds of $|T(j\omega)|$, then proceed to step 7. If not, repeat Step 5 with modified weighting functions $W_{un}(s)$ until the achieved maximal changes $\Delta|T_1(j\omega)|$ satisfy exactly the permitted bounds at several frequencies. Then proceed with step 7.

Stage 2:

Step 7. Design of the prefilter $F(s)$ to achieve the input-output tracking specifications of $|T(j\omega)| = |F(j\omega)| \, |T_1(j\omega)|$, Eq.(4.2.3).

Step 8. Evaluation of the design in the time and the frequency domains, and refinement of the solution if necessary.

The following example illustrates the above design steps.

Example 4.8.7.   This example is the same as Example 4.3.1 which is next solved in the H_∞-optimization framework.

Solution: The solution of this problem follows the above eight design steps. Some of them were already performed, hence, they will only be referenced. The uncertain plant is defined as:

$$P(s) = k/[(s + a)(s + b)]; k = [1–10], a = [1–5], b = [0.2 – 1].$$

Step 1. See step 1 in Example 4.3.1. The permitted changes $\Delta|T(j\omega)|$ in dB are taken from Example 4.3.1, Fig.4.3.9.

Step 2. See example 4.8.6. In practice, $|(P/P_n - 1)|$ is plotted for different choices of $P_n(s)$ until the most favorable one is detected in the sense that the lowest gain $|W_{MP}(j\omega)|$ is attained. In this example, $P_n(s) = 10/[(s+0.2)(s+1)]$ was the most favorable choice, with which a maximum value of 0.95 is attained for the uncertainty $|(P/P_n - 1)|$. Hence, let us choose $W_{MP}(s) = 0.95$.

Step 3. The choice of $W_S(s)$ is more complicated.
With the first approach, defining specifications on $S_n(s)$, $P_n(s) = 5.5/[(s+3)(s+0.6)]$ was chosen to find the maximum changes in $|(P/P_n - 1)|$, and $|T_n| = (|T|_{max} + |T|_{min})/2$ was chosen to find the permitted changes in $|(T/T_n - 1)|$. The resulting maximum changes, as well as $|S_n(j\omega)|$ at some important frequencies, are summarized in Table 4.8.2 below.
When the second approach for choosing $S_n(s)$ is used, calculate first $|P(j\omega)/P_n(j\omega)|$ for most of the plant cases. The results are shown in Fig.4.8.14. From this figure we can find the maximum $\Delta|P(j\omega)|/|P_n(j\omega)|$ for the chosen frequencies used in Table 4.8.2. Using Eq.(4.8.36), we can calculate the needed $|S_n(j\omega)|$, from which $1/W_S(s)$ is finally approximated. See Table 4.8.2.

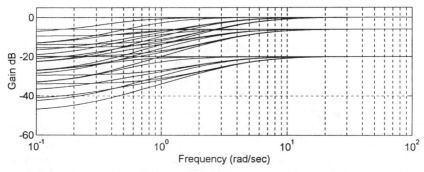

Figure 4.8.14. $|P(j\omega)/P_n(j\omega)|$ for extreme plant cases in $\{P(j\omega)\}$.

Table 4.8.2. Data for calculating $W_S(s)$

ω rad/sec	0.2	0.3	0.5	0.7	1.0	1.5	2.0	3.0	5.0
First approach of finding $|S|$ dB									
$\max[|\Delta T| / |T_n|]$	0.06	0.1	0.17	0.27	0.47	0.65	0.73	0.81	0.9
$\max[|\Delta P| / |P_n|]$	0.98	0.98	0.98	0.98	0.98	0.97	0.96	0.95	0.94
$k_{nom}=5.5;\ a_n=3;\ b_n=0.6$									
$|S_n|$ db=	−24	−20	−15	−11.4	−7	−4	−3	−2	−1
$\max[|\Delta T|/|T_n|]/\max[|\Delta P|/|P_n|]$									
Second approach of finding $|S|$ db									
$d\ln|T| = \max \Delta|T(j\omega)|$ dB	0.4	1.0	2.0	4.0	6.0	11.0	13.0	17.0	—
$d\ln|P| = \max \Delta|P(j\omega)|$dB	42	38	36	34	34	30	28	25	
$|S_n| = d\ln|T|\ /d\ln|P|$ (dB)	−40	−32	−25	−19	−15	−9	−7	−3	

The resulting $|S_n(j\omega)|$ in dB, based on the second approach, is adopted for the cur-
rent design, because it is more conservative. A little cut-and-try with Bode plots
allows us to find an adequate $W_S(s)$, namely,

$$W_S(s) = \frac{(s + 5)(s + 7)}{1.5(s + 0.01)(s + 0.1)}.\ W_{un}(s)\text{ is chosen for the first design iteration to be:}$$

$$W_{un}(s) = 0.001.$$

Step 4. Eq.(4.8.32) is always satisfied since $|W_{MP}| = 0.98 < 1;\quad \forall\omega$.

Step 5–1. The compensator $G(s)$ is obtained by solving the H_∞ -norm sensitivity
problem with the use of the *hinfsyn* algorithm of the μ-Analysis and Synthesis
Toolbox. $G(s)$ is found to be

$$G(s) = 1.66 \times 10^9 \frac{(s + 0.1997)(s + 1)(s + 1.695)}{(s + 0.01)(s + 0.1)(s + 164.41)(s + 2.146 \times 10^6)}$$

The detailed Matlab program for the solution is documented in Table 4.8.3.

Step 6–1. The obtained suboptimal controller $G(s)$ is used to calculate $|T_1(j\omega)|$ for
all plants in the set $\{P(s)\}$. These are shown in Fig.4.8.15. It is not surprising that
all the resulting $|T_1(j\omega)|$'s lie outside the permitted upper and lower bounds, also
shown. But it is also observed that the overall changes $\Delta|T_1(j\omega)|$'s are much
smaller than what is allowed per the specified bounds. For instance, at ω = 1
rad/sec, $\Delta|T_1(j1)| < 2$ dB while at this frequency a tolerance of 10 dB is prescribed.
Return to step 5 for ameliorating the solution in the sense of decreasing adequately

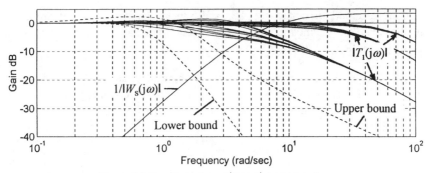

Figure 4.8.15.   Bode plots of $|T_1(j\omega)|$, 1st trial design.

the magnitude of $|L_n(j\omega)|$, or equivalently, of increasing adequately the magnitude of $|S(j\omega)|$ in the useful frequency range.

Step 5–2. $W_{un}(s)$ is increased to 0.007 in the second design iteration, $W_{un}(s) = 0.007$. After rerunning the H_∞-norm optimization program, the following compensator is derived

$$G(s) =$$

$$\frac{10^8(1.9065s^5 + 9.95s^4 + 19.19s^3 + 16.917s^2 + 6.54s + 0.7704)}{s^6 + 1.46\times10^6 s^5 + 9.6\times10^7 s^4 + 1.98\times10^8 s^3 + 1.14\times10^8 s^2 + 1.04s + 9.26\times10^4}$$

$$\approx 1.906 \times 10^8 \, \frac{(s+0.2)(s+1)(s+2.02)}{(s+0.01)(s+0.1)(s+63.59)(s+1.46\times10^6)}$$

Step 6–2. The newly obtained suboptimal controller $G(s)$ is used to calculate $|T_1(j\omega)|$ for all plant cases. These are shown in Fig.4.8.16. It is observed that the changes $\Delta|T_1(j\omega)|$ in the useful frequency range $\omega = 0.4$ to 0.7 rad/sec match fairly

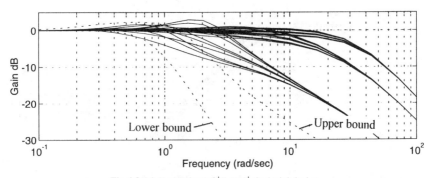

Fig.4.8.16. Bode plots of $|T_1(j\omega)|$, 2nd trial design.

well the specified tolerances, Eq.(4.3.2). But these changes in $|T_1(j\omega)|$ are much smaller than the specified tolerances in the high frequency range. Compare with the QFT solution in Fig.4.3.14.

Step 7. The prefilter $F(s)$ is next designed to achieve the tracking specifications by shifting all $|T_1(j\omega)|$'s within the permitted bounds of $|T(j\omega)|$ in Fig.4.8.17. (Compare with the QFT solution in Fig.4.3.15). The designed filter

$$F(s) = \frac{2.727(s+0.22)}{(s+0.3)(s+1)(s+2)}$$

achieves completely the second degree-of-freedom specifications, i.e., the input-output tracking specifications, Eq.(4.2.3).

It is interesting to compare the achieved nominal sensitivity function $|S_n(j\omega)|$ and $1/|W_S(j\omega)|$, displayed in Fig.4.8.18, which also shows $|T_{1n}(j\omega)|$ and $|T_n(j\omega)| = |F(j\omega)T_{1n}(j\omega)|$. The obtained nominal $|S_n(j\omega)|$ does not exactly follow the specified $1/W_S(j\omega)$. But this is a direct consequence of the theoretical inability of the H_∞-norm optimization algorithm to satisfy exactly both $|W_S(j\omega)S_n(j\omega)| = 1$ and $|W_{MP}(j\omega)T_{1n}(j\omega)| = 1$ equalities. This was explained in Section 2.5.4.

Step 8. Evaluation of the design follows.
1- *Stability margins.* The loop transmission functions are shown on the Nichols chart in Fig.4.8.19 for comparison with those obtained by the QFT solution, and which are displayed in Fig.4.3.13. It is important to realize that, as required, none of the loop transmission functions cross the contours of constant $|T_1| = 3$dB and $|S| = 3$dB. As a result, no large overshoots in the time responses will occur for command and disturbance inputs. See Section 3.2.2.

Large gain and phase margins of 17 dB and 50° respectively, are achieved for the same reason. See Section 2.5.2.

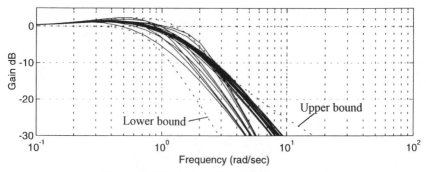

Figure 4.8.17. Bode plots of $|T(j\omega)| = |F(j\omega)||T_1(j\omega)|$.

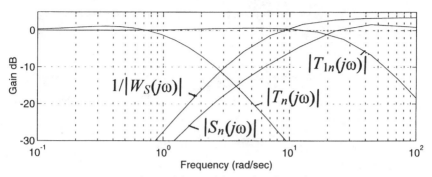

Figure 4.8.18. $|W_S(j\omega)|$, $|T_{1n}(j\omega)|$, $|T_n(j\omega)|$ and $|S_n(j\omega)|$ Bode plots.

2- *Step time response*. As can be observed in Fig.4.8.20, the step time responses for all the family of plants are well within the permitted bounds. Compare with the results in Fig.4.3.16 obtained by the QFT solution. The resulting step responses are very similar for both QFT and H_∞ design paradigms.

3- *Sensor noise amplification*. To remind the reader, sensor noise amplification is one of the most annoying problems in control engineering. Excessive noise am-

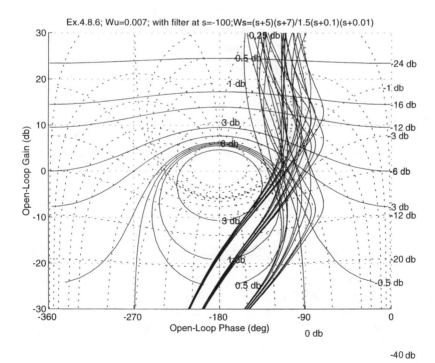

Figure 4.8.19. $L(j\omega)$'s on the combined Nichols & Inverted Nichols charts.

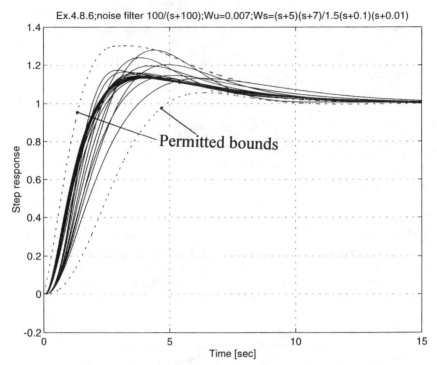

Figure 4.8.20. Step time responses for some extreme plant cases.

plification can preclude the possibility of using a preferred engineering control scheme (Sidi 1997a). The control compensator $G(s)$ achieved in Step 5–2 is a transfer function with virtually the same number of poles and zeros (one of the poles is located at $s = -1.46\ 10^6$), hence, a tremendous amplification of the sensor noise n is to be expected, with imminent saturation of the plant input u in Fig 4.8.13. The resulting average value, obtained by calculating the sensor noise amplification for all the plants in the set $\{P(s)\}$, amounts to $1.1147\ 10^5$ (RMS)! With such a tremendous noise amplification, there is no practical engineering solution.

To overcome this problem, a noise filter is added to the nominally obtained $G(s)$ using classical frequency-domain design principles. When a filter $100/(s+100)$ was added, the average noise amplification for all plants in the set $\{P(s)\}$ was substantially decreased to 746 (RMS). The satisfactory results in Figs. 4.8.16 to 4.8.20 are obtained with the modified compensator including this noise filter. The QFT design in Example 4.3.1 emerges with an average noise amplification of about 1000 (RMS). In the QFT design technique, the sensor noise amplification is directly controlled during the $L_n(j\omega)$ loopshaping process.

The full MATLAB program for solving Example 4.8.7 is given in Table 4.8.3 below.

Table 4.8.3. Matlab Program for Solving Example 4.8.7.

```
%mu486.m, 23 August 98, TDOF design Example 4.8.7.
%preparation of sensitivity weighting function
%Ws = (s + 5)(s + 7)/1.5(s + 0.01)(s + 0.1);
nws = [1  12  35]; dws = 1.5*[1  0.11  0.001]; Ws = nd2sys(nws,dws,1.0)
%preparation of Wmp weighting function;
%Wmp = 0.98
nwmp = 0.98*[1];dwmp = [1]; Wmp = nd2sys(nwmp,dwmp,1.0)
%preparation of Wu weighting function;
%Wu = 0.98
nwu = 0.007*[1]; dwpm = [1]; Wmp = nd2sys(nwu,dwu,1.0)
%end of computation of Ws, Wmp and Wu;.
%computation of nominal plant P = 10/(s + 0.2)(s + 1)
np = [10]; dp = [1 1.2 0.2]; P = nd2sys(np,dp,1.0)
%%%%%
%preparation of augmented plant Paug
systemnames = 'P Wmp Wu Ws';
inputvar = '[Wmp; Wu; Ws; −P + w]';
input_to_P = '[u]'; input_to_Wmp = '[P]'; input_to_Wu = '[u]'; input_to_Ws = '[-
P+w]';
sysoutname = 'Paug';
cleanupsysic = 'yes';
sysic;
%end of Paug preparation
%start of Hinf algorithm;
nmeas = 1; nu =1; gmn = 0.5; gmx = 50; tol = 0.00001;
[khinf,ghinf,gopt] = hinfsyn(Paug, nmeas, nu, gmn, gmx, tol, 2);
%end
Calculation of suboptimal compensator
[a,b,c,d] = unpck(khinf);
[numg,deng] = ss2tf(a,b,c,d);
roots(numg)
roots(deng)
end;
%
%numerator polynomial of obtained controller
numg = 10^8 *(0.000 1.9061 9.9514 19.188 16.917 6.5443 0.7704)
%roots of numerator of obtained controller
roots(numglmi)
−2.0208e + 000
−1.0000e000
−9.999e − 0.001 + 1.2602e−005i
−9.999e − 0.001 − 1.2602e−005i
−2.000e − 001
%
```

%denominator polynomial of obtained controller
denglmi = 1.0000e + 0 1.46e + 6 9.604e + 7 1.9794e + 8 1.1367e + 8 1.04e + 7 9.296e + 4
%roots of denominator of obtained controller
roots(deng)
−1.4623e + 006
−6.3591e + 001
−1.0000e + 000
−1.0000e + 000
−1.0000e − 001
−1.0000e − 002

This completes the H_∞-optimization design procedure of Example 4.8.7.

4.8.7. Comparison between 'Classical' and 'H$_\infty$' Control Designs.

After solving the TDOF uncertain feedback problem by both the 'classical' and the 'modern H_∞' design approaches, it is worthwhile to compare them.
1- As a matter of fact, the design objectives are identical and these are stated in the frequency- domain for both approaches.
2- In the classical design approach, maximum peaking in the sensitivity function $|S(j\omega)|$ and in the complementary sensitivity function $|T_1(j\omega)|$ are kept under control by designing the nominal loop transmission $L_n(j\omega)$. When perturbed by the uncertainty of the plant, this loop transmission avoids crossing the prohibited constant gain contours of $|T_1|$ and $|S|$ in the Nichols and in the inverted Nichols charts. With the modern design technique, maximum peak values are controlled by correctly defining the corresponding weighting functions, such as $W_S(s)$.
3- Uncertainty modeling in both approaches consists in preparing templates on the Nichols chart for the classical approach, and templates on the complex plane for the modern H_∞ approach. While in the classical approach, the templates are used extensively in the entire design procedure. The disk-shaped templates used with the H_∞ paradigm are transformed to equivalent weighting functions and used when the standard mixed sensitivity feedback problem is solved.
4- In the classical approach, minimization of sensor noise amplification is performed by directly keeping the loop transmission magnitude as low as possible at high frequencies. In the H_∞ -control design approach, sensor noise amplification is minimized by defining a weighting function $W_{un}(s)$, introduced in the mixed sensitivity performance vector, and also by correctly choosing parameters of the H_∞ -norm optimization algorithm, such as 'tol' in *hinfsyn*. Nevertheless, the final controller will need additional manipulation at high frequencies in order to achieve a sufficiently low sensor noise amplification.
5- Input-output tracking specifications are defined similarly in both design approaches. In the classical approach, tracking sensitivity specifications are controlled by drawing sensitivity permitted bounds on the nominal loop transmission

$L_n(j\omega)$ in the Nichols chart. In the H_∞ design approach, the tracking sensitivity specifications are basically achieved by defining adequately the weighting function $W_S(s)$ pertaining to the sensitivity transfer function $S_n(s)$.

6- In the classical control design approach, an optimal loop transmission function $L_n(s)$ is manipulated first. Then the compensator $G(s)$ is derived, $G(s) = L_n(s) / P_n(s)$. In the H_∞-control design approach, the compensator $G(s)$ is designed directly via the H_∞-optimization process so that the selected weighted specifications of the feedback system are satisfied in some optimal way.

4.9. Summary

This chapter dealt with the design of single-input/single-output feedback control systems in which a LTI uncertain plant is embedded. The treated control design techniques are in the frequency- domain, and they solve simultaneously for tracking and also for disturbance rejection specifications, under the constraint of decreasing as much as possible the effect of sensor noise amplification at the input to the plant. The 'classical' design technique explained in this chapter is very transparent, providing the designer with the insight to make the necessary trade-offs at every step in the design process. The fundamental technique treated in this chapter is the basis for solving many control problems in which the uncertain plant can be multi-input/multi-output, or nonlinear (Horowitz 1976), linear time varying, (Horowitz and Sidi, 1978a), etc.

The robust design technique for the TDOF structure is also solved using the H_∞ -norm paradigm. Modeling of plant uncertainty is first treated and exemplified. Then the standard H_∞ -regulator problem is explained and used to solve real problems in which uncertainties of the plant are large. This design approach is less transparent. But if a good feeling exists for choosing the necessary weighting functions, then very appealing solutions are attainable with fast computerized algorithms. Iterating system weighting functions might be necessary to achieve the best solution.

The results obtained with both design techniques are quite similar.

The material explained and discussed in this chapter is a basis for the design of MIMO uncertain feedback systems, the 'classical design approach' being treated in Chapter 6. The 'modern H_∞ -control design approach' is treated in Chapter 8.

Chapter 5 _____

Single-Input
Multi-Output Uncertain
Feedback Systems

5.1 Introduction

The sensor noise amplification problem was first introduced in Section 2.4.1 for
SISO feedback systems. It was there stressed that excessive sensor noise amplification can cause to saturation of the input to the plant, followed by prevention
of satisfactory functioning of the feedback system. The effect of the sensor noise
amplification problem is specially pronounced in uncertain feedback control systems in which, due to severe tracking sensitivity specifications, the control network emerges with large magnitude in the high frequency range in which the sensor noise is usually concentrated. The sensor noise amplification effect can be
diminished if additional states of the plant are accessible for measurements. In
this chapter, it is assumed that the plant consists of cascaded sub-plants, so that
more than one loop can be closed. This enables us to obtain, using the Nichols
chart, permitted bounds on the outer and the inner loop transmission functions
which satisfy design specifications despite plant uncertainties (Horowitz and Sidi
1973). The design technique is based on the QFT for SISO systems explained in
Chapter 4.

5.2. Statement of the Problem.

This chapter presents a synthesis theory for the following problem (Horowitz
1962). There is given a linear time-invariant plant consisting of n cascaded parts
with transfer functions $P_i(s)$, $n = 2$ in Fig.5.2.1, $n = 3$ in Fig 5.3.1. The useful

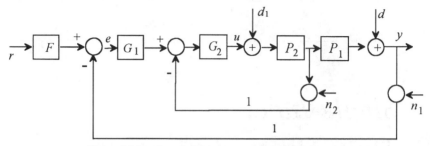

Figure 5.2.1.   Canonical 2-loop cascaded feedback structure

signal input to the system is denoted by $r(t)$. The system output $y(t)$ can only be controlled by $r(t)$ via this constrained plant with uncertain parameters. Sensors with known noise characteristics are available to measure the outputs of the n plant parts, allowing a feedback structure with n independent feedback loops as shown in Figs.5.2.1 and 5.3.1 for $n = 2, 3$ respectively. It is important to note that in this design technique, feedback from each plant element can only influence the main plant input u, otherwise, 'plant modification' will be effected, which is not permissible here. For an overall plant consisting of n sub-plants, the physical possibility of accessing the system output, and of using the prefilter $F(s)$, allows us to increase the degrees of freedom to $n+1$.

We have seen in Chapter 4 that in problems with significant plant uncertainty, and/or narrow tolerances on the system response, the resulting single-loop transmission $L(j\omega)$ tends to have a large bandwidth, far greater than that of $T(j\omega)$. This leads to a large frequency range in which the sensor noise is greatly amplified. This tends to saturate the early stages of the plant. A valid and an important criterion from a practical point of view in multiple-loop design is, therefore, minimization of the net effect of the combined sensor noise sources, i.e. n_1 and n_2 in Fig.5.2.1, n_1, n_2 and n_3 in Fig.5.3.1.

Here again it is assumed that the time-domain tolerances may be reasonably translated into frequency-domain sensitivity specifications, those on magnitude sufficing for minimum-phase systems. The goal of the design technique is to achieve satisfactory system performance despite significant parameter uncertainty and disturbances, but with decreased sensor noise amplification compared to the single-loop design treated in previous chapters.

5.2.1.   *Design Philosophy*

For uncorrelated uncertainty of P_1 and P_2 parameters, the best one can do is to ease the burden on the outer loop L_1, by admitting that a perfect inner loop L_2 can be designed so that there is no uncertainty at all in $P_{2e} = L_2/[1+L_2]$, where $L_2 = G_2 P_2$, Fig.5.2.1. There remains then the single-loop system of Fig.5.2.1a, in which L_1 can be designed to handle the uncertainty of P_1 only.

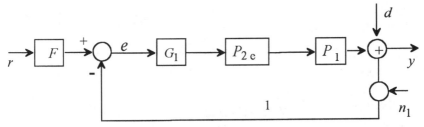

Figure 5.2.1a. Equivalent single-loop structure.

The resulting L_1 is therefore more economical in bandwidth than its counterpart in the single-loop system, since, from a practical point of view, only the uncertainty of P_1 is to be handled. Next, one finds what uncertainty of P_{2e} can actually be tolerated with the above design of L_1. As will be seen from Fig.5.2.8, a design of L_1 based upon specific bounds of uncertainty of P_1 can in fact nearly always handle a larger range of P_1 uncertainty. The final step is to determine the L_2 needed so that the resulting P_{2e} does indeed stay within the bounds found by the previous step. It will be demonstrated that the resulting two-loop design can be highly superior to a single-loop design. The same quantitative sensitivity specifications can be achieved, but with considerably less effect of sensor noise as shown in Figs.5.2.15 and 5.2.16.

As explained in Section 2.4.1, the sensor noise amplification problem is specially pronounced in the high frequency range $\omega > \omega_a$, which is denoted in Fig.5.2.2. In this frequency range, both P_1 and P_2 templates approach their ultimate form of a vertical straight line of length $K_i = 20 \log_{10}(k_{i\,max}/k_{i\,min})$, $i = 1,2$. Assuming no uncertainty in P_{2e}, and P_1 being in its highest gain plant condition, the loop transmission function will touch the boundary B_h from below, $L_1(j\omega)$ in Fig.5.2.2. If we assume that there is no closed-loop around P_2, then L_1 must be redesigned to L_1'' to take care of the uncertainty in P_2, which in the high frequency range amounts to K_2 dB. The consequence is an increase of the sensor noise amplification (see Section 5.2.3). Since a perfect inner loop L_2 cannot be designed, by closing a practically achievable loop around P_2, the uncertainty in $P_{2e} = G_2 P_2$ $/(1+G_2 P_2)$ can be sufficiently decreased in the high frequency range to, say, α dB $< K_2$ dB. Thus we obtain a loop transmission function $L_1'(j\omega)$ which is more economical than $L_1''(j\omega)$ in bandwidth and, consequently, in noise amplification. $L_1'(j\omega)$ is also shown in the figure.

The choice of α is not straightforward. We have to perform several design trials with different α's, and extrapolate to find that particular α which minimizes the root mean square of the amplified sensor noise at the input to the plant. A measure of noise amplification can be calculated by the following equation:

$$U_n^2 = \int_0^\infty \left[|T_{n1}|^2 \, \Phi_{n1} + |T_{n2}|^2 \, \Phi_{n2} \right] d\omega \qquad (5.2.1)$$

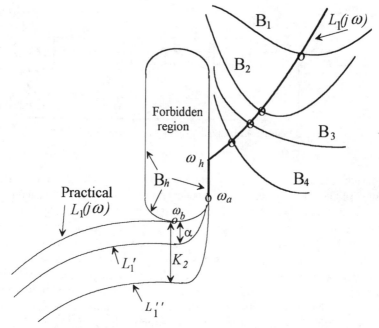

Figure 5.2.2.   Pertinent L_1 design data, optimum and suboptimum L_1' and L_1'' on Nichols chart.

U_n is the root mean square at the plant input due to the amplified sensor noises n_1 and n_2; T_{un1} and T_{un2} are the transfer functions from the noise sources n_1 and n_2 respectively at the plant input u in Fig.5.2.1; Φ_{n1} and Φ_{n2} are the noise power spectra. Notice that T_{un1} and T_{un2} depend on α. The optimized U_n also depends on Φ_{n1} and Φ_{n2}. As related to U_n in Eq.(5.2.1), the parameter α is the tradeoff factor between the two loops L_1 and L_2, i.e. optimization of the overall design is with respect to α.

Having chosen a preliminary α (or, equivalently, a certain $L_1'(j\omega)$ as shown in Figure 5.2.2), we have to design an adequate L_2 for which the resulting P_{2e} does not spoil the design specifications of L_1 when P_2 changes over its permitted range.

5.2.2.   Bounds on L_2

The technique presented here is based on the SISO design technique detailed in Chapter 4. Of special importance to the explanation is the defined suboptimal (and practical) loop transmission function in Fig.4.3.6, as modified and shown in Fig.5.2.2.

It is convenient at this stage to divide the frequency spectrum into the following ranges:

$R_1 : \omega > \omega_a$.
$R_2 : \omega_a > \omega > \omega_h$.
$R_3 : \omega < \omega_h$.

Additional sub-ranges can be defined for a more elaborated design (Horowitz and Sidi 1973), but the above three ranges suffice to illustrate the generality of obtaining the bounds on L_2.

Let us suppose that L_1 was designed under the assumption that $\Delta\log P_{2e} = 0$. The suboptimal and practical $L_1(j\omega)$ in Fig.5.2.2, lies outside the forbidden region B_h and above, or, on the permitted bounds at the lower frequencies in R_3. The first step is to find the permissible range of $\Delta\log P_{2e}$, such that the design of $L_1(j\omega)$, based on $\Delta\log P_{2e} = 0$, is not spoiled. For example, in the range R_2, $\omega_a > \omega > \omega_h$, L_1 is permitted to move to the right in the Nichols chart. In R_3, L_1 is permitted to move to the right and above the bounds B_1, B_2, B_3 etc. Changes in P_2 tend to move L_1 'up', which is admissible in R_2 and in R_3. However, in the range R_1, especially in the reduced range $\omega_b > \omega > \omega_a$, there is some problem because in this range L_1 is not permitted to move 'up', unless it enters inside the forbidden B_h boundary.

The second step is to deduce the resulting bounds on L_2 from the relation $\Delta\log P_{2e} = \Delta\log[L_2/(1+L_2)]$, with $L_2 = P_2G_2$ and P_2 extending over its range of uncertainty. In this section it will be explained how bounds on L_2 can be obtained in R_1 to R_3, so that the L_1 design will not be spoiled (Sidi 1973, Horowitz 1992). The result is the *generality* of the derived bounds on L_2 over the ranges R_i, $i = 1, 3$.

The next step is to find the bounds on L_2 to satisfy the constraints on P_{2e} as P_2 ranges within its own region of uncertainty. For this purpose, it is useful to have a single expression relating the mapping into each other of the triangular wedges of P_2 and P_{2e} of Fig.5.2.3 by the relation $P_{2e} = L_2/[1+L_2]$, $L_2 = P_2 G_2$. It is easily found that

$$P_{2e} \text{ in } B_2 O B_1 \ \forall \ P_2 \text{ in } A_2 O' A_1 \text{ iff}$$

$$\theta_1 - \theta_i \le \arg[1 + L_2] \le \theta_x - \theta_2 \qquad (5.2.2)$$

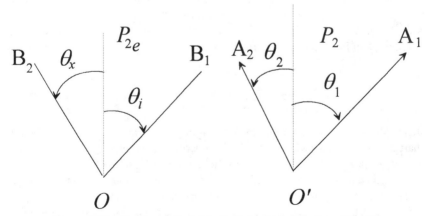

Figure 5.2.3. Mapping of dln P_2 into dln P_{2e} by dln P_2 / dln $P_{2e} = 1/(1+L_2)$

Let $l_2 = 1/L_2$, so that Eq.(5.2.2) becomes $\theta_2 - \theta_x \leq \arg [l_2 /(1+l_2)] \leq \theta_i - \theta_1$. In the inverted Nichols chart, when the rectangular axes are those of l_2, the loci of constant $\arg [l_2 /(1 + l_2)]$ are available, so that the acceptable $l_2 = 1/L_2$ region is easily found. Since $\log l_2 = -\log l_2$ and $\arg l_2 = -\arg L_2$, the boundaries of L_2 on the L_2 Nichols chart are obtained by reflecting the l_2 boundaries twice, once about the zero dB axis and once about the vertical $-180°$ axis. By using the above argumentation, we can find bounds on L_2 in the different frequency ranges R_i, $i = 1,3$. Some examples follow.

Derivation of Bounds on L_2 in range R_1, $\omega > \omega_a$

Let us suppose that, in this range, P_1 and P_2 have already attained their high frequency range form of $P_1(s) = k_1 /s^{e_1}$ and $P_2(s) = k_2 /s^{e_2}$, $s\to\infty$, where e_i is the excess of poles over zeros assigned to P_i. Hence, the template of P_2 in this frequency range is a vertical line of length

$$K_2 = 20 \log (k_{2max}/k_{2min}) \text{ dB} \qquad (5.2.3)$$

Let us define the nominal k_2 as k_{2min}.

The practical L_1 shown in Fig.5.2.2 shows that in this frequency range, changes in P_2 (but also in P_{2e}) will cause changes in L_1 which will tend to enter inside the forbidden region B_h. This difficulty can be solved by manipulating the optimal L_1 so that it remains the same at frequencies below ω_a. An additional gain margin of α dB is provided at $\omega > \omega_a$. The new loop transmission L'_1 will be a little bit less economical in bandwidth; its magnitude at $s\to \infty$ will augment; and the sensor noise amplification $|T_{un1}|$ will slightly increase, depending on the value of α. However, due to changes in P_2, (and consequently also in P_{2e}), L'_1 will not enter the forbidden region B_h.

We are next confronted with the problem of finding bounds on L_2 such that the maximum changes in P_2 will not drive L'_1 inside the forbidden region B_h in Fig.5.2.2. The graphical technique for deriving these bounds involves using a Nichols chart of $-P_{2e}$, shown in Fig.5.2.4. This is useful, because from the definition of L_2 in Fig.5.2.1 and 5.2.1a, we find that

$$-L_2 = \frac{(-P_{2e})}{1+(-P_{2e})}. \qquad (5.2.4)$$

Hence, the superposed contours of constant magnitude and phase on the Nichols chart of $-P_{2e}$ give the values of $-L_2$. The permissible range of $L_1(j\omega)$, due only to changes in P_{2e} is the entire plane excluding region B_h in Fig.5.2.2.

It is convenient to sketch the lower part of B_h and $L_1(j\omega)$ on transparent paper, point A corresponding to some frequency in $\omega > \omega_a$. The rectangular open-loop axes on the Nichols chart belong to $-P_{2e}$. We are interested in finding a per-

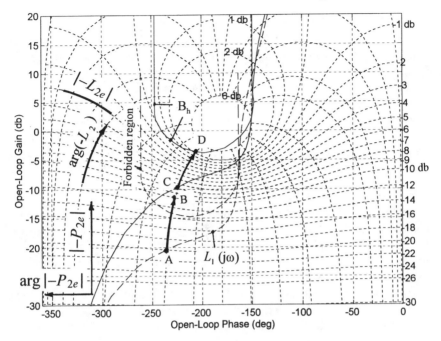

Figure 5.2.4. Determination of bounds on L_2 in the range R_1.

mitted value of $-L_2$ such that despite the maximum changes in P_2, L_1' will not enter the forbidden region B_h. To achieve this, lay the paper with point A on some trial value of open-loop gain and phase of $-P_{2e}$ on the Nichols chart in Fig.5.2.4. Consider first some trial value of the nominal $-P_{2e}$ ($j\omega$), say, at point $(-P_{2e}) = [-20.2$ dB; $-235°]$, where $(-L_2) = [-20$dB; $-240°]$ (the closed-loop constant gain and phase contours of the Nichols chart). As P_2 increases in magnitude from its nominal (minimum) value at point A, $-L_2 = -P_2 G_2$ moves towards point B on the contour of constant $\arg(-L_2) = -240°$, a distance equivalent to 10dB (assuming that, according to Eq.5.2.3, the maximum change of $|P_2|$ is $K_2 = 10$dB). The corresponding $L_1 = P_{2e} P_1 G_1$ moves to point B which is inside the forbidden region B_h (dotted curve) and point A [-20.2dB, -235°] comes to be a bad trial choice. Next, move the transparent paper so that point A is relocated at point C, $[-9.5$dB; $-225°]$. Changing the magnitude of $-L_2$ by 10dB on the contour of constant phase equal to $-240°$, will bring L_1 to point D which lies on the boundary of the permitted region B_h (plain curve). The point C $[-9.5$dB; $-225°]$ is, therefore, a permitted location of $-L_2$ at the frequency pertaining to point A on $L_1(j\omega)$. By repeating the above procedure, additional permitted points for different contours of constant phase of $-L_2$ can be found, until a complete boundary is obtained.

Universal bounds on $L_2(j\omega)$ in the frequency range R_1, $\omega > \omega_a$

Fig.5.2.5 shows two L_1 's providing phase margins of $PM = 45°$ and additional gain margins of $\alpha = 4$dB and 9dB, respectively. They are named $L_{1:\alpha=4dB}$ and $L_{1:\alpha=9dB}$. Frequencies normalized to ω_a are also indicated on them. The procedure of obtaining the bound on L_2 in R_1 can be repeated for different α' s and K_2' s in dB at several frequencies in the range $\omega > \omega_a$, until a family of universal bounds on L_2 is obtained as in Figs.5.2.6a, b, c and d ($\alpha = 4$ and 9 dB and $K_2 = 20$ and 30 dB).

Bounds on $L_2(j\omega)$ for additional α's and K_2's can be derived if needed. In the remaining frequency ranges R_2 and R_3, the bounds on L_2 are less universal. We shall now explain their derivation for some common template forms of P_2.

Bounds on L_2, in range R_2, $\omega_a > \omega > \omega_h$.

Consider ω_x in R_2 with $L_1(j\omega_x)$ at point A, shown in Fig.5.2.7. In this high frequency range, $P_1 = k_1 s^{-e_1}$, so that the P_1 template at this frequency is a vertical line of length AA' equal to $K_1 = 20 \log_{10} (k_{1\,max}/k_{1\,min})$ dB. Note that $L_1(j\omega_x)$ may lie anywhere on AA' due to uncertainty of k_1 and that this design was obtained on the assumption that $\Delta \log P_{2e} = 0$. However, with $\Delta \log P_1 = 0$ and finite changes in P_2, $\Delta \log P_{2e} \neq 0$, so that the range of $\Delta \log P_1 P_{2e} = \Delta \log L_1$ is now the region ABB'A' in Fig.5.2.7. However, this does not spoil the design of $L_1(j\omega_x)$ at A, because no part of ABB'A' lies in the forbidden region B_h. In this way it is easily

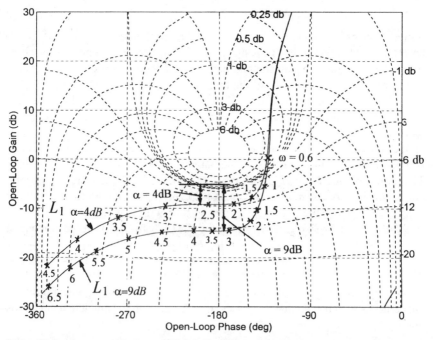

Figure 5.2.5. $L_{1:\alpha=4dB}$ and $L_{1:\alpha=9dB}$ on Nichols chart. The numbers are frequencies normalized to ω_a.

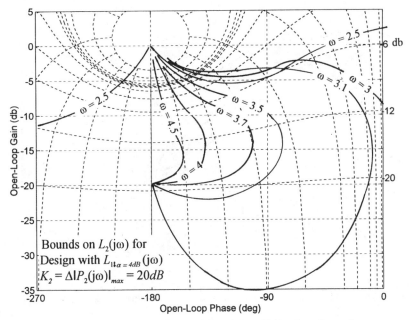

Figure 5.2.6a. Bounds on L_2 for $\alpha = 4$dB and $K_2 = 20$dB, where the numbers refer to those normalized frequencies on the appropriate $L_{1:\alpha=4dB}$ *in Fig.5.2.5*

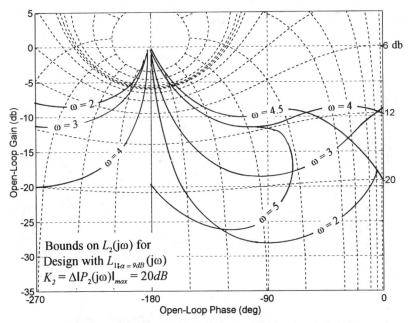

Figure 5.2.6b. Bounds on L_2 for $a = 9$dB and $K_2 = 20$dB, where the numbers refer to those normalized frequencies on the appropriate $L_{1:\alpha=9dB.}$ in Fig.5.2.5

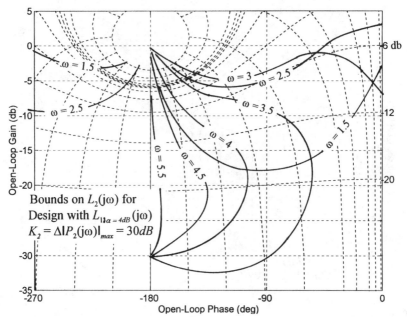

Figure 5.2.6c. Bounds on L_2 for a = 4dB and K_2 = 30dB, where the numbers refer to those normalized frequencies on the appropriate $L_{1:\alpha=4dB.}$ in Fig.5.2.5.

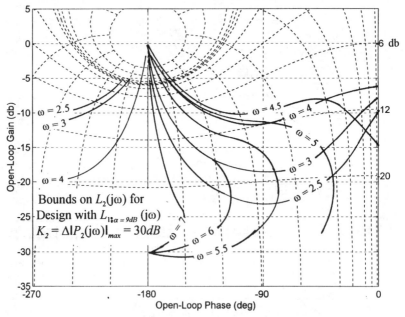

Figure 5.2.6d. Bounds on L_2 for α = 9dB and K_2 = 30dB, where the numbers refer to those normalized frequencies on the appropriate $L_{1:\alpha=9dB}$ in Fig.5.2.5

seen that the permissible range of variation of P_{2e} is the entire plane except for B_h, i.e. the same as for L_1, even though the design of L_1 was based on $\Delta P_{2e} = 0$.

The next step is to find the bounds on L_2 to satisfy the above constraints on P_{2e} as P_2 ranges within its own region of uncertainty. Suppose that the template of $P_2(j\omega_x)$ in R_2 has the form shown in Fig.5.2.7, and that the nominal plant condition is located at the lowest gain region of the template. It is easily shown on the Nichols chart (Sidi 1973), that if the loop transmission $L_2(j\omega_x)$ is situated in the right half plane of the Nichols chart (arg $L > -180°$), then any change $\Delta P_2(j\omega_x)$ will cause changes in P_{2e} accompanied with a phase-lead augmentation. Since $L_1 = P_1 G_1 P_{2e}$, we conclude that L_1 will not move towards the forbidden region limited by B_h. To sum up, the right half plane of the Nichols chart is a permitted region for $L_2(j\omega)$ in R_2.

Bounds on L_2 in range R_3, $\omega < \omega_h$.

The final example of finding the bounds on L_2 from those on L_1 is taken in R_3, as shown in Fig.5.2.8. In this range, the graphical technique for obtaining the bounds on L_2 depends very much on the form of the template of P_2 and also on the features of the bounds on L_1. Generalization, therefore, is not possible. An example will illustrate the general procedure for obtaining the bounds on L_2. The permitted variation in $|T(j\omega)|$ has been taken to be 3dB. The nominal L_1 is located at point J and the assumed template of P_1 lies between $|T(j\omega)| = 0.2$ and -2.8 dB, giving a total change of 3dB. However, this choice of L_1 can obviously handle a much larger range

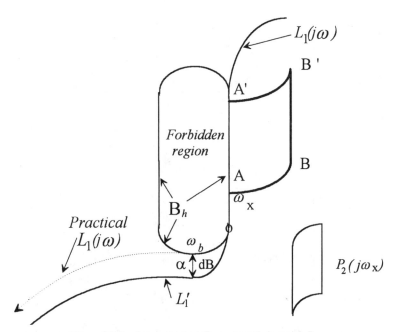

Figure 5.2.7.   Determination of bounds on L_2 in region R_2.

of uncertainty, in fact the entire range in between the contours of $|T(j\omega)| = 0.2$ dB and $|T(j\omega)| = -2.8$ dB. Since $\Delta\log L_1 = \Delta\log P_{2e} + \Delta\log P_1$ and the range of $\Delta\log P_1$ is known, one may determine the permissible range of $\Delta\log P_{2e}$. As the following shows, together they result in points inside the above larger region of permissible L_1 variation. Consider a test point for acceptable P_{2e} at, say, point U in Fig.5.2.8a. The variation of $P_1(j\omega)$ must now be relative to point U, i.e. U takes the place of point J, as shown by the dashed contour B' in Fig.5.2.8a. One simply positions the template of P_1 so that J lies on U and checks whether any point of the shifted template lies outside the region bounded by $|T(j\omega)| = 0.2$ dB and $|T(j\omega)| = -2.8$ dB. As seen in the figure, since such points do exist, point U is not a permissible value for P_{2e}. In this way, the permissible range of P_{2e}, shown in Fig.5.2.8a, was determined. In general, the P_{2e} range can be enclosed in a wedge of the form shown in Fig.5.2.3. If the template of P_2 can also be enclosed, then Eq.(5.2.2) can be used for an estimate of the acceptable range of L_2. Obviously, generalization is not possible in R_3, but, as will be shown, this is of secondary importance.

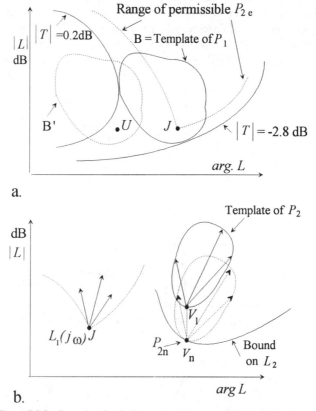

Figure 5.2.8　Procedure for finding acceptable range of P_{2e} in region R_3.

Now, we can proceed to find the permissible range of L_2 (see Fig.5.2.8b). Assume that at some frequency ω in R_3, $L_1(j\omega)$ lies at point J. If we lay the $P_2(j\omega)$ template such that the nominal plant condition is located at point V, then we can find what the change in P_{2e} will be (using the contours of constant gain and phase on the Nichols chart) after we move from $P_{2\,nom}$ to the remaining plant conditions of P_2 (using the rectangular open-loop axes of the Nichols chart). We transpose the changes of P_{2e} caused by changes in P_2 to point J on which $L_1(j\omega)$ is situated, and check whether $L_1(j\omega)$ moves inside the permissible P_{2e} range. If the answer is positive for all plant conditions of P_2, then point V is a permissible location for $L_2(j\omega)$. We then lower the template and locate $P_{2\,nom}$ at points $V_1, V_2 \ldots$ until we reach point V_n at which changes in P_2 will cause changes in P_{2e} such that changes in $L_1(j\omega)$ barely satisfy the range of permissible P_{2e}. The procedure is repeated at additional open-loop phase locations of point V until a continuous boundary for permissible $P_{2e}(j\omega)$ is obtained. The procedure is repeated at several substantial frequencies in R_3. The final stage in finding bounds on L_2 follows the procedure explained in this section using Eq.(5.2.2). A family of such bounds in R_3 will be derived in the solution of Example 5.2.1 (see Fig.5.2.11).

5.2.3 The Sensor Noise Amplification Problem

In significant plant uncertainty problems, we have seen in Chapter 4 that there is a strong tendency for the design to be such that the sensor noise is so highly amplified as to saturate the plant input u. In Fig. 5.2.1, we are concerned with two noise sources, n_1 and n_2. The noise response functions for the two-loop problem are given by

$$T_{un1} \triangleq \frac{u}{n_1} = \frac{-G_1 G_2}{1 + G_2 P_2 + G_1 G_2 P_1 P_2} = \frac{-\left(\dfrac{L_1}{P_1 P_2}\right)}{1 + L_1}$$

$$\approx \frac{-L_1}{P_1 P_2}, \quad \omega >> \omega_{co} \tag{5.2.5}$$

and

$$T_{un2} \triangleq \frac{u}{n_2} = \frac{-\left(\dfrac{L_2}{P_2}\right)}{(1 + L_1)(1 + L_2)}$$

$$\approx \frac{-L_2}{P_2}, \quad \omega >> \omega_{co} \tag{5.2.6}$$

The noise component in u is most important in the high frequency range where the useful command and disturbance components due to d_i are relatively small, rather than in the low frequency range where they are relatively large. Hence, Eqs.(5.2.5) and (5.2.6) show that it is desirable to decrease $|L_1|$ and $|L_2|$ versus ω as fast as possible in the high frequency range (see also Section 2.4).

Example 5.2.1. There is a given plant with an internal measurement point, so that two cascaded plants can be defined in the following way:

$P_1 = k_1 \omega_n{}^2/[(s^2+2\xi \omega_n s + \omega_n{}^2)]$; $k_1 = 1$, ω_n and ξ defined as in Example 4.4.1, Fig.4.4.4.

$P_2 = k_2 /[(1+s/A)(1+s/B)]$; $k_2 = [1\text{–}5.250]$, $A = [1\text{–}3]$, $B = [10\text{–}20]$

We shall exemplify the solution with an excess gain margin of $\alpha = 4\text{dB}$. Finally, the same problem will be solved in a single-loop system in order to underline the superiority of a two-loop feedback structure in decreasing the sensor noise amplification.

Solution. In the first stage of the design procedure, a sub-optimal L_1 is manipulated with the assumption that, with the feedback around P_2, the uncertainties in P_{2e} are virtually eliminated. In the second stage, a practical L_2 is designed so that the achieved L_1 in the previous stage is not perturbed by uncertainties in P_2. The different design steps follow.

Step 1. Definition of plant parameters

The parameters of some defined cases of P_1 and P_2 are summarized in Table 5.1.
    Note that according to the definition of the two cascaded plants, the length of

Table 5.1: Parameters of the two cascaded plants

$P_1 = \dfrac{\omega_n^2}{s^2+2\,\xi\omega_n s + \omega_n^2}$			$P_2 = \dfrac{A\,B\,k_2}{(s+A)(s+B)}$			
Case	$2\xi\omega_n$	$\omega_n{}^2$	Case	A	B	K_2
1	10	29	1	1	10	1.0
3	4	8	2	1	10	5.25
5	0	8	3	3	20	5.25
7	−4	8	4	3	20	1.0
8	−6	13	5	1	20	1.0
10	4	40	6	3	10	5.25
11	0	36	7	1	20	5.25
14	−6	45				
15	10	125				
19	0	100				
21	−6	109				

their templates at very high frequencies become: $K_{1max} = \omega^2_{n\,max}/\omega^2_{n\,min} = 125/8$ = 24 dB, and $K_{2\,max} = (A_{max}\,B_{max}\,k_{2\,max})/(A_{min}\,B_{min}\,k_{2\,min}) = 30$ dB. These numbers are important in the problem solution to come.

The nominal cases are chosen as No.3 for P_1 and No.1 for P_2.

Step 2. Basic characteristics of $L_1(s)$ in R_1

In this step of designing L_1, it is assumed that only uncertainties in P_1 are taken into account. This is admissible if the loop around P_2 is such that uncertainties of P_{2e} are virtually eliminated. The bounds on L_1 in the low frequency range are found in the usual way, as explained in Chapter 4. These are shown in Fig.5.2.9 for the suboptimal $L_{1\,nom}$ (case 3 is the nominal plant). The achieved optimal $L_{1\,nom}$ (case 3) for the choice of $\alpha = 4$dB is shown in Fig.5.2.10. It can be seen from the figure that $L_{1\,max}$ (case 15) lies 4dB below the constant gain contour of $|T_1| = 3$dB in the Nichols chart, as required. This additional $\alpha = 4$dB gain margin allows us to design a practical inner-loop $L_2(j\omega)$ for the known uncertainties in P_2.

Step 3. Derivation of bounds on $L_2(s)$

Based on the achieved suboptimal L_1, we have to find in this step the bounds on L_2 such that despite uncertainties in P_2, the designed L_2 will not disturb the L_1 characteristics obtained in Step 2. We will next find bounds on L_2 in the three frequency regions, R_1 to R_3.

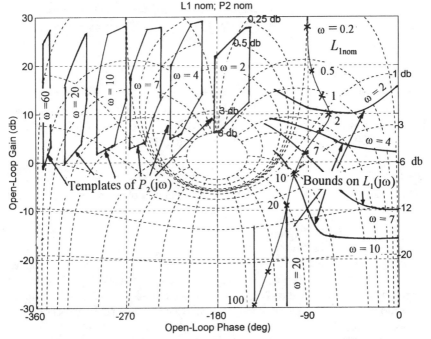

Figure 5.2.9. Bounds on $L_1(j\omega)$ and achieved $L_1(j\omega)$ at low frequencies. Templates of $P_2(j\omega)$ at $\omega = 2, 4, 7, 10, 20$ and 60 rad/sec also shown.

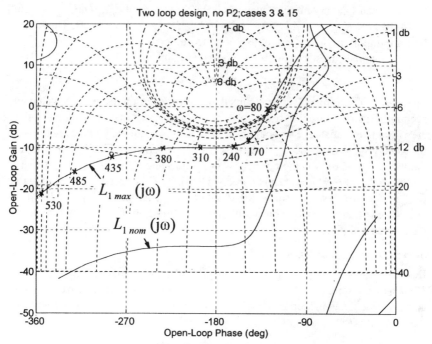

Figure 5.2.10. $L_{1\,nom}(j\omega)$ of nominal case No.3 and $L_{1\,max}(j\omega)$ of Case No.15, for which $L_1(j\omega)$ reaches its maximum gain at high frequencies; the additional *GM* is $\alpha = 4$dB.

$R_1:\ \omega > \omega_a = 80$ rad/sec.
In this range the permitted bounds on L_2 are found by using the universal bounds in Fig.5.2.6. The resulting bounds on L_2 at the high frequencies $\omega = 120, 200, 240, 280, 320, 360$, and 440 rad/sec are shown in Fig.5.2.11.

$R_2:\ 10 = \omega_h < \omega < \omega_\alpha = 80$ rad/sec.
In this region, as already explained, the entire right half plane of the Nichols chart is the permitted region of L_2.

$R_3:\ 0 < \omega < \omega_h = 10$ rad/sec
As an example, let us find the permitted bounds on L_2 at $\omega = 7$ rad/sec. L_1 is displayed in Fig. 5.2.12 at the low frequency range. The template of $P_2(j7)$ is used to derive the permitted bound on $L_2(j7)$, as explained in Section 5.2.2. This template is positioned on the Nichols chart in such a way that the nominal case lies at $L_1(j7)$. The permissible change in $|T_1|$ at that frequency is $\Delta|T_1(j7)| = 14$ dB. The extreme magnitudes of $|T_1(j7)|$ are $+3.0$ at point A, and -2 dB at point B, with an overall

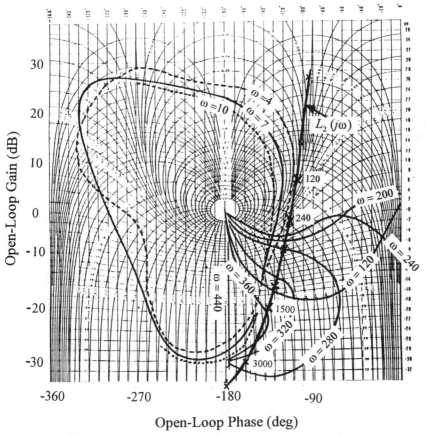

Figure 5.2.11. Boundary on L_{2nom} at different frequencies, and the obtained L_{2nom}.

change of $3.0 + 2.0 = 5.0$ dB, which is below the specified value of 14 dB. However, if we permit $|T_1(j7)|_{max} = 3.0$ dB only, then we have to relocate the nominal case of the template to point X so that $|T_1(j7)|_{max} < 3.0$ dB. The extreme magnitudes of $|T_1(j7)|$ are now such that $\Delta|T_1(j7)| = 3.5$dB only, much below the allowed 14dB. In the same manner, we find points $X_1, X_2, \ldots$ etc., where we can place the nominal case of the $P_1(j7)$ template so that $|T_1(j7)|_{max} < 3.0$ dB and the overall $\Delta|T_1(j7)| < 14$ dB, despite changes in $T_2(j7) = P_{2e}(j7)$ due to the uncertainty of P_2 at that frequency. The curve passing through $[X_1, X_2, \ldots X_n]$ is the boundary of the permitted region where $L_1(j7)$ can be moved due to uncertainties of $P_{2e}(j7)$. The template of $P_2(j7)$ is used to obtain the range of permissible $P_{2e}(j7)$, as exemplified in Fig.5.2.8. By use of Eq.(5.2.2) and the explanation in Section 5.2.2, the bound on $L_2(j7)$ is finally obtained and shown in Fig.5.2.12. Additional bounds in R_3 can be derived, for instance, at $\omega = 4$ and 10 rad/sec. These are also shown in Fig.5.2.11.

An important conclusion can be stated by interpreting the resulting bounds in R_1 and R_3, all shown in Fig.5.2.11. As is readily seen in this figure, the bound in R_1 with the lowest magnitude is at $\omega = 120$ rad/sec, while the emerging bounds in R_3 at the low frequencies have much lower magnitude levels. These are also located to the left of the $-135°$ argument axis. This means that if L_2 contains at least one integrator, then L_2 in the region R_3 will be quite distanced from the appropriated bounds and the effect of changes in P_{2e} (due to uncertainties in P_2) on L_1 will be very limited. Thus, no redesign is actually necessary in the low frequency range of L_1 to compensate for changes in P_{2e}.

Step 4. Design of $L_2(s)$

Based on the obtained bounds in $R_1 - R_3$, an $L_2(j\omega)$ was designed which is shown in Fig.5.2.11. The achieved $L_2(j\omega)$ is not perfect and does not lie on all the bounds at all frequencies. But it does satisfies them with a relatively simple control network $G_2(s)$.

Changes in L_1 at high frequencies due to changes in P_{2e} are shown in Fig.5.2.13. As is clearly perceived, when L_1 is at its maximum gain conditions and the maximum changes in P_{2e} are applied, the overall L_1 does not cross the forbidden contour of constant $|T| = 3$dB.

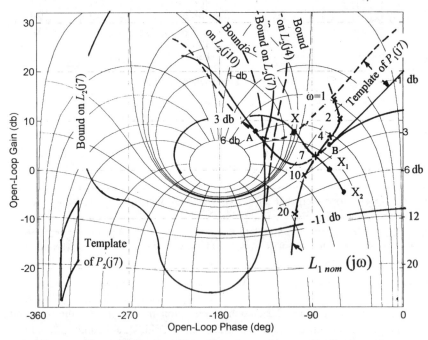

Figure 5.2.12.   Derivation of boundary on L_2 at $\omega = 7$ rad/sec

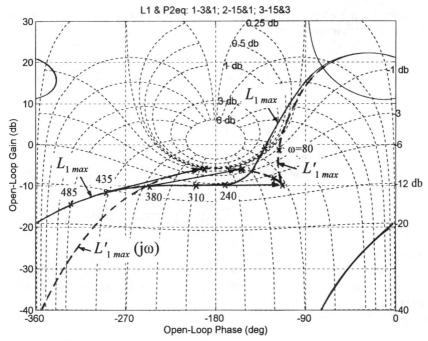

Figure 5.2.13.   Acceptable alteration of nominal L_1 due to changes in P_{2e}.

Step 5. Control networks derivation.
Due to the complexity of the problem, the resulting control networks become quite complex too. To find $G_1(s)$ we know that according to Fig.5.2.1a,

$$G_1(s) = L_{1\ nom} / (P_{1\ nom}\ P_{2e\ nom}) \tag{5.2.7}$$

Having designed L_1 for the known $P_{1\ nom}$ does not allow finding $G_1(s)$ because $P_{2e\ nom}$ is not yet known. After $L_{1\ nom}$ was found in Step 2 for a defined additional gain margin of α dB, we could design $L_{2\ nom}$ in Step 3 for the nominal $P_{2\ nom}$ case, thus obtaining $G_2(s)$:

$$G_2(s) = L_{2\ nom} / P_{2\ nom} \tag{5.2.8}$$

Next, we find $P_{2e\ nom}$ from the single-loop relation

$$P_{2\ e\ nom} = L_{2\ nom} / (1 + L_{2\ nom}). \tag{5.2.9}$$

Incorporating $P_{2e\ nom}$ in Eq.(5.2.7) allows us to find $G_1(s)$.

Since Case 3 was chosen nominal for $P_{1\ nom}$ and Case 1 for $P_{2\ nom}$, we obtain the following control networks:

$$G_1(s) = \frac{5}{8s} \frac{s^2 + 4s + 8}{0.001s + 1} \frac{1.05s + 1}{1.954s + 1} \frac{1.087s + 1}{0.19s + 1} \frac{0.0576s + 1}{0.164s + 1} \frac{0.0384s + 1}{0.0265s + 1} \times$$

$$\frac{0.0074s + 1}{0.02s + 1} \frac{s/970 + 1}{s/9700 + 1} \frac{0.00045s + 1}{s^2/450^2 + 0.65s/450 + 1} \times$$

$$\frac{1}{s^2/450^2 + 0.65s/450 + 1} \frac{s^2/270^2 + 2*0.57s/270 + 1}{s^2/(500 \times 1300) + (1/500 + 1/1300)s + 1}$$

$$G_2(s) = \frac{350}{s} \frac{0.1s^2 + 1.1s + 1}{s/200 + 1} \frac{s/500 + 1}{s/1000 + 1} \frac{s/1300 + 1}{s^2/4500^2 + 1.6s/4500 + 1}$$

Step 6. Design of F(s).
Design of the prefilter $F(s)$, the third degree of freedom, is accomplished in the usual way (see Section 4.3.6 and specially Example 4.4.1). The designed prefilter emerges as:

$$F(s) = \frac{1.06s + 1}{0.67s + 1} \frac{0.417s + 1}{0.667s + 1} \frac{1}{s^2/9 + 1.4s/3 + 1}$$

Step 7. Minimization of the noise amplification by choosing the optimizing α.
In order to find out the optimizing parameter α, we have to repeat steps 1 to 6 with different α's, until the minimum U_n is achieved in Eq.(5.2.1) for the known Φ_{n1} and Φ_{n2}. This step was not carried out here in order to save space. The reader is referred to Horowitz and Sidi (1973) and Horowitz (1992) for further results in optimizing α.

Step 8. Solution with single-loop configuration.
This stage is performed in order to compare the two-loop and the single-loop solutions of the same uncertain feedback problem. The resulting single-loop L is shown in Fig.5.2.17. Since, with a single-loop design, L has to take care of the full range of uncertainty in P_2, L_{nom} in this figure is lower than $L_{1\ nom}$ in Fig.5.2.10, (pertaining to the two-loop design), by the full range of changes in P_2, amounting to 30dB, (less $\alpha = 4$dB). This increases significantly the bandwidth of L_{nom}, and consequently, the sensor noise amplification also. In Figs. 5.2.15 and 5.2.16 are also shown the single-loop sensor noise amplification transfer functions $|T_{un}|$.

Step 9. Evaluation of the design.
With the obtained control networks $G_1(s)$, $G_2(s)$, and $F(s)$, we can evaluate the designed two-loop uncertain feedback system.

1.-Satisfaction of the step time response specifications.

Step time responses for the plant case conditions of Table 5.1 are shown in Fig.5.2.14. These have to be compared with step time responses that pertain to the solution of the same problem with a single-loop feedback system. These are shown in Fig.5.2.18. The resulting time responses for both single-loop and two-loop control solutions are very similar.

2.-Sensor noise amplification.

The two-loop design was performed in order to decrease the sensor noise amplification. The resulting $|T_{un1}|$ and $|T_{un2}|$ are shown in Fig.5.2.15 for plant cases No.3 (P_1) and No.1 (P_2), and in Fig.5.2.16 for plant cases No.15 (P_1) and No.3 (P_2). These are to be compared with the sensor noise amplification resulting in a single-loop feedback system that solves the same feedback control problem (see Step 8). The resulting $|T_{un}|$ obtained with the single-loop solution for the same plant cases are superimposed in Figs.(5.2.15) and (5.2.16). $|T_{un}|$ is roughly elevated by more than 100dB relative to $|T_{un1}|$ and $|T_{un2}|$. It is found that in RMS values, $|T_{un}|/|T_{un1}| > 2800$ for both plant conditions.

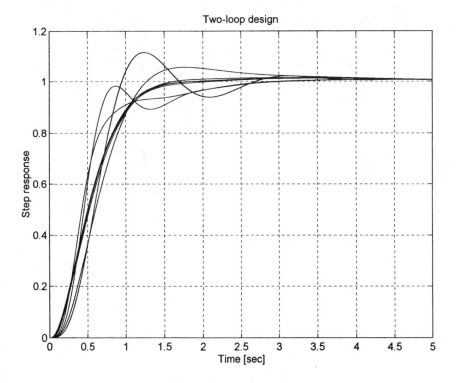

Figure 5.2.14. Step time responses for the two-loop feedback system design.

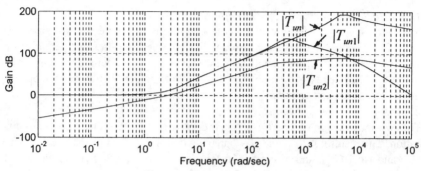

Figure 5.2.15. $|T_{un1}|$, $|T_{un2}|$ and $|T_{un}|$ for cases No.3 (P_1) and No.1 (P_2)

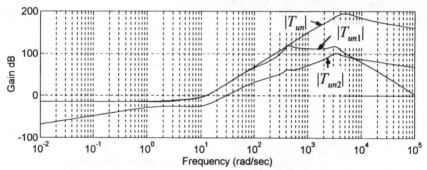

Figure 5.2.16. $|T_{un1}|$, $|T_{un2}|$ and $|T_{un}|$ for cases No.15 (P_1) and No.3 (P_2)

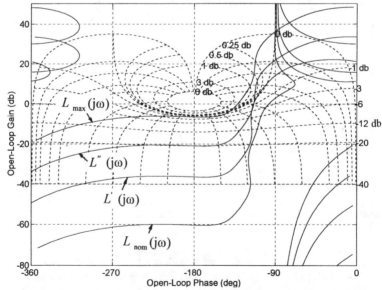

Figure 5.2.17. L_1 for single-loop design at extreme plant conditions of P_1 and P_2.

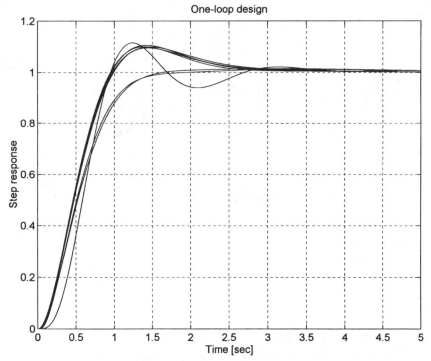

Figure 5.2.18.   Step time responses for the single-loop design
and different plant conditions of P_1 and P_2.

The final conclusion is that there is a real advantage in using the two-loop configuration, should a second sensing point be available for measuring.

5.3.   Extension to Three Loops

The synthesis philosophy that has been presented can be obviously extended step-
by-step to a larger number of cascaded loops in order to obtain general contours
and optimum L_i transmission functions in the high frequency range. If three cascaded sensing points in the plant are available, as in Fig. 5.3.1, then the design of
the outermost loop L_1 with its α parameter, is followed by the design of L_2.
This was previously done, but in this case P_2 (of the previous section) becomes
$P_2 P_{3e}$ of Fig.5.3.1. It is assumed that $\Delta \log P_{3e} = 0$. After L_2 has been so determined, one finds what range of $\Delta \log P_{3e}$ is actually tolerable, and also what are the
bound on L_3 such that P_{3e} lies within this tolerable range. We can find the permitted bounds on L_3 in the same way we found the boundary on L_2 using the techniques in Section 5.2.2.

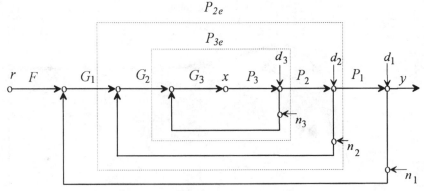

Figure 5.3.1.   Canonical 3-loop cascaded feedback system.

Comparative results for a 3-loop design can be found in Horowitz and Sidi (1973), Horowitz and Wang (1979), Horowitz and Loecher (1981).

5.4   Summary

It was demonstrated in this chapter that existence of additional sensing points to the principal output sensing point in a cascaded plant allows us to decrease the sensors noise amplification at the input to the plant, without practically disturbing the input-output tracking performances attainable with a single-output uncertain feedback system. Optimization and standardization of single-loop design of systems with large parameter uncertainties enables standardization of cascaded multiple-loop design of such systems.

Chapter 6 _____

MIMO Robust Feedback Systems Solved with Nyquist/Bode-based Design Techniques

6.1 Introduction

Most SISO design techniques are basically well-defined and lead to systematic control solutions despite physical constraints caused by unstable and nonmini-mum-phase plants. Knowledge of the unfriendly plant characteristics, helps the designer to foresee potential difficulties when designing a control system, and to estimate the limits of achievable control specifications.

The situation is much more difficult and undefined with MIMO feedback control systems. This is the reason for the existence of a vast body of literature about design approaches for solving even the basic MIMO feedback problem with no uncertainties in the plant. A very limited list of works dealing with the MIMO problem with no plant uncertainty, also solved in the Nyquist/Bode oriented frequency-domain framework, include:Rosenbrock (1970), MacFarlane and Belletrutti (1973), Mac-Farlane and Postlethwaite (1977), MacFarlane and Kouvaritakis (1977), Rosenbrock and Munro (1978), MacFarlane et al.(1978), Kouvaritakis (1979), MacFarlane (1977), Owens (1981), Maciejowski (1989), Skogestad and Postlethwaite (1996).

Before dealing with the MIMO uncertain plant problem, it is instructive to give a short introduction to MIMO feedback systems designed in the frequency-domain framework in which the plant has no discernible uncertainties. This subject is treated in Section 6.2, where the generalized Nyquist stability criterion dealing with stability of MIMO feedback systems is presented with the task of introducing briefly the Characteristic Locus Design Method. Basic design methods such as 'direct diagonalization' of the open-loop transfer matrix, 'noninterection by inversion' of the plant transfer matrix, 'sequential loop closing', etc., are also treated and illustrated with solved examples. Internal stability and **Q**-parametrization for MIMO systems are introduced for future use. The above mentioned design techniques are not sufficiently adequate to solve the 'MIMO uncertain plant feedback system problem'.

The basic design technique explained in Section 6.3 for solving the MIMO highly uncertain feedback problem was invented by Horowitz (1979b). It extensively uses the QFT design techniques for SISO uncertain plants feedback systems which were presented in Chapter 4. Since the first publication of this design technique, numerous papers on the subject have been published, including Horowitz and Sidi (1980), Horowitz and Breiner (1981), Horowitz and Loecher (1981), Horowitz (1982), Yaniv and Horowitz (1986), Horowitz (1992), Yaniv (1991, 1995), and many others.

6.1.1. Introductory Definitions for MIMO Feedback Systems.

The standard MIMO TDOF feedback structure is shown in Fig.6.1.1.

When the MIMO feedback system is treated, we are interested in the same transfer functions as defined for SISO systems. However, in MIMO systems, the open-loop transfer matrix $\mathbf{L}(s)$ is defined differently, according to the location where the loop is opened. For instance, if the loop is opened at the plant output, then

$$\mathbf{L}_o(s) = \mathbf{P}(s)\mathbf{G}(s). \tag{6.1.1}$$

But if the loop is opened at the plant input, we have

$$\mathbf{L}_i(s) = \mathbf{G}(s)\mathbf{P}(s). \tag{6.1.2}$$

Accordingly, we define *output sensitivity* $\mathbf{S}_o(s)$ and *input sensitivity* $\mathbf{S}_i(s)$ transfer function matrices. The important transfer functions in Eqs.(2.1.1) to (2.1.7) for SISO feedback systems are expressed for MIMO feedback systems by the following matrix equations:

$$\mathbf{y}(s) = (\mathbf{I}+\mathbf{PG})^{-1}\mathbf{PG}\,\mathbf{r_1}(s) = (\mathbf{I}+\mathbf{L}_o)^{-1}\,\mathbf{L}_o\,\mathbf{r_1}(s); \qquad \mathbf{T_1}(s) \stackrel{def}{=} (\mathbf{I}+\mathbf{PG})^{-1}\mathbf{PG} \tag{6.1.3}$$

$$\mathbf{y}(s) = (\mathbf{I}+\mathbf{PG})^{-1}\mathbf{PGF}\,\mathbf{r}(s) = (\mathbf{I}+\mathbf{L}_o)^{-1}\,\mathbf{L}_o\mathbf{F}\,\mathbf{r}(s); \qquad \mathbf{T}(s) \stackrel{def}{=} (\mathbf{I}+\mathbf{PG})^{-1}\mathbf{PGF} \tag{6.1.4}$$

$$\mathbf{y}(s) = (\mathbf{I}+\mathbf{PG})^{-1}\mathbf{d}(s) = (\mathbf{I}+\mathbf{L}_o)^{-1}\,\mathbf{d}(s); \qquad\qquad \mathbf{S}_o(s) \stackrel{def}{=} (\mathbf{I}+\mathbf{PG})^{-1} \tag{6.1.5}$$

$$\mathbf{u}(s) = (\mathbf{I}+\mathbf{GP})^{-1}\mathbf{d_1}(s) = (\mathbf{I}+\mathbf{L}_i)^{-1}\,\mathbf{d_1}(s); \qquad\qquad \mathbf{S}_i(s) \stackrel{def}{=} (\mathbf{I}+\mathbf{GP})^{-1} \tag{6.1.6}$$

$$\mathbf{u}(s) = -\ (\mathbf{I}+\mathbf{GP})^{-1}\mathbf{G}\ \mathbf{n}(s) = -\ (\mathbf{I}+\mathbf{L}_i)^{-1}\mathbf{G}\ \mathbf{n}(s); \quad \mathbf{T}_{un}(s) \overset{def}{=} -(\mathbf{I}+\mathbf{GP})^{-1}\mathbf{G}(s)$$
$$(6.1.7)$$

$$\mathbf{u}(s) = -\ (\mathbf{I}+\mathbf{GP})^{-1}\mathbf{G}\ \mathbf{d}(s) = -\ (\mathbf{I}+\mathbf{L}_i)^{-1}\mathbf{G}\ \mathbf{d}(s); \quad \mathbf{T}_{ud}(s) \overset{def}{=} -(\mathbf{I}+\mathbf{GP})^{-1}\mathbf{G}(s)$$
$$(6.1.8)$$

$$\mathbf{u}_1(s) = -\ (\mathbf{I}+\mathbf{GP})^{-1}\mathbf{GPd}_1(s) = -(\mathbf{I}+\mathbf{L}_i)^{-1}\mathbf{L}_i\ \mathbf{d}_1(s); \quad \mathbf{T}_i(s) \overset{def}{=} (\mathbf{I}+\mathbf{GP})^{-1}\ \mathbf{GP}$$
$$(6.1.9)$$

By combining Eqs.(6.1.3) and (6.1.5), or Eqs.(6.1.6) and (6.1.9) we readily find that

$$\mathbf{T}_1(s) + \mathbf{S}_o(s) = \mathbf{I}; \ \mathbf{T}_i(s) + \mathbf{S}_i(s) = \mathbf{I}. \qquad (6.1.10)$$

Note that the output vectors $\mathbf{y}(s)$ in eqs.(6.1.3) to (6.1.5) result for different applied input vectors, namely, $\mathbf{r}_1(s)$, $\mathbf{r}(s)$ and $\mathbf{d}(s)$ respectively. The vectors $\mathbf{u(s)}$ in Eqs.(6.1.6) to (6.1.8) result for the applied input vectors $\mathbf{d}(s)$, $\mathbf{d}_1(s)$ and $\mathbf{n}(s)$ respectively. The meaning of $\mathbf{y}(s)$ and $\mathbf{u(s)}$ in these equations is, hence, related to the activating input vector.

6.2. Design of MIMO Feedback Systems with Certain Plants

6.2.1. Complexity of the $n \times n$ Feedback System Problem

Solution of the MIMO feedback problem is inherently difficult because of the existence of n^2 scalar loop transmission elements in $\mathbf{L}_0 = \mathbf{PG}$. There are also n^2 uncertain plant elements $p_{ij}(s)$ in $\mathbf{P}$. Moreover, there is no simple and direct relation between the elements $l_{ij}(s)$ of $\mathbf{L}_0$ and the elements $t_{ij}(s)$ of the input-output transfer matrix $\mathbf{T}(s)$. To illustrate this difficulty, in a 2×2 feedback system with a simplified diagonal control matrix $\mathbf{G}(s) = diag(g_{11}, g_{22})$, we find that the element t_{11} of $\mathbf{T}(s)$ in Eq.(6.1.4) is:

$$t_{11} = \frac{p_{11}g_{11}f_{11} + p_{12}g_{22}f_{21} + g_{11}g_{22}f_{11}(p_{11}p_{22} - p_{12}p_{21})}{1 + p_{11}g_{11} + p_{22}g_{22} + g_{11}g_{22}(p_{11}p_{22} - p_{12}p_{21})}$$

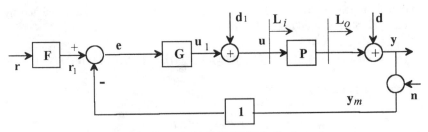

Figure 6.1.1.   Canonical MIMO TDOF feedback structure.

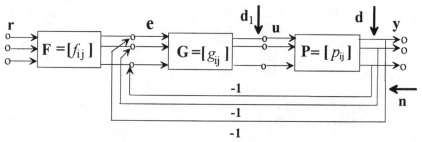

Figure 6.2.1.   A MIMO two-degree-of-freedom matrix structure.

There are three more transfer functions of similar complexity for the remaining input-output elements t_{22}, t_{21} and t_{12}. Evidently, it is difficult to design the elements of $\mathbf{G}(s)$ and of $\mathbf{F}(s)$ so that a specified input-output transfer function matrix $\mathbf{T}(s)$ is achieved.

The design of the MIMO control problem is greatly simplified if a basically non-interacting feedback system is of interest. This is usually the case. *Noninteraction* means simply that the design assures noninteraction between the different main channels of the controlled system. In other words, it is desired that the input-output transfer function matrix $\mathbf{T}(s)$ be diagonal. With this assumption, the $n \times n$ MIMO feedback system design can be reduced to n SISO feedback system designs.

Even with this simplifying assumption, the design procedures are not straight-forward due to different physical and mathematical complications. An existing design technique may be applicable to a class of problems, but not adequate for solving a problem of a different nature. The purpose of this section is to introduce some design techniques, to illustrate their use by design examples and to provide the reader with a choice of design techniques which are the most appropriate for his specific problem.

Note. It is convenient, when dealing with MIMO TDOF feedback systems, to use the subscript '$_{uf}$' which stands for the *'unity-feedback'* closed-loop transfer function, for instance $t_{uf\,ij}(s)$.

6.2.2.   *Design by Direct Diagonalization of the Open-Loop Transfer Function Matrix.*

In this approach, the open-loop transfer function matrix $\mathbf{L}(s)$ is diagonalized by zeroing the off-diagonal terms. From Eq.(6.1.4)

$$\mathbf{T}(s) = [\mathbf{I} + \mathbf{P}(s)\mathbf{G}(s)]^{-1}\mathbf{P}(s)\mathbf{G}(s)\mathbf{F}(s) = [\mathbf{I} + \mathbf{L}(s)]^{-1}\mathbf{L}(s)\mathbf{F}(s). \qquad (6.2.1)$$

We have to diagonalize

$$\mathbf{L}_o(s) = \mathbf{PG} = \begin{bmatrix} p_{11}g_{11} + p_{12}g_{21} & p_{11}p_{12} + p_{12}g_{22} \\ p_{21}g_{11} + p_{22}g_{21} & p_{21}g_{12} + p_{22}g_{22} \end{bmatrix} \qquad (6.2.2)$$

This can be achieved by putting

$$g_{12} = -g_{22}p_{12}/p_{11}; \quad g_{21} = -g_{11}p_{21}/p_{22} \tag{6.2.3}$$

Eq.(6.2.2) then becomes

$$\mathbf{L}_o(s) =$$

$$\begin{bmatrix} (p_{11} - p_{12}p_{21}/p_{22})g_{11} & 0 \\ 0 & (p_{22} - p_{12}p_{21}/p_{22})g_{22} \end{bmatrix} = \begin{bmatrix} g_{11}\Delta p/p_{22} & 0 \\ 0 & g_{22}\Delta p/p_{11} \end{bmatrix} \tag{6.2.4}$$

where

$$\Delta p = p_{11}p_{22} - p_{12}p_{21} \tag{6.2.5}$$

The plant transfer function matrix is transformed to a new diagonal one with equivalent entries

$$p_{11eq} = \Delta p / p_{22}; \ p_{22eq} = \Delta p / p_{11}; \ p_{12eq} = p_{21eq} = 0. \tag{6.2.6}$$

Now we are faced with two SISO feedback systems which can be solved individually by designing adequate control networks $g_{11}(s)$ and $g_{22}(s)$. A numerical example follows.

Example 6.2.1.
The transfer function matrix of a 2×2 plant is:

$$\mathbf{P}(s) = \frac{1}{(s+1)(s+5)} \begin{bmatrix} s+2 & -s \\ s+5 & 2 \end{bmatrix}.$$

Hence, the elements of the plant matrix are:

$$p_{11} = (s+2)/D(s); \ p_{12} = -s/D(s);$$
$$p_{21} = (s+5)/D(s); \ p_{22} = 2/D(s); \ D(s) = (s+1)(s+3)$$

Design an input-output noninteracting feedback system with the following specifications:
1- Velocity error coefficients of the two derived SISO systems are $K_{v1} = 10$; $K_{v2} = 20$.
2- Crossover frequencies $\omega_{co1} = 2\text{rad/sec}$; $\omega_{co2} = 5\text{rad/sec}$.
3- $PM \geq 40°$ in both channels.
4- Specified bandwidths of the input-output closed-loop transfer functions are:
$\omega_{-3dB1} = 2\text{rad/sec}$; $\omega_{-3dB2} = 5\text{rad/sec}$ respectively.
5- Maximum overshoots in $|t_{11}(j\omega)|$ and $|t_{22}(j\omega)|$ are to be less than 3dB.

Solution.

Stage 1: Derive the conditions for noninteraction.
By use of Eq.(6.2.3) we find:

$$g_{12} = -g_{22}[-s/(s + 2)] = g_{22} \, s/(s + 2); \, g_{21} = -g_{11}(s + 5)/2.$$

Stage 2: find the equivalent plants p_{11eq} and p_{22eq}.
By use of Eqs.(6.2.5) and (6.2.6) we find:

$$\Delta p = (s^2 + 7s + 4)/D^2(s); \, p_{11eq} = (s^2 + 7s + 4)/2D(s);$$
$$p_{22eq} = (s^2 + 7s + 4)/(s + 2)D(s)$$

Stage 3: Design of $l_{11eq} = p_{11eq} \, g_{11}$ and $l_{22\,eq} = p_{22eq} \, g_{22}$.
Loopshaping of the loop transmission functions follows the procedures explained in Chapter 2, (Example 2.3.3), using the Bode plots and the Nichols chart. First, an integrator is incorporated in $g_{11}(s)$ and $g_{22}(s)$ with appropriate gains in order to achieve the specified velocity error coefficients. (See Appendix G). The obtained

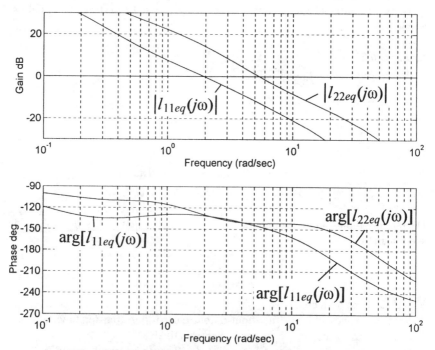

Figure 6.2.2.   Bode plots of $l_{11}(j\omega)$ and $l_{22}(j\omega)$; $l_{12}(j\omega) = l_{21}(j\omega) = 0$.

$l_{11eq} = l_{11}$ and $l_{22eq} = l_{22}$ are shown in Fig.6.2.2. All specified specifications on the loop transmission functions are exactly achieved.

Stage 4: Control networks $g_{11}(s)$ and $g_{22}(s)$.
The loop transmission functions l_{11eq} and l_{22eq} are achieved first by showing p_{11eq} and p_{22eq} on the Bode diagram, and next by manipulating their Bode plots with the control networks $g_{11}(s)$ and $g_{22}(s)$. The obtained compensators that achieve the open-loop design specifications are:

$$g_{11}(s) = \frac{800}{s} \frac{(s+1)}{(s+0.1333)(s+20)^2}; \; g_{22}(s) = \frac{7500}{s} \frac{(s+0.5)(s+4.545)}{(s+0.25)(s+45.45)(s+50)}.$$

Stage 5: Closed-loop specifications and the prefilter matrix $F(s)$.
We shall use in this solution a diagonal matrix $F(s)$. Knowledge of $l_{11}(s)$ and $l_{22}(s)$ allows us to calculate the unity-feedback transfer functions $t_{uf11}(s)$ and $t_{uf22}(s)$. Their Bode plots are manipulated by the prefilters $f_{11}(s)$ and $f_{22}(s)$ until the closed-loop specified performances on $|t_{11}(j\omega)|$ and $|t_{22}(j\omega)|$ are satisfied. The elements of the designed diagonal matrix $F(s)$ are: $f_{11}(s) = 1.5/(s+1.5)$, $f_{22}(s) = 2.8/(s+2.8)$ and $f_{12}(s) = f_{21}(s) = 0$. The resulting $|t_{11}(j\omega)| = |t_{uf11}(j\omega)f_{11}(j\omega)|$ and $|t_{22}(j\omega)| = |t_{uf22}(j\omega)f_{22}(j\omega)|$ are plotted in Fig.6.2.3. It can be seen that the closed-loop transfer function specifications are fulfilled.

The unity-step time responses of the outputs and of the output errors are shown in Fig.6.2.4 below.

In the case of Example 6.2.1, no design difficulties are met since p_{11eq} and p_{22eq} are minimum-phase and stable. With this kind of plant, all desired specifications can be achieved, as we have seen in Chapters 2 and 3. However, this pleasant situation does not always exist. In some cases, p_{11eq} and/or p_{22eq} may become nonminimum-phase transfer functions, with the inevitable consequence of creating design limitations, (treated in Chapters 3 and 4). For instance, if in Example 6.2.1 $p_{12}(s)$ changes sign, then $p_{11eq}(s)$ becomes NMP, namely, $p_{11eq}(s) = -(s-1)(s+4)/D^2(s)$. Also, if $p_{22}(s)$ is NMP, then $p_{11eq}(s)$ becomes unstable.

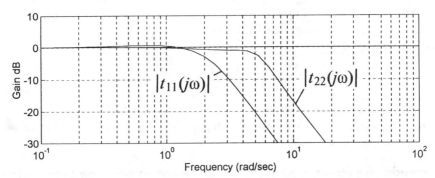

Figure 6.2.3. Closed-loop magnitudes $|t_{11}(j\omega)| = |t_{uf11}(j\omega)f_{11}(j\omega)|$, and $|t_{22}(j\omega)| = |t_{uf22}(j\omega)f_{22}(j\omega)|$.

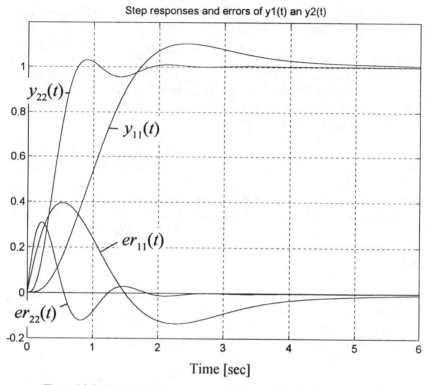

Figure 6.2.4.   Unity-step time responses of outputs $y_{ii}(t)$ and output errors $er_{ii}(t)$

6.2.3.   *Noninteraction by Inverse-Based Controller*

An additional design technique for noninteracting MIMO feedback systems is based on first preceding the plant by a control matrix that renders the matrix $\mathbf{P}(s)\mathbf{G}_1(s)$ to be diagonal, (Ovens 1981), namely, $\mathbf{P}(s)\mathbf{G}_1(s) = \mathbf{P}_{eq}(s) = \mathbf{Q}_{diag}(s)$ with diagonal elements $q_{ii}(s)$ whose characteristics are to be fixed according to the nature of the elements of $\mathbf{P}(s)$. To find the controller transfer function matrix $\mathbf{G}_1(s)$ we have to invert the plant transfer function matrix:

$$\mathbf{G}_1(s) = \mathbf{P}(s)^{-1}\,\mathbf{Q}_{diag}(s) \qquad\qquad (6.2.7)$$

The desired loop transmission functions $l_{11}(s)$ are then achieved by inserting a second diagonal control transfer function matrix $\mathbf{G}_2(s)$. The feedback structure is shown in Fig.6.2.5.

Since the elements of $\mathbf{P}(s)$ are generally proper or strictly proper, the elements of the inverted matrix $\mathbf{P}^{-1}(s)$ may not be strictly proper, neither proper. Therefore, the ele-

Equivalent plant matrix

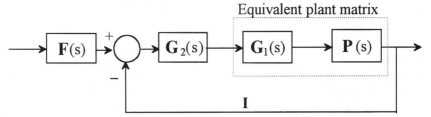

Figure 6.2.5. Noninteracting structure obtained by inversion of the plant transfer matrix.

ments of $\mathbf{Q}(s)$ must be fixed such that the elements of the control matrix $\mathbf{G}_1(s)$ will be at least proper, in order to make it possible to realize them. It is assumed here that each one of the elements of $\mathbf{G}_1(s)$ are realized separately. Using this procedure, the generally nondiagonal plant matrix $\mathbf{P}(s)$ is first substituted with a diagonal equivalent plant matrix $\mathbf{Q}(s)$, which makes it much easier for design purposes. Later, the noninteracting design specifications are achieved with the second diagonal control matrix $\mathbf{G}_2(s)$, as in Example 6.2.1. The following example clarifies this design procedure.

Example 6.2.2. The constrained plant and specifications are identical to those in Example 6.2.1.

Solution.

Express the elements of $\mathbf{G}_1(s)$ with the elements of $\mathbf{Q}(s)$, namely, with $q_{11}(s)$ and $q_{22}(s)$ which are still unfixed. We find that the elements $p'_{ij}(s)$ of the inverted transfer matrix $\mathbf{P}^{-1}(s)$ are

$$p'_{11}(s) = 2\, b(s);\ p'_{21}(s) = -(s+5)b(s);\ p'_{12}(s) = sb(s);\ p'_{22}(s) = (s+2)b(s);$$
$$b(s) = (s+1)(s+3)/(s^2+7s+4)$$

As expected, all the elements of $\mathbf{P}^{-1}(s)$, except $p'_{11}(s)$, are improper. The control matrix $\mathbf{G}_1(s)$ becomes

$$\mathbf{G}_1(s) = \frac{(s+1)(s+3)}{s^2+7s+4} \begin{bmatrix} 2q_{11}(s) & sq_{22}(s) \\ -(s+5)q_{11}(s) & (s+2)q_{22}(s) \end{bmatrix}$$

To make the elements of $\mathbf{G}_1(s)$ of least realizable order, $q_{11}(s)$ and $q_{22}(s)$ can be chosen as first order poles whose locations in the s-plane are of no importance. It seems logical, however, to put them close to the specified crossover frequencies at $\omega_{co} = 2$ and 5 rad/sec. Hence, we choose

$$q_{11}(s) = q_{22}(s) = 1/(s+5)$$

and the equivalent diagonal plant matrix becomes

$$Q(s) = \mathbf{P}_{eq} = \frac{1}{s + 5} \begin{bmatrix} 1 & 0 \\ 0 & 1 \end{bmatrix}$$

This plant is diagonal, and can be stabilized by a diagonal control matrix $\mathbf{G}_2(s)$ comprising two elements $g_{211}(s)$ and $g_{222}(s)$, so that the open and the closed-loop specifications of the two SISO loops are achieved. With this choice of $\mathbf{P}_{eq}$, the control transfer matrix $\mathbf{G}_1(s)$ becomes:

$$\mathbf{G}_1(s) = \frac{(s + 1)(s + 3)}{(s^2 + 7s + 4)(s + 5)} \begin{bmatrix} 2 & s \\ -(s + 5) & (s + 2) \end{bmatrix}$$

The design details are omitted, but they are similar to those in Example 6.2.1. The resulting control networks $g_{211}(s)$ and $g_{222}(s)$ of the diagonal control matrix $\mathbf{G}_2(s)$ are

$$g_{211} = \frac{300}{s} \frac{(s + 1)}{(s + 0.2)(s + 30)}; g_{222} = \frac{3000}{s} \frac{(s + 2)(s + 5.555)}{(s + 0.625)(s + 16.6)(s + 40)}$$

The achieved open and closed-loop performances are virtually identical to those in Example 6.2.1 (see Figs.6.2.2, 6.2.3 and 6.2.4). Examples 6.2.1 and 6.2.2 ended up with similar results, but are solved in quite different ways.

A note about the complexity of the control networks achieved in the solution of the two examples is in order. There is a tendency to claim that it is very important to realize simple control transfer functions in order to eliminate the complexity of dynamic electronic networks. And there are algorithms that have been developed to diagonalize the MIMO system with constant gain matrices (See, for instance, Rosenbrock 1969, Owens 1981). In the author's opinion, with today's advanced microprocessor technology, there is no difficulty in realizing complex control networks. It does not seem reasonable to sacrifice performance in order to save on the complexity of the needed control networks. This belief is central to all the problems and examples in the book.

6.2.4. Sequential Loop Closing Design Technique

This is one of the simplest approaches for MIMO system design. It consists in solving separated SISO feedback loops one at a time (Maciejowski 1989). No perfect noninteraction is achieved because no provision is made initially for satisfying such a requirement. A byproduct partial noninteraction is achieved by ensuring high gains to the individual SISO feedback loops.

Figure 6.2.6 is a structure for the regular sequential loop-closing procedure. With this approach, the precompensating control matrix $\mathbf{G}_1(s)$ does not exist. It is set as a unity diagonal matrix. With this design technique, stability of the overall system is preserved in a natural way. Suppose that the first loop is closed with all over loops left open. This first loop is naturally designed as stable. When a second

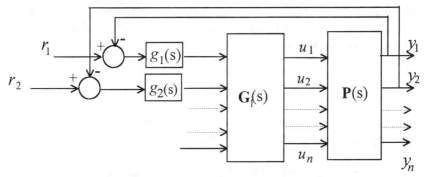

Figure 6.2.6. A structure for sequential loop closing

loop is closed, the dynamics of the first closed-loop are taken into consideration. This results in the second loop preserving the stability of the system with the first two closed loops. Thus, sequentially closing stable loops preserves the global stability of the MIMO system. If, according to the specifications of the design problem, one of the loops is to have a larger bandwidth than the remaining loops, it is to be designed first. In this case, it will have a reduced effect on the other loops to be closed sequentially. In principle, with this design approach, the interaction between the different channels will be weaker in the low frequency range, where high gains are required. Above the crossover frequencies, the interaction will be more pronounced. The practical implication is that cross channel transients are to be anticipated in the time-domain. It is understood that after closing channel i, the open-loop transfer function of the $(i-1)$th channel is deteriorated to some extent. Only the last, the nth open-loop transmission function remains intact. It is suggested that a second design iteration be performed. This means that the first designed loop is opened and improved, then closed again. Next, the second loop is opened and ameliorated, and so on, until the last loop is finally improved too. There is no proof that the design iterations converge, but, intuitively, this approach may work. In order to appreciate the simplicity of the sequential loop-closing design technique, the problem presented in Example 6.2.1 is solved next in Example 6.2.3 with this design technique.

Example 6.2.3. The constrained plant and specifications are identical to those in Example 6.2.1.

Solution:

Stage 1. First loop-closing: design of $l_{20}(s)$.
We begin with the design of the fastest loop for which the specified crossover frequency is $\omega_{co} = 5$ rad/sec. In order to satisfy the K_v specification, an integrator

with a gain of 30 is first provided. Notice that the plant of this loop is $p_{22}(s)$. In order to satisfy all the specifications of this loop transmission function, the control network $g_2(s)$ is found to be

$$g_2(s) = \frac{174 \times 10^3}{s} \frac{(s+3.57)^2}{(s+38.46)^2(s+50)}.$$

The achieved loop transmission $l_{2o}(j\omega)$ is shown in Fig. 6.2.7. The 'o' in the subscript helps to remember that the 1st loop $l_1(s)$ is open.

Stage 2. Second loop-closing: design of $l_1(s)$, with $l_{2o}(s)$ closed.
The plant in this loop is not the nominal $p_{11}(s)$. By closing the second loop $l_{2o}(s)$, an equivalent plant is obtained instead. To achieve all the open-loop specifications of $l_1(s)$, the following control network was obtained

$$g_1(s) = \frac{100}{s} \frac{(s+1)}{(s+0.125)(s+50)}.$$

Bode plots of the loop transmission $l_1(s)$ are also shown in Fig.6.2.7. All open-loop specifications are completely achieved.

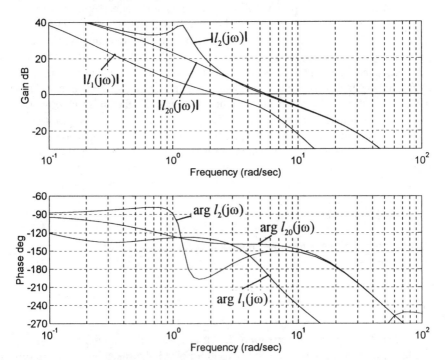

Figure 6.2.7. Bode plots of $l_1(j\omega)$, $l_2(j\omega)$ and $l_{2o}(j\omega)$.

Stage 3. Check the achieved design.
Due to closing of the first loop $l_1(s)$, $l_{20}(s)$ is altered to $l_2(s)$, which is also shown in Fig.6.2.7. We notice that $l_2(s)$ has the same crossover frequency of $l_{20}(s)$, namely, $\omega_{co} = 5$rad/sec as specified, but its phase margin is reduced to 30°. Worst than this, the bode plots of $l_2(j\omega)$ show that this loop is now conditionally stable. (A second design iteration can help to recover, at least partially, the initially achieved characteristics of $l_{20}(s)$ in Stage 1. Nonetheless, the design in this example will be accomplished without an additional iteration).

Stage 4. Design of prefilters $f_{11}(s)$ and $f_{22}(s)$.
The prefilters $f_{11}(s)$ and $f_{22}(s)$ are designed in order to achieve the closed-loop specifications, and these are:

$$f_{11}(s) = 1.5/(s+1.5); f_{22}(s) = 2.5/(s+2.5); f_{12}(s) = f_{21}(s) = 0$$

Both prefilters are very similar to those obtained in the solution of the previous examples 6.2.1 and 6.2.2. The obtained closed-loop $|t_{ij}(j\omega)|$'s are shown in Fig.6.2.8.

The unit-step time responses of all $t_{ij}(s)$, $i, j = 1, 2$, are shown in Fig.6.2.9. The direct channel responses $y_{11}(t)$ and $y_{22}(t)$ are very similar (but not identical) to those achieved with the noninteracting techniques presented in Examples 6.2.1 and 6.2.2, Fig.6.2.4. However, $y_{12}(t)$ and $y_{21}(t)$ are not zero (see Fig.6.2.9). $y_{12}(t)$ has a quite pronounced transient at the beginning of the step response, while $y_{21}(t)$ is very small. This is the price to be paid for not designing intentionally for noninteraction. This drawback can be overcome by using a more elaborated nondiagonal transfer matrix $\mathbf{F}(s)$.

The sequential loop closing technique treated in this subsection was ameliorated by Mayne (1973, 1979), and is called sequential return-difference method. It first uses a precompensator matrix $\mathbf{G}_1(s)$ as in Fig.6.2.6, whose primary purpose is to take care of difficulties due to the plant nature. Next, the original method of sequential loop closing is applied.

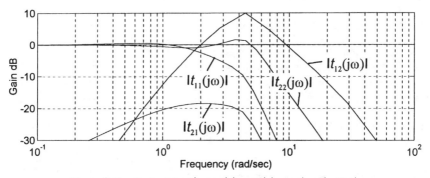

Figure 6.2.8. Bode plots of $|t_{11}(j\omega)|$, $|t_{22}(j\omega)|$, $|t_{12}(j\omega)|$ and $|t_{21}(j\omega)|$.

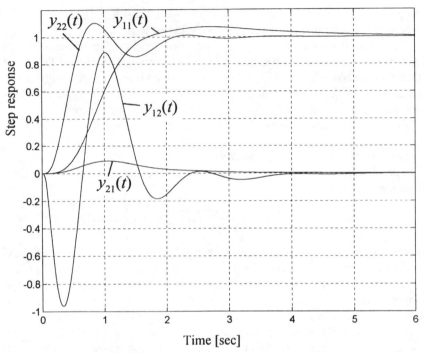

Figure 6.2.9. Output time responses $y_{11}(t)$, $y_{22}(t)$, $y_{12}(t)$
and $y_{21}(t)$ to unit-step input commands.

A different class of design techniques is based on applying the Nyquist stability criterion to MIMO feedback systems. These techniques emerged in the late 1960s, and culminated in the 1970s with sophisticated design philosophies such as *the characteristic-locus methods* (MacFarlane, Kouvaritakis 1977), *Nyquist-array methods,* and *the inverse Nyquist-array methods* (Rosenbrock 1970, Rosenbrock and Munro 1978, and others). These methods are based on the MIMO interpretation of the SISO Nyquist stability criterion.

6.2.5. The Generalized Nyquist Stability Criterion

The explanation of the generalized Nyquist stability criterion in the following section and its use in the design of MIMO systems is based on MacFarlane (1970), Mac-Farlane and Belletrutti (1973), MacFarlane and Postlethwaite (1977), Kouvaritakis (1979), Stevens (1981) and others. First, some preliminary definitions are necessary.

Characteristic transfer functions, and corresponding eigenvector functions
(see Appendix B).

These functions are the heart in the implementation of the Nyquist stability criterion to MIMO feedback systems. They have their origin and parallel in the theory of eigenvalues and eigenvectors of constant square matrices. The only difference is that these eigenvalues and eigenvectors are themselves frequency dependent.

Let us define a $n \times n$ square matrix $\mathbf{Q}(s)$ and assume also that there are no hidden unstable modes in this system (for a definition see App.B, Section B.4.3). If $\mathbf{Q}(s)$ is not identically singular, then it is possible to find a set of n eigenvalues $\{q_i(s), i = 1, 2, \ldots n\}$ which are functions of the complex Laplace variable s. A set of n eigenvectors can be also found for these eigenvalue functions. The eigenvalues are determined by the solution of the characteristic equation

$$\det[\mathbf{Q}(s) - q(s)\mathbf{I}_n] = q^n + a_1(s)q^{n-1} + a_2(s)q^{n-2} + \ldots + a_n(s) = 0 \quad (6.2.8)$$

I_n–a unity diagonal matrix of order n.

The above characteristic equation leads to a polynomial in $q(s)$ whose coefficients are rational functions of s. It defines an *algebraic function* of the complex variable s (Bliss 1966). Let us call the n solutions as *eigenvalue transfer functions,* or *characteristic transfer functions, $q_i(s)$.* Since these functions are the solution of a n order characteristic equation, they will not generally be rational functions of s. They might be irrational functions, and, as such, have to be treated in the context of Riemann surfaces (Weyl 1955). To each eigenvalue function, we can find its corresponding eigenvector, also a function of s, generally not rational. By definition, these eigenvector functions are obtained by solving the n equations

$$\mathbf{Q}(s) \mathbf{w}_i(s) = q_i(s) \mathbf{w}_i(s); \ i = 1, 2, \ldots, n \quad (6.2.9)$$

where $\mathbf{w}_i(s)$ are vectors, also called *characteristic directions*. If we define a matrix

$$\mathbf{W}(s) = [\mathbf{w}_1(s) \ \mathbf{w}_2(s) \ \mathbf{w}_3(s) \ldots \mathbf{w}_n(s)] \quad (6.2.10)$$

and its inverse $\mathbf{V}(s)$ (which exists because $\mathbf{w}_i(s)$ are linearly independent vectors),

$$\mathbf{V}(s) = \mathbf{W}^{-1}(s) = [\mathbf{v}_1(s) \ \mathbf{v}_2(s) \ \mathbf{v}_3(s) \ldots \mathbf{v}_n(s)] \quad (6.2.11)$$

then, by standard algebraic theory (see, for instance, Warner 1965), we can obtain a diagonal matrix $\mathbf{\Lambda}^Q(s)$ whose entries are the eigenvalue transfer functions $q(s)$

$$\mathbf{\Lambda}^Q(s) = \mathbf{W}^{-1}(s)\mathbf{Q}(s)\mathbf{W}(s) = \mathbf{V}(s)\mathbf{Q}(s)\mathbf{W}(s) \quad (6.2.12)$$

and conversely

$$\mathbf{Q}(s) = \mathbf{W}(s)\mathbf{\Lambda}^Q(s) \ \mathbf{V}(s) \quad (6.2.13)$$

The above equations are important for future use.

Characteristic loci.

As we have seen, the characteristic transfer functions $q_i(s)$ are functions of the complex variable s, so that the frequency response of each $q_i(j\omega)$ can be calculated and plotted in the complex plane. Any closed contour in the s-plane can be mapped, by each of the characteristic transfer functions, on graphs in the complex plane. When s goes once around the Nyquist contour as in Fig.2.3.1, the graphs are called *characteristic loci,* or *eigenvalue loci.* There exist commercial programs for drawing such graphs, for instance, *cgloci(a,b,c,d,Type,w)* in the Matlab Robust Toolbox. A procedure for obtaining the characteristic loci, by solving Eq.(6.2.8) first, and then finding analytically $q_i(j\omega)$, $i = 1, n$, does not seem to be feasible. The practical procedure to obtain these graphs is as follows:

1- Select a frequency ω at which the complex values of the eigenvalues $q_i(j\omega)$ are to be calculated.
2- Compute the matrix $\mathbf{Q}(j\omega)$ at that frequency.
3- Compute the eigenvalues of $\mathbf{Q}(j\omega)$ at that frequency, which are the complex values of the characteristic loci $q_i(j\omega)$ $i = 1, n$ at the same frequency.
4- Plot the complex values of all $q_i(j\omega)'$s.
5- Repeat the procedure for a sufficient number of frequencies until the characteristic loci are continuously plotted.

In this context it is useful to define the *spectral radius* of the matrix $\mathbf{Q}(j\omega)$ as the maximum modulus of its eigenvalues $q_i(j\omega)$ (at each frequency),

$$\rho[\mathbf{Q}(j\omega)]: = \max_{i=1,n} |q_i(j\omega)|. \tag{6.2.14}$$

The characteristic functions of $\mathbf{Q}(s)$ are the MIMO counterpart of the usual loop transmission of SISO systems. The eigenvalue graphs may show some strange features when compared to the SISO Nyquist frequency dependent plot. For instance, for a SISO transmission function of order 0, which means no integrators in the loop, the Nyquist plot in the complex plane originates on the real axis at $s = 0$. This might not be the case with the characteristic loci because the eigenvalues of a matrix with all its elements real, may be complex. Moreover, the characteristic loci may not be closed loci in the complex plane. This very important point is discussed next.

Adaptation of the Nyquist stability criterion to MIMO systems

Define a square matrix $\mathbf{P}(s)$ as the transfer function matrix of the plant and the control matrix $\mathbf{G}(s)$ in a series connection: $\mathbf{L}_0(s) = \mathbf{P}(s)\mathbf{G}(s)$ if the loop is opened at the output to the plant $\mathbf{P}(s)$; $\mathbf{L}_i(s) = \mathbf{G}(s)\mathbf{P}(s)$ if the loop is opened at the input to the plant $\mathbf{P}(s)$, as shown in Fig.6.1.1. Assume also that there are no hidden, unstable modes in this system. We wish to analyze the stability of this system in a unity-feedback MIMO structure. As with the SISO system, we define for the MIMO feedback system the *return difference matrix* $\mathbf{F}(s) = \mathbf{I} + \mathbf{L}(s)$ evaluated at some break point in the feedback multivariable structure. With these definitions, stability of the closed-loop feedback system is identified with the location of the zeros of the numerator of $\det\mathbf{F}(s)$. (Do not confuse $\mathbf{F}(s)$ defined here with the prefilter matrix in Figs.6.1.1 and 6.2.1).

Let

OLCP(s) = the open-loop characteristic polynomial of a complete feedback system with all loops broken at the input or at the output of the MIMO plant in Fig.6.1.1 (See Eqs.(6.1.1) and (6.1.2); see also Eq.(B.4.8)).

CLCP(s) = the closed-loop characteristic polynomial of a complete feedback system with all feedback loops closed, as shown in Fig.6.1.1,(see also Eq.(B.4.12)). It is easily shown that

$$\det \mathbf{F}(s) = \frac{CLCP(s)}{OLCP(s)}\, c \qquad (6.2.15)$$

where CLPC(s) and OLCP(s) are respectively the system closed-loop and open-loop characteristic polynomials, and c is a constant that does not interfere when the closed loop poles are evaluated. In fact, $c = \det \mathbf{F}(\infty)$ (see MacFarlane and Postlethwaite, 1979).

As for the SISO case, assume that the determinant in Eq.(6.2.15) has z zeros and p poles in the closed RHP. As s traverses the Nyquist contour clockwise, shown in Fig.2.3.1, then the mapping of this contour by $\det[\mathbf{I} + \mathbf{L}(s)]$ will encircle the origin $N = z-p$ times in the same direction as the direction of the Nyquist contour. (Here again, p is the number of open-loop unstable poles located in the closed RHP, and z is the number of closed-loop unstable poles). Hence, for a stable closed-loop feedback system, the number of encirclements of the origin equals $N = -p$ so that the number z of closed-loop unstable poles will be zeroed (See Section 2.3.1). We would like to shift the stability critical point in the complex plane from the origin to $[-1, j0]$. In SISO feedback systems, just one loop transmission $L(j\omega)$ can be plotted in the complex plane. For MIMO feedback systems, there are n such functions, where n is the order of the square loop transmission matrix $\mathbf{L}(s)$. If $\lambda_i(s)$ is an eigenvalue function of $\mathbf{L}(s)$, it can be shown that $1+ \lambda_i(s)$ is an eigenvalue function of $\mathbf{I} +\mathbf{L}(s)$. To proceed further, we have to find the *eigenvalue functions* of the matrix $\mathbf{F}(s) = \mathbf{I} +\mathbf{L}(s)$, namely, the set $f_i(s)$; $i = 1, n$. But since the determinant is the product of the eigenvalues, it follows that

$$\det \mathbf{F}(s) = \prod_{i=1}^{n} f_i(s) \qquad (6.2.16)$$

or, in terms of $\mathbf{L}(s)$,

$$\det [\mathbf{I}+\mathbf{L}(s)] = \prod_{i=1}^{n} [1 + \lambda_i(s)]. \qquad (6.2.17)$$

By using once more the principle of the argument (See Churchill 1960), it is deduced that we can determine closed-loop stability of MIMO feedback systems by counting the total number of encirclements of the origin $[0, j0]$ by the frequency dependent plots of all $1 + \lambda_i(j\omega)$, or by counting the total number of encirclements of the Nyquist stability critical point $[-1, j0]$ by all the characteristic loci $\lambda_i(j\omega)$. Formal proof of the generalized Nyquist stability criterion can be found in MacFarlane (1970), Barman and Katzenelson (1973), MacFarlane (1977), Postlethwaite and MacFarlane (1977), Desoer C. and Wang (1980), or Smith (1984).

A formal statement of the generalized Nyquist stability criterion follows.

Theorem 6.1.   If a square, rational open-loop transfer function matrix $\mathbf{L}(s)$ has p unstable (Smith-McMillan) poles (see Rosenbrock 1974), then the closed-loop feedback system with *return ratio matrix* $\mathbf{L}(s)$ is stable, if and only if, the characteristic loci of $\mathbf{L}(s)$, taken all together, encircle the Nyquist stability point $[-1, j0]$ p times anticlockwise. It is assumed that no unstable pole-zero cancellations exist in $\mathbf{L}(s)$.

There are two problems involved with the above presentation:
1- The eigenvalue functions of a rational transfer function matrix are generally not rational functions. The unpleasant consequence is that individual characteristic loci corresponding to a mapping of the closed Nyquist contour **may not be closed loci in the complex plane.** Fortunately, it can be proven that the set of all loci join at the boundary points and give a set of closed graphs on the complex plane. These graphs can be used to unambiguously count the number of encirclements of the critical point $[-1, j0]$ (Macfarlane 1977).
2- The generalized Nyquist stability criterion is well-suited for stability analysis when the characteristic loci can be drawn in the complex plane. With today's commercial mathematical tools, there is no problem in plotting these loci in the frequency-domain and in investigating the stability of the MIMO feedback system in terms of changing parameters of the plant or of the controller. However, the converse action is not possible due to the fact that the individual characteristic loci depend on all the elements of the compensator transfer matrix, which are introduced along different paths of the MIMO feedback system. For instance, let us suppose that

$$\mathbf{G}(s) = \begin{bmatrix} g_1(s) & 0 \\ 0 & g_2(s) \end{bmatrix}; \mathbf{L}(s) = \begin{bmatrix} l_{11}(s) & l_{21}(s) \\ l_{12}(s) & l_{22}(s) \end{bmatrix}. \tag{6.2.18}$$

The eigenvalue functions can be derived by solving the quadratic equation in $\lambda(s)$:

$$\lambda^2(s) + [l_{11}(s)g_1(s) + l_{22}(s)g_2(s)]\,\lambda(s) + g_1(s)g_2(s)[l_{11}(s)\,l_{22}(s) - l_{21}(s)l_{12}(s)] = 0 \tag{6.2.19}$$

The solution to this equation yields $\lambda_1(s)$ and $\lambda_2(s)$, each of them depending on both $g_1(s)$ and $g_2(s)$. There does not seems to be a way of loopshaping satisfactorily each of one of the characteristic loci by any one of these controllers alone. A solved example will clarify this difficulty.

Example 6.2.4.   Plot the characteristic loci of

$$\mathbf{L}(s) = \frac{1}{(s+2)(s+4)} \begin{bmatrix} (s-1) & 2 \\ -s & (s-3) \end{bmatrix}$$

and investigate the stability of the closed-loop system in terms of the constant controller matrix

$$\mathbf{G}(s) = \begin{bmatrix} k_1 & 0 \\ 0 & k_2 \end{bmatrix}$$

Solution: Since we deal with a 2×2 transfer function matrix, two characteristic loci are to be plotted. The Matlab program used to calculate them is listed in Table 6.2.1.

The derived characteristic loci are shown in Fig.6.2.10. In this figure there exist two closed contours that may encircle the critical point $[-1, j0]$. There are no encirclements of this point with nominal $k_1 = k_2 = 2.5$, and stability is assured. With

Table 6.2.1. Matlab program for deriving the characteristic loci in Example 6.2.4

```
%Ex.6.2.4.m sigma & cgloci analysis, 2 June 1998
%use 'robust toolbox'
%loop opened at input of K (output of L, LK)
rad = 180/pi; figure(1); clf
w1 = logspace(-2, 2, 1000);
denol = [1  6  8]; n11 = [0  1 -1]*k1; n21= [0 -1  0]*k1;
n12 = [0 0 2]*k2; n22 = [0 1 -3]*k2;
numol = [n11; n21; n12; n22];
[a1,b1,c1,d1] = tfm2ss(numol, denol, 2, 2);
[cg, ph] = cgloci(a1,b1,c1,d1,1,w1);
cg1 = cg(1,:); cg2 = cg(2,:); ph1 = ph(1,:); ph2 = ph(2,:);
cg1db = 20*log10(cg1); cg2db = 20*log10(cg2);
real1 = cg1 '.*cos(ph1/rad)'; imaj1 = cg1 '.*sin(ph1/rad)';
real2 = cg2 '.*cos(ph2/rad)'; imaj2 = cg2 '.*sin(ph2/rad)';
figure(1); plot(real1,imaj1, 'r'); hold on;
figure(1); plot(real1,-imaj1, 'r:'); hold on;
figure(1); plot(real2, imaj2, 'b:'); hold on;
figure(1); plot(real2,-imaj2, 'b'); hold on;
figure(1); grid; title('k1 = 2.5; k2 = 2.7');
end
```

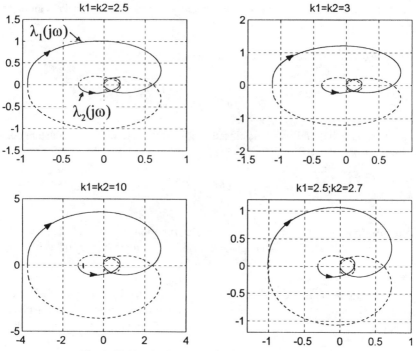

Figure 6.2.10.   The two characteristic loci for the open-loop transfer function matrix in Example 6.2.4 for different k_1 and k_2

$k_1 = k_2 = 3$, there is a single clockwise encirclement of the critical point, and instability is deduced. When both controller gains are appreciably augmented to $k_1 = k_2 = 10$, then there ensue two encirclements of $[-1, j0]$, but in opposite directions. Hence, there is a null net encirclement of the critical point, and stability is once more preserved. The sensitivity of this system to k_2 is much higher than that to k_1 because when k_1 is kept nominal at $k_1 = 2.5$, and the nominal k_2 is changed to $k_2 > 2.7$, then instability of the MIMO system occurs. But, when $k_2 = 2.5$, then k_1 can be increased to as much as $k_1 = 8.0$, while stability is still preserved. Fig.6.2.11 shows stability regions for k_1 and k_2 gains.

From Eq.(6.2.19) it was intuitively concluded that even for the simplest 2×2 MIMO feedback system, it is not feasible to manipulate favorably and separately the two characteristic loci using the control networks $g_1(s)$ and/or $g_2(s)$. The next section briefly explores a design technique based on *commutative controllers* that present a way of partially circumventing the last difficulty.

6.2.6.   The Characteristic Locus Design Method

Complete and detailed explanation and development of this techniques can be found in MacFarlane and Belletrutti (1973), Kouvaritakis (1979), MacFarlane and

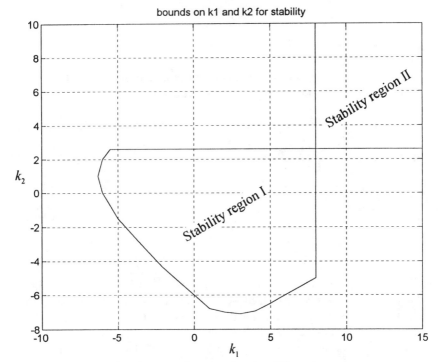

Figure 6.2.11. Gain space $k_1 - k_2$ stability regions.

Kouvaritakis (1979). A short presentation of this design technique follows (see also Maciejowski 1989).

The basic idea is to find a way of individually manipulating each characteristic loci by a single compensator. This will allow us to use a kind of SISO Nyquist type design procedure for each characteristic loci. Mathematically, this can be achieved in the following way:

Suppose that we have a $n \times n$ plant transfer function matrix $\mathbf{P}(s)$. A spectral decomposition of this matrix can be obtained by use of Eq.(6.2.13).

$$\mathbf{P}(s) = \mathbf{W}(s)\Lambda^\mathbf{P}(s)\mathbf{W}^{-1}(s) \tag{6.2.20}$$

with the usual definition for $\mathbf{W}(s)$ and $\Lambda^\mathbf{P}(s)$. The characteristic functions of $\mathbf{P}(s)$ are named $\lambda_i(s)$; $i = 1,n$.

$$\Lambda^\mathbf{P}(s) = \text{diag}[\lambda_1(s), \lambda_2(s), \lambda_3(s), \ldots, \lambda_n(s)] \tag{6.2.21}$$

Suppose that a compensator transfer function matrix $\mathbf{G}(s)$ of the same order of $\mathbf{P}(s)$ can be achieved such that its spectral decomposition is of the form

$$G(s) = W(s)\Lambda^G(s)W^{-1}(s) \tag{6.2.22}$$

$$\Lambda^G(s) = \text{diag}[\gamma_1(s), \gamma_2(s), \gamma_3(s), \ldots, \gamma_n(s))] \tag{6.2.23}$$

where $\gamma_i(s)$ are the compensator matrix characteristic functions. With these assumptions, the return ratio matrix $L(s)$ becomes

$$-L(s) = -W(s)\Lambda^G(s)\Lambda^P(s)W^{-1}(s) = -W(s)\Lambda^L(s)W^{-1}(s) \tag{6.2.24}$$

where

$$\Lambda^L(s) = \Lambda^G(s)\Lambda^P(s) = \text{diag}[l_1(s), l_2(s), l_3(s), \ldots, l_n(s)] \tag{6.2.25}$$

and

$$l_i(s) = \lambda_i(s)\gamma_i(s) \tag{6.2.26}$$

Eq.(6.2.25) indicates that if the compensator transfer matrix $G(s)$ can be designed to have the same characteristic eigenvectors as those of the plant matrix $P(s)$, then the return ratio matrix $L(s)$, which is the open-loop transfer function matrix, has eigenvalue functions which are the products of the plant and of the compensator eigenvalues. In this new situation, design of the MIMO feedback system is simplified to the design of n conventional SISO feedback systems. The compensator then becomes a series connection of three matrices which are respectively $W(s)$, $\Lambda^G(s)$ and $W^{-1}(s)$. It is important to realize that if the compensator has the structure of Eq.(6.2.22), then $P(s)$ and $G(s)$ commute, which means that

$$G(s)P(s) = P(s)G(s) \tag{6.2.27}$$

Compensators satisfying Eq.(6.2.27) are named *commutative compensators*.

As explained previously, the annoying problem with this approach is that, the elements of the eigenvector matrices are generally irrational functions which cannot be practically realized. We are then left with the alternative of finding a realizable rational approximation to $W(s)$ and $W^{-1}(s)$, say $A(s)$ and $B(s)$ respectively. This is not an easy task. Many researchers in the 1980s spent a lot of energy in developing techniques and algorithms to achieve the desired approximation of $A(s) \approx W(s)$ and $B(s) \approx W^{-1}(s)$, at least at a number of important frequencies from the overall system point of view (See the ALIGN algorithm of Kouvaritakis 1974). Additional design procedures for adequately approximating $W(s)$ and $W^{-1}(s)$ can be found in Kouvaritakis and Edmonds (1978), Edmunds and Kouvaritakis (1979) and Maciejowski (1989).

MIMO feedback system design techniques based on the inverse Nyquist array of Rosenbrock (1970) were invented in the 1970s. These techniques are beyond the scope of the present book.

The design procedures for MIMO feedback systems treated and demonstrated with solved examples in this section seem to be successful only because the plant has no uncertainties. Once the parameters of the plant transfer function matrix change, the achieved performances will strongly deteriorate. This fact is clearly perceived for the characteristic locus design techniques treated in this section; changes of parameters of the plant transfer function matrix $\mathbf{P}(s)$ give rise to appreciable changes in the eigenvector matrix $\mathbf{W}(s)$, and the approximations achieved with $\mathbf{A}(s)$ and $\mathbf{B}(s)$ do not hold anymore. The noninteraction property achieved in sections 6.2.2 to 6.2.4 will be completely spoiled, the stability margins will remain satisfactory only for the nominal plant condition, etc.

6.2.7. Internal Stability in MIMO Feedback Systems

Internal stability for SISO feedback systems was discussed briefly in Section 2.2.3. It was shown that stability of any input-output transfer function of the closed-loop system does not guarantee 'internal stability' if the plant or the control compensator contains RHP poles and/or zeros. RHP pole-zero cancellations between the plant and the compensator dynamics may end up with stable input-output transfer functions, but with unstable transfer functions between other points of the feedback system. This phenomena is next analyzed for MIMO feedback systems (For details see Vidyasagar 1985, Maciejowski 1989).

In the analysis to follow, it is efficient to manipulate the standard feedback structure of Fig.6.1.1 to that of Fig. 6.2.12. But first it is important to define the notion of 'Well-Posedness' of such feedback loops.

Well-posedness of feedback loops.

When a canonical feedback loop as in Fig.6.2.12 is considered, $\mathbf{G}(s)$ and $\mathbf{P}(s)$ being real rational proper transfer function matrices with constant coefficients, it is important to first ascribe the necessary conditions for physically realizability of the closed-loop system. A common definition follows for such systems:

Definition 6.2.1. A feedback system is called *well-posed* if all closed-loop transfer matrices are *well-defined* and *proper*.

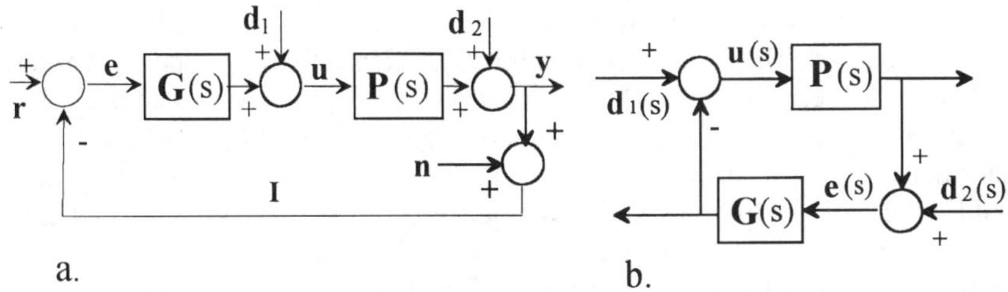

Figure 6.2.12. Standard feedback structure for internal stability investigation.

A simple example will clarify the meaning of this definition.

Example 6.2.5.   A 2×2 plant transfer function matrix $\mathbf{P}(s)$ is given by $p_{11}(s) = (-s+2)/(2s+3)$; $p_{12}(s) = 0$; $p_{21}(s) = 1/s$; $p_{22}(s) = -(s-2)/(s+3)$. Choose initially the controller transfer matrix $\mathbf{G}(s)$ to be given by $g_{11}(s) = g_{22}(s) = 1$; $g_{21}(s) = g_{12}(s) = 0$. Calculate the transfer matrix $\mathbf{T}(s)$ with input vector $\mathbf{d}_2(s) = [d_{21}\ d_{22}]^T$ and output vector $\mathbf{u}(s) = [u_1\ u_2]^T$; $\mathbf{u}(s) = \mathbf{T}(s)\,\mathbf{d}_2(s)$. It is easily found that $t_{11}(s) = -(2s+3)/(s+5)$; $t_{22}(s) = -(s+3)/5$; $t_{12}(s) = 0$; $t_{21}(s) = (s+3)(2s+3)/[5s(s+5)]$.

Since $t_{22}(s) = -(s+3)/5$ *is not proper*, we conclude that the feedback system cannot be physically realized since $u_2 = -[(s+3)/5]\,d_{22}$.

Next, choose $g_{11}(s) = -1/p_{11}(s) = -(2s+3)/(-s+2)$; $g_{22}(s) = 1$; $g_{21}(s) = g_{12}(s) = 0$. With this choice

$$[\mathbf{I}+\mathbf{G}(s)\mathbf{P}(s)] = \begin{bmatrix} 0 & 0 \\ p_{21}(s) & 1+p_{22}(s) \end{bmatrix}$$

which is not invertible, and the closed-loop transfer matrix $\mathbf{T}(s)$ cannot be evaluated. It does not exist. The system is not *well-defined*. Hence, with both choices of $\mathbf{G}(s)$ in this example, the feedback problem is not *well-posed*. To summarize, the feedback system in Fig.6.2.12 is well posed iff the transfer matrix $\mathbf{T}(s)$ exists and is proper.

Internal stability

First, let us define stability of a transfer function matrix. By definition, a transfer function matrix is *exponentially stable* iff it is proper and has no poles in the closed RHP. Next, assume that the feedback system in Fig.6.2.12 is well-posed. Then the system is defined as *internally stable* if the closed-loop transfer function matrix $\mathbf{T}(s)$ in the following equation (with $\mathbf{r} = \mathbf{0}$, $\mathbf{e} = \mathbf{y}$)

$$\begin{bmatrix} \mathbf{u}(s) \\ \mathbf{e}(s) \end{bmatrix} = \begin{bmatrix} \mathbf{T}_{11}(s) & \mathbf{T}_{12}(s) \\ \mathbf{T}_{21}(s) & \mathbf{T}_{22}(s) \end{bmatrix} \begin{bmatrix} \mathbf{d}_1(s) \\ \mathbf{d}_2(s) \end{bmatrix} = \mathbf{T}(s) \begin{bmatrix} \mathbf{d}_1(s) \\ \mathbf{d}_2(s) \end{bmatrix} \tag{6.2.28}$$

is exponentially stable. As with the definition for SISO feedback systems, a MIMO feedback system is internally stable if, and only if, for each of the bounded external input vectors $\mathbf{r}$, $\mathbf{n}$, $\mathbf{d}_1$ and $\mathbf{d}_2$, the internal vectors $\mathbf{u}$, $\mathbf{e}$ and the output vector $\mathbf{y}$ are also bounded. The main purpose of this definition is to exclude pole-zero cancellations between the plant transfer function matrix $\mathbf{P}(s)$ and the compensator transfer function matrix $\mathbf{G}(s)$, exactly as was done for the SISO case. Thus, internal stability is assured if all the transfer function matrices $\mathbf{T}_{ij}(s)$ are exponentially stable. We have to differentiate between different classes of systems, related to some general characteristics of $\mathbf{P}(s)$ and of $\mathbf{G}(s)$, as well as to find conditions on the system transfer function matrix $\mathbf{T}(s)$ for internal stability. Two important theorems are stated. Their proofs are omitted and can be found in Maciejowski (1989).

1- *P(s) and G(s) are both unstable transfer function matrices.*

In this case, internal stability exists if the four $T_{ij}(s)$ are exponentially stable.

Let us next assume that at least one of the transfer function matrices is exponentially stable. For instance, $G(s)$ is exponentially stable, but $P(s)$ is not.

2- $G(s)$ *is exponentially stable.*

In this case the following theorem holds.

Theorem 6.2: If $G(s)$ is exponentially stable, then the feedback system of Fig.6.2.12 is internally stable if, and only if, $T_{21}(s) = [I+P(s)G(s)]^{-1} P(s)$ is exponentially stable. The proof consists in showing that if the above condition holds, then $T_{11}(s)$, $T_{22}(s)$ and $T_{12}(s)$ are also exponentially stable.

The next theorem is a useful variant of Theorem 6.2.

Theorem 6.3: If $G(s)$ is exponentially stable, then $T_{21}(s)$ is exponentially stable if and only if A: $\det[I+P(s)G(s)]$ has no zeros in the closed RHP (including infinity), and B: $[I+P(s)G(s)]^{-1}P(s)$ is analytic (which means that it has no poles) at every closed RHP pole of $P(s)$ (including infinity).

3- *P(s) is exponentially stable,* $G(s)$ *is not.*

Theorems 6.2 and 6.3 can be restated for the dual of **2.**

Example 6.2.6. Given the plant transfer function matrix $P(s) = \begin{bmatrix} \dfrac{1}{s-1} & \dfrac{1}{s+2} \\ 0 & \dfrac{1}{s-3} \end{bmatrix}$

and a diagonal compensator transfer function matrix $G(s) = \begin{bmatrix} g_{11}(s) & 0 \\ 0 & g_{22}(s) \end{bmatrix}$, find if

the closed-loop feedback system is internally stable for the following compensators

$$1 - G(s) = \begin{bmatrix} 3 & 0 \\ 0 & 10 \end{bmatrix}$$

$$2 - G(s) = \begin{bmatrix} \dfrac{s-1}{s+2} & 0 \\ 0 & \dfrac{2(s-3)}{s+2} \end{bmatrix}$$

Solution. We shall compute $\mathrm{num}\{\det[I+P(s)G(s)]\}$ and $T_{21}(s) = [I +P(s)G(s)]^{-1}P(s)$ for both compensator transfer function matrices.

1. $\mathrm{num}\{\det[I + P(s)G(s)]\} = (s + 2)(s + 7)$, stable roots.

$$T_{21} = \begin{bmatrix} \dfrac{1}{s+2} & \dfrac{(s-3)(s-1)}{(s+2)^2(s+7)} \\ 0 & \dfrac{1}{s+7} \end{bmatrix},$$

hence, internal stability follows.

2. num$\{\det[\mathbf{I} + \mathbf{P}(s)\mathbf{G}(s)]\} = (s + 3)(s + 4)$, stable roots, but,

$$\mathbf{T}_{21} = \frac{(s + 2)}{(s + 3)(s + 4)} \begin{bmatrix} \dfrac{s+4}{s-1} & 1 \\ 0 & \dfrac{s+3}{s-3} \end{bmatrix},$$

hence, no internal stability exists! This happens because zeros of the compensators have canceled unstable poles in elements of the plant transfer function matrix. See also Section 2.2.3.

The consequences of Theorems 6.2 and 6.3 are clearly identified in this example.

6.2.8. *Q- Parametrization*

Q-parametrization was introduced and analyzed for SISO feedback systems in Section 3.7. In this section, the MIMO problem will be treated using a similar design philosophy, known in the literature as *Youla-parametrization,* Youla et al (1976b). The task of this design technique is to find a stabilizing controller $\mathbf{G}(s)$ that yields internal stability to the MIMO closed-loop system. The general form of this controller, defined in parametric form, is important since in this form, it always yields an internally stable feedback system. The parameters of the controller can be changed adequately so that desired system performances are obtained, while stability of the closed-loop is preserved.

First, the $\mathbf{T}_{ij}(s)$ in Eq.(6.2.28) are explicitly expressed for future use. From Fig.6.2.12 we see that

$$\mathbf{e} = \mathbf{d}_2 + \mathbf{Pu}; \mathbf{u} = \mathbf{d}_1 - \mathbf{Ge} \qquad (6.2.29)$$

from which we easily get

$$\mathbf{T}_{11} = (\mathbf{I} + \mathbf{GP})^{-1} \qquad (6.2.30a)$$

$$\mathbf{T}_{12} = -\mathbf{G}(\mathbf{I} + \mathbf{PG})^{-1} \qquad (6.2.30b)$$

$$\mathbf{T}_{21} = \mathbf{P}(\mathbf{I} + \mathbf{GP})^{-1} \qquad (6.2.30c)$$

$$\mathbf{T}_{22} = (\mathbf{I} + \mathbf{PG})^{-1} \qquad (6.2.30d)$$

and finally

$$\mathbf{u} = (\mathbf{I} + \mathbf{GP})^{-1}\mathbf{d}_1 - \mathbf{G}(\mathbf{I} + \mathbf{PG})^{-1}\mathbf{d}_2 \qquad (6.2.31)$$

$$\mathbf{e} = \mathbf{P}(\mathbf{I} + \mathbf{GP})^{-1}\mathbf{d}_1 + (\mathbf{I} + \mathbf{PG})^{-1}\mathbf{d}_2 \qquad (6.2.32)$$

Once again, we differentiate between two cases to be treated, namely, MIMO systems with 'stable' and with 'unstable' plant transfer function matrices.

1: Q-parametrization: stable plants.

Define first the matrix

$$\mathbf{Q}: = \mathbf{G}(\mathbf{I} + \mathbf{PG})^{-1} \tag{6.2.33}$$

It can be proven that if the plant $\mathbf{P}(s)$ is stable and if we choose a stable matrix $\mathbf{Q}$, this guarantees that the feedback system in Fig. 6.2.12 is stable. This means that all $\mathbf{T}_{ij}$ in Eqs.(6.2.30) are also stable. The proof is almost immediate. Let us express all $\mathbf{T}_{ij}$ in Eq.(6.2.30) in term of $\mathbf{Q}$. By definition, $\mathbf{T}_{12} = -\mathbf{Q}$. The remaining relations are obtained by use of the matrix identity $(\mathbf{A} + \mathbf{BC})^{-1} = \mathbf{A}^{-1} - \mathbf{A}^{-1}\mathbf{B}(\mathbf{A}^{-1}\mathbf{B} + \mathbf{C}^{-1})^{-1}\mathbf{A}^{-1}$, by which, $(\mathbf{I} + \mathbf{GP})^{-1} = \mathbf{I} - \mathbf{G}(\mathbf{G} + \mathbf{P}^{-1})^{-1}$ and $(\mathbf{I} + \mathbf{PG})^{-1} = \mathbf{I} - \mathbf{P}(\mathbf{P} + \mathbf{G}^{-1})^{-1}$. The rest immediately follows.

$$\mathbf{T}_{11} = (\mathbf{I} + \mathbf{GP})^{-1} = \mathbf{I} - \mathbf{QP} \tag{6.2.34a}$$

$$\mathbf{T}_{12} = -\mathbf{G}(\mathbf{I} + \mathbf{PG})^{-1} = -\mathbf{Q} \tag{6.2.34b}$$

$$\mathbf{T}_{21} = \mathbf{P}(\mathbf{I} + \mathbf{GP})^{-1} = \mathbf{P}(\mathbf{I} - \mathbf{QP}) \tag{6.2.34c}$$

$$\mathbf{T}_{22} = (\mathbf{I} + \mathbf{PG})^{-1} = \mathbf{I} - \mathbf{PQ} \tag{6.2.34d}$$

But the above transfer function matrices are all stable if $\mathbf{P}$ and $\mathbf{Q}$ are stable. The parameters of the plant transfer function matrix are fixed, but those of $\mathbf{Q}$ can be freely chosen, as long as it remains a stable matrix. Next, a pure synthesis procedure can be followed. (See Truxal 1955, Zames 1981). The stabilizing controller $\mathbf{G}(s)$ can be extracted from the definition of $\mathbf{Q}(s)$

$$\mathbf{G}(s) = (\mathbf{I} - \mathbf{QP})^{-1}\mathbf{Q} = \mathbf{Q}(\mathbf{I} - \mathbf{PQ})^{-1} \tag{6.2.35}$$

The solution is apparently straightforward. However, stabilization is not the only factor to be achieved. The transfer function matrix $\mathbf{Q}(s)$ must be defined so that additional specifications are satisfied, such as required stability margins, input-output closed-loop characteristics and so on. These points were treated in some length in Chapter 3 for the SISO case.

2: Q- parametrization: unstable plants.

$\mathbf{Q}$-parametrization for the MIMO feedback system is a much more elaborate procedure than that for the SISO case, since *matrix coprime factorization* of the plant rational transfer function matrix is involved. There are two ways for achieving the coprime factorization, namely, 'left' or 'right' coprime factorization.

A right coprime factorization of $\mathbf{P}(s)$ is

$$\mathbf{P}(s) = \mathbf{N}_r(s)\mathbf{M}_r^{-1}(s) \tag{6.2.36}$$

in which $\mathbf{N}_r(s)$ and $\mathbf{M}_r(s)$ are coprime polynomial matrices. For latter applicability in achieving stability, $\mathbf{N}_r(s)$ must include all the RHP-zeros of $\mathbf{P}(s)$, while $\mathbf{M}_r(s)$ should contain as RHP-zeros all the RHP-poles of $\mathbf{P}(s)$. In order to avoid pole-zero cancellation when forming $\mathbf{N}_r(s)\mathbf{M}_r^{-1}(s)$, no common RHP-zeros should exist in $\mathbf{N}_r(s)$ and $\mathbf{M}_r(s)$. This is achieved by the coprimeness of both matrices. Coprimeness is characterized by the satisfaction of the well known Bezout identity, already discussed and used in Section 3.7.4. The meaning of this identity is that there exist two polynomial matrices $\mathbf{U}_r(s)$ and $\mathbf{V}_r(s)$ such that

$$\mathbf{U}_r(s)\mathbf{N}_r(s) + \mathbf{V}_r(s)\mathbf{M}_r(s) = \mathbf{I} \tag{6.2.37}$$

In a similar way, a left coprime factorization of $\mathbf{P}(s)$ is

$$\mathbf{P}(s) = \mathbf{M}_l^{-1}(s)\,\mathbf{N}_l(s) \tag{6.2.38}$$

Once more, the following Bezout identity is to be satisfied

$$\mathbf{N}_l(s)\mathbf{U}_l(s) + \mathbf{M}_l(s)\mathbf{V}_l(s) = \mathbf{I} \tag{6.2.39}$$

where $\mathbf{N}_l(s)$ and $\mathbf{M}_l(s)$ are coprime. Here again we are interested in finding a controller $\mathbf{G}(s)$ defined in parametric form that stabilizes the plant $\mathbf{P}(s)$. For that purpose **any** stable transfer matrix $\mathbf{Q}(s)$, satisfying $\det[\mathbf{V}_r(\infty) - \mathbf{Q}(\infty)\mathbf{N}_l(\infty)] \neq 0$, can be chosen in order to obtain the stabilizing controller, defined in parametric form as follows

$$\mathbf{G}(s) = [\mathbf{V}_r(s) - \mathbf{Q}(s)\mathbf{N}_l(s)]^{-1}[\mathbf{U}_r(s) + \mathbf{Q}(s)\mathbf{M}_l(s)] \tag{6.2.40}$$

where $\mathbf{V}_r(s)$ and $\mathbf{U}_r(s)$ satisfy Eq.(6.2.37).

For additional and more detailed treatment of the subject, see Vidyasagar (1985).

The main objective of this short presentation of $\mathbf{Q}$-parametrization is to point out the possibility of finding a generalized controller structure, defined in parametric form, that stabilizes the MIMO feedback system and whose parameters can be varied freely until a stable closed-loop system with satisfactory properties is obtained.

It is important to note that the parametrization of all stabilizing controllers can also be expressed in the state-space formulation. In fact, algorithms for solving H_∞-norm optimization problems in automatic control are mostly formulated in this formulation (See Doyle et al. 1989, Zhou et al.1996, Zhou and Doyle 1998 and Chapter 8).

6.3. Uncertain MIMO Feedback Systems, Classical Approach-Statement of the Problem

Fig. 6.2.1 is repeated here as Fig.6.3.1 for the reader's convenience. $\mathbf{P} = [p_{ij}(s)]$ in Fig.6.3.1 is an $n \times n$ plant transfer function matrix in which each element is real rational, with a finite number of poles and with an excess of poles over zeros $e_{ij} > 0$. Due to uncertainty of the plant parameters of the element $p_{ij}(s)$, we can define a class of all possible parameter combinations, $\mathcal{M} = \{m\}$. Let $\mathcal{P}_{ij}$ denote the set of $p_{ij}(s)$, $\mathcal{P}$ the set of $\mathbf{P}$ transfer function matrices generated by the uncertainty, and $\mathcal{T}_{ij}$ the set of acceptable $t_{ij}(j\omega)$ so generated, (see Horowitz1979 and Horowitz and Sidi 1980).

The compensating $n \times n$ transfer function matrices $\mathbf{F} = [f_{ij}(s)]$ and $\mathbf{G} = [g_{ij}(s)]$ consist of LTI compensating networks each with a finite excess of poles over zeros. They must ensure that the elements of the closed-loop transfer function matrix $\mathbf{T} = [t_{ij}(s)]$ are internally stable and satisfy conditions similar to these of the SISO problem in Eq.(4.2.3), namely,

$$a_{ij}(\omega) \le |t_{ij}(j\omega)| \le b_{ij}(\omega) \quad \forall m \in \mathcal{M} \tag{6.3.1}$$

in the MIMO case. The system transfer function matrix $\mathbf{T}$ is to be 'basically non-interacting' (i.e. ideally one wants $t_{ij} \equiv 0$, $i \neq j$ which is impossible due to the uncertainty of $\mathbf{P}$).

As we have seen in Chapter 3, there exist approximated relations in translating $|T(j\omega)|$ into step time response $y(t)$, for instance. Thus, bounds in time-domain tolerances can be translated into frequency-domain tolerances to each $|t_{ij}(j\omega)|$.

6.3.1. Complexity of the $n \times n$ Feedback System Problem

As already discussed in Section 6.2.1, solution of the MIMO problem is inherently difficult, because of the existence of n^2 scalar loop transmissions in $\mathbf{L} = \mathbf{PG}$. There are also n^2 uncertain plant elements $p_{ij}(s)$. Moreover, each element of $\mathbf{L}$ and of $\mathbf{T}$ are complicated mixtures in elements of $\mathbf{G}$ and of $\mathbf{P}$, (see for example t_{11} in Section 6.2.1).

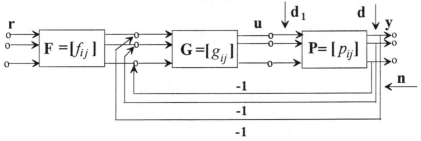

Figure 6.3.1. A MIMO two-degree-of-freedom matrix structure, $\mathbf{y} = \mathbf{T} \mathbf{r}$, $\mathbf{T} = [t_{ij}]$

The design technique presented next circumvents the already mentioned difficulties by converting the $n \times n$ complex structure into n equivalent single-loop feedback systems. Design techniques for SISO systems were presented in previous chapters, especially in Chapter 4, in which the SISO uncertain plant feedback problem was solved.

6.3.2. Derivation of a Synthesis Technique Based on QFT

The elements of the vectors $\mathbf{r}, \mathbf{d}, \mathbf{d_1}, \mathbf{n}, \mathbf{u}$ and $\mathbf{y}$ in Fig.6.3.1 are the reference inputs to the feedback system, the disturbances, the sensor's noises, the control signals at the inputs to the plant, and the system outputs respectively. The elements of $\mathbf{P}^{-1} = [p'_{ij}]$ are used a great deal and are denoted by $1/q_{ij}$ to indicate their nature as inverses of transfer functions, so $q_{ij} = 1/p'_{ij}$ is the inverse of the ijth element of $\mathbf{P}^{-1}$. Let $\mathcal{Q}_{ij}$ denote the set of q_{ij}. The sets $\mathcal{P}_{ij}$, $\mathcal{T}_{ij}$ and $\mathcal{P}$ were defined in the previous section.

With this notation, each one of the inputs to the plant is

$$u_i = p'_{i1} y_1 + p'_{i2} y_2 + \ldots + p'_{in} y_n = y_1/q_{i1} + y_2/q_{i2} + \ldots + y_n/q_{in}, \text{ or,}$$

$$u_i = p'_{ii}y_i - d_i, \ d_i \stackrel{def}{=} -\sum_{k \neq i} p'_{ik}y_k = -\sum_{k \neq i} y_k/q_{ik} \tag{6.3.2}$$

and y_i can be expressed in the following form

$$y_i = (u_i + d_i)/p'_{ii} = (u_i + d_i)q_{ii} \tag{6.3.3}$$

Obviously, for these equations to hold, a necessary condition is that $\mathbf{P}$ is nonsingular for $\forall m \ \mathcal{M}$. With the above definitions, the feedback structure in Fig.6.3.1 can be transformed to that in Fig.6.3.2a, in which $\mathbf{G}$ may consist of n^2 compensation functions at most. To simplify the design technique, it is convenient to choose a diagonal matrix $\mathbf{G}$ consisting of n elements g_{ii} only. With this simplifying choice of $\mathbf{G}$, the structure of Fig.6.3.2b emerges, in which we detect n classical single loops with equivalent disturbances d_i. Each y_i can be expressed in terms of the different input-output transfer functions t_{ij}.

Looking again at Fig.6.3.1, we find that

$$\mathbf{u} = \mathbf{G}(\mathbf{Fr} - \mathbf{y}), \quad \mathbf{y} = \mathbf{Pu} = \mathbf{PG}(\mathbf{Fr} - \mathbf{y}), \quad (\mathbf{I} + \mathbf{PG})\mathbf{y} = \mathbf{PGFr}, \ \mathbf{y} = (\mathbf{I} + \mathbf{PG})^{-1}\mathbf{PGFr}$$

thus,

$$\mathbf{T} = [t_{ij}] = (\mathbf{I} + \mathbf{PG})^{-1} \mathbf{PGF} = (\mathbf{G} + \mathbf{P}^{-1})^{-1} \mathbf{GF} \tag{6.3.4}$$

hence

$$(\mathbf{G} + \mathbf{P}^{-1})\mathbf{T} = \mathbf{GF} \tag{6.3.5}$$

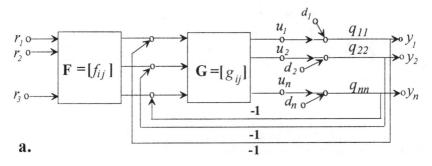

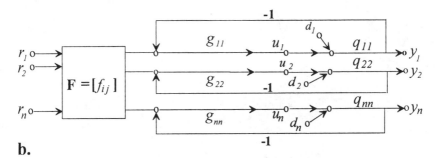

Figure 6.3.2.   **a.** Equivalent MIMO plant structure;
b. Transformation to equivalent n single-loop problems

Expressions for $[t_{ij}]$ can be readily derived from the last equation which, for a diagonal **G**, becomes

$$\begin{bmatrix} g_{11}+p'_{11} & p'_{12} & \cdot & p'_{1n} \\ p'_{21} & g_{22}+p'_{22} & \cdot & p'_{2n} \\ \cdot & \cdot\cdot & & \cdot \\ p'_{n1} & p'_{n2} & \cdot & g_{nn}+p'_{nn} \end{bmatrix} \begin{bmatrix} t_{11} & t_{12} & \cdot & t_{1n} \\ t_{21} & t_{22} & \cdot & t_{2n} \\ \cdot & \cdot & & \cdot \\ t_{n1} & t_{n2} & \cdot & t_{nn} \end{bmatrix} = \begin{bmatrix} g_{11}f_{11} & g_{11}f_{12} & \cdot & g_{11}f_{1n} \\ g_{22}f_{21} & g_{22}f_{22} & \cdot & g_{22}f_{2n} \\ \cdot & \cdot & & \cdot \\ g_{nn}f_{n1} & g_{nn}f_{n2} & \cdot & g_{nn}f_n \end{bmatrix}$$

$$(6.3.6)$$

From Eq.(6.3.6) it follows that

$$t_{11} = \frac{\dfrac{g_{11}}{p'_{11}}f_{11} - \dfrac{p'_{12}t_{21}+p'_{13}t_{31}+ \ldots + p'_{1n}t_{n1}}{p'_{11}}}{1+\dfrac{g_{11}}{p'_{11}}} = \frac{\dfrac{g_{11}}{p'_{11}}f_{11} - \dfrac{\sum\limits_{k=1}^{n} p'_{1k}t_{k1}}{p'_{11}}}{1+\dfrac{g_{11}}{p'_{11}}} \quad (6.3.7)$$

and the expression for each t_{ij} in terms of q_{ij} becomes

$$t_{ij} = \frac{\dfrac{g_{ii}}{p'_{ii}}f_{ij} - \dfrac{d_{ij}}{p'_{ii}}}{1 + \dfrac{g_{ii}}{p'_{ii}}} = \frac{g_{ii}q_{ii}f_{ij} - q_{ii}d_{ij}}{1 + g_{ii}q_{ii}} \overset{\Delta}{=} \tau_{ij} - \tau_{dij}; \quad d_{ij} = \sum_{k \neq i}^{n} p'_{ik} t_{kj} = \sum_{k \neq i}^{n} \frac{t_{kj}}{q_{ik}}$$

$$(6.3.7a)$$

in which the set $\mathscr{D}_{ij} = [d_{ij}]$ are the sets of disturbances generated by letting t_{ij} and q_{ij} in Fig.6.3.2 to range over their respective sets $\mathscr{T}_{ij}$ and $\mathscr{D}_{ij}$. It is important to realize that each consists of two parts having different meanings, namely,

$$\tau_{ij} = \frac{g_{ii}q_{ii}f_{ij}}{1 + g_{ii}q_{ii}}, \quad \tau_{dij} = \frac{q_{ii}d_{ij}}{1 + g_{ii}q_{ii}} \qquad (6.3.7b)$$

Define

$$|d_{ij}|_{max} = \sup_{\forall m} \sum_{k \neq i}^{n} |p'_{ik}| \, |b_{ij}| \quad ; |\tau_{dij}|_{max} = \left| \frac{q_{ii}}{1 + g_{ii}q_{ii}} \right| |d_{ij}|_{max} \qquad (6.3.7c)$$

Then,

$$0 < |\tau_{ij}| \pm |\tau_{dij}|_{max} \in [a_{ij}, b_{ij}], \forall m \in \mathcal{M} \qquad (6.3.7d)$$

with b_{ij} as defined in Eq.(6.3.1).

This expression corresponds to the single loops in Fig.6.3.2b. For a $n \times n$ feedback system, n^2 input-output transfer functions can be defined as lying within specified bounds, Eq.(6.3.1). This implies that n^2 prefilters $f(s)$ are to be found during the design process. Eqs.(6.3.7) were obtained with the assumption that a diagonal compensating transfer matrix $\mathbf{G}(s)$ is used, hence, n transfer functions $g_{ii}(s)$ only are to be designed.

The design technique presented here consists in finding n $g_{ii}(s)$ and $n^2 f_{ij}(s)$ compensating functions so that Eqs.(6.3.7) are satisfied for each t_{ij} (s) within their specified bounds as per Eq.(6.3.1) for $\forall m$ $\mathcal{M}$. Under these conditions, it was proven by Horowitz (1979b) using Schauder's fixed point theorem, that these same n $g_{ii}(s)$ and $n^2 f_{ij}(s)$ are the solution to the stated synthesis problem.

Eq.(6.3.7a) has transformed the $n \times n$ problem to n single-loop problems that can be designed sequentially. Each single-loop uncertain feedback system can be designed with the QFT technique presented in Chapter 4.

Since in Eq.(6.3.7a) the phase angles of τ_{ij} and of τ_{dij} are unknown until the final stage of the design process is completed, it is assumed that the expected maximum $|t_{ij}|$ will amount to $|t_{ij}| \overset{\Delta}{=} |\tau_{ij}| + |\tau_{dij}|_{max}$. For any permitted change in $|t_{ij}|$, only a part of it can be assigned to $|\tau_{ij}|$ due to the existence of $|\tau_{dij}|$. The larger d_{ij} is, the smaller the permitted changes in $|\tau_{ij}|$ will be, thus forcing a higher magnitude of the loop transmission function $l_{ii} = g_{ii}q_{ii}$. However, this may affect favorably the burden on the remaining t_{ij}'s. A design tradeoff between assumed maximum values of $|\tau_{ij}|$ and of $|\tau_{dij}|$ becomes inevitable, as will be illustrated later.

Remark 1. Eq.(6.3.1) specifies lower and upper bounds on each $|t_{ij}(j\omega)|$. In practical engineering problems, some of the input-output transfer functions are required to have only specified upper bounds, i.e., $a_{ij}(j\omega) = 0$, $i \neq j$. For this type of system, termed *basically noninteracting,* we wish to obtain zero effect of command input r_i on output y_j, i.e., $t_{ji} = 0$, $i \neq j$. However, because of the uncertainty of the plant, this can never be achieved for all plant conditions. In this case, some of the specifications will be bounded as follows:

$$|t_{ij}(j\omega)| \leq b_{ij}(\omega), \; i \neq j$$

Remark 2. If we are interested in a diagonal transfer function matrix **T**, the filter transfer function matrix **F** can be chosen as a diagonal, thus, $f_{ij} = 0$, $i \neq j$.

The design technique of this section will be explained with the 2 × 2 MIMO uncertain feedback problem, and will be illustrated with a solved 2 × 2 design example.

6.3.3. The 2 × 2 Uncertain Feedback System Design Problem

Let us illustrate the design technique with a 2 × 2 feedback system in which **G** is diagonal. By Eq.(6.3.7)

$$t_{11} = \frac{g_{11}q_{11}f_{11}}{1+g_{11}q_{11}} - \frac{\frac{q_{11}}{q_{12}}t_{21}}{1+g_{11}q_{11}} \qquad t_{12} = \frac{g_{11}q_{1}f_{12}}{1+g_{11}q_{11}} - \frac{\frac{q_{11}}{q_{12}}t_{22}}{1+g_{11}q_{11}} \qquad (6.3.8a,b)$$

$$t_{21} = \frac{g_{22}q_{22}f_{21}}{1+g_{22}q_{22}} - \frac{\frac{q_{22}}{q_{21}}t_{11}}{1+g_{22}q_{22}} \qquad t_{22} = \frac{g_{22}q_{22}f_{22}}{1+g_{22}q_{22}} - \frac{\frac{q_{22}}{q_{21}}t_{12}}{1+g_{22}q_{22}} \qquad (6.3.9a,b)$$

In the 2 × 2 feedback problem we have to deal with 2 loop transmissions, $l_1(j\omega)$ $= g_{11}(j\omega)q_{11}(j\omega)$ and $l_2(j\omega) = g_{22}(j\omega)q_{22}(j\omega)$. In the design of $l_1(j\omega)$, we have to satisfy the two identities in Eqs. (6.3.8a,b). These must be satisfied for the worst specification conditions of Eq.(6.3.1), and for the entire set $\mathcal{Q}_{ij}$ generated for $\forall m \in \mathcal{M}$. Notice that in each one of the single-loops to be designed, and for which specifications on t_{ij} are to be satisfied, the effect of the remaining t_{ij} channels appear as a disturbance d_{ij} defined in Eq.(6.3.7a). This interaction between the single-loop systems depends on the performance tolerances.

To illustrate this effect, let us suppose that we deal with a basically noninteracting system so that a diagonal **F** can be used, $f_{ij} = 0$, $i \neq j$. With the last assumption, Eqs.(6.3.8) and (6.3.9) are simplified to

$$t_{11} = \frac{g_{11}q_{11}f_{11}}{1 + g_{11}q_{11}} - \frac{\frac{q_{11}}{q_{12}}t_{21}}{1 + g_{11}q_{11}} = \tau_{11} - \tau_{d11}; \quad t_{12} = -\frac{\frac{q_{11}}{q_{12}}t_{22}}{1 + g_{11}q_{11}} = -\tau_{d12} \quad (6.3.10a,b)$$

and

$$t_{21} = -\frac{\frac{q_{22}}{q_{21}}t_{11}}{1 + g_{22}q_{22}} = -\tau_{d21}; \quad t_{22} = \frac{g_{22}q_{22}f_{22}}{1 + g_{22}q_{22}} - \frac{\frac{q_{22}}{q_{21}}t_{12}}{1 + g_{22}q_{22}} = \tau_{22} - \tau_{d22} \quad (6.3.11a,b)$$

Initially, let us specify $|t_{12}| < b_{12} = 0.1$ and $|t_{21}| < b_{21} = 0.1$. Suppose next that b_{12} and b_{21} are decreased by a factor of 10. In this case, τ_{d11} and τ_{d22} will be decreased by the same factor, so that a larger part of the permitted bounds of $|t_{11}|$ and $|t_{22}|$ can be allocated to $|\tau_{11}|$ and to $|\tau_{22}|$ respectively, as per Eq.(6.3.10a) and (6.3.11b). Thus, the bandwidth needed for the loop transmissions $l_1(j\omega)$ and $l_2(j\omega)$ is decreased. However, the same bandwidth will tend to increase drastically in order to satisfy Eqs.(6.3.10b) and (6.3.11a) in which the permitted upper bounds were decreased by the same factor of 10. Similarly, if the bounds on $|t_{ii}|$, namely b_{11} and b_{22}, are decreased, then d_{21} and d_{12} become smaller in Eqs.(6.3.10b) and (6.3.11a). But the feedback requirements in Eqs.(6.3.10a) and (6.3.11b) become consequently more stringent. Thus, tradeoffs between the tolerances of these bounds are necessary (without violating the original input-output tracking specifications), in order to emerge with g_{11} and g_{22} with minimal magnitudes, especially in the high frequency range where the sensor noise is the most pronounced.

Modification of the tolerances

The above interaction between the single-loop performances, defined by Eqs.(6.3.10) and (6.3.11), can be illustrated in the following way. Suppose that at some frequency, say $\omega = 1$, $b_{11} = 0.9$ and $a_{11} = 0.4$, a difference of 0.5, which must be split up between τ_{11} and τ_{d11} in Eq.(6.3.10a). Suppose that we allow arbitrarily $|\tau_{d11}|_{max} = 0.2$. If we define the bounds on $|\tau_{11}|$ as $[b'_{11}, a'_{11}]$, then it is necessary that $a'_{11} = 0.4 + 0.2 = 0.6$ and $b'_{11} = 0.9 - 0.2 = 0.7$. Thus, the new bounds on $|\tau_{11}|$ will be within the range $[0.7, 0.6]$, which is quite a severe demand. This happens because the phases of τ_{11} and τ_{d11} are not known in advance, and their maximum values must be added or subtracted arithmetically in Eqs.(6.3.7a). The latter choice of the modified bounds seems to be bad, because with such bounds, l_1 will emerge with very large magnitudes. When $[b'_{11}, a'_{11}]$ is modified, the influence of these bounds on the remaining inequalities must be foreseen.

Precisely as in Chapter 4, we have to loopshape first a nominal loop transmission $l_{1n} = g_{11} q_{11n}$. The latter is altered according to plant changes, that is, $l_1 = l_{1n}q_{11}/q_{11n}$. The demands on l_{1n} due to τ_{11}, τ_{d11} and to τ_{d12} in Eqs.(6.3.10a,b) can be written

$$\Delta\left|\frac{l_1}{1 + l_1}\right|_{dB} \leq \left(\frac{b'_{11}}{a'_{11}}\right)_{dB} \quad (6.3.12)$$

$$\left| \frac{1}{1 + l_{1n} q_{11}/q_{11n}} \right| \leq \left| \frac{q_{12}}{q_{11}} \frac{b_{d11}}{b_{21}} \right| \tag{6.3.13}$$

$$\leq \left| \frac{q_{12}}{q_{11}} \frac{b_{12}}{b_{22}} \right| \tag{6.3.14}$$

Similarly, demands on l_{2n} can be obtained from Eqs.(6.3.11a,b). These can be written

$$\Delta \left| \frac{l_2}{1 + l_2} \right|_{dB} \leq \left(\frac{b'_{22}}{a'_{22}} \right)_{dB} \tag{6.3.15}$$

$$\left| \frac{1}{1 + l_{2n} q_{22}/q_{22n}} \right| \leq \left| \frac{q_{21}}{q_{22}} \frac{b_{d22}}{b_{12}} \right| \tag{6.3.16}$$

$$\leq \left| \frac{q_{21}}{q_{22}} \frac{b_{21}}{b_{22}} \right| \tag{6.3.17}$$

The two single-loop problems defined so far by the inequalities in Eqs.(6.3.12) to (6.3.17) can be solved by the QFT design technique presented in Chapter 4.

Constraints at high frequencies

The above design problem is solvable as long as d_{ij} is bounded. This is indeed the case since b_{ij} and a_{ij} in Eq.(6.3.1) are bounded. In Eqs.(6.3.8) and (6.3.10) we use the maximum values of $|t_{ij}|$, such that $|t_{11}|_{max} = b_{11}$, $|t_{21}|_{max} = b_{21}$ and so on. As $\omega \to \infty$, $l_{ii} \to 0$, and $|\tau_{11}|$ and $|\tau_{21}|$ can be disregarded in Eqs.(6.3.8a) and (6.3.9a) by making $|f_{11}|$ and $|f_{21}|$ sufficiently small at high frequencies. Now, Eqs.(6.3.7), (6.3.7c) and (6.3.7d) generally require $|t_{ij}|_{max} > 2|t_{dij}||d_{ij}|_{max}$. At high frequencies this leads to $b_{11} > 2b_{21}|q_{11}/q_{12}|$ and $b_{21} > 2b_{11}|q_{22}/q_{21}|$, requiring $1 > 4|p_{12}p_{21}|/|p_{11}p_{22}|$ as $\omega \to \infty$. Thus, a constraint on **P** in the high frequency range is

$$|p_{11} p_{22}| > 4|p_{12} p_{21}| \quad \forall m \ \mathcal{M} \tag{6.3.18}$$

If this inequality does not hold, the $p_{ij}(s)$ can be renamed by changing their subscripts so that the inequality holds.

An additional constraint on the t_{ij}, $i \neq j$ specified tolerances for the 2×2 basically noninteracting system treated here follows from Eq.(6.3.11a). This equation can be rewritten as

$$\frac{t_{21}}{\frac{q_{22}}{q_{21}} t_{11}} = - \frac{1}{1 + g_{22} q_{22}} \ .$$

Since at high frequencies, as $\omega \to \infty$, $g_{22}q_{22} \to 0$ it follows also that

$$b_{21} = |t_{21}|_{max} \geq |t_{11}q_{22}/q_{21}|_{max} \qquad (6.3.19)$$

Generally this condition can be easily fulfilled since, as $\omega \to \infty$, so does $|t_{11}| \to 0$.

At this explanatory stage a design example is vital. Once again, an example with simple low order plant transfer functions is solved in order to simplify the computational effort and to obtain a transparent insight into the design procedure. Problems with much more complicated plants, a chemical MIMO plant, for example, can be solved with the same degree of easiness. In any case, the computational burden will be transferred to the computer.

Example 6.3.1.   The plant family is defined by $p_{ij} = k_{ij}/(1+sA_{ij})$, with correlated uncertain parameters as given in Table 6.3.1.

The performance tolerances on $|t_{ij}(j\omega)|$ are shown in Figs.(6.3.3) to (6.3.5). A basically noninteracting system is desired.

Solution. Each one of the two single loops will now be designed. Some preliminary relations must first be obtained. The different design steps follow.

Step 1. Translation of time-domain specifications into frequency-domain specifications.

In this example, the translation step is omitted; the specifications are given directly in the frequency-domain. The specifications of $|t_{11}|$ are the same as those defined in main Example 4.3.1 (Section 4.3.8), while the specifications for $|t_{22}|$ are those defined in Example 4.4.1 (Section 4.4). The specified bounds $b_{11}, a_{11}, b_{22}, a_{22}, b_{12}$ and b_{21} are next displayed in linear scale. This is done by translating the logarithmic magnitude Bode plots, shown in Figs.6.3.3 to 6.3.5, into Bode plots in linear magnitude scale, shown in Figs.6.3.6 to 6.3.8.

Table 6.3.1. Plant parameters

Case No	k_{11}	k_{22}	k_{12}	k_{21}	A_{11}	A_{22}	A_{12}	A_{21}	$\dfrac{k_{11}k_{22}}{k_{12}k_{21}}$	$\dfrac{k_{11}k_{22}}{A_{11}A_{22}}$	$\dfrac{k_{12}k_{21}}{A_{12}A_{21}}$
1	1	2	0.5	1	1	2	2	3	4	1	0.08
2	1	2	0.5	1	0.5	1	1	2	4	4	0.25
3	1	2	0.5	1	0.2	0.4	0.5	1	4	25	1
4	4	5	1	2	1	2	2	3	10	10	0.33
5	4	5	1	2	0.5	1	1	2	10	40	1
6	4	5	1	2	0.2	0.4	0.5	1	10	250	4
7	10	8	2	4	1	2	2	3	10	40	1.3
8	10	8	2	4	0.5	1	1	2	10	160	4
9	10	8	2	4	0.2	0.4	0.5	1	10	1,000	16

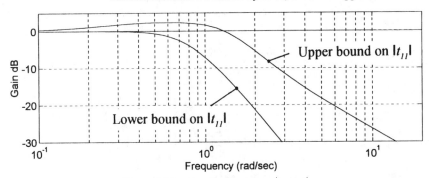

Figure 6.3.3. Specified bounds on $|t_{11}(j\omega)|$.

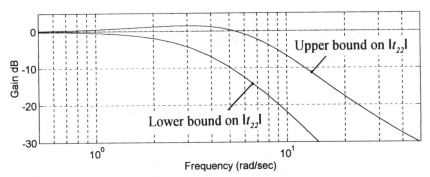

Figure 6.3.4. Specified bounds on $|t_{22}(j\omega)|$.

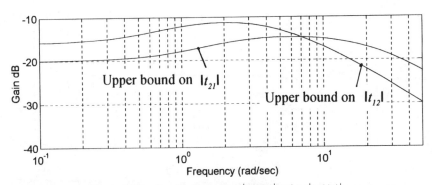

Figure 6.3.5. Specified bounds on $|t_{12}(j\omega)|$ and on $|t_{21}(j\omega)|$.

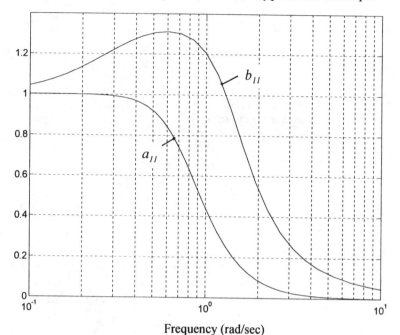

Figure 6.3.6. $b_{11}(\omega)$ and $a_{11}(\omega)$ in linear scale.

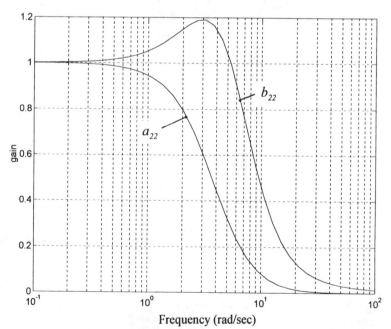

Figure 6.3.7. $b_{22}(\omega)$ and $a_{22}(\omega)$ in linear scale.

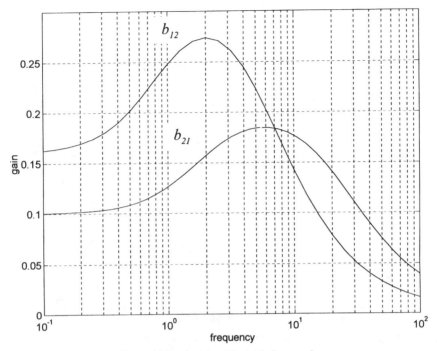

Figure 6.3.8. $b_{12}(\omega)$ and $b_{21}(\omega)$ in linear scale.

Step 2. Preparation of templates.

The elements $q_{ij}(s)$ are found from the inverse matrix $\mathbf{P}^{-1}$. From Figs. 6.3.3 and 6.3.4 we find out that $0.2 < \omega < 20$ is the important frequency range. Hence, templates for the uncertain plant were prepared, and bounds on $l_{1n} = g_{11}q_{11n}$ and $l_{2n} = g_{22}q_{22n}$ were derived on the Nichols chart at $\omega = [0.2, 0.5, 1, 2, 4, 7, 10, 20]$. Templates of q_{11} and q_{22} are shown in Figs. 6.3.9 and 6.3.10 for the plant cases in Table 6.3.1. Case 3 is chosen as the nominal plant.

Step 3. Modification of the specified bounds-preliminary stage.

The design technique is based on adequate modification of the bounds of $|\tau_{ii}|$ and $|\tau_{dii}|$. These depend, accordingly to Eqs.(6.3.10) and (6.3.11), on the maximum values of $|q_{11}/q_{12}|$ and of $|q_{22}/q_{21}|$. These are shown in Figs.6.3.11 and 6.3.12 for the family of plants given in Table 6.3.1. Table 6.3.2 is prepared to facilitate the next design steps.

Sensitivity bounds for satisfying Eqs.(6.3.10a) and (6.3.11b) are given in rows 2 and 3 for l_1. In the first place, we choose from row 4, $|\tau_{d1}| = 0.05$, and modify accordingly the initially defined bounds a_{11} and b_{11} to a'_{11} and b'_{11}, also given in rows 5, 6 of the table.

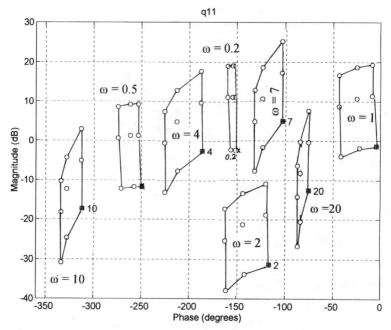

Figure 6.3.9.   Templates of the equivalent plant $q_{11}(j\omega)$ at some substantial frequencies.

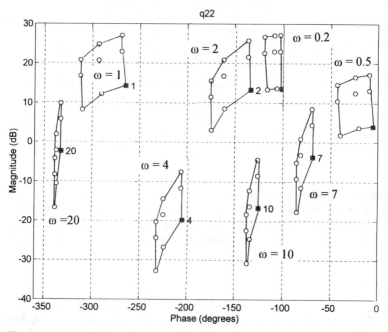

Figure 6.3.10.   Templates of the equivalent plant $q_{22}(j\omega)$ at some substantial frequencies

Table 6.3.2.   Extreme design parameters

1	ω	0.2	0.5	1	2	4	7	10	20
2	b_{11}	1.15	1.26	1.2	0.55	0.18	0.08	0.05	0.02
3	a_{11}	1	0.92	0.42	0.08	0.02	~ 0		
4	$|\tau_{d1}|_{max} = b_{d1}$	0.05	0.05	0.05	0.05	0.05	0.04		
5	b'_{11}	1.1	1.21	1.15	0.5	0.13	0.04		
6	a'_{11}	1.05	0.97	0.47	0.13	0.07	0.04		
7	b_{22}	1.01	1.02	1.08	1.15	1.15	0.78	0.45	0.13
8	a_{22}	10.98	0.95	0.8	0.43	0.18	0.09	0.02	
9	b_{12}	0.17	0.2	0.25	0.27	0.25	0.19	0.15	0.08
10	b_{21}	0.1	0.11	0.13	0.16	0.18	0.18	0.17	0.14
11	$\left|\dfrac{q_{11}}{q_{12}}\right|_{max}$	0.25	0.25	0.25	0.25	0.25	0.25	0.25	0.25
12	$\left|\dfrac{q_{22}}{q_{21}}\right|_{max}$	0.98	0.9	0.72	0.48	0.35	0.34	0.33	0.33
13	$\left|\dfrac{q_{11}}{q_{12}}b_{21}\right|_{max}$	0.03	0.03	0.03	0.04	0.05	0.04	0.04	0.04
14	$\left|\dfrac{q_{11}}{q_{12}}b_{22}\right|_{max}$	0.25	0.26	0.27	0.29	0.29	0.2	0.11	0.03
15	$\left|\dfrac{q_{22}}{q_{21}}b_{11}\right|_{max}$	1.13	1.13	0.86	0.26	0.06	0.03	0.02	0.01
16	$\left|\dfrac{q_{22}}{q_{21}}b_{12}\right|_{max}$	0.17	0.18	0.18	0.13	0.09	0.06	0.05	0.04
17	$b_{d1}\left/\left|\dfrac{q_{11}}{q_{12}}b_{21}\right|\right._{max}$	1.67	1.67	1.67	1.25	1	1	>1.5	>1.5
18	$b_{12}\left/\left|\dfrac{q_{11}}{q_{12}}b_{22}\right|\right._{max}$	0.68	0.77	0.9	0.93	0.86	0.95	1.4	2.6
19	$b_{21}\left/\left|\dfrac{q_{22}}{q_{21}}b_{11}\right|\right._{max}$	0.08	0.09	0.15	0.62	3	6	8.5	14

Step 4a. Derivation of bounds on the loop transmission $l_{1n}(j\omega)$ ***on the Nichols chart.***

In the design of l_1, we use the respective extreme values in rows 5, 6, 17 and 18, in order to find bounds on the Nichols chart that will guarantee that Eq.(6.3.12) to (6.3.14) are satisfied. The technique of deriving the bounds was explained in detail in Chapter 4. Bounds on l_1, to satisfy Eq.(6.3.12), are shown in Fig.6.3.13. Bounds on l_1, to satisfy Eq.(6.3.13), are shown in Fig.6.3.14, and bounds on l_1, to

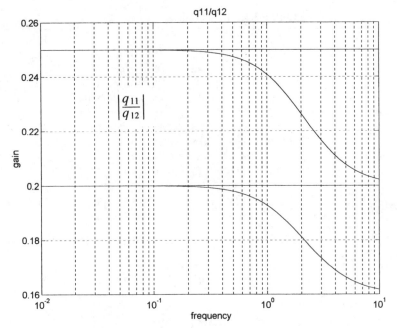

Figure 6.3.11. $|q_{11}/q_{12}|$ for the 9 cases in Table 6.3.1

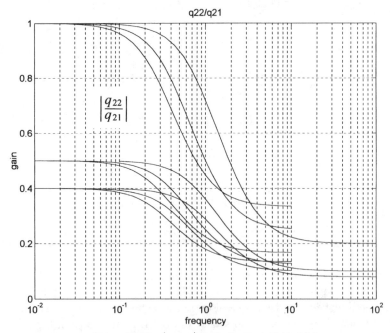

Figure 6.3.12. $|q_{22}/q_{21}|$ for the 9 cases in Table 6.3.1

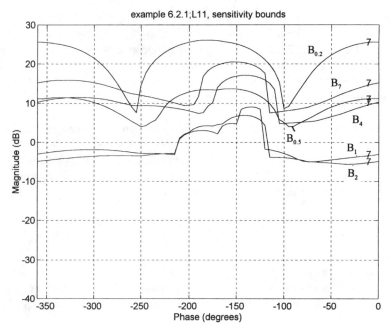

Figure 6.3.13. Sensitivity bounds on $l_{1n}(j\omega)$ to satisfy τ_{11} in Eq.(6.3.12).

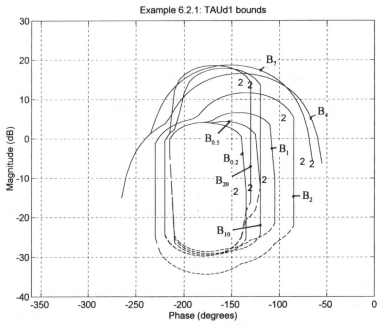

Figure 6.3.14. Disturbance bounds on $l_{1n}(j\omega)$ to satisfy τ_{d11} in Eq.(6.3.13).

satisfy Eq.(6.3.14), are shown in Fig.6.3.15. The intersection of all these bounds are shown in Fig.6.3.16. It is clearly perceived in the latter figure that since the bounds at $\omega = 1$ and 2 rad/sec lie below the bound at $\omega = 4$, they can be ignored and deleted. The same is true for the bound at $\omega = 0.5$, which lies completely below the bound at $\omega = 7$. Fig.6.3.17 shows the remaining necessary bounds for designing the loop transmission function l_{1n}.

Step 5a. Derivation of the loop transmission function $l_{1n}(j\omega)$ and of g_{11}.
Fig.6.3.17 shows the designed nominal $l_{1n}(j\omega)$ for the nominal case 3 in Table 6.3,1 that satisfies the necessary bounds; l_1 $(j7)$ and l_1 $(j20)$ lie practically on B_7 and B_{20}. The obtained l_1's for the remaining plants in the set $\mathcal{P}$ are shown in Fig.6.3.18. The obtained control network $g_{11}(s)$ is

$$g_{11}(s) = \frac{793}{s} \frac{s^2 + 2 \times 1 \times 70s + 70^2}{s^2 + 2 \times 3 \times 70s + 70^2} \frac{500^2}{s^2 + 2 \times 0.5 \times 500s + 500}$$

Step 6a. Design of the prefilter $f_{11}(s)$
By use of the Nichols chart, or by analytical computation, the unity-feedback $|t_{uf11}|$'s are derived. These are shown in Fig.6.3.19. All lie outside the permitted bounds a'_{11}

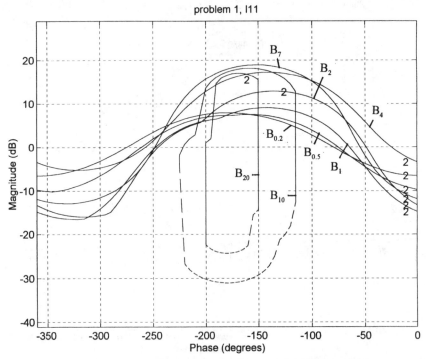

Figure 6.3.15.   Disturbance bounds on $l_{1n}(j\omega)$ to satisfy $|t_{12}|$ in Eq.(6.3.14).

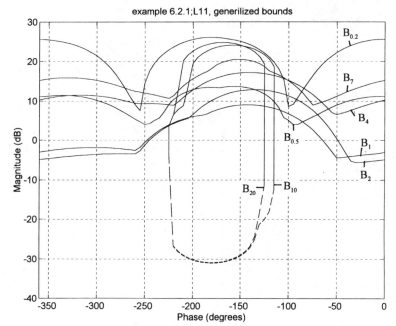

Figure 6.3.16.   Intersection of all bounds on $l_{1n}(j\omega)$
to satisfy simultaneously Eqs.(6.3.12) to (6.3.14)

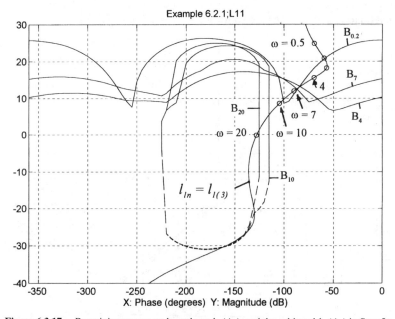

Figure 6.3.17.   Remaining necessary bounds on $l_{1n}(j\omega)$, and the achieved $l_{1n}(j\omega)$ in Step 5a.

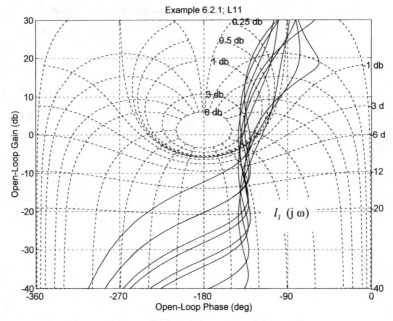

Figure 6.3.18. Loop transmissions $l_1(j\omega)$ for the set $\mathcal{P}$.

and b'_{11}. A simple filter $f_{11}(s)$ is derived to relocate the obtained $|t_{uf11}|$'s within the permitted bounds of $|t_{11}|$ which are shown in the same figure. The filter emerges as

$$f_{11}(s) = \frac{2.25(s + 0.2)}{(s + 0.3)(s + 1)(s + 1.5)}$$

This concludes the design stage of the first SISO feedback system around q_{11}. Next, we repeat steps 4a to 6a for designing the second SISO feedback system around q_{22}.

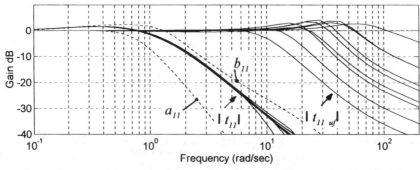

Figure 6.3.19. $|t_{uf11}|$'s and $|t_{11}| = |t_{uf11}f_{11}|$ for all plant cases.

Step 4b. Derivation of bounds on the loop transmission $l_{2n}(j\omega)$.
Proceeding exactly as in Step 4a, the bounds on l_2 are obtained. These are shown in Fig.6.3.20.

Step 5b. Derivation of the loop transmission function $l_{2n}(j\omega)$ ***and of*** g_{22}.
l_{2n} is designed in the usual way, and $l_2(j1)$ lies on the bound B_1, which practically fixes the lowest achievable gain bandwidth. The nominal l_2 is shown in Fig.6.3.20. The obtained controller is $g_{22}(s)$

$$g_{22}(s) = \frac{l_2}{q_{22}} = \frac{557}{s} \frac{(s+2.55)(s+28.9)(s+63.7)}{(s+19.22)(s+86.6)(s+157)} \frac{300^2}{s^2+2\times0.4\times300s+300^2}$$

The loop transmissions for all plant conditions are shown in Fig.6.3.21.

Step 6b. Design of the prefilter $f_{22}(s)$.
By use of the Nichols chart or by analytical computation, the unity-feedback $|t_{uf22}(j\omega)|$'s are derived and plotted versus frequency. All of them lie outside the permitted bounds a'_{22} and b'_{22}. A simple filter $f_{22}(s)$ is derived to relocate all $|t_{uf22}|$'s within the permitted bounds of $|t_{22}|$, as shown in Fig.6.3.22. The needful prefilter emerges as

$$f_{22}(s) = \frac{1.25(s+20)}{s^2+2\times0.64\times5s+5^2}$$

Step 7. Evaluation of the design.
Evaluation of the design in regard to the specifications on $|t_{11}|$ and $|t_{22}|$ could be performed with the two separate SISO feedback system simulations. However, in order to check compliance with the remaining t_{12} and t_{21} specifications, a complete 2×2 simulation must be programmed. This may be done by using, for example, Matlab/Simulink (see Fig.6.3.23). By use of this simulation, the resulting $|t_{21}|$'s and $|t_{12}|$'s are computed and plotted in figs.6.3.24 and 6.3.25 respectively. The results show that the specifications are satisfied.

The results in Figs.6.3.18, 6.3.19, 6.3.21 and 6.3.22 were obtained by two separate SISO simulation setups. But, identical results were obtained by running the complete 2×2 simulation.

Some comments are mandatory in order to conclude this design example.
1. It is seen in Fig.6.3.19 that all $|t_{11}|$'s are well inside the specified performance bounds. But, the maximal $\Delta|t_{11}|$ are much smaller than the changes which the bounds a_{11} and b_{11} allow. Thus, from the sensitivity point of view, a design with a lower gain bandwidth l_1 could be achieved. However, due to the harsh constraints on $|t_{21}|$ ($\equiv b_{21}$) and to the required high bandwidth of $|t_{22}|$ ($\equiv b_{22}$), the inequalities in Eqs.(6.3.13) and (6.3.14) cause the bounds on l_1 to become more elevated on the Nichols chart than the bounds due to sensitivity requirements on $|t_{11}|$, Eq.(6.3.12). To be more precise, let us look at Fig.6.3.15. The bounds at $\omega = 4$

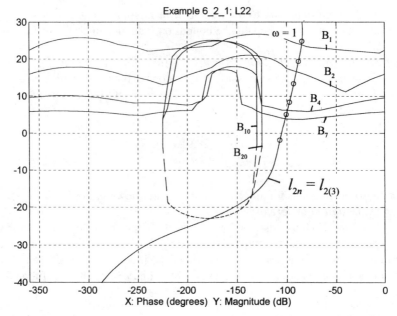

Figure 6.3.20.   Remaining necessary bounds on $l_{2n}(j\omega)$, and achieved $l_{2n}(j\omega)$ in Step 5b.

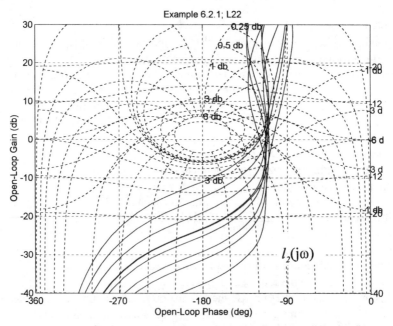

Figure 6.3.21.   Loop transmissions $l_2(j\omega)$ for all plant conditions.

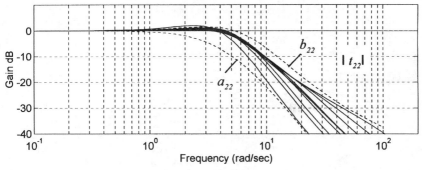

Figure 6.3.22. $|t_{22}(j\omega)|$'s for all plant cases.

and 7 rad/sec are the most elevated. The results in Fig.6.3.25 show that in the range $2 < \omega < 5$, the extreme $|t_{12}|$'s are quite close to the bound b_{12} on $|t_{12}|$. This points to the fact that at these frequencies, g_{11} emerges with nearly the lowest possible magnitude. On the other hand, the bounds at the same frequencies in Fig.6.3.13, for satisfying the sensitivity specifications on $|t_{11}|$, lie below the bounds pertaining to the $|t_{12}|$ specifications. Thus, there is an overdesign in l_1, and the permitted $\Delta|l_1/(1+l_1)|$ is not sufficiently exploited. (see Fig.6.3.19).

2. The above reasoning leads to the conclusion that a careful tradeoff between $|\tau_{ij}|$ and $|\tau_{dij}|$ in the partitioning of t_{ii}, $i = 1, n$ in Eqs.(6.3.7a) and (6.3.7b) can help in

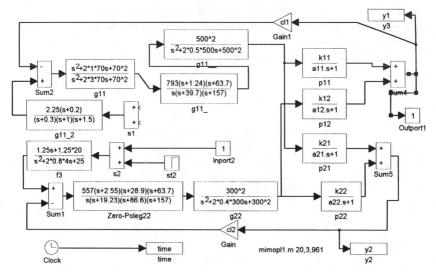

Figure 6.3.23. 2×2 complete simulation for checking the original 2x2 MIMO feedback system.

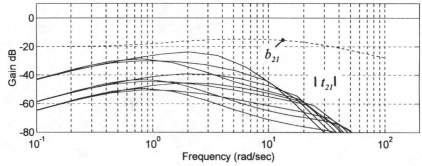

Figure.6.3.24. $|t_{21}(j\omega)|$'s for all plant cases.

obtaining a design solution with smaller gain bandwidths of the control networks $g_{11}(s)$ and $g_{22}(s)$, thus decreasing the sensor noise amplification in both channels.

The above conclusion is contrary to the SISO uncertain plant feedback problem. In this problem, once the specifications are defined, the outcome control solution satisfies the specifications in a unique and optimal way from the point of view of sensor noise amplification at the input to the plant. (See Section 4.3.4). In other words, the QFT solution for the MIMO uncertain plant problem is not unique. Several iterations might be necessary in order to satisfy the specifications with a more economical bandwidth by different choices of τ_{ij} and of τ_{dij}, Eq.(6.3.7b)

The general interacting case

Eqs.(6.3.8) and (6.3.9) are the equations for the design of the general 2×2 feedback problem. In case we are confronted with a design problem in which $|t_{ij}|$, $i \neq j$ have both upper **and** lower specified bounds, then we cannot use a diagonal prefilter matrix **F**. This fact by itself complicates the design stages, because more tradeoffs in choosing initial values for τ_{dij} will be necessary to achieve a more eco-

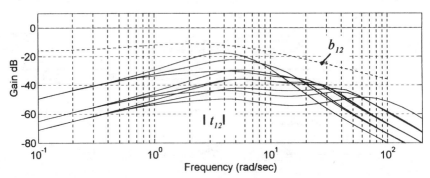

Figure.6.3.25. $|t_{12}(j\omega)|$'s for all plant cases.

nomical design in bandwidth. However, the basic design technique remains the same, (see, for instance, Yaniv 1995).

6.3.4. The 3 × 3 feedback system design problem.

The solution of the 3 × 3 feedback problem is much more complicated than the solution of the 2 × 2 problem, but a design process is still feasible. The constraint at high frequencies on the plant elements for existence of a solution as $s \to \infty$, becomes,

$$|p_{11}p_{22}p_{33}| > |p_{11}\,p_{23}p_{32}| + |p_{12}p_{21}p_{33}| + |p_{12}p_{23}p_{31}| + |p_{13}p_{22}p_{31}| + |p_{13}p_{21}p_{32}|$$

$$(6.3.20)$$

Design problems of 3 × 3 uncertain feedback systems were successfully solved by Horowitz and Loecher (1981), Horowitz et al.(1981), Horowitz et al.(1982).

6.4 Summary

This chapter dealt with the uncertain $n \times n$ feedback system problem. First, some basic features of MIMO feedback systems in the frequency-domain were stated and applied to the design of such systems in which the plant has no uncertainty. Diagonalization of the open-loop transfer function matrix is a common procedure that enormously facilitates MIMO system design. Noninteraction, by inversion of the plant transfer function matrix, and sequential loop closing were presented and illustrated by solved examples. Conditions for internal stability of MIMO feedback systems were then presented. The outline of the Q-parametrization design procedure for stabilizing feedback systems with stable and unstable plant transfer function matrices was also presented. Next, the basic QFT was used to solve the MIMO uncertain plant feedback problem. The basic idea is to decompose the MIMO problem into n SISO design problems, for which design techniques in the frequency-domain exist.

As for the SISO uncertain plant feedback system problem, it is of practical interest to solve the MIMO uncertain plant feedback system problem by use of the more recent and advanced H_∞-norm optimization paradigm. This will be carried out in Chapter 8.

Chapter 7 _____

Introductory to Design Techniques in the State-Space Framework

7.1 Introduction.

Chapter 6 culminated in the solution of the 'MIMO uncertain feedback problem' with the QFT design technique. Our next and final goal involves solving the same problem within the H_∞-control framework. In the literature, when in the latter framework, scientists and engineers prefer the term 'MIMO robust control'. Both expressions are used interchangeably in the text. The frequency-domain approach for analyzing feedback control systems was adopted in the previous chapters. This domain is 'natural' to control engineers, since, when faced with a transfer function, there is an immediate mental connection with nature; the poles describe clearly the dynamical properties of the physical system. On the other hand, conversion of the differential equations of a physical system to the 'state-space form' results in matrices that tell us nothing about the nature of its dynamics.

Since most of the optimization algorithms used in the H_∞ paradigm are solved within the state-space formulation, and since important definitions and theorems from the state-space oriented literature will be used to the solution of the MIMO uncertain feedback problem, a short tutorial overlook on state-space theory can be beneficial. Section 7.3 presents an overview of such subjects as the Linear Quadratic Regulator (LQR) in which all the states of the system can be measured, and hence, full state-feedback is applied for regulating the feedback system. Implicit and explicit model- following methods based on the LQR design principles are also treated and exemplified. Next, in Section 7.4, the Linear-Quadratic-Gaussian (LQG) problem is reviewed briefly. In this famous conjecture, some of the states cannot be measured, and in addition, since process and sensor noises are included, all the states must be estimated optimally (The Kalman-Bucy filter). Only then can the solution of the full-state feedback control problem be implemented. The 'separation principle' and the solution of the LQG problem are reviewed. The LQG Loop Transfer Recovery (LQG/LTR) method, innovated by Doyle and Stein (1979), is introduced next in order to further improve the LQG design technique. There exists a vast literature of excellent books and technical papers dealing with control design in the state-space framework, from which we will quote important facts and theorems, generally, without proofs. Just to mention some of them, Athans and Falb (1969), Athans (1971), Anderson and Moore (1971, 1990), Kvakernaak and Sivan (1972), Bryson and Ho (1975), Dorato et al.(1995) and many others.

7.2.   MIMO Feedback Control in the State-Space Framework

The structure of the control problem to be solved in the state-space formulation is shown in Fig.7.2.1. In practice, plants and compensators are described in the form of transfer functions, whose properties in the frequency-domain can be obtained by measurements on the control hardware with appropriate instrumentation. This is maybe the reason why practicing control engineers prefer working with transfer functions. But, to be fair, the transfer functions are obtained from the solution of linear differential equations which can be converted to the state-space formulation. It is well known that the set of linear differential equations expressing the dynamics of physical hardware can be put in the following state-space form, (see also Appendix B),

$$\frac{d}{dt}\mathbf{x} = \mathbf{A}(t)\mathbf{x}(t) + \mathbf{B}(t)\mathbf{u}(t) \tag{7.2.1a}$$

$$\mathbf{y}(t) = \mathbf{C}(t)\mathbf{x}(t) + \mathbf{D}(t)\mathbf{u}(t) \tag{7.2.1b}$$

in which $\mathbf{x}$, $\mathbf{u}$ and $\mathbf{y}$ are the state, the control and the output vectors respectively. $\mathbf{A}$, $\mathbf{B}$, $\mathbf{C}$ and $\mathbf{D}$ are matrices of appropriate order. By use of the Laplace transformation, it is easily found that if the matrices $\mathbf{A}$, $\mathbf{B}$, $\mathbf{C}$ and $\mathbf{D}$ are time invariant, then

$$\mathbf{y}(s) = \mathbf{C}(s)[s\mathbf{I}-\mathbf{A}]^{-1}\mathbf{Bu}(s) + \mathbf{Du}(s) = \{\mathbf{C}(s)[s\mathbf{I}-\mathbf{A}]^{-1}\mathbf{B} + \mathbf{D}\}\mathbf{u}(s) \tag{7.2.2}$$

and the transfer function matrix relating the output vector $\mathbf{y}(s)$ to the input vector $\mathbf{u}(s)$ is identified as

$$\mathbf{P}(s) = \mathbf{C}(s)[s\mathbf{I}-\mathbf{A}]^{-1}\mathbf{B} + \mathbf{D} \tag{7.2.3}$$

The feedback control structure in Fig.7.2.1 is very general. The **Plant,** the state-feedback gain matrix $\mathbf{K}_c$ obtained with the Linear Quadratic Regulator (LQR) solution (presented in Section 7.3), and the famous Kalman-Bucy Filter (presented in Sec-

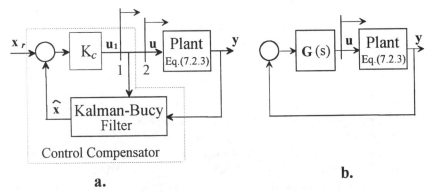

Figure 7.2.1.   State-feedback realization including a Kalman-Bucy filter.

tion 7.4) can be described in state-space formulation or in transfer function matrix form as in Chapter 6. The control compensator from **y** to **u** in Fig.7.2.1a can also be expressed in transfer function matrix form, (**G**(s) in Fig.7.2.1b), for time invariant systems. The state-space formulation was initiated in the early 1960s by Kalman and his numerous followers to solve the LQG problem. The essence of the LQG paradigm is to optimize some quadratic performance measure, related to a known constrained plant (process), when input disturbances to the plant and sensor noises are present. The solution to this problem is best performed in state-space formulation (Section 7.4).

K$_c$ in Fig.7.2.1a is the LQR optimal state-feedback gain controller. **K**$_c$ emerges as a matrix of order $n \times m$, where n is the state order of the plant **P**(s), and m is the number of inputs to the plant. Unfortunately, in real physical systems, all of the states can never be measured. There remain very few measurable states, or output variables, which are linear combinations of the states. In order to implement the optimal controller **K**$_c$, which uses all the system states, the unmeasurable states must be estimated (or observed) first. This is the task of the Kalman-Bucy Filter, which not only estimates the states that cannot be measured, but also optimally filters the sensor and the process noises present in all practical systems. The following sections review quadratic performance criterion design methods which are an essential basis to H_∞-norm optimization algorithms used in control design.

7.3.   The Linear Quadratic Regulator (LQR) Problem

In this section the optimal LQR problem is stated and solved.

The basic optimization problem treated in this section is that of finding an optimal state-feedback control law $\mathbf{u} = -\mathbf{K}_c\mathbf{x}$ that minimizes a quadratic performance index of the form

$$J = \int_0^T (\mathbf{x}^T\mathbf{Q}\mathbf{x} + \mathbf{u}^T\mathbf{R}\mathbf{u})dt + \mathbf{x}^T(T)\mathbf{M}\mathbf{x}(T) \qquad (7.3.1)$$

where $\mathbf{Q}$, $\mathbf{M}$ and $\mathbf{R}$ are symmetric matrices; $\mathbf{Q}$ and $\mathbf{M}$ are nonnegative definite; and $\mathbf{R}$ is a positive-definite. The constrained system dynamics are given by

$$\frac{d}{dt}\mathbf{x} = \mathbf{A}\mathbf{x} + \mathbf{B}\mathbf{u} \qquad (7.3.2)$$

The control goal is to keep the state of the system vector $\mathbf{x}(t)$ as close as possible to the state $\mathbf{x}_r = \mathbf{0}$ denoted in Fig.7.2.1a. The term $\mathbf{x}^T\mathbf{Q}\mathbf{x}$ in Eq.(7.3.1) is a measure of control accuracy. The term $\mathbf{u}^T\mathbf{R}\mathbf{u}$ is a measure of control effort and the term $\mathbf{x}^T(T)\mathbf{M}\mathbf{x}(T)$ is a measure of control accuracy at the terminal time T. This is called a *regulator problem* because the objective of the regulator is to maintain the state of the feedback system close to the zero state. The performance measure consists of quadratic terms in elements of the state and the control vectors. From here stems the expression *optimal* **Linear Quadratic Regulator** (LQR) *problem*. The solution to this problem consists in finding an optimal control law of the form

$$\mathbf{u} = -\mathbf{K}_c\,\mathbf{x}. \qquad (7.3.3)$$

$\mathbf{K}_c$ is generally called the optimal state-feedback matrix.

There are different approaches for finding this optimal control law, one of them is the **dynamic-programming approach** proposed by Bellman (1952). Another common approach is based on the **Hamilton-Jacobi Equation,** Craggs (1973). Formal derivation of the optimal control-law using these two fundamental approaches can be found in Athans and Falb (1966), Anderson and Moore (1971, 1990), Bryson and Ho (1975), Dorato et al.(1995). To save repeating the derivations, only the final results will be presented here.

The optimal controller for the LQR problem is found by solving the following matrix Riccati equation, which is obtained by using the data defined in Eqs.(7.3.1) and (7.3.2):

$$-\frac{d}{dt}\mathbf{P} = \mathbf{A}^T\mathbf{P} + \mathbf{P}\mathbf{A} + \mathbf{Q} - \mathbf{P}\mathbf{B}\mathbf{R}^{-1}\mathbf{B}^T\mathbf{P} \qquad (7.3.4)$$

with boundary (terminal) condition

$$\mathbf{P}(T) = \mathbf{M} \qquad (7.3.5)$$

Finally, the optimal control-law and controller are given by

$$\mathbf{u}(t) = -\mathbf{K}_c(t)\mathbf{x}\,(t) \qquad (7.3.6)$$

$$\mathbf{K}_c(t) = \mathbf{R}^{-1}\,\mathbf{B}^T\mathbf{P}(t) \qquad (7.3.7)$$

From Eq.(7.3.7) it is evident why the matrix **R** ought to be **positive-definite.** Eqs.(7.3.6) and (7.3.7) are the solution of the general LQR problem. The state-feedback gain matrix $\mathbf{K}_c(t)$ will be time variant even if only one of the matrices **A, B, Q, R** are time variant, and/or the terminal time T, also named *time-to-go,* is finite. The optimal control-law $\mathbf{u}(t) = -\mathbf{K}_c(t)\mathbf{x}(t)$ is time variant because it is derived from the solution of a Riccati equation which is time variant. On the other hand, if all the matrices **A, B, Q, R** are constant, and the terminal time T is infinite, then the Riccati equation becomes constant, too. It is then called the *Algebraic Riccati Equation* (ARE). The resulting optimal controller then becomes a constant matrix $\mathbf{K}_c$. Both cases of time varying and constant $\mathbf{K}_c$ will be discussed and exemplified in this section.

7.3.1 The General Case

An analytical closed form solution is possible only for very special and simple problems. The following procedure is usually followed in the solution of the general case.

Solution of the Riccati equation

First, the *Hamiltonian matrix* is formed

$$\mathbf{H} = \begin{bmatrix} \mathbf{A} & -\mathbf{BR}^{-1}\mathbf{B}^T \\ -\mathbf{Q} & -\mathbf{A}^T \end{bmatrix} \tag{7.3.8}$$

The solution of the nonlinear Riccati equation in Eq.(7.3.4) is obtained by solving the system of linear equations

$$\frac{d}{dt}\begin{bmatrix} \mathbf{X} \\ \mathbf{Y} \end{bmatrix} = \mathbf{H}\begin{bmatrix} \mathbf{X} \\ \mathbf{Y} \end{bmatrix} \tag{7.3.9}$$

with boundary conditions

$$\begin{bmatrix} \mathbf{X}(T) \\ \mathbf{Y}(T) \end{bmatrix} = \begin{bmatrix} \mathbf{I} \\ \mathbf{M} \end{bmatrix} \tag{7.3.10}$$

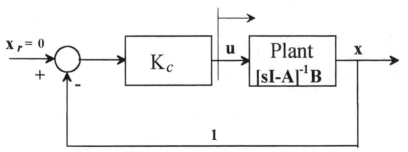

Figure 7.3.1. Control structure for the LQR problem.

$\mathbf{X}(t)$ and $\mathbf{Y}(t)$ are $n \times n$ matrices. The solution $\mathbf{P}(t)$ of the Riccati equation is obtained from the solutions of the above matrices, namely,

$$\mathbf{P}(t) = \mathbf{Y}(t)\mathbf{X}^{-1}(t) \qquad (7.3.11)$$

(See Dorato et al. 1995 for the proof.)

The Hamiltonian matrix is used by many of the software programs in Matlab tools (control, robust, μ) to solve LQR, LQG, H_∞ and other control problems. When the matrices $\mathbf{A}, \mathbf{B}, \mathbf{Q}$ and $\mathbf{R}$ are constant, an explicit solution is available (See Anderson and Moore, 1990, Dorato et al., 1995.)

With most design techniques based on quadratic performance measure, choice of the weighting matrices $\mathbf{Q}, \mathbf{R}$ and $\mathbf{M}$ is a major problem. It is up to the control engineer to choose the appropriate elements of these matrices so that preferred control performances can be achieved. Some intuition is necessary in choosing them.

The next example illustrates the meaning of a linear quadratic regulator and the problem in choosing the parameters of the weighting matrices.

Example 7.3.1.   Find an optimal controller that minimizes the performance index

$$J = \int_0^T (x^2 + u^2)dt + x^T(T)mx(T)$$

subject to

$$\frac{d}{dt}x = ax + u \qquad (7.3.12)$$

Solution: In this algebraic case, $\mathbf{A} = [a]$; $\mathbf{B} = [b]$; $\mathbf{Q} = [q]$; $\mathbf{R} = [r]$; $\mathbf{M} = [m]$; where $a = 2, b = 1$ and $T = 5$ sec; q, r and m are the design parameters. The matrix Riccati equation becomes the scalar nonlinear differential equation

$$\frac{d}{dt}p = ap + ap + q - p^2 b^2 r^{-1} = q + 2ap - b^2 r^{-1} p^2 \qquad (7.3.13)$$

with boundary conditions $p(T) = m$.

The solution to this first order differential equation can be obtained by separation of variables,

$$\int \frac{dp}{q + 2ap - b^2 r^{-1} p^2} + c = -\int dt$$

or, see Petit Bois (1961),

$$\frac{1}{\sqrt{4qb^2r^{-1} + 4a^2}} \ln \frac{2b^2r^{-1}p - 2a + \sqrt{4qb^2r^{-1} + 4a^2}}{2b^2r^{-1}p - 2a - \sqrt{4qb^2r^{-1} + 4a^2}} + c = -t. \quad (7.3.14)$$

To find c, we put in Eq.(7.3.14) $p(T) = m$. We get
$$c = -T - c_1 \text{ where}$$

$$c_1 = \frac{1}{2\sqrt{qb^2r^{-1} + a^2}} \ln \frac{b^2r^{-1}m - a + \sqrt{qb^2r^{-1} + a^2}}{b^2r^{-1}m - a - \sqrt{qb^2r^{-1} + a^2}} \quad (7.3.15)$$

and finally, with $x = 2[qb^2r^{-1} + a^2]^{1/2}$, the solution of the Riccati equation becomes

$$p(t) = \frac{1}{2b^2r^{-1}} \frac{e^{x(T + c_1 - t)}(2a + x) - 2a + x}{e^{x(T + c_1 - t)} - 1}. \quad (7.3.16)$$

The optimal time varying control function $K(t)$ is then

$$K(t) = p(t)b/r$$

In this scalar example, we will choose at random initial values for the free design parameters q, r and m. Next, we will change these parameters in a logical way until the best results of $x(t)$, $u(t)$ and $J(t)$ are obtained.

1st design parameter choice; $q = 1, r = 1$ and $m = 5$.

With this choice of the design parameters, we find that $x = (20)^{1/2}$. From Eq.(7.3.14) we get the equation

$$\frac{1}{\sqrt{20}} \ln \frac{2p - 4 + \sqrt{20}}{2p - 4 - \sqrt{20}} + c = -t,$$

from which we find that $c_1 = 0.4304089$, and $c = -5 - 0.4304089 = -5.43$. The solution of the Riccati equation is finally

$$p(t) = \frac{0.236065 + 4.23607 \, e^{(T + c_1 - t)\sqrt{20}}}{e^{(T+c_1-t)\sqrt{20}} - 1} = \frac{0.236065 + 4.23607 \, e^{(5.43 - t)\sqrt{20}}}{e^{(5.43 - t)\sqrt{20}} - 1}.$$

The above equation satisfies the boundary conditions at $t = T = 5\text{sec}, p(T) = m = 5$. With the given data in this example, the optimum control gain becomes

$$K_c(t) = 1 \times 1 \times p(t) = p(t).$$

The resulting $x(t)$, $J(t)$, the time varying gain $K_c(t) = p(t)$ and the control input $u(t) = -K_c(t)x(t)$ for the initial condition $x(0) = 1$ are shown by the plain lines of Fig.7.3.2.

Choice of another set of design parameters (q, r and m) will lead to a different time response of $x(t)$. Some intuition is used to fix them so that an improved result is achieved. By analyzing the results in Fig.7.3.2, it is observed that the gain $K_c(t)$ is fairly constant in the first 4.7 sec, and that $x(t)$ is virtually zeroed at $t = 2$ sec.

Can the regulation time be shortened? Intuitively, if the value of r is reduced, then the control $u(t)$ is less constrained. It consequently tends to increase, thus speeding the regulation process, but, at the expense of an increased performance measure $J(T)$. This design factor is next illustrated numerically with a reduced parameter r.

2nd design parameter choice: $q = 1, r = 0.01$ *and* $m = 5$.
With this choice of design parameters, $x = (416)^{1/2}$, $c_1 = 0.0862$ and the solution of the Riccati equation becomes

$$p(t) = \frac{0.082 + 0.122\, e^{(T+c_1-t)20.39}}{e^{(T+c_1-t)20.39} - 1} = \frac{0.082 + 0.122 e^{(5.086-t)20.39}}{e^{(5.086-t)20.39} - 1}.$$

Due to the much lower value of r than in the 1st design parameters, a much larger control effort $u(t)$ is now obtained. But the regulating process is also much faster.

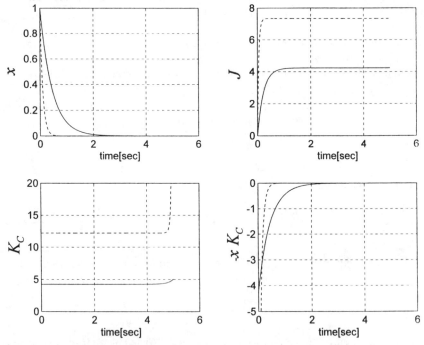

Figure 7.3.2.   Time histories of $x(t)$, $K_c(t)$, $-x(t)K_c(t)$ and $J(t)$.
Solid lines: $q = 1, r = 1, m = 5$. Dashed lines: $q = 1, r = 0.01, m = 5$.

The resulting variables are also shown by the dashed lines in Fig.7.3.2. The performance measure $J(T)$ with the second choice of r ($= 0.01$) is increased from 4.2 to 7.4, but the output $x(t)$ is virtually zeroed at less than 0.5 sec., a much shorter period than that achieved with the first choice of r ($= 1$).

This very simple example emphasizes that even for a first order time invariant linear system, but with a finite terminal time, the solution of the optimal controller is not trivial, as far as the solution of the Riccati equation is concerned. The situation is essentially aggravated when more complex system dynamics are considered. Easier analytical solutions are obtained for those control problems in which the Riccati equation becomes time invariant.

7.3.2. The Steady-State LQR Problem

This section deals with an LQR problem where the terminal time is infinite ($T\rightarrow\infty$), the constrained dynamic system (the plant) is time invariant, and the **Q** and **R** matrices have constant elements. With these assumptions, we are faced with the *steady-state LQR problem,* which can be solved with the (stationary) *Algebraic Riccati Equation* (ARE), given by

$$0 = \mathbf{A}^T\mathbf{P} + \mathbf{PA} + \mathbf{Q} - \mathbf{PBR}^{-1}\mathbf{B}^T\mathbf{P} \qquad (7.3.17)$$

The optimal state-feedback matrix $\mathbf{K}_c$ is obtained from the steady-state solution of **P** satisfying the above equation. When this very common problem is solved, the optimal control-law is time invariant,

$$\mathbf{u}(t) = -\mathbf{K}_c\mathbf{x}(t) \qquad (7.3.18)$$

since the elements of the optimal state-feedback control matrix $\mathbf{K}_c$ emerge constant

$$\mathbf{K}_c = \mathbf{R}^{-1}\mathbf{B}^T\mathbf{P}. \qquad (7.3.19)$$

Certain conditions are required for the existence of the steady-state LQR solution and for the stability of the controlled system. These conditions are related to some fundamental properties and concepts of linear systems described in state-space formulation, such as 'controllability' and 'observability', (both introduced by Kalman 1965), 'stabilizability' and 'detectability'. We only interpret here their physical meaning. For a deeper treatment of these system properties, the reader is referred to Ogata (1967), Kwakernaak and Sivan (1972), Kailath (1980), and to Appendix B.

Refer to Eqs.(7.2.1). In these equations, $\mathbf{x}(t)$ is the state vector, $\mathbf{u}(t)$ is the input vector whose elements are applied to the system at different input points, and $\mathbf{y}(t)$ is the output vector of the dynamic system, whose elements are a linear combination of the state variables. The elements of matrix $\mathbf{A}(t)$ depend on the parameters of the defined plant. The elements of matrix $\mathbf{B}(t)$ show how the input vector $\mathbf{u}(t)$

affects the state variables. The elements of matrix $C(t)$ show how the output variables are related to the state variables, and the matrix $D(t)$ shows how the control variables, which are the elements of $u(t)$, directly affect the output vector $y(t)$. ($D = 0$ in many practical systems). With the above basic definitions in the state-space formulation, we can consider the notions of 'controllability' and 'observability'. Assume that the matrices A, B, C and D are constant for this discussion.

Controllability

'Controllability' is defined from Eq.(7.2.1a). *Controllability* is the important property that for any t_0, it is possible to construct an unconstrained control vector $u(t)$ which will transfer any known initial state $x(t_0)$ to any desired final state $x(t_1)$ in a finite time interval $t_0 \leq t \leq t_1$. The mathematical test for controllability is easily shown to be as follows (consult one of the cited references). Suppose A is of order $n \times n$. For the system in Eq.(7.2.1a) to be controllable, the rank of the matrix

$$G = [B \mid AB \mid A^2 B \mid \ldots \mid A^{n-1} B]$$

must be of order n,

$$rank\ G = n \tag{7.3.20}$$

or, equivalently, if and only if there is a set of n linearly independent column vectors of G. This is also equivalent to the condition that no pole-zero cancellations occur in the transfer function matrix P of Eq.(7.2.3), Ogata (1967). In this context, we can define 'stabilizability': a system is named *stabilizable* if the uncontrollable modes are stable.

Observability

'Observability' is defined from Eqs.(7.2.1b) as follows. The measured output elements are in the output vector $y(t)$. A system is said to be *observable* in the time interval $t_0 \leq t \leq t_1$, if for every t_0 and some t_1, every state $x(t_0)$ can be determined from the measured output vector $y(t)$ on $t_0 \leq t \leq t_1$. In other words, each change in the state $x(t)$ will be sensed in the output vector $y(t)$. The mathematical test for observability consists in building the matrix

$$H = [C^T \mid A^T C^T \mid \ldots \mid \ldots \mid (A^{n-1})^T C^T]$$

and checking its rank. The system is observable if

$$rank\ H = n \tag{7.3.21}$$

or equivalently, if and only if, there is a set of n linearly independent column vectors of H. In this context, we can define 'detectability'. A system is named *detectable* if the unstable modes are observable.

The above concepts have a great impact upon the solution of the matrix Riccati equation, especially when we come to discuss design techniques based on the H_∞-norm optimization in the next chapter.

With these definitions and observations, we can proceed further with the ARE problem. As already mentioned, it is common to use symmetric Q matrices. To guarantee this, let us choose $Q = Q_1^T Q_1$ with Q positive definite. A very important theorem on existence and solution of the steady-state LQR solution is stated next (See Anderson and Moore 1971).

Theorem 7.3.1. Given the LQR problem with $M = 0$, R positive definite, and $Q = Q_1^T Q_1$, where the pair (A, B) is controllable and the pair (A, Q_1) is observable, there exists a solution to the steady-state LQR problem. This means, a positive-definite matrix P, which is a unique solution to the ARE (Eq.7.3.17), and that the optimal closed-loop system, i.e., $\frac{d}{dt}x = (A - B K_c)x(t)$, where $K_c = R^{-1}B^T P$, is asymptotically stable.

The proof is omitted, and can be found, for example, in Dorato et al.(1995).

Naturally, the system must be 'observable from the performance index', which means that all movement of the system will be sensed in the performance index. To be more precise, stabilizability and detectability are also necessary conditions for the existence and stabilization of the closed-loop system. This guaranties that unstable subsystems are stabilized. Moreover, stabilizability and detectability are required from the system dynamics so that the Hamiltonian matrix H (Eq.(7.3.8)) will not have eigenvalues on the imaginary axis. This property is very important when dealing with algorithms for H_∞-norm optimization (See for instance Glover and Doyle 1988).

7.3.3 Selection of the Q, R and M Matrices.

As we have seen in Example 7.3.1, the performances achieved with the LQR solution depend on the choice of the Q, R and M matrices. To have some freedom in influencing individually the states $x(t)$ and the control effort $u(t)$, it is advisable to choose them diagonal, so that each entry on the diagonal tends to influence directly the related elements of $x(t)$ or $u(t)$. Intuitively, to make a variable 'small' in the time-domain, the related entry on the diagonals of Q, R or M must be chosen 'large' enough, so that the variable is sensed more strongly in the performance measure J in Eq.(7.3.1). Unfortunately, 'large' has no meaning unless being such, comparatively to the remaining diagonal terms of all Q, R or M. As already mentioned, selection of these matrix elements is not an easy task. Numerous papers deal with this 'selection problem', (See Tyler and Tuteur 1966, Stein 1979, and others.) When the 'model following' LQR oriented design techniques is treated in the next section, this issue will be clarified to some extent. Finally, this is the place to point out that, from the point of view of the control designer, the problem of choosing the Q, and R matrices is greatly relieved when design techniques based on the H_∞-norm optimization are used. The control engineer is then able to achieve the design specifications by defining appropriate weighting functions with physical meaning.

The following example is solved with the LQR paradigm.

Example 7.3.2. Design an optimal steady-state regulator for the inverted pendulum shown in Fig.7.3.3, and investigate the influence of the selected **Q** and **R** matrices on: 1) the maximum angular deviation $\theta(t)$ of the stabilized pendulum; 2) maximum linear motion deviation of the cart $x(t)$; and 3) control effort $u(t)$. Maximum allowable deviation in x is 0.2 m. (Similar models are reported in Kailath 1980, Doyle et al. 1992, and Dorato et al. 1995.)

The linearized equations of motion of the pendulum about the 'up' position and for $M = 1\ kg$, $m = 0.5\ kg$, $l = 0.5\ m$, and $g = 9.81\ m\ s^{-2}$ are given in state-space form as follows:

$$
\frac{d}{dt}\begin{bmatrix} x_1 \\ x_2 \\ x_3 \\ x_4 \end{bmatrix} = \frac{d}{dt}\mathbf{x} = \begin{bmatrix} 0 & 1 & 0 & 0 \\ 0 & 0 & -mg/M & 0 \\ 0 & 0 & 0 & 1 \\ 0 & 0 & (M+m)g/Ml & 0 \end{bmatrix}\begin{bmatrix} x_1 \\ x_2 \\ x_3 \\ x_4 \end{bmatrix} + \begin{bmatrix} 0 \\ 1/M \\ 0 \\ -1/Ml \end{bmatrix}u = \mathbf{Ax + Bu}
$$

where

$$
\begin{bmatrix} x_1 \\ x_2 \\ x_3 \\ x_4 \end{bmatrix} \equiv \begin{bmatrix} x \\ \frac{d}{dt}x \\ \theta \\ \frac{d}{dt}\theta \end{bmatrix}; \mathbf{A} = \begin{bmatrix} 0 & 1 & 0 & 0 \\ 0 & 0 & -4.905 & 0 \\ 0 & 0 & 0 & 1 \\ 0 & 0 & 29.43 & 0 \end{bmatrix}; \mathbf{B} = \begin{bmatrix} 0 \\ 1 \\ 0 \\ -2 \end{bmatrix}
$$

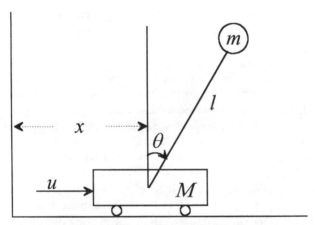

Figure 7.3.3. An Inverted Pendulum

Solution: Let us first select the matrices $\mathbf{Q}$ and $\mathbf{R}$ almost randomly,

$$\mathbf{Q} = \text{diag}(20, 2, 20, 2); \mathbf{R} = [10].$$

Use the subroutine *lqr(A,B,Q,R)*, (a subroutine in Matlab Control Toolbox) with which the following optimal state-feedback control matrix is obtained

$$\mathbf{K}_c = [-1.414, -2.6505, -38.38, -7.484]$$

The plain lines of Fig.7.3.4 show simulated time responses of some of the states, and of the control effort for an initial condition of $x_3(0) = \theta(0) = 10\ deg$ from the vertical reference axis. Examination of the variables θ and x obtained with the initially chosen $\mathbf{Q}$ and $\mathbf{R}$ leads to the following practical conclusions:

1) The maximum deviation of the cart amounts to $x_{max}(t) = 0.4\ m$. Assuming that for the real system at hand this deviation of $x(t)$ is not available, a redesign must be performed by changing properly $\mathbf{Q}$ and $\mathbf{R}$.

2) The undershoot of $\theta(t)$ is acceptable. Its final deviation is zeroed after 5 *sec*.

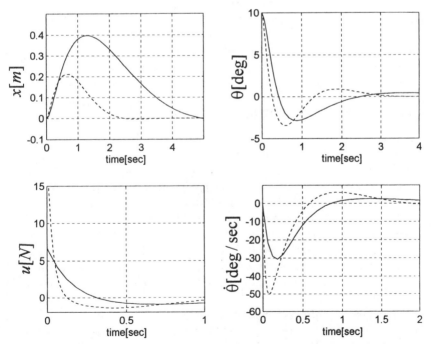

Figure.7.3.4. Motion of stabilized inverted pendulum for two different choices of $\mathbf{R}$: $\mathbf{R} = [10]$ − solid lines and $\mathbf{R} = [0.05]$ − dashed lines. $\mathbf{Q} = \text{diag}(20,2,20,2)$.

Since the maximum admissible deviation of $x(t)$ is only 0.2 m, we have to improve the solution in the sense of achieving a smaller deviation of $x(t)$, by allowing a larger and a faster control effort $u(t)$. This can be achieved by decreasing the elements of the control effort matrix to $\mathbf{R} = [0.05]$, for instance. The calculated new state-feedback control matrix $\mathbf{K}_c$ then becomes

$$\mathbf{K}_c = [-20., -19.515, -98.3, -21.52]$$

The time responses of the feedback system with the new optimal state-feedback control matrix $\mathbf{K}_c$ are shown by dashed lines in Fig.7.3.4. The maximum deviation in $x(t)$ is now very close to 0.2 m, while the maximum effort $u(t)$ has increased by a factor of nearly 3.

To summarize, a tradeoff between the amplitudes of the different system variables can be achieved by choosing accordingly the elements of the $\mathbf{Q}$ and $\mathbf{R}$ matrices.

Remark. An important remark is essential here. In this simple design example, the closed-loop feedback system is activated by a control variable $u(t)$ that uses information from all the states which are assumed to be measurable. The states in this example are the angle $\theta(t)$ of the pendulum arm from the vertical axis and its derivative $\dot{\theta}(t)$, as well as the linear deviation $x(t)$ from the origin and its derivative $\dot{x}(t)$. Normally, as in this simple system, all of the states cannot be measured unless very expensive and cumbersome instrumentation is used. In the above Example 7.3.2, a more practical solution is to measure the states $\theta(t)$ and $x(t)$ only, with inexpensive potentiometers, and to estimate the missing states. This possibility will be investigated in section 7.4 where the LQG problem is stated, analyzed and illustrated.

7.3.4. Model Following LQR Oriented Design Techniques

The **LQR** design technique, as presented previously, solved the optimal regulator problem, in which no input command was to be tracked. It can be modified so that a reference input command is followed successfully. There are two basic control methods for that task, known in the literature as the *explicit* and the *implicit model following*. The implicit model-following was introduced by Kalman et al.(1964). (see also Tyler and Tuteur 1966). These design techniques were developed in the mid-1960s and 1970s to design flight control systems for advanced aircraft. They are still in use today. The basic line of thought of each one of the model following methods will be described next. The explanation follows closely Kreindler and Rothschild (1976). (See also Asseo 1970, Motyka 1974 and Hirzinger 1974).

Some equations from previous sections, used in the derivation of the model following controller, are rewritten here for the reader's convenience. It is understood that $\mathbf{A}$, $\mathbf{B}$, $\mathbf{C}$, $\mathbf{Q}$ and $\mathbf{R}$ are constant matrices, and that the terminal time T is infinite. With these assumptions, an algebraic Riccati equation is solved for both model-following methods.

$$\frac{d}{dt}\mathbf{x} = \mathbf{A}\mathbf{x} + \mathbf{B}\mathbf{u} \tag{7.3.22}$$

$$\mathbf{y} = \mathbf{C}\mathbf{x} \tag{7.3.23}$$

$$J = \int_0^\infty (\mathbf{x}^T\mathbf{Q}\mathbf{x} + \mathbf{u}^T\mathbf{R}\mathbf{u})dt \tag{7.3.24}$$

Minimization of the performance index in Eq.(7.3.24) results in the linear control law of the form

$$\mathbf{u} = -\mathbf{K}\mathbf{x} \tag{7.3.25}$$

in which $\mathbf{K}$ is a constant matrix.

In many design problems, especially in flight control, we are interested in a closed-loop feedback system, expressed in a state-space form,

$$\frac{d}{dt}\mathbf{x} = (\mathbf{A} - \mathbf{B}\mathbf{K})\mathbf{x} \tag{7.3.26}$$

which behaves as closely as possible as a model of desirable dynamics, expressed in the form

$$\frac{d}{dt}\mathbf{z} = \mathbf{A}_m\mathbf{z} \tag{7.3.27}$$

where $\mathbf{A}_m$ represents the desirable dynamics of the model. The plant dynamics matrix A is generally of a high order, while the model dynamics $\mathbf{A}_m$ can be of a much lower order, obtained by using, for instance, the concept of dominant complex pole pair of second-order model of $T(s)$ treated in Chapter 3. Consequently, their dimensions will not be equal. Hence, $\mathbf{z}$ of the model will be compared to $\mathbf{y}$ (in Eq.(7.3.23)) of the same dimension.

The basic idea in solving the model-following problem consists in changing the quadratic performance index J, according to the model to be achieved for the model-following task. The control-law for the implicit model-following is derived next.

Implicit model-following

In implicit model-following, the standard LQR performance index J is modified as follows

$$J_{impl} = \int_0^\infty \left[\left(\frac{d}{dt}\mathbf{y} - \frac{d}{dt}\mathbf{y}_m \right)^T \mathbf{Q} \left(\frac{d}{dt}\mathbf{y} - \frac{d}{dt}\mathbf{y}_m \right) + \mathbf{u}^T \mathbf{R}\mathbf{u} \right] dt \qquad (7.3.28)$$

The problem is difficult to solve analytically for this form of J_{impl}. But, if we assume that a good design has been achieved, so that the output of the system follows nicely the model output, then $\mathbf{y} \approx \mathbf{y}_m$ and the performance index can be changed to

$$J_{impl} = \int_0^\infty \left[\left(\frac{d}{dt}\mathbf{y} - \mathbf{A}_m\mathbf{y} \right)^T \mathbf{Q} \left(\frac{d}{dt}\mathbf{y} - \mathbf{A}_m\mathbf{y} \right) + \mathbf{u}^T \mathbf{R}\mathbf{u} \right] dt \qquad (7.3.29)$$

where $\mathbf{Q}$ and $\mathbf{R}$ are respectively, positive semi-definite and positive definite matrices. By using Eqs.(7.3.22), and (7.3.23) in Eq.(7.3.29) we get

$$J_{impl} = \int_0^\infty (\mathbf{x}^T \mathbf{Q}_{eq}\mathbf{x} + 2\mathbf{u}^T \mathbf{R}\mathbf{S}_{eq}\mathbf{x} + \mathbf{u}^T \mathbf{R}_{eq}\mathbf{u}) dt \qquad (7.3.30)$$

with the definitions

$$\mathbf{Q}_{eq} = (\mathbf{C}\mathbf{A} - \mathbf{A}_m\mathbf{C})^T\mathbf{Q}(\mathbf{C}\mathbf{A} - \mathbf{A}_m\mathbf{C}), \qquad (7.3.31)$$

$$\mathbf{S}_{eq} = \mathbf{B}^T\mathbf{C}^T\mathbf{Q}(\mathbf{C}\mathbf{A} - \mathbf{A}_m\mathbf{C}) \qquad (7.3.32)$$

and

$$\mathbf{R}_{eq} = \mathbf{R} + \mathbf{B}^T\mathbf{C}^T\mathbf{Q}\mathbf{C}\mathbf{B} \qquad (7.3.33)$$

Unfortunately, in the implicit model-following performance index in Eq.(7.3.30), there is a cross-product term in the integral. Thus J_{impl} deviated somehow from the standard definition of J in the LQR problem. This difficulty does not exist for the following system classes:

1) Systems in which

$$\mathbf{C}\mathbf{B} = 0 \qquad (7.3.34)$$

because then $\mathbf{S}_{eq}$ reduces to zero, and $\mathbf{R}_{eq} = \mathbf{R}$.

There are systems where Eq.(7.3.34) inherently holds, or systems which can be brought to this form.

2) Systems in which $\mathbf{S}_{eq}$ is forced to be zero.

There are additional classes of practical problems in which one has $\mathbf{S}_{eq} = \mathbf{0}$. In the following example, suppose that the system to be controlled can be brought to the form

$$\mathbf{A} = \begin{bmatrix} \mathbf{A}_{11} & \mathbf{A}_{12} \\ \mathbf{0} & \mathbf{A}_{22} \end{bmatrix}; \mathbf{B} = \begin{bmatrix} \mathbf{0} \\ \mathbf{B}_2 \end{bmatrix}; \mathbf{A}_m = \begin{bmatrix} \mathbf{A}_{m11} & \mathbf{A}_{m12} \\ \mathbf{0} & \mathbf{A}_{m22} \end{bmatrix}. \tag{7.3.35}$$

In this case, for $\mathbf{A}_{m22} = \mathbf{A}_{22}$, $\mathbf{C} = \mathbf{I}$ is diagonal, and $\mathbf{Q}$ is given in block-diagonal form, namely,

$$\mathbf{Q} = \begin{bmatrix} \mathbf{Q}_{11} & \mathbf{0} \\ \mathbf{0} & \mathbf{Q}_{22} \end{bmatrix} \tag{7.3.36}$$

so that we find finally that

$$\mathbf{S}_{eq} = \mathbf{0}; \mathbf{R}_{eq} = \mathbf{R} + \mathbf{B}_2{}^T\mathbf{Q}_{22}\,\mathbf{B}_2. \tag{7.3.37}$$

We also find that

$$\mathbf{Q}_{eq} = [(\mathbf{A}_{11} - \mathbf{A}_{m11}) \quad (\mathbf{A}_{12} - \mathbf{A}_{m12})]^T \mathbf{Q}_{11} [(\mathbf{A}_{11} - \mathbf{A}_{m11}) \quad (\mathbf{A}_{12} - \mathbf{A}_{m12})] \tag{7.3.38}$$

3) Systems in which $\mathbf{S}_{eq} \neq \mathbf{0}$.

In this general case, it can be shown that the system is transformable to the regular LQR form by performing some transformations on variables (Anderson and Moore 1971). By completing the square of the integrand in Eq.(7.3.30), we obtain the following identity:

$$\mathbf{u}^T\mathbf{Ru} + 2\mathbf{x}^T\mathbf{Su} + \mathbf{x}^T\mathbf{Qx} = (\mathbf{u} + \mathbf{R}^{-1}\mathbf{S}^T\mathbf{x})^T\mathbf{R}(\mathbf{u} + \mathbf{R}^{-1}\mathbf{S}^T\mathbf{x}) + \mathbf{x}^T(\mathbf{Q} - \mathbf{SR}^{-1}\mathbf{S}^T)\mathbf{x} \tag{7.3.39}$$

After defining

$$\mathbf{u}_1 = \mathbf{u} + \mathbf{R}^{-1}\mathbf{S}^T\mathbf{x} \tag{7.3.40}$$

the original system of Eq.(7.3.26) is equivalent to

$$\frac{d}{dt}\mathbf{x} = (\mathbf{A} - \mathbf{BR}^{-1}\mathbf{S}^T)\mathbf{x} + \mathbf{Bu}_1 \tag{7.3.41}$$

and a newly defined performance index is obtained,

$$J = \int_0^\infty [\mathbf{x}^T(\mathbf{Q} - \mathbf{SR}^{-1}\mathbf{S}^T)\mathbf{x} + \mathbf{u}_1^T\mathbf{Ru}_1]dt \tag{7.3.42}$$

The ARE to be solved is finally found to be:

$$0 = P(A - BR^{-1} S^T) + (A^T - SR^{-1} B^T)P - PBR^{-1} B^TP + Q - SR^{-1} S^T \quad (7.3.43)$$

The optimal state-feedback control gain matrix is then

$$K = R^{-1} (B^TP + S^T) \quad (7.3.44)$$

A design example at this stage is imperative to clarify the meaning of implicit model-following.

Example 7.3.3.   The lateral control system of an aircraft will be considered. The airframe dynamics, including the dynamics of the actuators is given by the two equations

$$\frac{d}{dt}\mathbf{x}_A = \frac{d}{dt}\begin{bmatrix} p \\ r \\ \beta \\ \emptyset \end{bmatrix} = \mathbf{A}_A \begin{bmatrix} p \\ r \\ \beta \\ \emptyset \end{bmatrix} + \mathbf{B}_A \begin{bmatrix} \delta_r \\ \delta_a \end{bmatrix} \quad (7.3.45)$$

and

$$\frac{d}{dt}\boldsymbol{\delta} = \frac{d}{dt}\begin{bmatrix} \delta_r \\ \delta_a \end{bmatrix} = \mathbf{A}_\delta \begin{bmatrix} \delta_r \\ \delta_a \end{bmatrix} + \mathbf{B}_\delta \begin{bmatrix} u_1 \\ u_2 \end{bmatrix} \quad (7.3.46)$$

where $\mathbf{A}_A$ and $\mathbf{B}_A$ are related to the airframe dynamics; $\mathbf{x}_A$ is the airframe state vector; p and r are the roll and the yaw rates respectively; β and $\emptyset$ are the sideslip and the bank (roll) angles respectively. $\mathbf{A}_\delta$ and $\mathbf{B}_\delta$ are related to the actuator dynamics, which cannot be neglected. They also help to satisfy Eq.(7.3.34). The inputs to the airframe are the rudder and aileron deviations, δ_r and δ_a respectively; the inputs to the actuators are u_1 and u_2. We also define an input dynamics, (a kind of command generator for testing the overall system behavior to input commands)

$$\frac{d}{dt}\mathbf{u}_c = \frac{d}{dt}\begin{bmatrix} u_{c1} \\ u_{c2} \end{bmatrix} = \mathbf{A}_c\mathbf{u}_c \quad (7.3.47)$$

Next, we have to define the dynamics of the model to be followed. The model dynamics to this example is defined as

$$\frac{d}{dt}\mathbf{z} = \frac{d}{dt}\begin{bmatrix} \mathbf{x}_m \\ \mathbf{u}_c \end{bmatrix} = \begin{bmatrix} \mathbf{A}_m & \mathbf{B}_m \\ 0 & \mathbf{A}_c \end{bmatrix}\begin{bmatrix} \mathbf{x}_m \\ \mathbf{u}_c \end{bmatrix} \quad (7.3.48)$$

which can be rewritten for simplicity as

$$\frac{d}{dt}\mathbf{z} = \mathbf{A}_z\mathbf{z} \quad (7.3.49)$$

Eqs.(7.3.45) and (7.3.46) can be also expressed as an augmented first order matrix differential equation

$$\frac{d}{dt}\begin{bmatrix} \mathbf{x}_A \\ \boldsymbol{\delta} \\ \mathbf{u}_c \end{bmatrix} = \begin{bmatrix} \mathbf{A}_A & \mathbf{B}_A & 0 \\ 0 & \mathbf{A}_\delta & 0 \\ 0 & 0 & \mathbf{A}_c \end{bmatrix} \begin{bmatrix} \mathbf{x}_A \\ \boldsymbol{\delta} \\ \mathbf{u}_c \end{bmatrix} + \begin{bmatrix} 0 \\ \mathbf{B}_\delta \\ 0 \end{bmatrix} \begin{bmatrix} u_1 \\ u_2 \end{bmatrix} \qquad (7.3.50)$$

which can be simplified to

$$\frac{d}{dt}\mathbf{x} = \mathbf{Ax} + \mathbf{Bu.} \qquad (7.3.51)$$

Also, remember that **y** in Eq.(7.3.23) is of the form

$$\mathbf{y} = \mathbf{Cx} \qquad (7.3.52)$$

From the realization point of view, **y, z** and **x** do not have the same dimension. To adjust adequately their dimensions, we define the matrix **C** in the following way

$$\mathbf{C} = \begin{bmatrix} \mathbf{I}(n_a,n_a) & \mathbf{0}(n_\delta,n_a) & \mathbf{0}(n_c,n_a) \\ \mathbf{0}(n_a,n_a) & \mathbf{0}(n_\delta,n_\delta) & \mathbf{I}(n_c,n_c) \end{bmatrix} \qquad (7.3.53)$$

where (n_a,n_a) is the order of the plant matrix A_a; (n_δ, n_δ)- that of the actuator model matrix A_δ; and (n_c, n_c)- that of the command generator matrix A_c.

The control structure is shown in Fig.7.3.5. The calculated optimal state-feedback control matrix $\mathbf{K}_{impl}$ can be decomposed into three lower order matrices $\mathbf{K}_1, \mathbf{K}_2$ and $\mathbf{K}_3$. Each pertains to the states of the plant, the actuator outputs and the command generator system inputs respectively.

The lateral-axis linearized equations for a common aircraft fighter and a model at 0.4 M and 36kft given in Kreindler and Rotschild (1974, 1976) are:

$$\mathbf{A}_m = \begin{bmatrix} -4.0 & 0.865 & -10.0 & 0 \\ 0.04 & -0.507 & 5.87 & 0 \\ 0 & -1 & -0.743 & 0.0586 \\ 1 & 0 & 0 & 0 \end{bmatrix}; \ \mathbf{B}_m = \begin{bmatrix} 3.3 & 20 \\ -3.13 & 0 \\ 0 & 0 \\ 0 & 0 \end{bmatrix}; \ \mathbf{C}_m = \begin{bmatrix} 1 & 0 & 0 & 0 & 0 & 0 \\ 0 & 1 & 0 & 0 & 0 & 0 \\ 0 & 0 & 1 & 0 & 0 & 0 \\ 0 & 0 & 0 & 1 & 0 & 0 \end{bmatrix}$$

$$\mathbf{A}_A = \begin{bmatrix} -0.679 & 0 & -14.8 & 0 \\ 0 & -0.38 & 1.58 & 0 \\ 0.163 & -1 & -0.135 & 0.075 \\ 1 & 0 & 0 & 0 \end{bmatrix}; \ \mathbf{B}_A = \begin{bmatrix} 25.32 & 2.655 \\ 1.237 & -1.175 \\ 0 & 0 \\ 0 & 0 \end{bmatrix}; \ \mathbf{C}_A = \begin{bmatrix} 1 & 0 & 0 & 0 \\ 0 & 1 & 0 & 0 \\ 0 & 0 & 1 & 0 \\ 0 & 0 & 0 & 1 \end{bmatrix}$$

The actuator dynamics are chosen as

$$\mathbf{A}_\delta = \begin{bmatrix} -20 & 0 \\ 0 & -10 \end{bmatrix}; \mathbf{B}_\delta = \begin{bmatrix} 20 & 0 \\ 0 & 10 \end{bmatrix}$$

With this choice of input data, the matrix $\mathbf{C}$ and the augmented matrix $\mathbf{Q}_1$ are

$$\mathbf{C} = \begin{bmatrix} \mathbf{I}(4,4) & \mathbf{0}(4,2) & \mathbf{0}(4,2) \\ \mathbf{0}(2,4) & \mathbf{0}(2,2) & \mathbf{I}(2,2) \end{bmatrix}; \mathbf{Q}_1 = \begin{bmatrix} \mathbf{Q}(4,4) & \mathbf{0}(4,2) \\ \mathbf{0}(2,4) & \mathbf{0}(2,2) \end{bmatrix}$$

$\mathbf{I}$ is a unity diagonal matrix, $\mathbf{0}$ is a null matrix.

Now, we can form the equivalent $\mathbf{Q}_{eq}$ and $\mathbf{R}_{eq}$ weighting matrices. In this example $\mathbf{Q}_{eq} = (\mathbf{CA} - \mathbf{A}_z\mathbf{C})^T \mathbf{Q}_1 (\mathbf{CA} - \mathbf{A}_z\mathbf{C})$. $\mathbf{S}_{eq} = 0$ since $\mathbf{CB} = 0$, and the model-following problem is transformed to the classical LQR problem from which the optimal state-feedback matrix is obtained. The routine *lqr(a,b,q,r)* (Robust tool-box, Matlab) is used for this task. The following weighting matrices $\mathbf{Q}$ and $\mathbf{R}$ were obtained in a cut-and-try process until a satisfactory solution was achieved: $\mathbf{Q} =$ diag(2,20,10,2) and $\mathbf{R} =$ diag(4,1). The obtained control gain matrix is:

$$\mathbf{K}_{impl} = \begin{bmatrix} 2.29 & -0.508 & -5.3 & 0.03 & 17.21 & 1.28 & -0.84 & -113.4 \\ 1.23 & -1.33 & 16.88 & 0.026 & 2.57 & 5.08 & -12.3 & -5.35 \end{bmatrix}$$

Time responses for this solution are shown in Figs.7.3.7 and 7.3.8, together with responses of the explicit model-following, to be treated next. The loop transmission functions obtained when each one of the two plant inputs is opened, the rudder and the aileron in our case, are shown on the Nichols chart in Fig.7.3.9

Explicit model-following

In this design technique, the standard LQR performance index is modified as follows,

$$J_{expl} = \int_0^\infty [(\mathbf{y} - \mathbf{z})^T\mathbf{Q}(\mathbf{y}-\mathbf{z}) + \mathbf{u}^T\mathbf{R}\mathbf{u}]dt \qquad (7.3.54)$$

This index tends to minimize the error between the plant's output vector $\mathbf{y}$ and the model's state vector $\mathbf{x}_m$. For reducing this optimization problem to a standard regulator problem, we define an augmented state vector and augmented system matrices $\mathbf{A}$ and $\mathbf{B}$.

The augmented state vector $\mathbf{x}$ includes the states of the plant $\mathbf{x}_a$ as well as those of the model $\mathbf{x}_m$, and of the command generator $\mathbf{x}_c$, namely,

$$\mathbf{x} = [\, \mathbf{x}_a\ \mathbf{x}_m\ \mathbf{x}_c\,]^T.$$

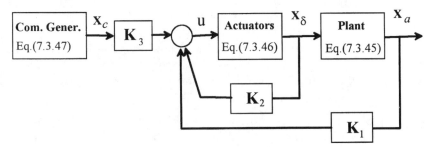

Figure 7.3.5. Feedback control structure for the implicit model-following.

With these definitions, the new state-space formulation of the system becomes

$$\frac{d}{dt}\mathbf{x} = \frac{d}{dt}\begin{bmatrix} \mathbf{x}_a \\ \mathbf{x}_m \\ \mathbf{x}_c \end{bmatrix} = \begin{bmatrix} \mathbf{A}_a & \mathbf{0} & \mathbf{0} \\ \mathbf{0} & \mathbf{A}_m & \mathbf{B}_m \\ \mathbf{0} & \mathbf{0} & \mathbf{A}_c \end{bmatrix}\begin{bmatrix} \mathbf{x}_a \\ \mathbf{x}_m \\ \mathbf{x}_c \end{bmatrix} + \begin{bmatrix} \mathbf{B}_a \\ \mathbf{0} \\ \mathbf{0} \end{bmatrix}\mathbf{u} = \mathbf{A}\mathbf{x} + \mathbf{B}\mathbf{u} \qquad (7.3.55)$$

If we choose $\mathbf{y} = \mathbf{Cx}$ and $\mathbf{z} = \mathbf{C}_m\mathbf{x}$, then we get from Eq.(7.3.54),

$$J_{expl} = \int_0^{\infty}(\mathbf{x}^T\mathbf{Q}_{eq}\mathbf{x}+\mathbf{u}^T\mathbf{R}\mathbf{u})dt \qquad (7.3.56)$$

in which

$$\mathbf{Q}_{eq} = \begin{bmatrix} \mathbf{C}^T\mathbf{Q}\mathbf{C} & -\mathbf{C}^T\mathbf{Q}\mathbf{C}_m \\ -\mathbf{C}_m^T\mathbf{Q}\mathbf{C} & \mathbf{C}_m^T\mathbf{Q}\mathbf{C}_m \end{bmatrix}, \qquad (7.3.57)$$

so that the performance index is again in the standard LQR form. (See Hirzinger 1974.) Therefore, Eqs.(7.3.55) and (7.3.56) define a standard regulator problem. The control signal is here given by

$$\mathbf{u} = \mathbf{K}_{impl}\mathbf{x} = \mathbf{K}_1\mathbf{x}_a + \mathbf{K}_2\,\mathbf{x}_m + \mathbf{K}_3\,\mathbf{x}_{c,.} \qquad (7.3.58)$$

It is easily seen that the model in the explicit model-following must be 'explicitly' implemented, in contrast to the implicit model-following method.

Example 7.3.4.   The flight control system of Example 7.3.3 is next solved using the explicit model-following design procedure. To find $\mathbf{Q}_{eq}$ we must first define the matrices $\mathbf{C}$ and $\mathbf{C}_m$. Taking into consideration the definition of the augmented system in Eq.(7.3.55), and being interested in controlling all the states in $\mathbf{x}_a$, namely the roll and yaw rates as well as the sideslip and bank angles, we easily find that

$$\mathbf{C} = [\ \mathbf{I}(4,4) \quad \mathbf{0}(4,6)\ ]; \ \mathbf{C}_m = [\ \mathbf{0}(4,4) \quad \mathbf{I}(4,4) \quad \mathbf{0}(4,2)\ ]$$

Once again, by a cut-and-try process, the following $\mathbf{Q}$ and $\mathbf{R}$ matrices were obtained for achieving a satisfactory control system: $\mathbf{Q} = \text{diag}(50,100,100,50)$; $\mathbf{R} = \text{diag}(3,2)$. The obtained control gain matrix is, (using lqr(a,b,q,r)),

$$\mathbf{K}_{expl} = \begin{bmatrix} 7.03 & 1.27 & -0.027 & 7.0 & -6.9 & -1.27 & -0.39 & -7.04 & -0.005 & -0.7 \\ 0.69 & -7.21 & 4.6 & 0.4 & -0.35 & 6.8 & -1.6 & -0.25 & -1.06 & 0.16 \end{bmatrix}$$

Some resulting time responses are shown in Figs.7.3.7 (roll input) and 7.3.8 (yaw input).

In both model-following methods, the input vector to the lateral dynamics of the airframe consists of two elements (aileron and rudder), while the output vector consists of four elements (roll and yaw rates and the sideslip and roll angles), hence, we can define, and achieve simultaneously, eight satisfactory transfer functions. With a fast roll exponential input, roll rate and bank angle follow very closely the model trajectory for both model-followers. The interaction with the yaw channel is low, as expected. But for both cases, the yaw rate and the sideslip responses do not look very similar to those of the model, although their magnitudes are significantly small. With a yaw input, the trajectories follow less accurately those of the model.

To better appreciate the achieved results, the time responses of the plant in open-loop are also shown. It is quite clear that the task of achieving a satisfactory tracking is fulfilled with both model-following methods. In Figs.7.3.7a and d, the explicit model-following controller follows the model exactly. Compare the resulting time

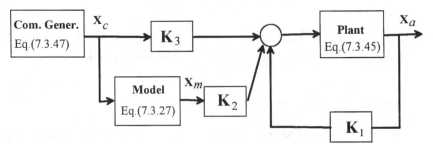

Figure 7.3.6.   Feedback control structure for the explicit
model-following (adapted from Kreindler & Rothschild 1976.)

responses with the plant's time responses. The implicit model-following time responses in the same figures are also quite satisfactory, but not perfect. In Figs.7.3.8*a* and *d*, the response of the explicit model-following is indistinguishable from the model's time response. Although the implicit model-following shows slightly less satisfactory results, see Fig. 7.3.7*d*, nevertheless, they are much better than that of the open-loop response of the plant. A better choice of the weighting matrices **R** and **Q** can ameliorate the design solution, but this is not pursued here. More about selection of the quadratic weighting matrices can be found in Harvey a nd Stein (1978).

It is difficult to decide which model-following method is superior. A lot of work has been dedicated to that purpose, and the reader is referred to the references cited, specially to Kreindler and Rotschild (1974, 1976). The only major difference between the two presented techniques is a necessity to physically implement the model in the controller of the explicit model-following.

A general remark is imperative here. The resulting optimal state-feedback constant matrix holds for only one specified flight condition. When a flight control system is designed, it must provide a solution for all flight conditions in the operational flight envelope. The state-feedback matrix then becomes a varying gain matrix adapted to all flight conditions, with elements that are dependent on the estimated altitude and Mach number, (obtained from static and dynamic pressure measurements).

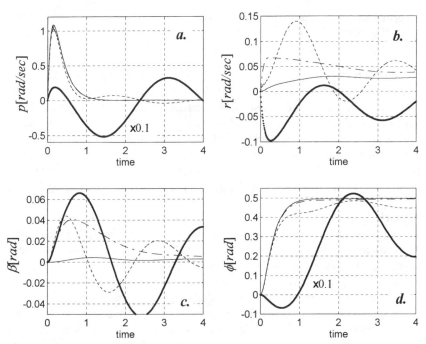

Figure 7.3.7. Time responses to a fast exponential roll input. Solid line: model; dashed line: implicit model following; dashdotted line: explicit model following; thick line: plant.

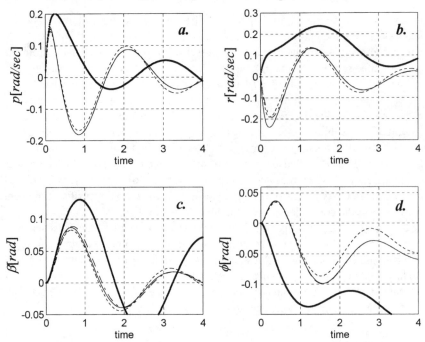

Figure 7.3.8. Time responses to a fast exponential yaw input. Solid line: model; dashed line: implicit model following; dashdotted line: explicit model following; thick line: plant.

An important feature in automatic control is the relative stability of the closed-loop feedback system (see Section 2.3). To clarify that point for the two model-following approaches, and in general for the LQR problem, the loop transmission functions obtained when each one of the two plant inputs is opened, (the rudder and the aileron inputs in our case), are shown on the Nichols chart in Fig.7.3.9. It is seen that the phase margins are large, close to 90 degrees and that the gain margins are infinite for both model-following methods. In the next section, it will be shown that for the LQR feedback design, the phase margin is at least 60 degrees.

Remark. Such large gain and phase margins are not at all practical from an engineering viewpoint. The loop transmission functions shown in Fig.7.3.9 contradict the classical definition of 'optimality' stated in Section 4.3.4, in which the excess of poles over zeros e tends to be equal or larger than 3, thus approaching at high frequencies a phase-lag of $-90e$ degrees. Hence, the solution obtained in the above two examples must be complemented with additional far-off poles for a realistic solution in which is adequately attenuated the magnitude of the loop transmission function at high frequencies. This is indispensable if we wish to limit the sensor noise amplification and to also attenuate the influence of structural modes, if these exist, which is generally the case.

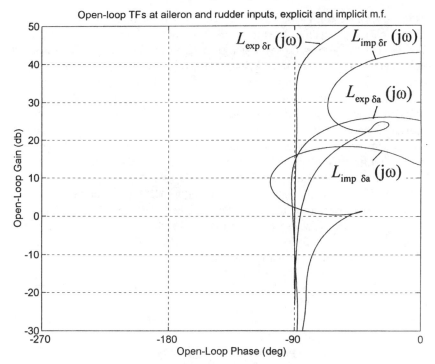

Figure 7.3.9.   Open-loop transfer functions for implicit and explicit model-following when the loop is opened at each one of the plant input channels, the rudder or the aileron.

7.3.5.   *Frequency Domain Characterization of Optimality in the LQR Oriented Design*

An important task in classical automatic control is achieving a well-behaved system in the frequency-domain, where the Nyquist stability properties are best shown. The optimal LQR problem was solved in previous sections in the time-domain. The optimal characteristics of the LQR solution are interpreted in this section in the frequency-domain by use of the classical notion of 'return difference', treated in Section 2.2.

Kalman inequality

In Kalman (1964), it is proven that if $\mathbf{K}$ in Eq.(7.3.18) is the optimal state-feedback gain matrix obtained for a single-input plant defined in Eq.(7.2.1a), then it holds that

$$|F(j\omega)| = |\,1 + L(j\omega)\,| = |\,1 + \mathbf{K}(j\omega\mathbf{I} - \mathbf{A})^{-1}\,\mathbf{B}\,| \geq 1 \qquad (7.3.59)$$

The geometrical interpretation of this inequality is important. For the single-input case, the region inside the circle of unity radius centered at the Nyquist critical point $[-1+j0]$ in Fig.7.3.10 must be avoided by the optimal transmission $L(j\omega) =$

$\mathbf{K\Phi}(j\omega)\mathbf{B}$, where $\mathbf{K}$ is the optimal state-feedback gain matrix obtained by solving the algebraic Riccati equation. The forbidden dashed region is avoided by $L_1(j\omega)$ shown in the figure, and also by $L_2(j\omega)$, which encircles this region. There is no reason why such encirclements cannot occur, as long as the correct number of encirclements of the critical point $[-1+j0]$ by any $L(j\omega)$ satisfies the Nyquist criterion for stability.

It is readily distinguished in the figure that as $\omega\rightarrow\infty$, arg $L_1(j\omega)\rightarrow -90°$, which de facto means that the excess of poles over zeros of $L(s)$ is just $e=1$. The conclusion is that from an engineering point of view, this solution is accompanied by a large sensor noise amplification at the input to the plant. Consequently, adequate noise filtering must be provide. At the same time, the basic characteristics of the LQR designed optimal $L(j\omega)$ must be retained.

In recent years, many authors have proved the MIMO version of this inequality. The first known proof appears in MacFarlane (1970). (See also Anderson and Moore 1971, Maciejowski 1989, Dorato et.al. 1995).

It is instructive to follow a proof for the MIMO version of the Kalman inequality. When Laplace transformed, Eq.(7.2.1a) becomes

$$\mathbf{x}(s) = (s\mathbf{I} - \mathbf{A})^{-1}\mathbf{B}u(s) = \mathbf{\Phi}(s)\mathbf{B}u(s) \tag{7.3.60}$$

where $\mathbf{\Phi}(s) = (s\mathbf{I} - \mathbf{A})^{-1}$, so that the plant transfer matrix can be rewritten as

$$\mathbf{P}(s) = (s\mathbf{I} - \mathbf{A})^{-1}\mathbf{B} = \mathbf{\Phi}(s)\mathbf{B}.$$

Taking into consideration the optimal state-feedback control matrix $\mathbf{K}$, we can obtain the loop transmission function matrix, 'return ratio matrix' in Bode's terminology, namely,

$$\mathbf{L}(s) = \mathbf{K}(s\mathbf{I} - \mathbf{A})^{-1}\mathbf{B} = \mathbf{K\Phi}(s)\mathbf{B} \tag{7.3.61}$$

and the 'return difference matrix' is clearly

$$\mathbf{F}(s) = \mathbf{I} + \mathbf{K}(s\mathbf{I} - \mathbf{A})^{-1}\mathbf{B} = \mathbf{I} + \mathbf{K}\,\mathbf{\Phi}(s)\mathbf{B} \tag{7.3.62}$$

with the system loop opened at $\mathbf{u}$ in Fig.7.3.1. To show Kalman's inequality, use is made of the algebraic Riccati equation Eq.(7.3.17), from which the optimal state-feedback matrix is obtained with the assumptions that $\mathbf{R}$ and $\mathbf{Q}$ are positive definite and positive semi-definite respectively. Add to the right side of Eq.(7.3.17) $s\mathbf{IP}$ and $-s\mathbf{PI}$ ($= -s\mathbf{IP}$) and rearrange to obtain

$$\mathbf{P}(s\mathbf{I} - \mathbf{A}) + (-s\mathbf{I} - \mathbf{A}^T)\mathbf{P} = \mathbf{Q} - \mathbf{PBR}^{-1}\mathbf{B}^T\mathbf{P}$$
$$= \mathbf{Q} - \mathbf{PBR}^{-1}\mathbf{RR}^{-1}\mathbf{B}^T\mathbf{P} = \mathbf{Q} - \mathbf{K}^T\mathbf{RK}$$

($\mathbf{Q} = \mathbf{Q_1}^T\mathbf{Q_1}$ to guarantee its positiveness, see Section 7.3.2). Multiply each term in the above equation on the left by $\mathbf{B}^T\mathbf{\Phi}^T(-s)$ and on the right by $\mathbf{\Phi}(s)\mathbf{B}$. Add $\mathbf{I}$ to each side of the equation to obtain

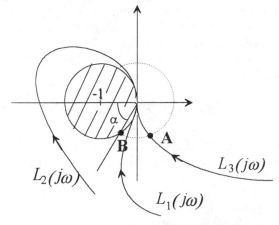

Figure 7.3.10.   Nyquist loci at input of optimally regulated single-input
plant, which avoid the forbidden region inside the unity-radius
circle centered at $[-1 + j0]$; $L_i(j\omega) = \mathbf{K}(s\mathbf{I} - \mathbf{A})^{-1}\mathbf{B}$.

$$\mathbf{I} + \mathbf{B}^T\Phi^T(-s)\mathbf{P}(s\mathbf{I}-\mathbf{A})\Phi(s)\mathbf{B} + \mathbf{B}^T\Phi^T(-s)(-s\mathbf{I}-\mathbf{A}^T)\mathbf{P}\Phi(s)\mathbf{B}$$
$$= \mathbf{I} + \mathbf{B}^T\Phi^T(-s)[\mathbf{Q} - \mathbf{K}^T\mathbf{R}\mathbf{K}]\Phi(s)\mathbf{B}.$$

After some standard algebraic operations, and remembering that $\Phi(s) = (s\mathbf{I}-\mathbf{A})^{-1}$, the above equation reduces to

$$\mathbf{I} + \mathbf{B}^T\Phi^T(-s)\mathbf{P}\mathbf{B} + \mathbf{B}^T\,\mathbf{P}\Phi(s)\mathbf{B} + \mathbf{B}^T\Phi^T(-s)\mathbf{K}^T\mathbf{R}\mathbf{K}\Phi(s)\mathbf{B}$$
$$= \mathbf{I} + \mathbf{B}^T\Phi^T(-s)\mathbf{Q}\Phi(s)\mathbf{B} \qquad (7.3.63)$$

Without loss of generality, we can choose $\mathbf{R} = \mathbf{I}$, so that $\mathbf{K} = \mathbf{B}^T\mathbf{P}$ and the last equation can be rewritten as

$$[\mathbf{I} + \mathbf{K}\Phi(-s)\mathbf{B}]^T[\mathbf{I} + \mathbf{K}\Phi(s)\mathbf{B}] = \mathbf{I} + \mathbf{B}^T\Phi^T(-s)\mathbf{Q}\Phi(s)\mathbf{B}.$$

Or, in terms of the return difference matrix, we finally get

$$\mathbf{F}^T(-s)\,\mathbf{F}(s) = \mathbf{I} + \mathbf{B}^T\Phi^T(-s)\mathbf{Q}\Phi(s)\mathbf{B} = \mathbf{I} + \mathbf{B}^T\Phi^T(-s)\mathbf{Q}\Phi(s)\mathbf{B}$$

Set $s = j\omega$ in this equation. Since the $\mathbf{Q}$ matrix is positive semi-definite, so is the entire second term in the right-hand side of the above equation at all ω. This implies the Kalman inequality for the MIMO case,

$$F^*(j\omega)F(j\omega) \geq \mathbf{I}; \ \forall\omega \qquad (7.3.64)$$

This inequality can also be expressed in the following form

$$\underline{\sigma}\,[\mathbf{F}(j\omega)] = \underline{\sigma}\,[\mathbf{I} + \mathbf{L}(j\omega)] \geq 1; \ \ \forall\omega \qquad (7.3.65)$$

where $\underline{\sigma}$ is the smallest singular value (defined in Appendix B) of the return difference matrix $\mathbf{F}(j\omega) = \mathbf{I} + \mathbf{L}(j\omega)$, and $\mathbf{L}(j\omega)$ is the return ratio matrix of the general MIMO feedback system opened at **u** in Fig.7.3.1.

For a single input feedback system, Eq.(7.3.65) reduces to the original Kalman inequality of Eq.(7.3.59).

7.3.6. Gain and Phase Margins for Optimal LQR Designed Feedback Systems

The additional dotted circle with unity radius, shown in Fig.7.3.10, is the geometrical loci of all Nyquist plots of optimal regulators at unity distance from the origin. To find the phase margin of any $L(j\omega)$, for instance, of the shown $L_3(j\omega)$, we have to find on the dotted unity circle the angle that will shift point **A** to the critical point $[-1+j0]$. However, since the forbidden region inside the critical unity circle must be excluded, point **B** becomes the boundary part of the dotted unity circle for permitted optimal Nyquist plots. Point **B** is clearly distanced 60° from the stability critical point, so that there is at least 60° of phase margin for any optimal LQR transmission function $L_i(j\omega)$. As far as the gain margins are concerned, L_1 $(j\omega)$ shows a net gain margin of infinity. If the loop transmission is conditionally stable, as L_2 $(j\omega)$ in the figure, its magnitude can be decreased by at least a factor of 2 before instability occurs. Hence, the optimal LQR loop transmission function has a decreasing gain margin of at least 2, or $+6$ db.

For the multi-loop LQR regulators, it was shown in Safonov and Athans (1977) that the above conclusions hold at each input channel $u_{i,}$ with all remaining loops closed. The proof, however, exists only for the case in which the weighting matrix **R** is not only positive definite, but also diagonal, $\mathbf{R} = \rho \, \text{diag}(\mathbf{I}); \rho > 0$.

These results have been proven in numerous papers and books using different mathematical approaches. (See, for instance, Maciejowsk 1989, Dorato et al.1995 and others).

The above results are illustrated by the loop transmission functions of Examples 7.3.3 and 7.3.4, which are shown in Fig.7.3.9.

To summarize, the linear quadratic optimal regulator has excellent relative stability performances, as well as gain and phase margins. But this is due to the fact that all states are measurable. When some of the states cannot be measured, these excellent stability performances are lost. This is discussed in the remaining sections of this chapter.

7.4. The Linear-Quadratic-Gaussian (LQG) Problem

After a short review of the LQR problem and its particular qualities, we can return to the original LQG problem stated in the beginning of this chapter. The LQG design technique is most realistic because it takes into consideration real practical difficulties that arise when not all the states of the plant, necessary to the LQR solution, are available for feedback. Moreover, since the measured outputs of the plant are generally noisy, a good filtration of the output signals is imperative for a practical engineering solution. The LQG problem and its applications are treated in several excellent books and papers (Athans 1971, Kwakernaak and Sivan 1972, Anderson and Moore 1990, and many others). The purpose here in presenting the material is to provide a short review of the subject needed for the next chapter.

There are two basic cases to be treated. The first one is the deterministic case in which the measured output vector **y** is not too noisy. We are then faced with the so called 'observers for the states of linear systems' (Luenberger 1963, 1965, 1971). Next, the Kalman-Bucy filter will be examined for the realistic cases in which the measurements of the output vector are substantially noisy.

7.4.1. The State Estimator Problem

The general structure of the LQG problem is shown in Fig.7.2.1. $\mathbf{K}_c$ is the state-feedback gain matrix, treated in Section 7.3, which implements the optimal LQR feedback law. The plant **P** can be expressed in its state-space formulation or in its transfer function matrix form. The important fact is that only the output vector **y** can be measured. The elements of **y** are linear combinations of the states x_i of the state vector **x**, (Eq.(7.2.1b)). The estimator, which is also called the 'observer', uses as its inputs, the control vector **u**, and the estimation error $\mathbf{y} - \mathbf{y}_e$, where **y** and $\mathbf{y}_e$ are the measured and the estimated output vectors. A basic structure for a deterministic observer is derived from Fig.7.2.1 and is shown in Fig.7.4.1. The definitions of the matrices in the figure are the same as those in Eqs.(7.2.1). (See also Anderson and Moore, 1971, 1990).

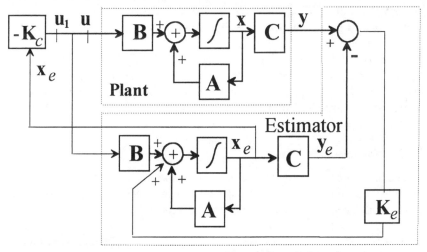

Figure 7.4.1. Detailed state-estimator feedback realization.

According to the feedback structure in the above figure, the basic estimator equation is

$$\frac{d}{dt}\mathbf{x}_e = \mathbf{A}\mathbf{x}_e + \mathbf{B}\mathbf{u} + \mathbf{K}_e(\mathbf{y} - \mathbf{y}_e)$$
$$= \mathbf{A}\mathbf{x}_e + \mathbf{B}\mathbf{u} + \mathbf{K}_e\mathbf{C}(\mathbf{x} - \mathbf{x}_e) \tag{7.4.1}$$

Subtract Eq.(7.4.1) from (7.2.1a) to get

$$\frac{d}{dt}(\mathbf{x} - \mathbf{x}_e) = (\mathbf{A}\mathbf{x} - \mathbf{x}_e) - \mathbf{K}_e\mathbf{C}(\mathbf{x} - \mathbf{x}_e)$$
$$= (\mathbf{A} - \mathbf{K}_e\mathbf{C})(\mathbf{x} - \mathbf{x}_e) \tag{7.4.2}$$

After defining the state estimation error as $\mathbf{e}_e = \mathbf{x} - \mathbf{x}_e$, we can rewrite Eq.(7.4.2) as

$$\frac{d}{dt}\mathbf{e}_e = (\mathbf{A} - \mathbf{K}_e\mathbf{C})\mathbf{e}_e \tag{7.4.2a}$$

We are left with the problem of designing the estimator gain matrix $\mathbf{K}_e$ so that the eigenvalues of the matrix $(\mathbf{A} - \mathbf{K}_e\mathbf{C})$ have negative real values, thus ensuring asymptotic stability. This leads to exponential decrease of any initial estimation error $\mathbf{e}_e = \mathbf{x} - \mathbf{x}_e$, until finally the estimated state vector $\mathbf{x}_e$ follows the real state vector $\mathbf{x}$ of the plant. The more negative the real part of the eigenvalues will be, the faster will the estimator follow the actual state, but, at the expense of a higher sensor noise amplification, if noise is actually superimposed on the measured output vector $\mathbf{y}$. The estimator gain matrix $\mathbf{K}_e$ can be designed using different techniques, such as that of pole placement (See for instance, Wonham 1967, Kailath 1980, Laub and Wette 1984 and many others).

Our next and final task in this chapter is to find a way to design an estimator in some 'optimal' way. If the noise characteristics of the controlled system are known, then the estimation of the states will be obtained with a minimum error in some optimal square integrating criterion to be defined. This leads to the Kalman-Bucy filter treated next.

7.4.2. Kalman-Bucy Filter

The number of papers and books related to this famous filter is virtually innumerable. The number of scientists that have dedicated their entire lives to this subject is remarkable. Basic treatment of the subject can be found in the previously cited references. However, for this short introduction, the original paper is mentioned here. (Kalman and Bucy 1961). The structure of the Kalman-Bucy Filter is similar to that shown in Fig.7.4.1. We only have to exchange the subscript '*e*,' which is shorthand for 'estimate', with 'f', shorthand for 'filter'. As a matter of fact, filtering is the primary purpose of the LQG theory. The filter is also consistently used if all the states are available for measurement, but are corrupted by noise.

When corrupting *process* and *output measurement noises* are added to the deterministic system, Eqs.(7.2.1) transform to

$$\frac{d}{dt}\mathbf{x} = \mathbf{Ax} + \mathbf{Bu} + \mathbf{w} \tag{7.4.3a}$$

$$\mathbf{y} = \mathbf{Cx} + \mathbf{v} \tag{7.4.3b}$$

where $\mathbf{w}$ and $\mathbf{v}$ are, respectively, stochastic white noise disturbances of the states of the controlled process and noise superimposed on the measured outputs. $\mathbf{w}$ and $\mathbf{v}$ have covariance matrices

$$E[\mathbf{w}(t_1)\,\mathbf{w}^T(t_2)] = \mathbf{W}\delta(t_1 - t_2) \geq \mathbf{0} \text{ (positive semi-definite)} \tag{7.4.4a}$$

and

$$E[\mathbf{v}(t_1)\,\mathbf{v}^T(t_2)] = \mathbf{V}\delta(t_1 - t_2) > \mathbf{0} \text{ (positive definite)} \tag{7.4.4b}$$

$\mathbf{W}$ and $\mathbf{V}$ are the intensities of the white noises $\mathbf{w}$ and $\mathbf{v}$ respectively. It is also assumed that $\mathbf{w}$ and $\mathbf{v}$ are uncorrelated with each other. In other words,

$$E(\mathbf{w}\,\mathbf{v}^T) = \mathbf{0} \tag{7.4.5}$$

Assume also that the system is detectable. Let us denote the filter state vector as $\mathbf{x}_f$, and the filter state error as $\mathbf{e}_f = \mathbf{x} - \mathbf{x}_f$. It is interesting to minimize the filter estimation error $\mathbf{e}_f$ in the usual quadratic index form

$$a_f = \lim_{t \to \infty} E\,[\mathbf{e}_f^T(t)\mathbf{e}_f(t)]. \tag{7.4.6}$$

Exactly as in the state estimation problem of Section 7.4.1, subtract Eq.(7.4.1) in which 'e,' the subscript for *estimator,* is exchanged with 'f' for *filter*, from Eq.(7.4.3a) and use Eq.(7.4.3b) to get

$$\frac{d}{dt}(\mathbf{x} - \mathbf{x}_f) = (\mathbf{A} - \mathbf{K}_f\mathbf{C})(\mathbf{x} - \mathbf{x}_f) + \mathbf{w} - \mathbf{K}_f\mathbf{v}. \tag{7.4.7}$$

The Kalman-filter gain matrix $\mathbf{K}_f$ is given by

$$\mathbf{K}_f = \mathbf{P}_f\mathbf{C}^T\,\mathbf{V}^{-1} \tag{7.4.8}$$

where $\mathbf{P}_f$ satisfies an algebraic Riccati equation, dual to Eq.(7.3.17), which, in terms of the matrices $\mathbf{W}$ and $\mathbf{V}$ becomes

$$\mathbf{P}_f \mathbf{A}^T + \mathbf{A} \mathbf{P}_f - \mathbf{P}_f \mathbf{C}^T \mathbf{V}^{-1} \mathbf{C} \mathbf{P}_f + \mathbf{W} = \mathbf{0} \qquad (7.4.9)$$

The optimizing $\mathbf{P}_f$ is also positive semi-definite and symmetric.

$$\mathbf{P}_f = \mathbf{P}_f^T \geq \mathbf{0} \qquad (7.4.10)$$

The important difference between Eqs.(7.4.9) and (7.3.17) is the fact that $\mathbf{W}$ and $\mathbf{V}$ stand for $\mathbf{Q}$ and $\mathbf{R}$ respectively in the LQR control problem. $\mathbf{Q}$ and $\mathbf{R}$ are weighting quadratic matrices used to tune the LQR control solution, while $\mathbf{W}$ and $\mathbf{V}$ are generally fixed by the physics of the engineering problem at hand, namely, by the statistical properties of the process and the sensor noises. Since these cannot be changed freely at will, the optimal filter is uniquely fixed by them. If, nonetheless, some of the elements of the vectors $\mathbf{w}$ and $\mathbf{v}$ cannot be even roughly prefigured, because of insufficient knowledge of the physical properties of the controlled system, then these elements can be used for tuning purposes in solving the LQG problem. Moreover, $\mathbf{V}$ must be positive definite and $\mathbf{W}$—positive semi-definite, Eqs.(7.4.4). If any element v_i of $\mathbf{v}$ does not exist, then $\det(\mathbf{V}) = 0$. This contradicts Eq.(7.4.4b) and no solution to the filter exists. This follows simply because the row i of $\mathbf{V}$ is given by $E(v_i \mathbf{v}^T)$. Thus $\det(\mathbf{V}) = 0$. In this case, a value must be provided for that missing v_i such that a good engineering solution is achieved. Also, if the elements of $\mathbf{v}$ are uncorrelated between them for all $i \neq j$, then $E(v_i v_j) = 0$ so that $\mathbf{V}$ become diagonal, $\mathbf{V} = \mathrm{diag}(v^2{}_{ii})$. It is evident that all covariance matrices $\mathbf{W}$, $\mathbf{V}$ and $\mathbf{P}$ are symmetric.

Eq.(7.4.9) is sometimes called the *Filter Algebraic Riccati Equation* (FARE), in contrast to the Control Algebraic Riccati Equation that was shortened to ARE.

7.4.3.   The Separation Principle and the Solution of the LQG Problem

A question of stability immediately arises. The control solution using the LQR principle emerges with a state-feedback gain matrix $\mathbf{K}_c$ that ensures a stable closed-loop design as long as the system is stabilizable. The filter solution, using the Kalman-Bucy principle, emerges with a filter gain matrix $\mathbf{K}_f$ that ensures a stable optimal filter if the system is detectable. When the LQR is closed with states estimated by the Kalman-Bucy filter, does the overall system remain stable? To answer this question, Eqs.(7.3.18), (7.4.3) and (7.4.7) are manipulated into the following combined Kalman-filter/optimal state feedback equation:

$$\frac{d}{dt} \begin{bmatrix} \mathbf{x} \\ (\mathbf{x} - \mathbf{x}_f) \end{bmatrix} = \begin{bmatrix} \mathbf{A} - \mathbf{B}\mathbf{K}_c & \mathbf{B}\mathbf{K}_c \\ \mathbf{0} & \mathbf{A} - \mathbf{K}_f \mathbf{C} \end{bmatrix} \begin{bmatrix} \mathbf{x} \\ (\mathbf{x} - \mathbf{x}_f) \end{bmatrix} + \begin{bmatrix} \mathbf{w} \\ \mathbf{w} - \mathbf{K}_f \mathbf{v} \end{bmatrix} \qquad (7.4.11)$$

Since the emerging matrix is triangular, it immediately follows that the eigenvalues of the LQG designed system are the union of the separated eigenvalues of the

Kalman-Bucy filter and those of the full state-feedback LQR system. This is the *separation principle*. From this principle, it follows that solution of the complete LQG problem consists in finding separately the solutions of the LQR and of the Kalman-Bucy filter problems. Hence, we are left with the freedom to use the **Q** and **R** matrices, as well as some of the **W** and **V** elements, for tuning satisfactorily the overall system.

Remark. The Kalman-Bucy filter introduces additional dynamics to the LQR solution. This means that the time-domain and frequency-domain responses will be different with or without state estimation and filtering.

A design example follows.

Example 7.4.1. The pendulum problem in Example 7.3.2 will be solved again, but now we assume that the linear velocity $dx(t)/dt$ of the cart and the angular rate $d\theta(t)/dt$ of the pendulum arm are unmeasurable. Noise sources are added to the linear x and to the angular θ position sensors. Moreover, some process noise with known characteristics is assumed to exist:

$\mathbf{v} = [v_1 \ v_2 \ ]^T$, $v_1 = 0.01$ and $v_2 = 0.01$. In other words, measurements noises of $0.01 \ m$ in x and 0.01 rad in θ are assumed. Also $\mathbf{w} = [w_1 \ w_2 \ w_3 \ w_4]$; $w_1 = 0.02$, $w_3 = 0.01$ are assumed to be know. Since the physical characteristics of w_2 and w_4 are completely unknown, these variables may be used freely as design parameters to obtain the best possible control solution.

Solution: Choose initially the **Q** and **R** matrices of the faster control solution in Example 7.3.2, $\mathbf{Q} = \text{diag}(20,2,20,2)$; $\mathbf{R} = [0.05]$, and also $w_2 = w_4 = 5.0$. Assuming that the elements of $\mathbf{w}$ and $\mathbf{v}$ are uncorrelated, the matrices **W** and **V** become diagonal,

$\mathbf{W} = \text{diag} (w_i^2) = \text{diag}(0.02^2 \ w_2^2, \ 0.01^2 \ w_4^2)$; $\mathbf{V} = \text{diag}(v_i) = \text{diag}(0.01^2 \ 0.01^2)$. With this data, use the Matlab subroutine *lqe* to obtain $\mathbf{K}_f$. The obtained optimal filter gain matrix is:

$$\mathbf{K}_{f1} = \begin{bmatrix} 31.69 & -0.081 \\ 500.1 & -5.05 \\ -0.081 & 32.58 \\ -0.145 & 530.4 \end{bmatrix}$$

If w_2 and w_4 are changed to $w_2 = w_4 = 0.001$, we get the following optimal filter gain matrix:

$$\mathbf{K}_{f2} = \begin{bmatrix} 2.2 & -1.29 \\ 1.28 & -9.64 \\ -1.291 & 10.74 \\ -7.07 & 58.0 \end{bmatrix}$$

Also, the obtained optimal state-feedback gain matrix for both cases is:

$$\mathbf{K}_c = [-20, -19.5, -98.31, -21.52].$$

The resulting system is simulated in the time-domain. The angular motion of the pendulum and the linear motion of the cart are shown for different choices of w_2 and w_4 in Fig.7.4.2 ($w_2 = w_4 = 5.0$) and in Fig.7.4.3 ($w_2 = w_4 = 0.001$). In both cases, the intensity of added white sensor noise was: $v_1 = 0.01m$, $v_2 = 0.01$ rad/sec. The states $x(t)$ and $\theta(t)$, obtained with the LQR solution (with no sensor noises), are plotted on the same figures (dashdoted lines), for comparison with the LQG solution. It is easily concluded that the second choice of $w_2 = w_4 = 0.001$ (resulting in $\mathbf{K}_{f2}$) leads to smoother motion than that with the first choice of w_2 and w_4 (resulting in $\mathbf{K}_{f1}$.). The important difference is in the control effort level u, which is much higher with the first choice of $w_2 = w_4 = 5.0$. For both cases, the state motion is quite different from that obtained with the LQR solution. The control effort level of u with the LQR solution is not shown, but it is much lower than that for both LQG solutions. The reason lies in the fact that with the LQG solu-

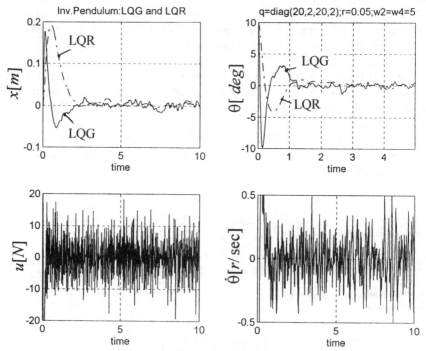

Figure 7.4.2. LQG solution of the pendulum problem with
$w_2 = w_4 = 5$, $w_1 = 0.02$, $w_3 = 0.01$, $v_1 = v_2 = 0.01$, $\mathbf{R} = [0.05]$, $\mathbf{Q} = \text{diag}(20,2,20,2)$.

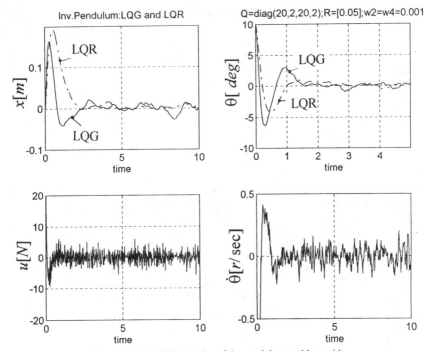

Figure 7.4.3. LQG solution of the pendulum problem with
$w_2 = w_4 = 0.001$, $w_1 = 0.02$, $w_3 = 0.01$, $v_1 = v_2 = 0.01$, **R** = [0.05], **Q** = diag(20,2,20,2).

tion, $dx(t)/dt$ and $d\theta(t)/dt$ are to be estimated. Because this action is accompanied with differentiation, the sensor noise is inevitably amplified. The filtration level of this noise depends on the choice of the Kalman-Bucy filter parameters.

Another point of interest is the fact that the minimum gain and phase margins achieved with the LQR design (Section 7.3.6) are not guaranteed anymore for the LQG design method. This effect is illustrated in Fig.7.4.4. $L_{LQR}(j\omega)$, obtained with the LQR design, shows that $PM = 72°$, the negative $GM > 10$ dB. The $L_{LQG}(j\omega)$ obtained with the LQG design shows that $PM = 31°$ and the negative $GM < 3.5$ dB. This bothering effect will be analyzed in the next section.

7.4.4. Loop Transfer Recovery (LTR)

It is pointed out in Doyle and Stein (1979) that the nice 'robust' features existing with the LQR design process, (Section 7.3.6 and Fig.7.4.4), are lost when not all the states are available for feedback purposes. Consequently, the LQG design technique that allows estimation of the missing states must be used instead. The emerging deficiency was illustrated in the last Example 7.4.1, Fig.7.4.4. The explanation to this phenomena is as follows.

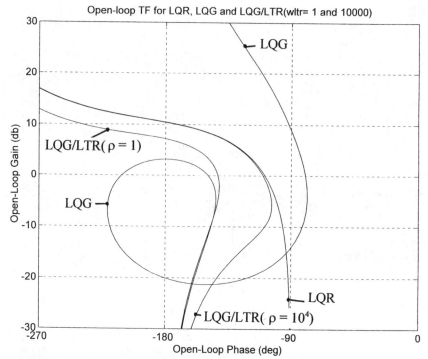

Figure 7.4.4.   Loop transmission function with the system opened at the plant input for LQR , LQG and LQG/LTR (with $\rho = 1$ and $\rho = 10^4$) designs.

Fig.7.2.1a shows the basic configuration of the LQG feedback system. When stability sensitivity to uncertainty of system parameters is analyzed, the feedback loop must be opened at the input **u** at point 2. It is very important to realize that the loop must be opened at this point, and not at $\mathbf{u}_1$ placed at point 1, shown in the same figure. If the loop is opened erroneously at point 1, then, sensitivity to uncertainties in the controller is checked. In this case, the unknown states are fully and correctly estimated, since the Kalman-Bucy filter also uses the input $\mathbf{u}_1$ in the state estimation process (**Plant** in the figure), as required by theory. Unfortunately, when the loop is opened at the physically correct place at point 2, the Kalman-Bucy filter is deteriorated because the filter does not sense the control input **u**. Thus, no correct observation of the unknown states is achieved. The inevitable consequence is that the robust properties of the LQR solution are lost, as seen in Fig.7.4.4 for $L_{LQG}(j\omega)$-LQG solution.

An observer-adjustment procedure exists to recover the lost relative stability properties of the LQR design when the loop is opened at point 2. This procedure is known as *Loop Transfer Recovery* (LTR), first treated in Doyle and Stein (1979).(See also Maciejowski 1989.)

$G(s)$ is the transfer function matrix from **y** to **u** in Fig.7.2.1b. The Kalman-Bucy optimal estimator structure is shown in detail in Fig.7.4.1. From this figure, the Kalman-Bucy filter equation without any stochastic noise is written (by putting $\mathbf{K}_e = \mathbf{K}_f$) as follows:

$$\frac{d}{dt}\mathbf{x}_f = \mathbf{A}\mathbf{x}_f + \mathbf{K}_f(\mathbf{y} - \mathbf{C}\mathbf{x}_f) - \mathbf{B}\mathbf{K}_c\mathbf{x}_f. \qquad (7.4.12)$$

Since $\mathbf{u} = -\mathbf{K}_c\mathbf{x}_f$ it easily follows that the compensator matrix is

$$\mathbf{G}(s) = \mathbf{K}_c[s\mathbf{I} - \mathbf{A} + \mathbf{K}_f\mathbf{C} + \mathbf{B}\mathbf{K}_c]^{-1}\mathbf{K}_f \qquad (7.4.13)$$

Using Eq.(7.2.3) with $\mathbf{D} = \mathbf{0}$, the open-loop transfer function matrix of the feedback system becomes, when the loop is broken at point 2 in Fig.7.2.1a,

$$\begin{aligned}\mathbf{L}_1(s) = \mathbf{L}_{LQG}(s) &= \mathbf{G}(s)\mathbf{C}[s\mathbf{I} - \mathbf{A}]^{-1}\mathbf{B} \\ &= \mathbf{K}_c[s\mathbf{I} - \mathbf{A} + \mathbf{K}_f\mathbf{C} + \mathbf{B}\mathbf{K}_c]^{-1}\mathbf{K}_f\mathbf{C}[s\mathbf{I} - \mathbf{A}]^{-1}\mathbf{B}.\end{aligned} \qquad (7.4.14)$$

On the other hand, if the loop is broken at point 1 ($\mathbf{u}_1$), then, from Fig.7.4.1, it follows immediately that $\mathbf{x} = \mathbf{x}_f$ (if the modeling of the Kalman-Bucy filter is exact). The filter estimation error is then nullified, $\mathbf{e}_f = 0$, and the filter dynamics do not interfere with the loop dynamics. Consequently, the open-loop transfer function matrix is identical to that obtained with the LQR solution, namely,

$$\mathbf{L}_2(s) = \mathbf{L}_{LQR}(s) = \mathbf{K}_c[s\mathbf{I} - \mathbf{A}]^{-1}\mathbf{B}. \qquad (7.4.15)$$

$\mathbf{L}_1(s)$ and $\mathbf{L}_2(s)$ are quite different, which explains why the relative stability properties of both LQR and LQG designs ought not to be similar. The task of the Loop Transfer Recovery (LTR) design technique is to make $\mathbf{L}_1(s)$ ($= \mathbf{L}_{LQG}(s)$) as close as possible to $\mathbf{L}_2(s)$ ($= \mathbf{L}_{LQR}(s)$). In order to achieve this objective, it can be shown that the covariance matrix $\mathbf{W}$, used in finding the Kalman-filter gain matrix $\mathbf{K}_f$ is to be augmented as follows

$$\mathbf{W}_{LTR} = \mathbf{W} + \rho^2(\mathbf{B}\mathbf{S}\mathbf{B}^T) \qquad (7.4.16)$$

where $\mathbf{S}$ is positive semi-definite. Exchange $\mathbf{W}$ with $\mathbf{W}_{LTR}$ in the filter algebraic Riccati equation, Eq.(7.4.9), and divide all the members by ρ^2 to obtain

$$\frac{\mathbf{P}_f\mathbf{A}^T}{\rho^2} + \frac{\mathbf{A}\mathbf{P}_f}{\rho^2} - \frac{\mathbf{P}_f\mathbf{C}^T\mathbf{V}^{-1}\mathbf{C}\mathbf{P}_f}{\rho^2} + \frac{\mathbf{W}}{\rho^2} + \mathbf{B}\mathbf{S}\mathbf{B}^T = \mathbf{0}. \qquad (7.4.17)$$

It is proven in Kwakernaak and Sivan (1972) that

$$\lim_{\rho^2 \to \infty} \frac{\mathbf{P}_f}{\rho^2} = 0 \tag{7.4.18}$$

if the transfer function $\mathbf{C}[s\mathbf{I} - \mathbf{A}]^{-1}\mathbf{B}$ has no right half plane zeros. Consequently, it follows from Eq.(7.4.17) that

$$\lim_{\rho^2 \to \infty} \frac{\mathbf{P}_f \mathbf{C}^T \mathbf{V}^{-1} \mathbf{C} \mathbf{P}_f}{\rho^2} = \lim_{\rho^2 \to \infty} \frac{\mathbf{P}_f}{\rho^2} \mathbf{C}^T \mathbf{V}^{-1} \mathbf{C} \frac{\mathbf{P}_f}{\rho^2} \rho^2 = \mathbf{BSB}^T. \tag{7.4.19}$$

From the definition of $\mathbf{K}_f$, Eq(7.4.8) and Eq.(7.4.19), we finally get

$$\lim_{\rho 2 \to \infty} \frac{\mathbf{K}_f \mathbf{V} \mathbf{K}_f^T}{\rho^2} = \mathbf{BSB}^T. \tag{7.4.20}$$

With no loss of generality, $\mathbf{S}$ can be chosen as unity diagonal, $\mathbf{S} = \mathbf{I}$, and it follows from Eq.(7.4.20) that

$$\lim_{\rho^2 \to \infty} \mathbf{K}_f = \rho \mathbf{B} \mathbf{V}^{-1/2}. \tag{7.4.21}$$

As the constant $\rho \to \infty$, $\mathbf{L}_{LQG}(s) \to \mathbf{L}_{LQR}(s)$. To prove this, we use the equalities in Eqs.(7.4.14) and (7.4.15), and the matrix identity

$$(\mathbf{I} + \mathbf{XY})^{-1}\mathbf{X} = \mathbf{X}(\mathbf{I} + \mathbf{YX})^{-1} \tag{7.4.22}$$

(easily proven by premultiplying by $(\mathbf{I} + \mathbf{XY})$ and postmultiplying by $(\mathbf{I} + \mathbf{YX})$ both sides).

$\mathbf{G}(s)$ in Eq.(7.4.13) can be expressed in terms of $\boldsymbol{\phi}_A(s) = [s\mathbf{I} - \mathbf{A}]^{-1}$ and $\boldsymbol{\phi}_c(s) = [s\mathbf{I} - \mathbf{A} + \mathbf{BK}_c]^{-1}$.

$$\mathbf{G}(s) = \mathbf{K}_c[s\mathbf{I} - \mathbf{A} + \mathbf{K}_f\mathbf{C} + \mathbf{BK}_c]^{-1}\mathbf{K}_f$$

$$= \mathbf{K}_c[\boldsymbol{\phi}_c^{-1}(s) + \mathbf{K}_f\mathbf{C}]^{-1}\mathbf{K}_f$$

$$= \mathbf{K}_c [\mathbf{I} + \boldsymbol{\phi}_c(s)\mathbf{K}_f\mathbf{C}]^{-1}\boldsymbol{\phi}_c(s)\mathbf{K}_f$$

which together with Eq.(7.4.22) becomes

$$\mathbf{G}(s) = \mathbf{K}_c \boldsymbol{\phi}_c(s)\mathbf{K}_f[\mathbf{I} + \mathbf{C}\boldsymbol{\phi}_c(s)\mathbf{K}_f]^{-1}$$

Use the resulting $\mathbf{K}_f$ in Eq.(7.4.21) for $\rho \to \infty$, and assume that $\mathbf{C}\boldsymbol{\phi}_c(s)\mathbf{K}_f >> \mathbf{I}$ to finally obtain

$$G(s) = K_c \phi_c(s) B [C\phi_c(s)B]^{-1.} \tag{7.4.23}$$

By using the definitions of $\phi_c(s)$, $\phi_A(s)$ and the identity in Eq.(7.4.22), it is easily shown that

$$\phi_c(s)B = \phi_A(s)B[I + K_c\phi_A(s)B]^{-1} \tag{7.4.24}$$

Eqs.(7.4.14), (7.4.23) and (7.4.24) lead to the final expression for $L(s)_{LQG.}$.

$$L(s)_{LQG} = G(s)C\phi_A(s)B = K_c\phi_A(s)B = K_c[sI - A]^{-1} B \tag{7.4.25}$$

and according to Eq.(7.4.15), $L(s)_{LQG} = L(s)_{LQR}$ when $\rho \to \infty$.

The meaning of the LTR design improvement is best illustrated with the following example.

Example 7.4.2. This example is a continuation of Example 7.4.1. The objective is to ameliorate the achieved open-loop transfer function $L_{LQG}(j\omega)$ (obtained by the LQG standard design technique), which shows very limited stability margins.

Solution: The autocorrelation matrix **W**, used in the solution of Example 7.4.1, is modified as per Eq.(7.4.16). Two resulting $L_{LQG/LTR}(j\omega)$ with $\rho = 1$ and $\rho = 10^4$ are also shown in Fig.7.4.4. When a low $\rho = 1$ is tried, the improvement is insufficient. (See the same figure.) If a very high ρ is chosen, for instance $\rho = 10^4$, the lost stability margins of the LQR design are almost completely recovered, with the additional merit that the achieved $L(j\omega)$ has a higher negative slope at high frequencies. This helps decrease the sensor noise amplification. (See Section 2.4 and Fig.2.4.1.)

7.5. Summary

Chapter 7 is a short exposition of design principles using the state-space formulation for linear systems. As such, these are well-suited to SISO as well as MIMO feedback systems. The design is based on optimization of a quadratic performance measure. When the constrained process, the plant, is time invariant and the regulation time is infinite, the optimal controller obtained by solving algebraic Riccati equations emerges with constant parameters. With all the states available for feedback purposes, the linear quadratic regulator is the solution. When not all the states are measurable, these must be estimated first. If process and sensor noises are present, the optimal Kalman-Bucy filter is used in the integrated design structure, known as the LQG problem. In order to remain with favorable relative stability margins with the LQG design technique, an improved technique known as the LQG/LTR should be used.

Unfortunately, the design methods presented in this chaper are incompatible for dealing with plants having bounded, but largely uncertain parameters. Nevertheless, these methods, expressed in state-space formulation, are the theoretical background to more advanced design techniques that solve the uncertain feedback system problem.

Chapter 8

MIMO Uncertain Feedback Systems Solved with H_∞-Norm Optimization Techniques

8.1 Introduction

The H_∞-norm optimization paradigm was introduced in Chapters 2 and 4 to solve the SISO uncertain feedback problem. Chapter 8 aims to solve the MIMO uncertain feedback problem in the framework of the same paradigm. As a prelude, Section 8.2 introduces the notion of 'singular values' that describe efficiently transfer function matrix characteristics such as matrix size, matrix norms, and also MIMO design performances. These are next used to define and solve the MIMO problem in the H_∞ workspace. Section 8.3 deals once more with the H_∞-Optimal Regulator Problem and its solution adapted to MIMO plants. An algorithm solving H_∞-norm optimization problems is also outlined in this section. Section 8.4 deals first with modeling of MIMO uncertain plants. Next, stability and robust properties for MIMO feedback systems in terms of transfer function matrices of the modeled uncertain plant are stated, and proved. Section 8.5 describes a design technique for solving the MIMO TDOF uncertain feedback problem. Much of the basic theoretical background material needed in this chapter can be found in Maciejowski (1989), Doyle et al. (1992), Kwakernaak (1993), Dorato and Cerone (1995), Skogestad and Postlethwaite (1996), Zhou, Doyle and Glover (1996), Zhou and Doyle (1998). Many other papers and books will be cited in the course of this chapter.

8.2. Singular Values and their Use in MIMO Feedback Systems.

The classical control designer is quite satisfied with Bode plots to describe the behavior of an algebraic transfer function by its frequency dependent magnitude and phase characteristics. The situation is much more complicated when transfer function matrices are involved in the MIMO feedback problem. There are two basic ways for describing magnitude characteristics of transfer function matrices, which are the 'characteristic (or eigenvalue) loci', treated briefly in Section 6.2.5, and the 'singular values'.

8.2.1. Singular Values as a Means to Express Transfer Function Matrix Size. (See Appendix B.)

The vector $\mathbf{y}(s)$ at the output of a matrix $\mathbf{P}(s)$ is not unique because it depends on the input vector $\mathbf{u}(s)$, which is specified by both its amplitude and direction. However, we can find upper and lower bounds of the ratio

$$\frac{\| \mathbf{P}(j\omega)\mathbf{u}(j\omega)\|}{\| \mathbf{u}(j\omega)\|} = \frac{\|\mathbf{y}(j\omega)\|}{\|\mathbf{u}(j\omega)\|} \equiv r(\omega) \tag{8.2.1}$$

and also of the ratio

$$\frac{\|\mathbf{P}^{-1}(j\omega)\mathbf{y}(j\omega)\|}{\|\mathbf{y}(j\omega)\|} \equiv q(\omega) \tag{8.2.2}$$

using matrix norms. Suppose that we keep the Euclidean norm of the input vector $\mathbf{u}$ constant, $\|\mathbf{u}(s)\| = 1$, for instance, but change the ratio between its elements. In this case, $r(\omega)$ will change too, depending on the direction of the input vector $\mathbf{u}(s)$.

For a vector norm $\|\mathbf{u}\|$, an *induced matrix norm* is defined as

$$\|\mathbf{P}\| = \sup_{\mathbf{u}\,\neq\,0} \frac{\|\mathbf{Pu}\|}{\|\mathbf{u}\|}. \tag{8.2.3}$$

(See Maciejowski 1989).
If $\|\mathbf{u}\|$ is the usual Euclidean vector norm, (which is a H_2-norm), it can be written as

$$\|\mathbf{u}\| = [\mathbf{u}^*\mathbf{u}]^{1/2}, \tag{8.2.4}$$

then the induced matrix norm is the spectral norm

$$\|\mathbf{P}\|_s = \bar{\sigma} \tag{8.2.5}$$

where $\bar{\sigma}$ is the positive square root of the maximum eigenvalue of $\mathbf{P}^*\mathbf{P}$ (or $\mathbf{PP}^*$). $\mathbf{u}^*$ and $\mathbf{P}^*$ denote the complex conjugate transposes of $\mathbf{u}$ and $\mathbf{P}$ respectively, since $\mathbf{u}$ and $\mathbf{P}$ can be complex. $r(\omega)$, as defined in Eq.(8.2.1), means 'gain', which is unique for the scalar case in which one input and one output are considered. For the matrix case, as already mentioned, this 'gain' depends on the input vector direction.

Singular values

A formal definition of singular values follows:

If **P** has n rows and m columns, and $n \geq m$, then the *singular values* of a constant matrix **P** are the positive square roots of **P*P** (if $n \leq m$, then **P P*** is considered):

$$\sigma_i(\mathbf{P}) = [\lambda_i(\mathbf{P^*P})]^{1/2} , n \geq m \qquad (8.2.6a)$$

$$\sigma_i(\mathbf{P}) = [\lambda_i(\mathbf{PP^*})]^{1/2}, n \leq m \qquad (8.2.6b)$$

where λ_i stands for the ith eigenvalue of (**P*P**) or (**PP***), and the notation $\sigma(\mathbf{P})$ is used for denoting the 'singular values' of a matrix **P**.

Principal gains

The singular values are sometimes called *principal gains* for frequency dependent matrices. They are denoted by $\sigma_i(\omega)$ to emphasis their frequency dependence. Singular values are by definition ordered as $\sigma_1 \geq \sigma_2 \geq \ldots \geq \sigma_n$ where $\sigma_i \geq \sigma_{i+1}$. σ_1 and σ_n are called the maximum and the minimum singular values respectively, denoted by $\sigma_{max} \equiv \bar{\sigma}$ and $\sigma_{min} \equiv \underline{\sigma}$. In other words, they indicate the maximum and minimum sizes, or magnitudes, of the matrix. ('principal gains' and 'singular values' are used interchangeably in the book).

Singular value decomposition of a matrix.

Any real or complex matrix **P** with n rows and m columns can be decomposed in the following form

$$\mathbf{P} = \mathbf{U\Sigma V^*} \qquad (8.2.7)$$

where $\mathbf{\Sigma}$ is a diagonal matrix whose elements are the singular values σ_i

$$\mathbf{\Sigma} = \text{diag} (\sigma_1, \sigma_2, \sigma_3, \ldots \ldots \ldots, \sigma_n) \qquad (8.2.8)$$

See Appendix B for details.

An important fact follows for square matrices which are invertible. In this case, by inverting Eq.(8.2.7), we find that

$$\mathbf{P^{-1}} = \mathbf{V\Sigma^{-1}U^*} \qquad (8.2.9)$$

from which it follows that, for frequency dependent matrices,

$$\|\mathbf{P^{-1}}(j\omega)\|_s = \frac{1}{\underline{\sigma}(\omega)} \qquad (8.2.10)$$

The last equation, together with Eq.(8.2.2), give the following important inequalities

$$\frac{\|\mathbf{P}^{-1}(j\omega)\mathbf{y}(j\omega)\|}{\|\mathbf{y}(j\omega)\|} \leq \frac{1}{\underline{\sigma}(\omega)} \qquad (8.2.11)$$

and

$$\frac{\|\mathbf{P}(j\omega)\mathbf{u}(j\omega)\|}{\|\mathbf{u}(j\omega)\|} \leq \bar{\sigma}(\omega). \qquad (8.2.12)$$

Insert $\mathbf{y}(j\omega) = \mathbf{P}(j\omega)\mathbf{u}(j\omega)$ in Eq.(8.2.11) to get

$$\frac{\|\mathbf{u}(j\omega)\|}{\|\mathbf{P}(j\omega)\mathbf{u}(j\omega)\|} \leq \frac{1}{\underline{\sigma}(\omega)}$$

or, after inversion of the last inequality, we get

$$\frac{\|\mathbf{P}(j\omega)\mathbf{u}(j\omega)\|}{\|\mathbf{u}(j\omega)\|} \geq \underline{\sigma}(\omega) \qquad (8.2.13)$$

Eqs.(8.2.12) and (8.2.13) together give the final result

$$\bar{\sigma}(\omega) \geq \frac{\|\mathbf{P}(j\omega)\mathbf{u}(j\omega)\|}{\|\mathbf{u}(j\omega)\|} = \frac{\|\mathbf{y}(j\omega)\|}{\|\mathbf{u}(j\omega)\|} \geq \underline{\sigma}(\omega) \qquad (8.2.14)$$

Thus, the bounds on $r(\omega)$ in Eq.(8.2.1) are given by the smaller and the larger principal gains of the given matrix $\mathbf{P}(j\omega)$, Eq.(8.2.14).

Note that in the last equation, as in Eq.(8.2.1), $\|\mathbf{P}(j\omega)\mathbf{u}(j\omega)\| = \|\mathbf{y}(j\omega)\|$, so that the 'gain' of the matrix $\mathbf{P}(j\omega)$ is characterized by the conventional input-output gain $\|\mathbf{y}(j\omega)\| / \|\mathbf{u}(j\omega)\|$ in which the input and output variables are 2-norm vectors. The 'gain' is bounded by the maximum and minimum principal gains and depends on the direction of the input vector $\mathbf{u}(j\omega)$.

In this context, the matrix norm to be used is the H_∞-norm of the matrix defined by the maximum singular value of the matrix,

$$\|\mathbf{P}(j\omega)\|_\infty = \max_{\omega \in R} \bar{\sigma}[\mathbf{P}(j\omega)] \qquad (8.2.15)$$

where R stands here for the 'real space'.

An example will clarify and illustrate the meaning of the last equation.

Example 8.2.1. A 2×2 plant transfer function matrix $\mathbf{P}$ is given, in which P_{ij} $(s) = k_{ij}/(sA_{ij} + 1)$: $P_{11}(s) = 10/(s\,0.2 + 1)$; $P_{22}(s) = 8/(s\,0.4 + 1)$; $P_{12}(s) = 2/(s\,0.5 + 1)$; $P_{21}(s) = 1/(s + 1)$;

1) Plot the smaller and the largest principal gains of **P**.

2) Plot the 'magnitude' of the matrix for different directions of the input vector $\mathbf{u}(j\omega) = [u_1\ u_2\ ]^T$, where $\|\mathbf{u}\| = 1$: $\mathbf{u}(j\omega) = [0.1\ 0.9954]^T$, $[0.3\ 0.9539]^T$, $[0.5\ 0.866]^T$ and $[0.7\ 0.714]^T$.

Solution: Since

$$\begin{bmatrix} y_1(j\omega) \\ y_2(j\omega) \end{bmatrix} = \begin{bmatrix} P_{11}(j\omega)\ P_{12}(j\omega) \\ P_{21}(j\omega)\ P_{22}(j\omega) \end{bmatrix} \begin{bmatrix} u_1(j\omega) \\ u_2(j\omega) \end{bmatrix},$$

the two outputs are

$$y_1(j\omega) = P_{11}(j\omega)u_1(j\omega) + P_{12}(j\omega)u_2(j\omega)\ ;\ y_2(j\omega) = P_{21}(j\omega)u_1(j\omega) + P_{22}(j\omega)u_2(j\omega).$$

The output norm is $\|\mathbf{y}(j\omega)\| = [y_1^2(j\omega) + y_2^2(j\omega)]^{1/2}$. The 'gain' of the matrix **P** is $\|\mathbf{y}(j\omega)\|/\|\mathbf{u}(j\omega)\|$. The Bode plots of the magnitudes for the assumed input vectors $\mathbf{u}(j\omega)$'s are shown in Fig.8.2.1 as solid lines, which are located well between the largest and smallest principal gains of the matrix, shown on the same figure as dashed lines.

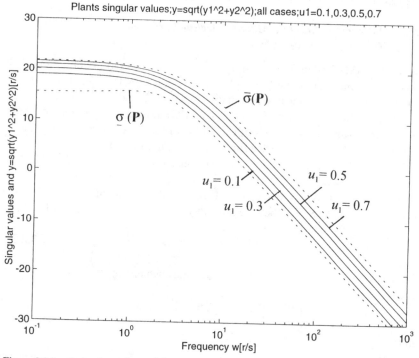

Figure 8.2.1. Bode plots of $\|\mathbf{y}(j\omega)\|/\|\mathbf{u}(j\omega)\|$ for $u_1^2 + u_2^2 = 1$; $u_1 = 0.1, 0.3, 0.5, 0.7$-solid lines; $\bar{\sigma}[\mathbf{P}(j\omega)]$ and $\underline{\sigma}[\mathbf{P}(j\omega)]$—dashed lines.

Some important singular value inequalities are listed below without proof. For proofs see Horn and Johnson (1991), Green and Limebeer (1995), Zhou et al. (1996). The following inequalities hold for matrices **A** and **B** of adequate order. (See also Appendix B).

$$\underline{\sigma}(\mathbf{A}) \leq |\lambda_i(\mathbf{A})| \leq \bar{\sigma}(\mathbf{A}) \qquad (8.2.16)$$

where λ_i are the eigenvalues of **A**. These are bounded between the maximum and minimum singular values of the matrix. Also,

$$\bar{\sigma}(\mathbf{AB}) \geq \bar{\sigma}(\mathbf{A})\bar{\sigma}(\mathbf{B}) \qquad (8.2.17)$$

$$\underline{\sigma}(\mathbf{A})\,\underline{\sigma}(\mathbf{B}) \leq \underline{\sigma}(\mathbf{AB}) \qquad (8.2.18)$$

$$\underline{\sigma}(\mathbf{A}) - 1 \leq \underline{\sigma}(\mathbf{I} + \mathbf{A}) \leq \underline{\sigma}(\mathbf{A}) + 1 \qquad (8.2.19)$$

$$\underline{\sigma}(\mathbf{A}) - 1 \leq 1/\underline{\sigma}(\mathbf{I}+\mathbf{A})^{-1} \leq \underline{\sigma}(\mathbf{A}) + 1 \qquad (8.2.20)$$

The last equation is useful when MIMO closed-loop systems are analyzed.

8.2.2. Singular Values as a Means to Define Performances in MIMO Feedback Systems

As for the SISO feedback system problem, we are interested in defining the following performance functions: disturbance rejection for MIMO feedback systems via the sensitivity transfer function matrix $\mathbf{S}(j\omega) = (\mathbf{I} + \mathbf{PG})^{-1}$; the unity-feedback transfer function matrix $\mathbf{T}_1(j\omega) = \mathbf{S}(j\omega)\mathbf{PG}$; the input-output tracking transfer function matrix $\mathbf{T}(j\omega) = \mathbf{S}(j\omega)\mathbf{PGF}$, the sensor noise amplification $\mathbf{T}_{un}(j\omega) = -(\mathbf{I} + \mathbf{GP})^{-1}\mathbf{G}$; and so on. (See Fig.(4. 2.1) or Fig.(6.2.1).)

In the SISO problem, the unity-feedback transfer function $T_1(j\omega)$ (also called the complementary sensitivity function) is related to the sensitivity function $S(j\omega)$ as per Eq. (2.2.2), namely $S(j\omega) + T_1(j\omega) = 1$. In the MIMO case, the transfer function matrices $\mathbf{T}_1(j\omega)$ and $\mathbf{S}(j\omega)$ obey the same identity in matrix form (Eq. (6.1.10)),

$$\mathbf{S}(j\omega) + \mathbf{T}_1(j\omega) = \mathbf{I}. \qquad (8.2.21)$$

There also exist two more important inequalities, which are

$$|\,1 - \bar{\sigma}(\mathbf{S})\,| \leq \bar{\sigma}(\mathbf{T}_1) \leq 1 + \bar{\sigma}(\mathbf{S}) \qquad (8.2.22)$$

and

$$|\,1 - \bar{\sigma}(\mathbf{T}_1)\,| \leq \bar{\sigma}(\mathbf{S}) \leq 1 + \bar{\sigma}(\mathbf{T}_1) \qquad (8.2.23)$$

Their proofs can be found in Maciejowski (1989).

General system requirements for SISO and MIMO closed-loop feedback systems were defined in different contexts in previous chapters. These can be translated for MIMO feedback systems in terms of the smallest and largest singular values. Similarly to the SISO feedback system case (Section 2.1), specifications for MIMO feedback systems can be defined in terms of the open-loop transfer function matrix, $\mathbf{L}(s) = \mathbf{P}(s)\mathbf{G}(s)$, or, closed-loop transfer function matrices such as $\mathbf{S}(j\omega)$, $\mathbf{T}_1(j\omega)$, $\mathbf{T}(j\omega)$, $\mathbf{G}(j\omega)\mathbf{S}(j\omega)$, etc. We may be interested requiring that $\underline{\sigma}[\mathbf{L}(j\omega)] \geq b$; $\omega \leq \omega_x$, or, for instance, it will be convenient to require that $\bar{\sigma}(\mathbf{S}) \leq a$; $\omega \leq \omega_x$ where $a < 1$ and ω_x is a frequency below which disturbance rejection is to be adequately achieved. In the same way, the magnitudes of the unity-feedback transfer function matrix $\mathbf{T}_1(j\omega)$ must be located within the limits $\bar{\sigma}$ [$\mathbf{T}_1$ $(j\omega)$] and $\underline{\sigma}[\mathbf{T}_1(j\omega)]$.

Closed-loop specifications can be derived from open-loop requirements such as:

1-Large $\underline{\sigma}[\mathbf{P}(j\omega)\mathbf{G}(j\omega)] = \underline{\sigma}[\mathbf{L}(j\omega)]$ in the frequency range in which the disturbance spectrum is concentrated. This requirement is effective for disturbance attenuation and for low-sensitivity to plant parameter uncertainties.

2-$\bar{\sigma}[\mathbf{P}(j\omega)\mathbf{G}(j\omega)]$ to be small at high frequencies where sensor noise is concentrated. This requirement is necessary for sensor noise attenuation and for attenuation of the effect of structural modes, which are generally located at high frequencies.

3-$\bar{\sigma}[\mathbf{P}(j\omega)\mathbf{G}(j\omega)]$ is to be as small as possible in the operational frequency range, in order to limit the control effort, but without contradicting **1-**.

In the classical design approach, definition of performances in terms of the open-loop transfer function matrix $\mathbf{L}(s)$ is preferred. In the modern H_∞ design approach, definition of performances in terms of closed-loop transfer function matrices is preferred. In this case, the specifications are expressed directly by closed-loop requirements such as:

1-Keep the sensitivity function small. Namely, keep $\bar{\sigma}[\mathbf{S}(j\omega)] = \bar{\sigma}[(\mathbf{I}+\mathbf{PG})^{-1}] = 1/\underline{\sigma}(\mathbf{I}+\mathbf{PG})$ as small as possible in the operational frequency range. This requirement is effective in attenuating the influence of external disturbances $\mathbf{d}_2$ at the output $\mathbf{y}$ in Fig.6.2.12a, and in rendering the system less sensitive to plant uncertainties.

2-To attenuate sufficiently the amplified sensor noise reaching the output vector $\mathbf{y}$, keep $\bar{\sigma}[\mathbf{I}-\mathbf{S}(j\omega)]$ as small as possible at the relevant noise spectrum range.

3-To achieve a low level of control effort $\mathbf{u}(j\omega)$, due to external disturbances and to sensor noises, $\bar{\sigma}[\mathbf{G}(j\omega)\mathbf{S}(j\omega)]$ must be kept low, especially in the high frequency range where the noise level is most pronounced and $\bar{\sigma}[\mathbf{S}(j\omega)] \to 1$. In the lower frequency range, where $\bar{\sigma}[\mathbf{S}(j\omega)]$ is low, a larger $\bar{\sigma}[\mathbf{G}(j\omega)\mathbf{S}(j\omega)]$ is less harmful from the sensor noise amplification point of view, as explained in Section 2.4.1.

Since there exist contradictions in the different requirements, tradeoffs between them are necessary in the design stage of the open-loop transfer function matrix $\mathbf{L}(s) = \mathbf{P}(s)\mathbf{G}(s)$. The design objective is to achieve high $\underline{\sigma}[\mathbf{L}(j\omega)]$ (which leads to low $\bar{\sigma}[\mathbf{S}(j\omega)]$) in the frequency ranges where the disturbances are most pronounced. Simultaneously, a low $\bar{\sigma}\,[\mathbf{L}(s)]$ is achieved in the higher frequency range where the sensor noise is concentrated.

Similarly to the SISO feedback system problem, we are faced with contradictory requirements, and some compromise between them becomes imperative. This compromise is achieved automatically in the solution of the Standard H_∞-Regulator Problem, presented in Section 2.5.5 for SISO feedback systems. The desired requirements on prescribed principal gains are achieved by choosing adequate weighting function matrices for MIMO feedback systems.

8.3.   Solution of the Standard H_∞-Regulator Problem.

8.3.1.   Introduction

The Standard H_∞-Optimal Regulator was introduced in Section 2.5.5 to solve the SISO mixed sensitivity problem. It was also used in Section 4.8.6 to solve the SISO TDOF uncertain plant feedback problem. In both cases, commercial algorithms were used to obtain the H_∞-optimal compensator $G(s)$. The purpose of this section is to clarify some important points and facts involved in programming of H_∞-optimization algorithms. Mathematical proofs can be found in published works which will be referred to when needed.

Definition of the Generalized plant

The general structure of the standard regulator problem is shown in Fig.8.3.1. $\mathbf{M}(s)$ is the *augmented* plant model. Also called *generalized,* this plant model includes the traditional physical plant $\mathbf{P}(s)$, and also all weighting function matrices related to the specific control problem. (See for example Figs. 2.5.2 and 4.8.13). To remind the reader, $\mathbf{w}$ is the vector of all external inputs (command, disturbances and sensor noises sources). $\mathbf{z}$ is a vector of fictitious outputs defining abstract mathematical errors and performance criterions (which are generally not physical outputs of the controlled system). $\mathbf{e}$ is a vector of error inputs to the controller $\mathbf{G}(s)$, obtained from the measurable physical outputs and the input commands. $\mathbf{u}$ is the physical control vector at the input to the plant.

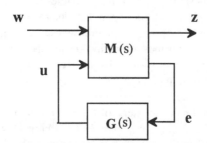

Figure 8.3.1   General structure for the standard H_∞-regulator problem.

The generalized plant $\mathbf{M}(s)$ can be partitioned as

$$\begin{bmatrix} \mathbf{z}(s) \\ \mathbf{e}(s) \end{bmatrix} = \mathbf{M}(s) \begin{bmatrix} \mathbf{w}(s) \\ \mathbf{u}(s) \end{bmatrix} = \begin{bmatrix} \mathbf{M}_{11}(s) & \mathbf{M}_{12}(s) \\ \mathbf{M}_{21}(s) & \mathbf{M}_{22}(s) \end{bmatrix} \begin{bmatrix} \mathbf{w}(s) \\ \mathbf{u}(s) \end{bmatrix} \qquad (8.3.1)$$

where $\mathbf{M}_{ij}$ are matrices of compatible order. In Fig.8.3.1, the closed-loop transfer function matrix $\mathbf{T}_{\mathbf{wz}}$ from $\mathbf{w}$ to $\mathbf{z}$ can be expressed by the so-called *Linear Fractional Transformation* (LFT). (For a more detailed treatment on linear fractional transformations, the reader is referred to Appendix B. See also Green and Limebeer 1995, or Zhou 1998).

$$\mathbf{T}_{\mathbf{wz}} = F_L(\mathbf{M}, \mathbf{G}) = \mathbf{M}_{11} + \mathbf{M}_{12}\mathbf{G}(\mathbf{I} - \mathbf{M}_{22}\mathbf{G})^{-1}\mathbf{M}_{21} \qquad (8.3.2)$$

or,

$$\mathbf{z} = F_L(\mathbf{M}, \mathbf{G})\,\mathbf{w} = \mathbf{T}_{\mathbf{wz}}\mathbf{w} \qquad (8.3.2')$$

Also

$$\mathbf{u} = \mathbf{G}(s)\mathbf{e} \qquad (8.3.3)$$

where $\mathbf{G}(s)$ is the controller to be designed.

The block diagram in Fig.8.3.1 represents a lower case linear fractional transformation described by Eq.(8.3.2). A simple example will help illustrate how the generalized plant is obtained from the physical plant and the weighting function matrices data.

Example 8.3.1. Obtain the generalized plant for the mixed sensitivity problem in Section 2.5.5 (after deleting the prefilter $\mathbf{F}$ and renaming the output variables) by using the matrix partitioning of Eq. (8.3.1). The generalized structure for the MIMO case is shown in Fig.8.3.2.

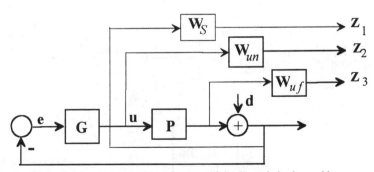

Figure 8.3.2. Structure of the mixed sensitivity H_∞-optimization problem.

Solution. The input vector to the generalized plant is $\mathbf{w} = [\mathbf{d}, \mathbf{u}]^T$. The performance output vector is $[\mathbf{z}_1, \mathbf{z}_2, \mathbf{z}_3]^T$, and the generalized output vector is $\mathbf{z} = [\mathbf{z}_1, \mathbf{z}_2, \mathbf{z}_3, \mathbf{e}]^T$. The transfer function matrix, relating the performance output vector $[\mathbf{z}_1, \mathbf{z}_2, \mathbf{z}_3]^T$ to the external input vector $\mathbf{d}$, is $\mathbf{M}_{11} = [\mathbf{W_S I}, \mathbf{0}, \mathbf{0}]^T$. The transfer function matrix relating the controller input vector $\mathbf{e}$ to the external input vector $\mathbf{d}$ is $\mathbf{M}_{21} = -\mathbf{I}$. The transfer function matrix relating the performance output vector $[\mathbf{z}_1, \mathbf{z}_2, \mathbf{z}_3]^T$ to the control input vector $\mathbf{u}$ is $\mathbf{M}_{12} = [\mathbf{W_S P}, \mathbf{W}_{un}\mathbf{I}, \mathbf{W}_{uf}\mathbf{P}]^T$. The transfer function matrix relating the controller input vector $\mathbf{e}$ to the control input vector $\mathbf{u}$ is $\mathbf{M}_{22} = -\mathbf{P}$.

State-space realization of the generalized plant

When a state-space version of an H_∞-optimization algorithm is implemented, $\mathbf{M}(s)$ is converted to its state-space realization form in the following way (see Appendix B):

$$\mathbf{M} = \left[\begin{array}{c|cc} \mathbf{A} & \mathbf{B}_1 & \mathbf{B}_2 \\ \hline \mathbf{C}_1 & \mathbf{D}_{11} & \mathbf{D}_{12} \\ \mathbf{B}_1 & \mathbf{D}_{21} & \mathbf{D}_{22} \end{array} \right] \tag{8.3.4}$$

De facto, $\mathbf{M}(s)$ is obtained by combining components, such as the plant $\mathbf{P}(s)$ and the different weighting function matrices in Fig.8.3.2. Each one of the real-polynomial transfer function matrices involved in the feedback system structure can be represented in the standard state-space matrix form used in all Matlab toolboxes,

$$\left[\begin{array}{c|c} \mathbf{A}\_ & \mathbf{B}\_ \\ \hline \mathbf{C}\_ & \mathbf{D}\_ \end{array} \right]$$

where the subscript (_) stands for the name of the transfer function matrix pertaining to the plant $\mathbf{P}$, and to the weighting function matrices $\mathbf{W}_S$, $\mathbf{W}_{un}$ and $\mathbf{W}_{uf}$ in Fig.8.3.2. (See Chiang and Safonov 1988, or Hvostov 1990). With this symbolism, the state-space realization of the elements in $\mathbf{M}$ of Eq.(8.3.4) become those in Eqs.(8.3.5):

$$\mathbf{A} = \begin{bmatrix} \mathbf{A_P} & \mathbf{0} & \mathbf{0} & \mathbf{0} \\ -\mathbf{B_{W_S}C_P} & \mathbf{A_{W_S}} & \mathbf{0} & \mathbf{0} \\ \mathbf{0} & \mathbf{0} & \mathbf{A_{W_{un}}} & \mathbf{0} \\ \mathbf{B_{W_{uf}}} & \mathbf{C_P} & \mathbf{0} & \mathbf{A_{W_{uf}}} \end{bmatrix} \in \mathfrak{R}^{n \times n}; \ \mathbf{B}_1 = \begin{bmatrix} \mathbf{0} \\ \mathbf{B_{W_S}} \\ \mathbf{0} \\ \mathbf{0} \end{bmatrix} \in \mathfrak{R}^{n \times m1} \tag{8.3.5a}$$

$$\mathbf{B}_2 = \begin{bmatrix} \mathbf{B_P} \\ -\mathbf{B_{W_S}D_P} \\ \mathbf{B_{W_{un}}} \\ \mathbf{B_{W_{uf}}D_P} \end{bmatrix} \in \mathfrak{R}^{n \times m2} \tag{8.3.5b}$$

$$C_1 = \begin{bmatrix} -D_{W_S}C_P & C_{W_S} & 0 & 0 \\ 0 & 0 & C_{W_{un}} & 0 \\ D_{W_{uf}}C_P & 0 & 0 & C_{W_{uf}} \end{bmatrix} \in \mathcal{R}^{p1 \times n}; \; C_2 = [-C_P \; 0 \; 0 \; 0] \in \mathcal{R}^{p2 \times n}$$

$$(8.3.5.c)$$

$$D_{11} = \begin{bmatrix} D_{W_S} \\ 0 \\ 0 \end{bmatrix} \in \mathcal{R}^{p1 \times m1} \; ; \; D_{12} = \begin{bmatrix} -D_{W_S}D_P \\ D_{W_{un}} \\ D_{W_{uf}}D_P \end{bmatrix} \in \mathcal{R}^{p1 \times m2} \quad (8.3.5d)$$

$$D_{21} = I \in \mathcal{R}^{p2 \times m1} \; ; \; D_{22} = -D_P \in \mathcal{R}^{p2 \times m2} \quad (8.3.5e)$$

8.3.2. Algorithms for the Solution of the Standard H_∞-Control Problem

In previous chapters, examples were solved by using commercial algorithms to solve the standard H_∞-regulator problem. The practicing engineer can use such existing software without devoting many hours to understand all the mathematical aspects and details that make them work. However, some superficial understanding is always necessary. The short explanation that follows is intended to give the reader a feeling of confidence that he understands the basic line of thought of the algorithm. Moreover, when the software programming fails to converge, he can then understand the appearing software notes and remarks on the screen concerning the failure. In this way, he can correct the programming of the problem setup, so that a successful solution emerges.

Optimization algorithms can be posed both in the frequency-domain and in the state-space frameworks. The mathematical details of frequency-domain based optimization algorithms can be found in Kwakernaak (1990a and 1993). However, most of the commercial H_∞ optimization algorithms for the solution of the standard regulator problem are solved in the state-space formulation (Doyle et al. 1989, Glover and Doyle 1988). Hence, a short presentation of the optimization algorithm detailed in the last two works follows. The presentation follows closely that in Skogestad and Postlethwaite (1997). (See also Hvostov, 1990. Detailed mechanization of H_∞-norm algorithms can be found in Balas et al., 1995).

The H_∞-norm optimization algorithm seeks to minimize $\|F_L(\mathbf{M}, \mathbf{G})\|_\infty$ over all stabilizing LTI controllers $\mathbf{G}(s)$. In an alternative way, used in the H_∞ optimization algorithms, we can specify some maximum value γ for the closed-loop $\mathbf{T}_{wz}$ RMS gain and ask if there exist a stabilizing linear controller $\mathbf{G}(s)$, with the state-space realization

$$G = \begin{bmatrix} A_G & | & B_G \\ - & -|- & - \\ C_G & | & D_G \end{bmatrix}$$

which ensures that $\mathbf{T_{wz}} = F_L(\mathbf{M, G})$ is stable, and that

$$\|F_L(\mathbf{M, G})\|_\infty = \max_{\mathbf{w}(t)\,\neq\,0} \frac{\|\mathbf{z}(t)\|_2}{\|\mathbf{w}(t)\|_2} < \gamma. \qquad (8.3.6)$$

γ is called the prescribed H_∞ performance factor and is a positive number.

The optimizing $\mathbf{G}(s)$ is hard to achieve directly, therefore we use 'γ—iterations'. The standard state-space optimization procedure for solving Eq.(8.3.6) can be repeated iteratively until the smallest γ is found, for which a compensator exists. Solution of the above equation yields in fact a 'suboptimal' compensator only. The final stage is obtaining the optimal controller $\mathbf{G}(s)$ that satisfies Eq.(8.3.6) with as low a prescribed performance factor γ as possible.

As for the SISO case, the most challenging stage in the MIMO H_∞-control design is to select correctly the different weighting function matrices, so that system control performances are adequately defined, and, finally, satisfied. It is hoped that the material in previous chapters, especially in Chapters 1 to 4 has helped the reader to acquire a good basis for defining the scalar weighting functions in the SISO feedback problem. Nonetheless, selection of weighting function matrices in the MIMO feedback problem is a much more elaborate process. The reason for this is that we are then faced with bounds on singular values, which belong to the entire matrix and not to its individual elements.

General control problem formulation

(The well-known 'Glover-Doyle (1988) algorithm' for general H_∞-norm optimization problems).

The state-space realization of the generalized plant $\mathbf{M}(s)$ in Fig.8.3.1 is given by Eq.(8.3.4). H_2 and H_∞ solution of control problems involve minimization of the H_2 and H_∞-norms of $F_L(\mathbf{M,G})$ respectively. It is of important to notice that both H_2 and H_∞ optimizations algorithms require the solutions of two Riccati equations. The obtained controllers are of state-dimension equal to that of the augmented plant $\mathbf{M}(s)$ in Eq.(8.3.1) and Fig.8.3.1. Both solutions exhibit a separation structure of the controller. See Section 7.4.3 where the 'separation principle' and the solution of the LQG problem (which is a special case of a H_2-optimization) are discussed. To summarize, all stabilizing controllers can be interpreted as observer/state feedback combinations. As such, two Riccati equations have to be solved.

For a solution to exist, some assumptions must be made for both the H_∞ and the H_2 optimization problems:

Assumptions on $\mathbf{M}(s)$ for feasibility of the optimal controller

1-$(\mathbf{A}, \mathbf{B}_2, \mathbf{C}_2)$ is stabilizable and detectable (see Section 7.2.2, and Appendix B).

2-$\mathbf{D}_{12}$ and $\mathbf{D}_{21}$ have full rank.

3-$\begin{bmatrix} \mathbf{A}-j\omega\mathbf{I} & \mathbf{B}_2 \\ \mathbf{C}_1 & \mathbf{D}_{12} \end{bmatrix}$ has full column rank for all ω.

4-$\begin{bmatrix} \mathbf{A} - j\omega\mathbf{I} & \mathbf{B}_1 \\ \mathbf{C}_2 & \mathbf{D}_{21} \end{bmatrix}$ has full row rank for all ω.

5-$\mathbf{D}_{11} = 0$ and $\mathbf{D}_{22} = 0$.

6-$\mathbf{D}_{12} = \begin{bmatrix} \mathbf{0} \\ \mathbf{I} \end{bmatrix}$; $\mathbf{D}_{21} = \begin{bmatrix} \mathbf{0} & \mathbf{I} \end{bmatrix}$.

7-$\mathbf{D}_{12}{}^T\mathbf{C}_1 = 0$ and $\mathbf{B}_1\mathbf{D}_{21}{}^T = 0$.

8-$(\mathbf{A}, \mathbf{B}_1)$ is stabilizable and $(\mathbf{A}, \mathbf{C}_1)$ is detectable.

Interpretation of constraining assumptions on M(*s*)

Interpretation of the above assumptions follows.

Assumptions 1 and 2 are required for the existence of the stabilizing controller
  G(*s*) and for sufficiency to ensure that the controller is proper, which means,
  physically realizable.
Assumptions 3 and 4 ensure that the obtained optimal controller does not cancel
  poles or zeros on the imaginary axis which might lead to closed-loop instability.
Assumption 5 is necessary for H_2-control. $\mathbf{D}_{11} = 0$ and $\mathbf{D}_{22} = 0$ make, in this case,
  $\mathbf{M}_{11}$ and $\mathbf{M}_{22}$ strictly proper. For H_∞ control design, these assumptions simplify
  the algorithm formulas.
Assumptions 6 and 7 are made for simplification of the algorithm and for its exposition.
Assumption 7 is common in H_2, for instance, when in the LQR or the LQG control
  designs there are no cross terms in the cost function, (see Section 7.3.4), and when
  the measurement noises are uncorrelated (the second assumption in 7).
Assumption 8 is needed for the existence of a stabilizing controller.

Solution of an H∞-optimization algorithm

With the above assumptions, the general standard H_∞-regulator problem of
Fig.8.3.1, formulated by Eqs.(8.3.2) and (8.3.3), ensures the existence of a stabi-
lizing controller such that $\|F_L(\mathbf{M,G})\|_\infty < \gamma$, Eq.(8.3.6), if and only if, using the no-
tations in Doyle et al.(1988), (see also Skogestad and Postlethwaite 1996 and Sec-
tion 7.3.1),
(i) $\mathbf{X}_\infty \geq \mathbf{0}$ is a solution to the algebraic Riccati equation

$$\mathbf{A}^T\mathbf{X}_\infty + \mathbf{X}_\infty\mathbf{A} + \mathbf{C}_1{}^T\mathbf{C}_1 + \mathbf{X}_\infty(\gamma^{-2}\mathbf{B}_1\mathbf{B}_1{}^T - \mathbf{B}_2\mathbf{B}_2{}^T)\mathbf{X}_\infty = 0 \qquad (8.3.7)$$

and such that $Re\ \lambda_i\ [\mathbf{A} + (\gamma^{-2}\mathbf{B}_1\mathbf{B}_1{}^T - \mathbf{B}_2\mathbf{B}_2{}^T)\mathbf{X}_\infty] < 0, \forall\ i$, and also
(ii) $\mathbf{Y}_\infty \geq 0$ is a solution to the algebraic Riccati equation

$$\mathbf{A}\mathbf{Y}_\infty + \mathbf{Y}_\infty\mathbf{A}^T + \mathbf{B}_1\mathbf{B}_1{}^T + \mathbf{Y}_\infty(\gamma^{-2}\mathbf{C}_1{}^T\mathbf{C}_1 - \mathbf{C}_2{}^T\mathbf{C}_2)\mathbf{Y}_\infty = 0 \qquad (8.3.8)$$

and such that $Re\ \lambda_i\ [\mathbf{A} + \mathbf{Y}_\infty(\gamma^{-2}\,\mathbf{C}_1{}^T\mathbf{C}_1 - \mathbf{C}_2{}^T\,\mathbf{C}_2)] < 0, \forall\ i$, and

(iii) $$\rho(\mathbf{X}_\infty\,\mathbf{Y}_\infty) < \gamma^2 \qquad (8.3.9)$$

All stabilizing controllers are then given by

$$\mathbf{G} = F(\mathbf{G}_c,\ \mathbf{Q}) \qquad (8.3.10)$$

where $\mathbf{Q}(s)$ is any stable proper transfer function matrix such that $\|\mathbf{Q}\|_\infty < \gamma$. (Q-parametrization. See also Section 6.2.8)

$$\mathbf{G}_c(s) :\overset{s}{=}
\left[\begin{array}{c|c}
\mathbf{A}_c & \mathbf{B}_c \\
\hline
\mathbf{C}_c & \mathbf{D}_c
\end{array}\right]
=
\left[\begin{array}{c|cc}
\mathbf{A}_\infty & -\mathbf{Z}_\infty\mathbf{L}_\infty & \mathbf{Z}_\infty\mathbf{B}_2 \\
\hline
\mathbf{F}_\infty & 0 & \mathbf{I} \\
-\mathbf{C}_2 & \mathbf{I} & 0
\end{array}\right]
\qquad (8.3.11)$$

where

$$\mathbf{F}_\infty = -\mathbf{B}_2{}^T\mathbf{X}_\infty, \quad \mathbf{L}_\infty = -\mathbf{Y}_\infty\mathbf{C}_2{}^T, \quad \mathbf{Z}_\infty = (-\mathbf{I} - \gamma^{-2}\,\mathbf{Y}_\infty\mathbf{X}_\infty)^{-1} \quad (8.3.12)$$

$$\mathbf{A}_\infty = \mathbf{A} + \gamma^{-2}\,\mathbf{B}_1\mathbf{B}_1{}^T\mathbf{X}_\infty + \mathbf{B}_2\mathbf{F}_\infty + \mathbf{Z}_\infty\mathbf{L}_\infty\mathbf{C}_2 \qquad (8.3.13)$$

The right side of Eq.(8.3.11) is the state-space realization of the controller $\mathbf{G}_c$, with elements obtained from the solution of the two Riccati equations, namely Eqs.(8.3.7) and (8.3.8). The transfer function matrix realization of $\mathbf{G}_c(s)$ is generally more convenient for use in practical engineering problems.

γ-iteration.

The H_∞ optimization algorithm as described above, finds a stabilizing controller that satisfies the inequality in Eq.(8.3.6). If we desire to achieve some γ_{min} to within a specified tolerance, then we use a bisection algorithm called 'γ iteration'. The iteration procedure is continued until the minimum value of γ is achieved for which a stabilizing controller exists and which is finally synthesized.

8.3.3.   Loopshaping of MIMO Feedback Control Systems with Fixed and Known Plants.

Loopshaping of MIMO feedback control systems with fixed and known plants follows exactly the procedure for SISO plants, as treated and illustrated in Section 2.5.7. Only the weighting functions selection becomes more involved.

In Chapter 7 we used the LQR methodology to solve the model-following control system. The same problem can be solved using the H_∞ design procedure by defining input-output tracking weighting functions based on the desired tracking model $\mathbf{A}_m$, Eq.(7.3.27). Moreover, by defining additional weighting function matrices appearing in the mixed sensitivity structure in Fig.8.3.2, additional system specification performances can be defined and achieved, such as disturbance rejection, steady state errors etc. A detailed comparison between both methodologies for this specific flight control problem can be found in Vincent et al.(1994). Additional practical use of H_∞ norm optimization for solving flight control problems can be found in Voulgaris and Valavani (1991), Rogers and Collins (1992) and in Niewoehner and Kaminer (1996).

We will not pursue this subject any more, because we are principally interested in the solution of the MIMO TDOF uncertain feedback problem.

8.4. Uncertainty, Robust Stability and Performance in MIMO Feedback Systems.

8.4.1. Introduction

Plant uncertainty modeling, robust stability and performance for SISO feedback systems were treated in Chapter 4. Four basic uncertain plant models were stated and analyzed, namely, 'multiplicative' and 'additive', 'inverse multiplicative' and so on. Each model is used according to the specific problem at hand (see Section 4.8.3). In a similar way, MIMO uncertain plant models can be implemented in the form of weighting function matrices.

Moreover, since generally for MIMO feedback systems $\mathbf{P}(s)\mathbf{G}(s) \neq \mathbf{G}(s)\mathbf{P}(s)$, uncertainties of the plant may exist at the input or at the output of the plant's transfer function matrix. Thus, 'output' and 'input' uncertainties are to be explicitly differentiated. Here again, robust stability and robust performance are the important system requirements to be achieved. Thus, necessary analytical conditions must be found to guarantee satisfaction of these requirements. Our final objective is to present a practical design procedure using H_∞-norm optimization to solve the MIMO TDOF uncertain feedback problem.

8.4.2. Uncertainty Modeling of MIMO Plants

Some important classes of models for uncertain MIMO plants are treated next.

Multiplicative uncertainty model

There exist multiple ways of modeling uncertainties of MIMO systems, a common one being, as for SISO plants, the *multiplicative uncertain model*. Different kinds of uncertainties can be lumped in this model. As already mentioned, uncertainty in the MIMO case can be defined at the input, or at the output of the plant, depending on where the loop is opened.

The generalized form of the MIMO output multiplicative uncertainty model takes the form

$$P(s) = [I + W_1(s)\Delta_O(s)W_2(s)]P_n(s); \ \bar{\sigma}[\Delta_O(j\omega)] < 1, \ \forall\omega \qquad (8.4.1)$$

where $P_n(s)$ is the nominal transfer function matrix of the plant (see Fig.8.4.1). For input multiplicative uncertainty, the model becomes

$$P(s) = P_n(s)[I + W_1(s)\Delta_I(s)W_2(s)]; \ \bar{\sigma}[\Delta_I(j\omega)] < 1, \ \forall\omega \qquad (8.4.2)$$

The last two equations allow us to represent unstructured uncertainties, but also the structured uncertainties which predominate at low frequencies. The weighting function matrices are stable transfer function matrices that characterize the frequency-modeling of the MIMO plant. It is not easy to construct individually all their elements, so that uncertainty of each one in the nominal transfer function matrix of the plant is adequately modeled. However, an easier, but more conservative way of modeling the whole uncertain plant transfer function matrix, is possible by choosing $W_1(s) = I$ and $W_2(s) = w(s)I$, in which $w(s)$ is a scalar function. Example 8.5.1 is solved using this approach. The 'output' and 'input' modeled uncertainties are then defined as follows:

Output multiplicative uncertainty model

By choosing $W_1(s) = I$, $W_2(s) = w_O(s)I$, we get the simplified model

$$P(s) = [I + w_{OM}(s)\Delta_{OM}(s)]P_n(s) ; \ \|\Delta_{OM}\|_\infty \leq 1 \qquad (8.4.3)$$

The subscript $(\_)_{OM}$ stands for "*Output Multiplicative*"
To find the scalar weighting function w_{OM}, we proceed as for the SISO case, but now we seek for the maximum changes of a matrix norm (singular values) due to uncertainties in $P(s)$.

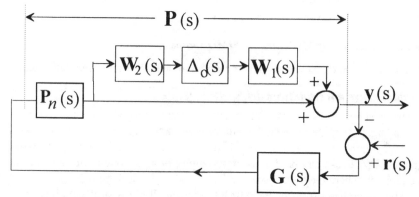

Figure 8.4.1. Output multiplicative uncertainty model. (Adapted from Fig.4.8.2).

$$\delta_{OM}(\omega) = \max_{P \in \{P\}} \bar{\sigma}[(\mathbf{P} - \mathbf{P}_n)\mathbf{P}^{-1}(j\omega)] \qquad (8.4.4)$$

and the related weighting function is determinated by the inequality

$$|w_{OM}(j\omega)| \ge \delta_{OM}(\omega); \quad \forall \omega \qquad (8.4.5)$$

Input multiplicative uncertainty model

In a similar way, we can write for the multiplicative uncertainty model

$$\mathbf{P}(s) = \mathbf{P}_n(s)[\mathbf{I} + w_{IM}(s)\mathbf{\Delta}_{IM}] \qquad (8.4.6)$$

The subscript $(\_)_{IM}$ stands for "*I*nput *M*ultiplicative".
Once again, we calculate first

$$\delta_{IM}(\omega) = \max_{P \in \{P\}} \bar{\sigma}[\mathbf{P}_n^{-1}(\mathbf{P} - \mathbf{P}_n)(j\omega)] \qquad (8.4.7)$$

from which the limiting function $|w_{IM}(j\omega)|$ can be obtained, namely,

$$|w_{IM}(j\omega)| \ge \delta_{IM}(\omega); \quad \forall \omega \qquad (8.4.8)$$

It is generally not difficult to find a $w_{IM}(s)$ that approximates $|w_{IM}(j\omega)|$.

Additional uncertainty models can be stated in a similar way, for instance, the *input* and *output inverse multiplicative models*, the *additive uncertainty model*, and its inverse version.

Inverse multiplicative uncertainty model

The inverse multiplicative uncertain plant model is adequate for modelling unstable MIMO plants. The two versions for inverse multiplicative models ('input' and 'output') are shown in Fig.8.4.2. The 'input inverse multiplicative' uncertainty model is defined as:

$$\mathbf{P}(s) = \mathbf{P}_n(s)[\mathbf{I} + \mathbf{W}_1(s)\mathbf{\Delta}(s)\mathbf{W}_2(s)]^{-1}; \quad \bar{\sigma}[\mathbf{\Delta}(j\omega)] < 1, \quad \forall \omega \qquad (8.4.9)$$

The 'output inverse multiplicative' uncertainty model is defined as:

$$\mathbf{P}(s) = [\mathbf{I} + \mathbf{W}_1(s)\mathbf{\Delta}(s)\mathbf{W}_2(s)]^{-1}\mathbf{P}_n(s); \quad \bar{\sigma}[\mathbf{\Delta}(j\omega)] < 1, \quad \forall \omega \qquad (8.4.10)$$

Additive uncertainty model

The additive uncertainty plant model is represented by the relation

$$\mathbf{P}(s) = \mathbf{P}_n(s) + \mathbf{W}_1(s)\mathbf{\Delta}_A(s)\mathbf{W}_2(s); \quad \bar{\sigma}[\mathbf{\Delta}_A(j\omega)] < 1, \quad \forall \omega \qquad (8.4.11)$$

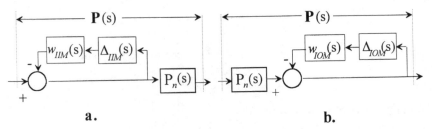

Figure 8.4.2.   Inverse multiplicative uncertainty models. **a:** 'input' and **b:** 'output'. (Adapted from Fig.4.8.4).

Here again, in order to make the model more practical for use, it is advised to put $W_2(s) = w_A(s)\mathbf{I}$ and $W_1(s) = \mathbf{I}$. The additive uncertainty plant model with the last assumptions is shown in Fig.8.4.3, where the subscript $(\_)_A$ stands for 'Additive', $(\_)_{IA}$ stands for '*I*nverse Additive'.

As already stated, the preferred choice of the model structure for the plant depends on the special characteristics of the uncertainty. Additional information on MIMO plant uncertainty modeling can be found in Doyle et al. (1982).

8.4.3.   Stability Considerations and the Small Gain Theorem.

As for the SISO feedback system case, the primary design objectives are to achieve 'robust stability' and 'robust performance' for all plant conditions in the MIMO uncertain plant set $\{\mathbf{P}(s)\}$. Conditions for robust stability and performance exist for each uncertainty model. Some important theorems for MIMO robust stability and robust performance have been proven in the literature for the previously defined uncertainty models of the plant, and limiting weighting functions (Doyle and Stein 1981, Lehtomaki 1981, Stein and Athans 1987, Skogestad and Postlethwaite 1996, Zhou 1998, and others). (One of these theorems will be proved here for illustrating how this is generally done). Since the proofs of these theorems, as

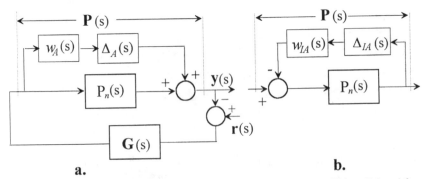

Figure 8.4.3.   Additive uncertainty models. **a:** *direct* additive, **b:** *inverse* additive. (Adapted from Figs.4.8.5 and 4.8.5a).

presented in Zhou (1998), are based on the 'small gain theorem', we will begin this discussion with its statement for the feedback structure shown in Fig.8.4.4 (adapted from Fig.6.2.12b).

Theorem 8.4.1   (*Small Gain Theorem*). Suppose that $\mathbf{M}(s)$ is a real rational stable transfer function matrix and let $\gamma > 0$. Then the closed-loop system shown in Fig.8.4.4 is well-posed and is internally stable for all $\mathbf{\Delta}(s)$, a real rational stable transfer function matrix, with

1- $\|\mathbf{\Delta}(s)\|_{\infty} \leq 1/\gamma$ if and only if $\|\mathbf{M}(s)\|_{\infty} < \gamma$

2- $\|\mathbf{\Delta}(s)\|_{\infty} < 1/\gamma$ if and only if $\|\mathbf{M}(s)\|_{\infty} \leq \gamma$.

The proof can be found in Desoer and Vidyasagar (1975), or in Zhou (1998). Note that the small gain theorem is independent of the feedback sign, since the norms of the transfer function matrices are only considered.

The following Lemma is also stated for a later use.

Lemma 8.4.1.   Suppose that $\mathbf{M}(s)$ is a real rational stable transfer function matrix and $\|\mathbf{M}\|_{\infty} > \gamma$.

Then there exists a $\sigma_0 > 0$ such that for any given $\sigma \in [0 - \sigma_0]$ there exists a stable $\mathbf{\Delta}(s)$ with $\|\mathbf{\Delta}\|_{\infty} < 1/\gamma$ such that $\det[\mathbf{I} - \mathbf{M}(s)\mathbf{\Delta}(s)]$ has a zero on the axis $\mathrm{Re}(s) = \sigma$.

The proof can be found in Zhou (1998).

8.4.4.   Robust Stability for MIMO Uncertain Feedback Systems

By use of the small gain theorem, conditions for robust stability can be stated and proved for different MIMO plant uncertainty models. Proof for the output multiplicative uncertainty model only will be given here, based on Fig. 8.4.1 and Eq.(8.4.3). The resulting theorems for other important uncertainty models will be only stated.

The proof of the following theorem follows closely Zhou (1998).

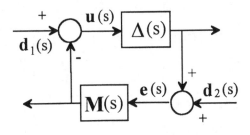

Figure 8.4.4.   Loop structure for stability analysis

(In the following discussions, $S_o(s)$ and $S_i(s)$ are the output and input sensitivity functions defined in Chapter 6 in Eqs.(6.1.5) and (6.1.6). $T_o(s) \equiv T_1(s)$ and $T_i(s)$ are the output and the input complementary sensitivity functions, Eqs.(6.1.3) and (6.1.9)).

Conditions for robust stability with output multiplicative uncertainty model, Eq.(8.4.1).

The following theorem gives the conditions for robust stability when the output multiplicative uncertainty model of the plant is known.

Theorem 8.4.2. Let $\{P(s)\}$ be the set of all plant transfer function matrices where $P(s) = (I + W_1 \Delta W_2) P_n$, $\Delta(s)$ is a stable transfer function matrix, and let $G(s)$ be a stabilizing controller for the nominal plant P_n. Then, the closed-loop system is well posed (definition 6.2.1) and internally stable for all stable $\Delta(s)$ with $\|\Delta\|_\infty < 1$ if and only if, $\|W_2 T_O W_1\|_\infty \leq 1$.

Proof. First, it is proven that the condition is necessary for robust stability. To do this, suppose by contradiction that $\|W_2 T_O W_1\|_\infty > 1$. Then, by Lemma 8.4.1, for sufficiently small $\sigma > 0$, there exists a stable Δ with $\|\Delta\|_\infty < 1$ such that $(I + \Delta W_1 T_0 W_2)^{-1}$ has at least one pole on the axis $\text{Re}(s) = \sigma$. This implies that

$$(I + PG)^{-1} = S_o(I + W_1 \Delta W_2 T_o)^{-1}$$

has at least one pole on the axis $\text{Re}(s) = \sigma$, since σ can always be chosen so that the unstable poles are not canceled by the zeros of S_o. Hence, $\|W_2 T_O W_1\|_\infty \leq 1$ is necessary for robust stability. The sufficiency follows from the small gain theorem. Hence, for the output multiplicative uncertainty model, robust stability is guaranteed, if and only if,

$$\|W_2 T_O W_1\|_\infty \leq 1 \tag{8.4.12}$$

In the above theorem, $T_o(s) \equiv T_1(s)$ of Eq.(6.1.3). $T_1(s)$ is the unity-feedback transfer function matrix of the nominal plant. When the practical assumptions $W_1(s) = I$ and $W_2(s) = w_o(s)I$ are adopted, this theorem is very similar to that pertaining to the SISO case. It states that when the uncertainty is defined as in Eq.(8.4.3), robust stability is maintained, if and only if, the unity-feedback transfer function matrix

$$T_1(s) = P_n(s)G(s)[I + P_n(s)G(s)]^{-1} \;(\equiv T_o(s)) \tag{8.4.13}$$

satisfies the inequality

$$\bar{\sigma}[T_1(j\omega)] \leq 1/w_{OM}(\omega) \tag{8.4.14}$$

The subscript $(_n)$ in the above equations stand for the nominal plant case. This condition will be used in Section 5 to solve the MIMO TDOF uncertain feedback problem, with the assumption that the output multiplicative plant uncertainty model is used.

Robust stability conditions for additional uncertainty models are stated without proofs. These can be found in Skogestad and Postlethwaite (1996), or in Zhou (1998).

Conditions for robust stability with $\|\Delta\|_\infty < 1$ *for:*

Input multiplicative uncertainty model
$(\mathbf{P}(s) = \mathbf{P}_n(s)\ [\mathbf{I}+\mathbf{W}_1(s)\Delta_{IM}(s)\mathbf{W}_2(s)], Eq.(8.4.2)\ ):$

$$\|\mathbf{W}_2\ \mathbf{T}_i\ \mathbf{W}_1\|_\infty \le 1 \tag{8.4.15}$$

$\mathbf{T}_i(s)$ is defined in Eq.(6.1.9).

Inverse input multiplicative uncertainty model
$(\mathbf{P}(s) = \mathbf{P}_n(s)[\mathbf{I} + \mathbf{W}_1(s)\Delta(s)\mathbf{W}_2(s)]^{-1}, Eq.(8.4.9)):$

$$\|\mathbf{W}_2\ \mathbf{S}_i\ \mathbf{W}_1\|_\infty \le 1 \tag{8.4.16}$$

Additive uncertainty model
$(\mathbf{P}(s) = \mathbf{P}_n(s) + \mathbf{W}_I(s)\Delta(s)\mathbf{W}_2(s), Eq.(8.4.11)):$

$$\|\mathbf{W}_2\ \mathbf{GS}_O\ \mathbf{W}_1\|_\infty \le 1 \tag{8.4.17}$$

8.4.5   Robust Performance of MIMO Uncertain Feedback Systems

Conditions for robust performance were stated and proven in Section 4.8.5 for SISO uncertain feedback systems, see Eq.(4.8.27). Very similar conditions for robust performance can be found for MIMO uncertain feedback systems, in terms of maximum singular values. However, only conditions for the output multiplicative uncertainty model, (Eq.(8.4.1)), will be treated in this chapter.

The analysis is based on the standard regulator problem structure in Fig.8.4.5, adapted from Fig.8.4.1.

Theorem 8.4.3.   Suppose that $\{\mathbf{P}(s)\} \in \{(\mathbf{I}+\mathbf{W}_1\Delta\mathbf{W}_2)\mathbf{P}_n: \Delta(s)$ is a real rational and stable transfer function matrix , $\|\Delta\|_\infty < 1$ $\}$, and $\mathbf{G}(s)$ internally stabilize $\mathbf{P}_n(s)$. Then the system robust performance is guaranteed if the following condition is satisfied:

$$\bar\sigma(\mathbf{W}_d)\bar\sigma(\mathbf{W}_sS_O) + \bar\sigma(\mathbf{W}_1)\bar\sigma(\mathbf{W}_2T_O) \le 1; \forall\ \omega. \tag{8.4.18}$$

The proof can be found in Zhou (1998).

This condition is closely equivalent to the robust performance condition for SISO feedback systems, Eq.(4.8.27). For example, by supposing that $\mathbf{W}_1 = \mathbf{I}$ and also $\mathbf{W}_d = \mathbf{I}$, the second term in the left side of the equation is exactly the condition for

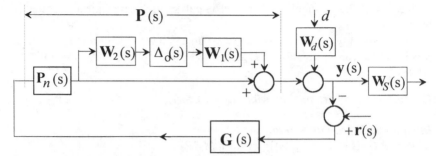

Figure 8.4.5.　Feedback structure for defining the robust performance conditions.

robust stability, while the addition of the first term is essential in generating the nominal performance condition.

When the standard mixed sensitivity problem in Fig.8.5.1 below is solved, the robust performance condition is automatically satisfied, exactly as in the SISO case.

8.5.　Design of MIMO TDOF Uncertain Feedback Systems

8.5.1.　Introduction

In the explanation and analysis of different items in the previous sections of this chapter, no use was made of the prefilter matrix $F(s)$ shown in Fig.8.5.1. The standard H_∞-regulator problem is defined for an ODOF feedback structure. If this structure can be physically complemented with the prefilter $F(s)$, then we are confronted with a MIMO TDOF uncertain feedback problem. The objective of this section is to use QFT principles for the solution of the MIMO TDOF feedback problem in the H_∞-norm optimization framework. (See also Section 4.8.6 and, Sidi 1999). An output multiplicative plant uncertainty model is used and the limiting weighting function $w_o(s)$ is obtained by use of Eqs.(8.4.4) and (8.4.5).

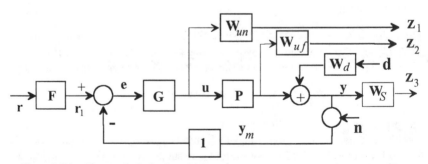

Figure 8.5.1.　The standard mixed sensitivity regulator problem for the uncertain plant {P }.

8.5.2. Design Procedure of the MIMO TDOF Uncertain Feedback System

With the definitions and the stated robust stability theorem in the last section 8.4, design procedure for the MIMO TDOF uncertain feedback system follows exactly the procedure for the SISO case, with the difference that we deal now with matrices. The standard mixed sensitivity H_∞-control structure to be used is shown in Fig.8.5.1. (The reader is recommended to reread Section 4.8.6). When QFT principles are used, the controller $\mathbf{G}(s)$ is responsible for solving the input-output tracking 'sensitivity specifications' for the entire set $\{\mathbf{P}(s)\}$. This means that all $T_{1ij}(j\omega)$, $i = j$, must satisfy the design specifications in Eq.(4.3.3). To achieve this goal, an adequate selection of the sensitivity weighting function matrix $\mathbf{W}_S(s)$ is necessary. However, this is generally insufficient. The reason is that the mixed sensitivity H_∞-norm optimization solution does not **exactly** satisfy the desired sensitivity transfer function matrix $\mathbf{S}(s)$, as explained in Section 2.5.4 for the SISO case. To circumvent this drawback, it is suggested to use the weighting function matrix $\mathbf{W}_{un}(s)$ as a tuning parameter. The sensitivity design specifications can be achieved by modifying the elements of $\mathbf{W}_{un}(s)$ in an iterative mode. As a byproduct, minimization of the sensor noise amplification at the plant inputs also follows.

The second-degree-of-freedom prefilter $\mathbf{F}(s)$ is next used to achieve the different tracking input-output specifications. This means that all $T_{ij}(j\omega)$ must satisfy the design specifications in Eq.(4.2.3).

The design procedure for the TDOF MIMO feedback system with large plant uncertainties is illustrated with a 2×2 plant design example.

Example 8.5.1. There is given a MIMO uncertain plant $p_{ij}(s) = k_{ij}(1 + s/A_{ij})$, with uncertainties defined in Table 8.5.1 below for nine plant cases. Tracking input-output specifications on $|T_{11}|$ and $|T_{22}|$ are shown in Fig.8.5.4 as permitted upper and lower bounds. $|T_{12}|$, $|T_{21}|$ and the sensor noise amplification are to be minimized. With no loss of generality, we set $\mathbf{W}_d = \mathbf{I}$.

Table 8.5.1. Plant parameters

Case No	k_{11}	k_{22}	k_{12}	k_{21}	A_{11}	A_{22}	A_{12}	A_{21}
1	1	2	0.5	1	1	2	2	3
2	1	2	0.5	1	0.5	1	1	2
3	1	2	0.5	1	0.2	0.4	0.5	1
4	4	5	1	2	1	2	2	3
5	4	5	1	2	0.5	1	1	2
6	4	5	1	2	0.2	0.4	0.5	1
7	10	8	2	4	1	2	2	3
8	10	8	2	4	0.5	1	1	2
9	10	8	2	4	0.2	0.4	0.5	1

Solution:

Step 1. The allowed changes $\Delta|T_{ii}|$, $i = 1, 2$, are detected from the permitted bounds on $|T_{11}(j\omega)|$ and $|T_{22}(j\omega)|$ shown in Fig.8.5.4. Design specifications ask for minimizing $|T_{12}(j\omega)|$ and $|T_{21}(j\omega)|$.

Step 2. Eq.(8.4.4) is calculated with different nominal plants, until the lowest limiting $\delta_{OM}(\omega)$ is obtained. Case 9 is finally chosen as the nominal plant case and $\delta_{OM}(\omega)$ is calculated for all plants in the set $\{P(s)\}$, and for all frequencies of interest. The results are shown in Fig.8.5.2. The limiting weighting function $w_{OM}(\omega)$ is also shown in the figure. $w_{OM}(\omega)$ corresponds to the weighting function $w_{OM}(s)$ $= 0.92(s + 1)/(s/1.09 + 1)$.

Step 3. The permitted $\Delta|T_{ii}(j\omega)|$, $i = 1, 2$, shown in Fig.8.5.4, are used in Table 8.5.2 in specifying S_{11} and S_{22}. In the MIMO problem, $\max\Delta|\sigma P(j\omega)|$ is used for calculating the sensitivity functions $S_{11}(s)$ and $S_{22}(s)$ according to Eq.(4.8.33). Since the difference $\sigma_{max}(j\omega) - \sigma_{min}(j\omega)$ in Fig.8.5.3 is larger that the gain uncertainty of each individual element in $P(s)$, the obtained $S_{11}(j\omega)$ and $S_{22}(j\omega)$ come to be more conservative. In this way, the uncertainties in P_{12} and P_{21} are also taken into consideration when designing the T_{11} and T_{22} channels. Table 8.5.2 includes all the necessary data for calculating the nominal sensitivity functions S_{11} and S_{22} (as defined in Eq.(4.8.33)). From this data, $w_{S11}(s)$ and $w_{S22}(s)$ are approximated as

$$w_{S11}(s) = 0.7(s + 12)/(s + 0.01) \text{ and } w_{S22}(s) = 0.7(s + 80)(s + 0.01)$$

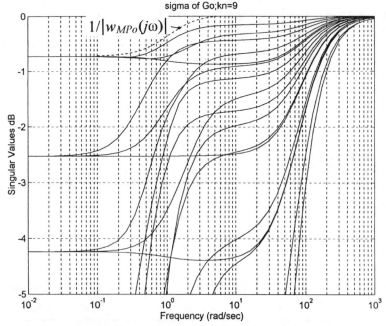

Figure 8.5.2.   Principal gains of $\sigma[(P-P_n)P^{-1}{}_n(j\omega)]$, $\equiv \{P\}$, for evaluating $w_{OM}(\omega)$.

Table 8.5.2. Data for calculating the needed nominal S_{11} and S_{22}.

w rad/sec	0.2	0.5	1	2	5	10	20
max$|\Delta\sigma\mathbf{P}|$	27	26	26	30	34	36	38
ΔP_{11} (db)	20	20	22	26	33	35	36
ΔP_{22} (db)	12	15	19	23	26	28	28
ΔT_{11} (db)	1	2.5	7	12	22	30	—
S_{11} (db)	-28	-20	-12	-8	-3	-1	—
ΔT_{22} (db)	0.1	0.2	1	3.5	9	13	15
S_{22} (db)	-47	-42	-28	-19	-11	-8	-8

Step 4-1. The compensator $\mathbf{G}(s)$ is obtained by solving the H_∞-sensitivity problem. The algorithm *hinfsyn* in μ-Analysis and Synthesis Toolbox is used. The initial choice of the control effort weighting function matrix $\mathbf{W}_{un}(s)$ in this first design iteration was as follows:

$$w_{un11} = 0.5; \; w_{un22} = 1; \; \mathbf{W}_{un}(s) = \text{diag}(\,0.5,\, 1)$$

Step 5-1. With this choice of $\mathbf{W}_{un}(s)$ in Step 4-1, the sensitivity specifications $\Delta|T_{11}(j\omega)|$ were completely satisfied. However, $\Delta|T_{22}(j\omega)|$ at low frequencies

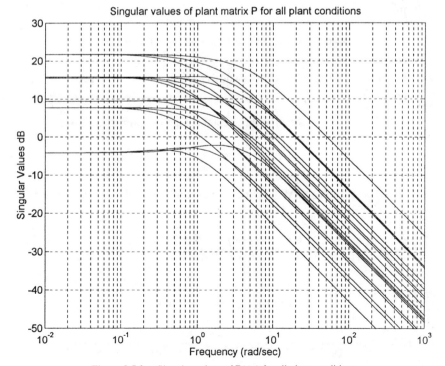

Figure 8.5.3. Singular values of $\mathbf{P}(j\omega)$ for all plant conditions.

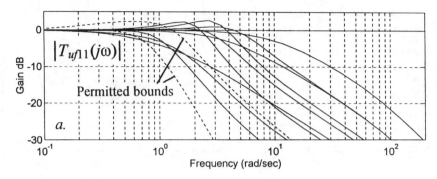

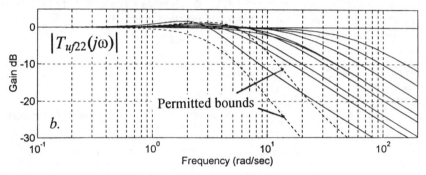

Figure 8.5.4. $|T_{uf11}(j\omega)|$ and $|T_{uf22}(j\omega)|$ for all plants in {**P**}

were larger than design specifications allowed. Hence, Step 4 was repeated with a different choice of w_{un22}.

Step 4-2. W$_{un}$(s) was modified in the second design iteration as follows:

$$w_{un11} = 0.5; \ w_{un22} = 0.5 \ ; \ \mathbf{W}_{un}(s) = \text{diag}(\, 0.5, 0.5).$$

With this second choice of **W$_{un}$**(s), the elements of the obtained controller matrix **G**(s) are (after cancellation of very close poles and zeros)

$$G_{11}(s) \cong 6.77 \, \frac{(s + 5)(s + 1.09)(s + 0.9997)}{(s + 142.4)(s + 1.1383)(s + 0.904)(s + 0.01)}$$

$$G_{22}(s) \cong 1.973 \times 10^5 \, \frac{(s + 2.5)(s + 1.09)(s + 0.983)}{(s + 4417)(s + 1.155)(s + 0.904)(s + 0.001)}$$

$$G_{21}(s) \cong -518.8 \, \frac{(s + 151)(s + 4.995)(s + 2.5)(s + 1.09)}{(s + 4417)(s + 142.48)(s + 1.138)(s + 0.904)(s + 0.01)}$$

$G_{12}(s) \cong$

$$266.989 \, \frac{(s - 588.7)(s + 5)(s + 2.64)(s + 1.09)(s + 1)}{(s + 4417)(s + 142.48)(s + 2.022)(s + 1.155)(s + 0.904)(s + 0.01)}$$

Step 5-2. The newly obtained suboptimal controller $\mathbf{G}(s)$ was once more used to calculate the unity-feedback $|T_{uf11}(j\omega)|$'s and $|T_{uf22}(j\omega)|$'s. These are shown in Fig.8.5.4 a and b respectively. The maximal magnitude changes $\Delta|T_{11}(j\omega)|$ and $\Delta|T_{22}(j\omega)|$ satisfy completely the sensitivity specifications.

Step 6-2. The prefilters $F_{11}(s)$ and $F_{22}(s)$ are next designed, in order to relocate the unity-feedback transfer functions $|T_{uf11}(j\omega)|$'s and $|T_{uf22}(j\omega)|$'s within their permitted input-output tracking bounds. The achieved prefilters are

$$F_{11}(s) = 0.6(s + 3.25)(s + 1/3.25)/[(s + 1)^2(s + 0.6)];$$
$$F_{22}(s) = 90/[(s + 3)(s + 30)]$$

The resulting $|T_{11}(j\omega)|$'s $= |F_{11}(j\omega)T_{uf11}(j\omega)|$'s and $|T_{22}(j\omega)|$'s $= |F_{22}(j\omega)T_{uf22}(j\omega)|$'s for all plant conditions are shown in Fig.8.5.5. The design specifications for tracking are achieved. Fig.8.5.6 shows the cross-channel transfer function

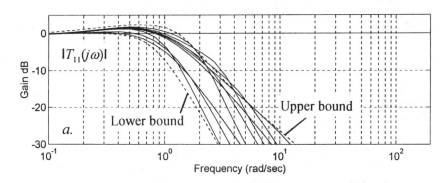

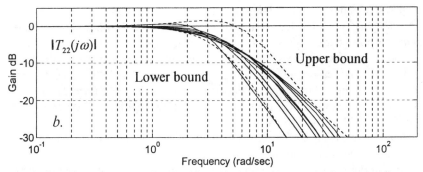

Figure 8.5.5. $|T_{11}(j\omega)| = |T_{uf11}(j\omega)| \, |F_{11}(j\omega)|$ and $|T_{22}(j\omega)| = |T_{uf22}(j\omega)| \, |F_{22}(j\omega)|$ for all **P** in {**P**}.

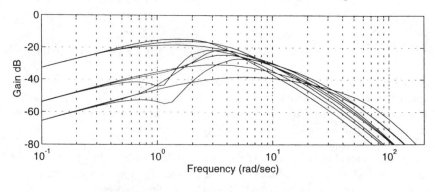

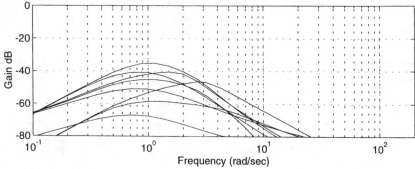

Figure 8.5.6. $|T_{12}(j\omega)|$ and $|T_{21}(j\omega)|$ for all **P** in {**P**}.

magnitudes $|T_{12}(j\omega)|$'s and $|T_{21}(j\omega)|$'s. They cannot be zeroed as wished because of plant uncertainties, but they are practically very small, as expected.

The defined weighting functions $1/|w_{S11}(j\omega)|$ and $1/|w_{S22}(j\omega)|$ and the achieved $|S_{11n}(j\omega)|$ and $|S_{22n}(j\omega)|$ are shown in Fig.8.5.7 for the second design iteration. The same figure also shows the achieved nominal $|T_{uf11}(j\omega)|$ and $|T_{uf22}(j\omega)|$.

Step 7. Evaluation of the design follows.

1-*Stability margins*. The loop transmission functions are shown for both channels in the Nichols charts of Figs.8.5.8 and 8.5.9. It is important to realize that none of the loop transmissions cross the forbidden contours of constant $|T_1| = 3\text{dB}$ and $|S| = 3\text{dB}$. For that reason, no large overshoots will be present in the time responses due to disturbances. Moreover, for the same reason, sufficient gain and phase margins are achieved for all the plant members in {**P**(s)}, at least 17 db and 45° respectively.

2-*Step time response*. The specified bounds on $|T_{11}(j\omega)|$ are the same as those in Fig.4.3.15. The step responses in Fig.4.3.16 correspond to these bounds. As can be seen in Fig.8.5.10a, the step time responses for all the plants in the set {**P**(s)} are well within the permitted time bounds. The specified bounds on $|T_{22}(j\omega)|$ are

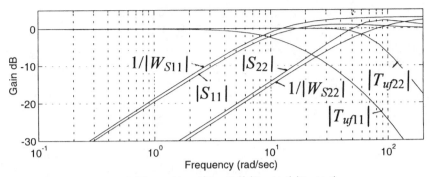

Figure 8.5.7. Achieved $|T_{uf11}(j\omega)|$, $|T_{uf22}(j\omega)|$, $|S_{11n}(j\omega)|$, $|S_{22n}(j\omega)|$, and the specified $1/|w_{S11}(j\omega)|$ and $1/|w_{S22}(j\omega)|$.

the same as those in Fig.4.4.2 and the step responses in Fig.4.4.3 correspond to them. As can be seen in Fig.8.5.10b, the step time responses for all plants in the set $\{\mathbf{P}(s)\}$ are also well within the permitted time bounds. Cross-channel time responses are shown in Figs.8.5.10c and d. Their amplitudes are negligible, except for transients with moderate amplitudes.

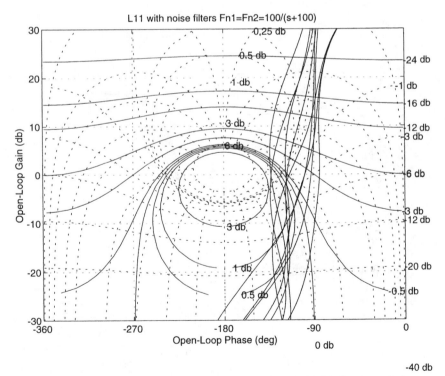

Figure 8.5.8. $L_1(j\omega)$, with loop opened at u_1, for all $\mathbf{P}$ in $\{\mathbf{P}\}$.

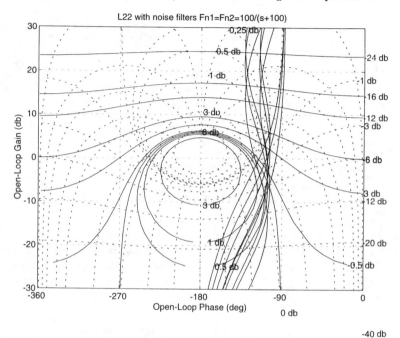

Figure 8.5.9. $L_2(j\omega)$, with loop opened at u_2, for all **P** in {**P**}.

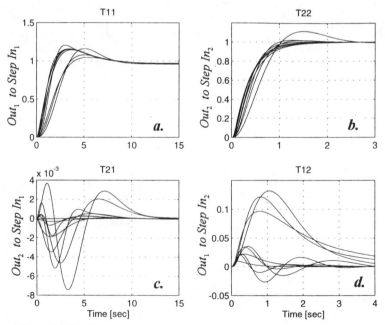

Figure 8.5.10.   Time responses of all **P**(s) in the set {**P**(s)} for a step input vector **r**.

3-*Disturbance responses.* It is important to check the achieved rejection level of disturbances. The frequency-responses of the relevant transfer functions are shown in Fig.8.5.11.

4-*Sensor noise amplification.* The control compensators obtained in Step 4-2 show that in practice these are transfer functions with the same number of poles and zeros (one of the poles in each $G_{ij}(s)$, $i, j = 1, 2$, is located very far from the active frequency range). Thus, a high sensor noise amplification, leading to saturation of the plant inputs u_1 and u_2 (defined in Fig .8.5.1) should be expected. The 'Tol.' parameter of the used optimization algorithm only partially influences the location of this very far-off pole. This is not as sufficient as needed. For this reason, noise filters are added to the nominally obtained **G**(*s*) elements, by using classical frequency design principles. When a filter $100/(s + 100)$ is added to all elements of **G**(*s*), the average noise amplification for both channels is quite low, in the order of 1.2 (RMS) for the first and 18.3 (RMS) for the second channel. These are acceptable values from an engineering point of view. The results in Figs.8.5.4 to 8.5.11 are obtained with the modified compensator including these noise filters. The Matlab program for solving Example 8.5.1 is listed in Table 8.5.3.

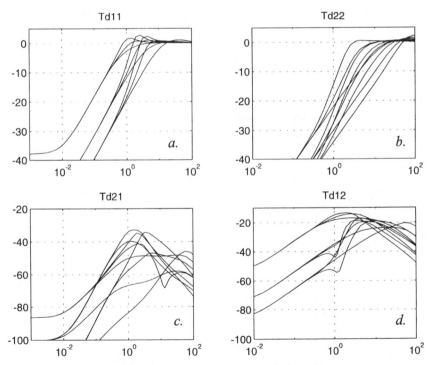

Figure 8.5.11. Output-to-disturbances frequency responses.

Table 8.5.3. Matlab Program for Solving Example 8.5.1

```
%based on mu486.m, 20 August 98, and TDOF design Example 4.8.6.
%uses mu-toolbox;
%definition of Wu is of importance and has to be carefully chosen;
%if 'too strong', it may lead to very small phase margins; clear;
%preparation of sensitivity weighting function
ws11=nd2sys([1 12],[1 0.01],1/1.4);
ws22=nd2sys([1 80],[1 0.01],1/1.4);
Ws=daug(ws11,ws22);
[aws,bws,cws,dws] = unpck(Ws);
%%%%
%preparation of Wt weighting function;
%wt=0.92(s + 1))/(s/1.09 + 1);
wt11=nd2sys([1 1],[1/1.09 1], 0.92);
wt22=nd2sys([1 1],[1/1.09 1], 0.92);
Wt=daug(wt11,wt22);
[awt,bwt,cwt,dwt] = unpck(Wt)
%%%%
%1st design trial;
%preparation of Wu weighting function;
wu11 = nd2sys([1   1],[1   1], 0.5); wu22 = nd2sys([1   1],[1   1], 0.5);
wu12 = nd2sys([1   1],[1   1], 0.0); wu21 = nd2sys([1   1],[1   1], 0.0);
Wu=daug(wu11,wu22);
[awu,bwu,cwu,dwu] = unpck(Wu);
%%%%
%end of computation of Ws, Wt and Wu;.
%set of plants;
aa11 = [1    0.5    0.2    1    0.5    0.2    1    0.5    0.2];
aa22 = [2    1    0.4    2    1    0.4    2    1    0.4];
aa12 = [2    1    0.5    2    1    0.5    2    1    0.5];
aa21 = [3    2    1    3    2    1    3    2    1];
kk11 = [1    1    1    4    4    4    10    10    10];
kk22 = [2    2    2    5    5    5    8    8    8];
kk12 = [0.5   0.5    0.5    1    1    1    2    2    2];
kk21 = [1    1    1    2    2    2    4    4    4];
%building nominal Gn matrix for case n;
kn=9;
p11n = nd2sys([1], [ aa11(kn), 1], kk11(kn));
p22n = nd2sys([1], [ aa22(kn), 1], kk22(kn));
p12n = nd2sys([1], [ aa12(kn), 1], kk12(kn));
p21n = nd2sys([1], [ aa21(kn), 1], kk21(kn));
P1n=sbs(p11n, p12n); P2n=sbs(p21n, p22n);
P = abv(P1n, P2n);
[ap,bp,cp,dp] = unpck(P);
%%%%
```

```
%preparation of augmented plant P
systemnames = 'P Ws Wu Wt';
inputvar = '[r(2); u(2)]';
outputvar = '[Ws; Wu; Wt; r-P]';
input_to_P = '[u]'; input_to_Ws = '[r-P]'; input_to_Wu = '[u]'; input_to_Wt = '[P]';
sysoutname = 'Paug';
cleanupsysic = 'yes';
sysic;
%end of Paug preparation
%start of Hinf algorithm;
nmeas = 2; nu = 2; gmn = 0.5; gmx = 1000; tol = 0.1;
[khinf,ghinf,gopt] = hinfsyn(Paug, nmeas, nu, gmn, gmx, tol, 2);
[ag,bg,cg,dg] = unpck(khinf);
end
```

Summary and conclusions.

Using the TDOF QFT/H_∞-control design technique for MIMO uncertain feedback systems, it is seen that the specifications are completely achieved, with two only design iterations. Specified input-output tracking characteristics in the time-domain are achieved by translating them as upper and lower permitted bounds in the frequency-domain, exactly as in the QFT design approach. The 'tracking sensitivity specifications' are achieved by solving the mixed sensitivity problem by H_∞-norm optimization. The outcome of this design stage is the controller matrix **G**(s). The 'tracking specifications' are achieved by using the second-degree-of-freedom, which is the prefilter matrix **F**(s).

Acceptable noise amplification is achieved by additional manipulation of the obtained nominal loop transmission functions in the higher frequency range, with classical Nyquist-Bode frequency design techniques. Additional approaches based on an H_∞ formulation of the QFT design technique can be found in Zhao and Jayasuriya (1998), and in Thompson and Pruyn (1999).

8.6. Summary

The purpose of this chapter was to introduce design principles to MIMO TDOF uncertain feedback systems using H_∞-norm optimization algorithms. MIMO plant properties and design specification are best described with the singular values of their corresponding transfer function matrices. First, MIMO plant uncertainty models were presented, then, based on these models, conditions for robust stability and robust performance were stated. The MIMO problem posed in this way is solved by H_∞-norm optimization algorithms. The basic mathematical principles of such algorithms are reviewed at some length in order to give the reader an understanding of their use. The MIMO TDOF highly uncertain feedback problem is solved within the H_∞-optimization design paradigm, in conjunction with classical QFT principles. A fully solved 2×2 uncertain feedback system example illustrates the combined H_∞/QFT design procedure and its efficient applicability to practical engineering problems.

Appendix A

Signal Flow Graphs

A.1. Introduction

Mason introduced 'Signal Flow Graphs' to represent graphically the relationship between signals (variables) in a set of linear equations, (Mason 1953). The signal flow graph shows the passage of signals through the feedback systems, and provides us with a clear insight to the feedback paths inside the system. Most important, the *gain formula* for signal flow graphs allows us to compute in a systematic way the relationship between signals inside the system.

A system of linear equations can be described by the set of equations:

$$x_j = \sum_{i=1}^{N} t_{kj} x_k; \quad j = 1,2,....,N \tag{A.1}$$

where the coefficient t_{kj} is called the *transmission,* or *gain function,* between the variable x_k and the variable x_j. The system variables are represented as *nodes;* the transmissions between two nodes are described as directed *branches.* The basic relationship between two signals $x_2 = t_{12} x_1$ is described graphically as in Fig.A.1.

It is important to notice that the transmissions can be constants, or transfer functions in the Laplace variable '*s*', in which case the signals are also in the *s*-domain.

An example of a set of linear equations described by signal flow graphs follows. This example will be used throughout the present appendix to illustrate the signal flow graph theory.

Example A.1. The set of equations is:

$$x_2 = t_{12} x_1 + t_{52} x_5$$
$$x_3 = t_{23} x_2 + t_{43} x_4$$
$$x_4 = t_{34} x_3 + t_{54} x_5$$
$$x_5 = t_{45} x_4 + t_{65} x_6$$
$$x_6 = t_{26} x_2 + t_{66} x_6$$
$$x_7 = t_{57} x_5$$

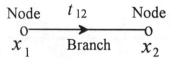

Figure A.1. Signal flow graph for the relationship $x_2 = t_{12} x_1$.

Graphical description of the signal flows are shown in Fig.A.2.

A summary of some basic properties of signal flow graphs follows:

1. The nodes represent signals (variables) of a system.
2. The directed branch from node x_k to node x_j represents the dependence of variable x_j upon the variable x_k, but not the reverse.
3. Signals flow along branches only in the direction of the arrows.
4. A signal flowing through a branch between two nodes x_k and x_j is multiplied by the gain of the branch t_{jk}, $x_k = t_{jk} x_j$

After the signal flow graph is drawn, the final aim of the theory is to compute the input-output relationship x_7/x_1 by use of a standard 'Mason gain formula' obtained by direct inspection of the signal flow graph.

A.2. Definitions for Signal Flow Graphs

Some basic definitions are used in dealing with signal flow graphs. (The definitions are exemplified with the variables, nodes and branches shown in Fig.A.2)

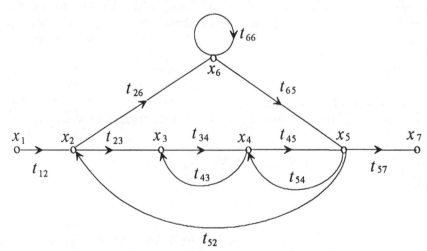

Figure A.2. Signal flow graph of the set of equations in Example A.1.

1. *Input node* (source): A node which has only outgoing branches (x_1).
2. *Output node* (sink): A node that has only incoming branches (x_7).
3. *Path:* Any continuous succession of branches traversed in the branch directions ($x_1 - x_2 - x_3 - x_4 - x_5 - x_7$).
4. *Forward path:* A path from the input node to the output node, along which no node is traversed more than once ($x_1 - x_2 - x_6 - x_5 - x_7$).
5. *Feedback path:* A path that begins and terminates on the same node, along which no node is traversed more than once ($x_2 - x_3 - x_4 - x_5 - x_2$).
6. *Path gain:* The product of all the branch gains encountered in traversing a path ($t_{12}\, t_{23}\, t_{34}\, t_{45}\, t_{57}$ for path $x_1 - x_2 - x_3 - x_4 - x_5 - x_7$)
7. *Loop gain:* The product of all the branch gains encountered in traversing a loop path ($t_{23}t_{34}\, t_{45}t_{52}$ for the loop path $x_2 - x_3 - x_4 - x_5 - x_2$).

With these definitions, we can proceed in stating the *Mason gain formula* that allows us to calculate the transmission gain by inspection of the signal flow graph.

A.3. Gain Formula for Signal Flow Graphs

A general gain formula for the transmission x_{out} / x_{in} has been derived by Mason, which allows us to write the input/output transmission by inspection:

$$G = \frac{x_{out}}{x_{in}} = \sum_k \frac{G_k \Delta_k}{\Delta} \qquad (A.2)$$

where G_k = gain of the kth forward path, x_{out} and x_{in} are the output and the input nodes respectively. Δ is defined as follows:

$$\Delta = 1 - \sum_m L_{m1} + \sum_m L_{m2} - \sum_m L_{m3} + \dots \qquad (A.3)$$

where L_{mr} = gain product of the mth possible combination of r nontouching loops. The practical meaning of Δ is:
$\Delta = 1 - $ (sum of all individual loop gains) + (sum of gain products of all possible combinations of two nontouching loops) $-$ (sum of the gain products of all possible combinations of three nontouching loops) $+ \dots$

Δ is called the *graph determinant.*
Δ_k is the *cofactor* of G_k, defined as follows:
Δ_k = remaining part of Δ after we delete from it all the loop gains of feedback paths touching the forward path k.

The general gain formula of Eq.(A.2) is very easy to use, as the following example will demonstrate.

Example A.2. Compute the transmission gain $G = x_7 / x_1$ of the signal flow graph in Fig.A.2 by use of Eq.(A.2).

Solution: by inspection we find that there are two forward paths from x_1 to x_7:

$$G_1 = t_{12} \, t_{23} \, t_{34} \, t_{45} \, t_{57}$$

$$G_2 = t_{12} \, t_{26} \, t_{65} \, t_{57}$$

Next, we have to find Δ, from which Δ_1 and Δ_2 can be derived by deleting the appropriate loops touching the forward paths G_1 and G_2 respectively. To find Δ we use Eq.(A.3):

$$\Delta = 1 - (t_{66} + t_{26} \, t_{65} \, t_{52} + t_{23} \, t_{34} \, t_{45} t_{52} + t_{34} t_{43} + t_{45} t_{54})$$
$$+ (t_{66} \, t_{23} t_{34} \, t_{45} \, t_{52} + t_{66} \, t_{34} t_{43} + t_{66} \, t_{45} \, t_{54} + t_{26} \, t_{65} \, t_{52} \, t_{34} t_{43})$$

The only loop gain not touching G_1 is t_{66}, hence:

$$\Delta_1 = 1 - t_{66}$$

The only loop gain not touching G_2 is $t_{34} \, t_{43}$, hence:

$$\Delta_2 = 1 - t_{34} \, t_{43}$$

To obtain $G = x_7 / x_1$, substitute G_1, G_2, Δ_1, Δ_2 and Δ in Eq.(A.2). This concludes the presentation of Mason's gain formula.

Appendix B

Mathematical Background Related to MIMO and to H_∞ Analysis and Design

B.1 Introduction

The purpose of this short appendix is to summarize for the reader's convenience some important mathematical definitions, notions and relations used in H_2 and H_∞ analysis and design. Of special importance are the notions of vector and matrix norms, singular values and eigenvalue functions, and the basic mathematical relations between them. Linear fractional transformation (LFT) is also introduced and illustrated. The material contained in this appendix can be found in more detailed form in Simmons (1963), Bliss (1966), Ogata (1967), Kolmogorov and Fomin (1970), Kailath (1980), Garnet (1981), Francis (1986), Horn and Johnson (1991), Rosenblum and Rovnyak (1994), Green and Limebeer (1995), Skogestad and Postlethwaite (1996), Zhou et al. (1996), Zhou (1998) and others.

B.2 Algebraic and Vector Norms.

In this appendix we are interested in norms belonging to the linear space of continuous functions. When signals in the time-domain are considered, for instance $x(t)$, they can be defined in $-\infty < t < \infty$ and take values in $\mathbf{C}^n$, where $\mathbf{C}$ is the field of complex numbers. When the frequency-domain space is considered, a function $x(j\omega)$ is defined for all frequencies $-\infty < \omega < \infty$ and takes values in $\mathbf{C}^n$. These functions can be mapped as well to the real field $\mathbf{R}$.

Different norms can be defined to express a 'size' of any variable 'x', which may be a scalar signal, a vector, a system transfer function or a matrix. Some definitions of 'norms' follow.

Definition B.1 A norm of x is a real number that satisfies the following properties:

1- $\|x\| \geq 0$
2- $\|x\| = 0 \Leftrightarrow x = 0$
3- $\|\alpha\, x\| = |\alpha|\, \|x\|, \quad \forall\, \alpha \in \mathbf{R} \qquad (\alpha$ is a complex scalar) $\qquad$ (B.2.1)
4- $\|x + y\| \leq \|x\| + \|y\| \qquad$ (the triangle inequality)

B.2.1   Time-Domain Scalar Functions

Some examples of time-domain scalar functions are as follows:
The simplest norm is the **1-norm**

$$\|x(t)\|_1 := \int_{-\infty}^{\infty} |x(t)|\, dt \qquad (B.2.2)$$

A very useful norm is the **2-norm**

$$\|x(t)\|_2 := \left[\int_{-\infty}^{\infty} |x(t)|^2\, dt \right]^{1/2} \qquad (B.2.3)$$

Being a square function, the 2-norm is generally related to 'energy'.
We can go further and define a **p-norm**

$$\|x(t)\|_p := \left[\int_{-\infty}^{\infty} |x(t)|^p\, dt \right]^{1/p} \qquad (B.2.4)$$

Finally, the ∞-**norm** of a signal is defined as

$$\|x(t)\|_\infty := \sup_t |x(t)| = \lim_{p \to \infty} \left[|x(t)|^p \right]^{1/p} \qquad (B.2.5)$$

B.2.2   Scalar System Functions

The two most familiar norms for scalar system functions are, once again, the 2-norm and the ∞-norm

System function 2-norm

$$\|F(j\omega)\|_2 := \left[\frac{1}{2\pi} \int_{-\infty}^{\infty} |F(j\omega)|^2\, d\omega \right]^{1/2} \qquad (B.2.6)$$

Derivation of the ∞-norm follows from the p-norm which is defined as:

System function p-norm

$$\|F(j\omega)\|_p := \left[\int_{-\infty}^{\infty} |F(j\omega)|^p \, d\omega \right]^{1/p} \tag{B.2.7}$$

from which follows the definition for ∞-**norm,**

System function ∞-norm

$$\|F(j\omega)\|_\infty := \sup_\omega |F(j\omega)| = \lim_{p\to\infty} \left[\int_{-\infty}^{\infty} |F(j\omega)|^p \, d\omega \right]^{1/p} \tag{B.2.8}$$

The idea beyond this definition is that by raising $|F(j\omega)|$ to infinite power, the peak value of this norm is displayed.

The p-norms as defined above are related in the literature to the definition of Hardy spaces. An H_2 norm is a bounded 2-norm of a stable scalar transfer function in the frequency- domain which is strictly proper. It has no poles on the imaginary axis. An H_∞-norm is a bounded ∞-norm of a stable scalar transfer function in the frequency-domain which is proper. It has no poles on the imaginary axis, in other words, no poles in $Re(s) \geq 0$. Hardy spaces and norms are extensively treated in Rosenblum and Rovnyak (1994). In this context, an important property for the H_∞ space is

$$\|GP\|_\infty \leq \|G\|_\infty \|P\|_\infty \tag{B.2.9}$$

B.2.3   Vector Norms

Here again all important norms stem from the vector p-norm defined as:

Vector p-norm

$$\|x\|_p := \left[\sum_i |x_i|^p \right]^{1/p} \tag{B.2.10}$$

from which definition follow the important norms:

Vector 1-norm

$$\|x\|_1 := \sum_i |x_i| \tag{B.2.11}$$

Vector 2-norm

$$\|x\|_2 := \left[\sum_i |x_i|^2 \right]^{1/2} \tag{B.2.12}$$

This is the usual Euclidean metric norm that measures the distance between two points.

Vector ∞-norm

$$\|x\|_\infty := \max_i |x_i| = \lim_{p\to\infty} \left[\sum_i |x_i|^p \right]^{1/p} \tag{B.2.13}$$

The meanings of Eqs.(B.2.5), (B.2.8) and (B.2.13) are equivalent. To better understand them, let us illustrate how one of them, for instance the last one, can be derived.

Proof: Suppose that $x_j = \max_i |x_i|$. With this assumption, the right side of Eq.(B.2.13) can be rewritten as

$$\lim_{p\to\infty} \left\{ \sum_i^m |x_i|^p \right\}^{1/p} = \lim_{p\to\infty} \left\{ x_j^p \left[\left(\frac{x_1}{x_j} \right)^p + \left(\frac{x_2}{x_j} \right)^p + .. + \left(\frac{x_j}{x_j} \right)^p + .. + \left(\frac{x_m}{x_j} \right)^p \right] \right\}^{1/p}$$

but since $\displaystyle\lim_{p\to\infty; i\neq j} \left(\frac{x_i}{x_j} \right)^p \to 0$ it follows that

$$\|x\|_\infty = \lim_{p\to\infty} \left[\sum_i^m |x_i|^p \right]^{1/p} = \lim_{p\to\infty} \left\{ x_j^p [0 + 0 + .. + 1 + .. + 0] \right\}^{1/p} = x_j = \max_i |x_i| \qquad \diamond$$

In a similar way Eqs.(B.2.5) and (B.2.8) are proven.

Matrix norms are defined quite differently and deserve a special section.

B.3.   Matrix Norms.

There are two particularly important matrix topics used in the analysis of a MIMO feedback system: *eigenvalues* and *singular values* of a transfer function matrix. Matrix norms evolve from the later.

B.3.1   *Singular Values and Principal Gains of Transfer Function Matrices*

The purpose of using *singular values* is to define matrix norms.

If A has n rows and m columns, and $n \geq m$, then the *singular values* of a constant matrix A are the positive square roots of A^*A (if $n \leq m$ then AA^* is considered)

$$\sigma_i(A) = [\lambda_i(A^*A)]^{1/2} \quad n \geq m \tag{B.3.1a}$$

$$\sigma_i(A) = [\lambda_i(AA^*)]^{1/2} \quad n \leq m \tag{B.3.1b}$$

where λ_i stands for the ith eigenvalue of $(\mathbf{A^*A})$ or $(\mathbf{AA^*})$, and the notation $\sigma(\mathbf{A})$ is used for noting the singular values of a matrix $\mathbf{A}$.

The singular values are sometimes called *principal gains* for frequency dependent matrices. They will be denoted by $\sigma_i(\omega)$ to emphasize their frequency dependence. Singular values are generally ordered as $\sigma_1 \geq \sigma_2 \geq \ldots \geq \sigma_n$ where $\sigma_i \geq \sigma_{i+1}$; σ_1 and σ_n are called the maximum and the minimum singular values respectively, denoted by $\sigma_{max} \equiv \bar{\sigma}$ and $\sigma_{min} \equiv \underline{\sigma}$. In other words, they point to the *maximum* and *minimum sizes,* or gains, of the matrix.

Singular-value decomposition of a matrix

Any real or complex matrix $\mathbf{P}$ with n rows and m columns can be decomposed into the following form

$$\mathbf{P} = \mathbf{U\Sigma V^*} \tag{B.3.2}$$

where Σ is a diagonal matrix whose elements are the singular values σ_i

$$\Sigma = \text{diag}(\,\sigma_1, \sigma_2, \sigma_3, \ldots \ldots ,\sigma_n) \tag{B.3.3}$$

For matrices which are not square we have to differentiate between cases for which $n \geq m$ or $n \leq m$. In Eq.(B.3.2) Σ is real, while $\mathbf{U}$ and $\mathbf{V}$ are complex unitary matrices, whose dimensions depend on n and m in the following way,

$$n \geq m : \mathbf{U} \in \mathcal{C}^{n \times m}; \Sigma \in \mathcal{R}^{m \times m}; \ \mathbf{V} \in \mathcal{C}^{m \times m}; \mathbf{U^*U} = \mathbf{I}_m; \mathbf{V^*V} = \mathbf{VV^*} = \mathbf{I}_m$$

$$n \leq m : \mathbf{U} \in \mathcal{C}^{n \times n}; \Sigma \in \mathcal{R}^{n \times n}; \ \mathbf{V} \in \mathcal{C}^{m \times n}; \mathbf{U^*U} = \mathbf{UU^*} = \mathbf{I}_n; \mathbf{V^*V} = \mathbf{I}_n$$

where $\mathcal{C}$ and $\mathcal{R}$ are the set of complex and real matrices. A *complex unitary matrix* $\mathbf{Q}$ is a matrix that satisfies the identity $\mathbf{Q^*} = \mathbf{Q}^{-1}$, and for which, all the eigenvalues and singular values have absolute value equal to one. It is important to realize that the singular values are unique.

An important fact follows for square matrices which are invertible. In this case, by inverting Eq.(B.3.2), we find that

$$\mathbf{P}^{-1} = \mathbf{V\Sigma}^{-1}\,\mathbf{U^*} \tag{B.3.4}$$

Definition of matrix norms

The meaning of matrix norm comes from the following discussion.

The 'output' $\mathbf{y}(s)$ of a transfer matrix $\mathbf{P}(s)$ is not unique because it depends on the input vector $\mathbf{u(s)}$ which is specified by both its amplitude and direction. However, we can find upper and lower bounds for the ratio

$$\frac{\|\mathbf{P}(j\omega)\mathbf{u}(j\omega)\|}{\|\mathbf{u}(j\omega)\|} = \frac{\|\mathbf{y}(j\omega)\|}{\|\mathbf{u}(j\omega)\|} \equiv r(\omega) \qquad (\text{B.3.5})$$

and also for the ratio

$$\frac{\|\mathbf{P}^{-1}(j\omega)\mathbf{y}(j\omega)\|}{\|\mathbf{y}(j\omega)\|} \equiv q(\omega) \qquad (\text{B.3.6})$$

using 'matrix norms'. Suppose that we keep the Euclidean norm of the input constant, $\|\mathbf{u}(s)\| = 1$ for instance, but change the ratio between its elements. In this case $r(\omega)$ will change too, depending on the direction of the input vector $\mathbf{u}(s)$.

For a vector norm $\|\mathbf{u}\|$, an *induced matrix norm* is defined as

$$\|\mathbf{P}\| = \sup_{\mathbf{u} \neq 0} \frac{\|\mathbf{Pu}\|}{\|\mathbf{u}\|} \qquad (\text{B.3.7})$$

(See Maciejowski 1989).
If $\|\mathbf{u}\|$ is the usual Euclidean vector norm,

$$\|\mathbf{u}\| = [\mathbf{u}^*\mathbf{u}]^{1/2} \qquad (\text{B.3.8})$$

then the *induced H$_\infty$ matrix norm* is the spectral norm

$$\|\mathbf{P}(s)\|_\infty \overset{def}{=} \max_\omega \bar{\sigma}[\mathbf{P}(j\omega)] \qquad (\text{B.3.9})$$

where $\bar{\sigma}$ is the maximum singular value, already defined in Eq.(B.3.1a) as $\sigma_i(\mathbf{P}) = [\lambda_i(\mathbf{P}^*\mathbf{P})]^{1/2}$. $\mathbf{u}^*$ and $\mathbf{P}^*$ denote the complex conjugate transposes of $\mathbf{u}$ and $\mathbf{P}$ respectively, since $\mathbf{u}$ and $\mathbf{P}$ can be complex vector and matrix. The induced gain, as defined by Eqs.(B.3.5) and (B.3.6), has the meaning of 'gain', which is unique for the scalar case in which one input and one output are considered. For the matrix case, as already mentioned, this 'gain' depends on the input vector direction.

Fortunately, the usual H$_\infty$ matrix norm defined in Eq.(B.3.9) has an important time-domain interpretation,

$$\|\mathbf{P}(s)\|_\infty = \max_{\mathbf{u}(t) \neq 0} \frac{\|\mathbf{y}(t)\|_2}{\|\mathbf{u}(t)\|_2} = \max_{\|\mathbf{u}(t)\|_2 = 1} \|\mathbf{y}(t)\|_2 \qquad (\text{B.3.10})$$

which is proven in Desoer and Vidyasagar (1975).

B.3.2. *Singular Value Inequalities*

Some important inequalities for singular values of matrices of adequate order are stated without proof. (See also Horn and Johnson, 1991; Green and Limebeer, 1995).

$$\underline{\sigma}(\mathbf{A}) \leq |\lambda_i(\mathbf{A})| \leq \bar{\sigma}(\mathbf{A}) \tag{B.3.11}$$

where λ_i are the eigenvalues of $\mathbf{A}$. These are bounded between the singular values.

$$\bar{\sigma}(\mathbf{A}^{-1}) = 1/\underline{\sigma}(\mathbf{A}) \tag{B.3.12}$$

$$\bar{\sigma}(\mathbf{AB}) \leq \bar{\sigma}(\mathbf{A})\,\bar{\sigma}(\mathbf{B}) \tag{B.3.13}$$

$$\underline{\sigma}(\mathbf{A})\,\underline{\sigma}(\mathbf{B}) \leq \underline{\sigma}(\mathbf{AB}) \tag{B.3.14}$$

$$\underline{\sigma}(\mathbf{A}) - 1 \leq \underline{\sigma}(\mathbf{I}+\mathbf{A}) \leq \underline{\sigma}(\mathbf{A}) + 1 \tag{B.3.15}$$

$$\underline{\sigma}(\mathbf{A}) - 1 \leq 1/\bar{\sigma}(\mathbf{I}+\mathbf{A})^{-1} \leq \underline{\sigma}(\mathbf{A}) + 1 \tag{B.3.16}$$

The above inequalities hold for matrices with constant, as well frequency dependent elements. For additional inequality relations, see Horn and Johnson (1991).

B.4.   State-Space Formulation of Linear systems

Most of the material in Chapters 6 to 8 is related to linear MIMO systems in which the plant and the controller are expressed in the state-space formulation. The object of this short section is to define some notions used in the book. For a deeper treatment of the subject, the reader is referenced to Ogata (1967) and to Kailath (1980).

B.4.1.   State-Space Formulation

The *state* of a dynamic system is the smallest collection of variables which must be specified at time $t = t_0$ in order to uniquely predict the behavior of the system for any time $t \geq t_0$ of any input set applied to the system, provided that every element of the input set is known for $t \geq t_0$. Such variables are called *state variables*.

Suppose that at least n variables $x_1, x_2, x_3, \ldots x_n$ are needed to describe completely the behavior of a system. Then the set of n state variables can be considered as n elements of a vector $\mathbf{x}$, which is called the *state vector*. A *state-space* is defined as an n-dimensional space in which $x_1, x_2, x_3, \ldots x_n$ are the coordinates.

A real linear system is generally described by a set of high order ordinary differential equations, that can be transformed into a set of first order differential equations. The latter set can be rewritten in terms of vector matrix notation

$$\frac{d}{dt}\mathbf{x} = \mathbf{A}(t)\mathbf{x}(t) + \mathbf{B}(t)\mathbf{u}(t) \tag{B.4.1}$$

$$\mathbf{y}(t) = \mathbf{C}(t)\mathbf{x}(t) + \mathbf{D}(t)\mathbf{u}(t) \tag{B.4.2}$$

In the above equation, $\mathbf{x}(t)$ is the 'state vector'; $\mathbf{u}(t)$ is the *input vector* whose elements are applied to the system at different input points; and $\mathbf{y}(t)$ is the output vector of the dynamic system, whose elements are combinations of the state variables. The elements of matrix $\mathbf{A}(t)$ depend on the parameters of the defined plant. The elements of matrix $\mathbf{B}(t)$ show how the input vector $\mathbf{u}(t)$ affects the state variables. The elements of matrix $\mathbf{C}(t)$ show how the output variables are related to the state variables. The matrix $\mathbf{D}(t)$ shows how the control variables, which are the elements of $\mathbf{u}(t)$, directly affect the output vector $\mathbf{y}(t)$. ($\mathbf{D} = 0$ in many practical systems).

B.4.2.   State-Space Realization and Minimal Realization

When the dynamic system is linear time invariant, then the Laplace transform of Eqs.(B.4.1) and (B.4.2) can be applied, to obtain after some algebraic operations:

$$\mathbf{y}(s) = \mathbf{C}(s)[s\mathbf{I}-\mathbf{A}]^{-1}\,\mathbf{Bu}(s) + \mathbf{Du}(s) = \{\mathbf{C}(s)[s\mathbf{I}-\mathbf{A}]^{-1}\,\mathbf{B} + \mathbf{D}\}\mathbf{u}(s) \tag{B.4.3}$$

From the above equation the definition of a transfer function matrix follows:

$$\mathbf{P}(s) = \mathbf{C}(s)[s\mathbf{I}-\mathbf{A}]^{-1}\,\mathbf{B} + \mathbf{D}. \tag{B.4.4}$$

It is also clear that any transfer function matrix $\mathbf{P}(s)$ can be realized in state-space formulation described by Eqs.(B.4.1) and (B.4.2), where the matrices $\mathbf{A}, \mathbf{B}, \mathbf{C}$ and $\mathbf{D}$ are time invariant. We say, then, that $(\mathbf{A}, \mathbf{B}, \mathbf{C}, \mathbf{D})$ is a state-space realization of $\mathbf{P}(s)$, sometimes denoted as

$$(\mathbf{A}, \mathbf{B}, \mathbf{C}, \mathbf{D}) \equiv \begin{bmatrix} \mathbf{A} & | & \mathbf{B} \\ - & | & - \\ \mathbf{C} & | & \mathbf{D} \end{bmatrix}$$

A state-space realization $(\mathbf{A}, \mathbf{B}, \mathbf{C}, \mathbf{D})$ of $\mathbf{P}(s)$ is called *minimal realization*, if the realized matrix $\mathbf{A}$ is of smallest possible dimension. This smallest dimension is called the *McMillan degree* of $\mathbf{P}(s)$.

B.4.3.   Basic Properties and Concepts from State-Space Theory.

Some fundamental properties and concepts of linear systems described in state-space formulation, are 'controllability', 'observability', (both introduced by Kalman

1965), and also 'stabilizability' and 'detectability'. The above system concepts are used when necessary and sufficient conditions are sought for the existence of a stable solution to different control problems. For a deeper treatment of these system properties, the reader is referred to Ogata (1967), Kwakernaak and Sivan (1972), Kailath (1980).

Controllability

Controllability is defined from Eq.(B.4.1). 'Controllability' is the important property that for any t_0 it is possible to construct an unconstrained control vector $\mathbf{u}(t)$ which will transfer any known initial state $\mathbf{x}(t_0)$ to any desired final state $\mathbf{x}(t_1)$ in a finite time interval $t_0 \leq t \leq t_1$. The mathematical test for controllability is easily shown to be as follows:

Suppose that $\mathbf{A}$ is of order $n \times n$. For the system in Eq.(B.4.1) to be controllable, the rank of the matrix

$$\mathbf{G} = [\mathbf{B}|\, \mathbf{AB} \mid \mathbf{A}^2\mathbf{B} \mid \dots \mid \mathbf{A}^{n-1}\mathbf{B}]$$

must be of order n,

$$rank\ \mathbf{G} = n \tag{B.4.5}$$

or equivalently, if and only if, there is a set of n linearly independent column vectors of $\mathbf{G}$. This is also equivalent to the condition that no pole-zero cancellations occur in the transfer function matrix of Eq.(B.4.4). See Ogata (1967).

Stabilizability

The concept of 'stabilizability' is closely related to the notion of 'controllability'. Let us suppose that the order of the above matrix $\mathbf{G}$ is less than n, say $n - 1$, which means that one of the modes included in the transfer function matrix $\mathbf{P}$ has been canceled. This mode cannot be controlled in the sense of 'controllability' just defined. However, as long as the canceled uncontrollable mode is not unstable, the system in closed-loop can be rendered exponentially stable by state-variable feedback. Moreover, if the uncontrollable system contains unstable modes that can be controlled by state-variable feedback, the system is then called *stabilizable*.

It is convenient and common to speak of the pair $(\mathbf{A},\mathbf{B})$ as being 'controllable' or 'stabilizable'.

Observability

Observability is defined from Eq.(B.4.2) as follows.
The measured output elements are in the output vector $\mathbf{y}(t)$. A system is said to be *observable* in the time interval $t_0 \leq t \leq t_1$, if for every t_0 and some t_1, every state $\mathbf{x}(t_0)$ can be determined from the measured output vector $\mathbf{y}(t)$ on $t_0 \leq t \leq t_1$. In other words, each change in the state $\mathbf{x}(t)$ will be sensed in the output vector $\mathbf{y}(t)$. The mathematical test for observability consists in building the matrix

$$H = [C^T \,|\, A^T C^T| \ldots | \ldots | (A^{n-1})^T \, C^T]$$

and checking its rank. The system is observable if

$$rank\ \mathbf{H} = n \qquad (B.4.6)$$

or equivalently, if and only if there is a set of n linearly independent column vectors of **H**.

Detectability

This property is dual to the notion of stabilizability. When supposing that the rank of **H** is smaller than n, say $rank\ \mathbf{H} = n - 1$, there exists one unobservable mode. But, as long as this mode is stable, there is nothing wrong with the fact that the system can be stabilized adequately. If the unstable modes are observable, then the system is called *detectable*.

It is convenient and common to speak of the pair (**A,C**) being 'observable' or 'detectable'.

Asymptotical stabilization by state-feedback

The following is an important property of state-feedback: if a system is controllable or stabilizable, there can always be found a constant control law $u(t) = -Kx(t)$ that makes the closed-loop system asymptotically stable.

Hidden Modes

Hidden modes are related to the two very important notions of controllability and of observability, defined previously. With the above definitions, we can consider the notion of *hidden modes*. A mode is defined as 'hidden' if in the state-space formulation it is not state controllable or observable, hence, it does not appear in the minimal realization defined in Section B.4.2. The notion of hidden modes is of special importance in feedback systems in which the plant includes 'hidden unstable modes'.

B.4.4.   Characteristic Polynomials in Feedback Control Systems

When stability analysis of a MIMO feedback system is performed, we are interested in two characteristic polynomials pertaining to the system return-ratio matrix $L(s)$ and to the system return-difference matrix $F(s) = 1 + L(s)$.

There exist matrices A_L, B_L, C_L, and D_L from which the state-space realization of $L(s)$ can be derived. Since according to the definition in Eq.(B.4.4),

$$L(s) = C_L[sI - A_L]^{-1} B_L + D_L \qquad (B.4.7)$$

we conclude that the poles of $L(s)$ are the roots of the *open-loop characteristic polynomial*

$$D_{ol}(s) = \det(s\mathbf{I} - \mathbf{A}_L) \tag{B.4.8}$$

In a similar way we can find the roots of the closed-loop system. Suppose that the system defined by $\mathbf{L}(s)$ is imbedded in a unity-feedback structure. In this case, it is not difficult to see that the sensitivity transfer function matrix takes the form:

$$\mathbf{S}(s) = (\mathbf{I} + \mathbf{L})^{-1} \tag{B.4.9}$$

By using the expression for $\mathbf{L}(s)$ in Eq.(B.4.7), we get $\mathbf{S}^{-1}(s) = \mathbf{C}_L[s\mathbf{I} - \mathbf{A}_L]^{-1}\mathbf{B}_L + \mathbf{D}_L + \mathbf{I}$, from which it readily follows that

$$\mathbf{S} = \mathbf{B}_L^{-1}(s\mathbf{I} - \mathbf{A}_L)\mathbf{C}_L^{-1} + (\mathbf{I} + \mathbf{D}_L)^{-1} \tag{B.4.10}$$

After few algebraic operations, we finally get

$$\mathbf{S}(s) = \mathbf{C}_L[s\mathbf{I} - \mathbf{A}_L + \mathbf{B}_L(\mathbf{I}+\mathbf{D}_L)^{-1}\mathbf{C}_L]^{-1}\mathbf{B}_L \tag{B.4.11}$$

Eq.(B.4.11) is of the same form of Eq.(B.4.7), except that the equivalent matrix $\mathbf{D} \equiv \mathbf{0}$. From this equation, we conclude that the poles of $\mathbf{S}(s)$ are the roots of the *closed-loop characteristic polynomial* given by:

$$D_{cl}(s) = \det[s\mathbf{I} - \mathbf{A}_L + \mathbf{B}_L(\mathbf{I}+\mathbf{D}_L)^{-1}\mathbf{C}_L] \tag{B.4.12}$$

B.5.   Eigenvalues and Eigenvectors of Transfer Function Matrices

As is well known, eigenvalues and eigenvectors of a real $n \times n$ square matrix $\mathbf{A}$ are the solution of the n order characteristic equation

$$\det(\mathbf{A} - \lambda\mathbf{I}) = 0. \tag{B.5.1}$$

The corresponding eigenvector $\mathbf{e}_i$ to each eigenvalue λ_i is the solution of the equation

$$(\mathbf{A} - \lambda_i\mathbf{I})\mathbf{e}_i = \mathbf{0} \tag{B.5.2}$$

which is equivalent to

$$\mathbf{A}\,\mathbf{e}_i = \lambda_i\,\mathbf{e}_i. \tag{B.5.3}$$

The eigenvalues are generally, for practical purposes, normalized to have an Euclidean norm equal to 1, or, $\mathbf{e}_i^T\,\mathbf{e}_i = 1$.

The eigenvalues of matrix $\mathbf{A}$ compose its *spectrum,* and the *spectral radius* of $\mathbf{A}$ is defined as

$$\rho(\mathbf{A}) \stackrel{def}{=} \max |\lambda_i| \tag{B.5.4}$$

The above definitions and facts hold also for transfer function matrices, for which *eigenvalue functions* are obtained. These functions are the heart of the implementation of the Nyquist stability criterion to MIMO feedback systems. They have their origin and parallel in the theory of eigenvalues and eigenvectors of constant square matrices. The only difference is that these eigenvalues are frequency dependent.

Let us define a $n \times n$ square matrix $\mathbf{Q}(s)$ and assume also that there are no hidden unstable modes in this system. If $\mathbf{Q}(s)$ is not identically singular, then it is possible to find a set of n eigenvalue functions, $q_i(s)$, $i = 1, n$, which are functions of the complex Laplace variable s. These are determined by the solution of the characteristic equation

$$\det[\mathbf{Q}(s) - q\mathbf{I}_n] = q^n(s) + a_1(s)q^{n-1}(s) + a_2(s)q^{n-2}(s) + \ldots + a_n(s) = 0 \tag{B.5.5}$$

$\mathbf{I}_n$-a unity diagonal matrix of order n.

The above characteristic equation leads to a polynomial in $q(s)$ whose coefficients are rational functions of s. It defines an *algebraic function* of the complex variable s, (Bliss 1966). Let us refer to the n solutions as *eigenvalue transfer functions*, or *characteristic transfer functions*, $q_i(s)$, $i = 1, n$. Since these functions are the solution of a n order characteristic equation, they will not generally be rational functions of s. They will be irrational functions, and, as such, have to be treated in the context of Riemann surfaces (Weyl 1955). For each eigenvalue function, we can find its corresponding eigenvector, also a function of s, generally not rational. By definition, these eigenvector functions are obtained by solving the n equations

$$\mathbf{Q}(s)\mathbf{w}_i(s) = q_i(s)\mathbf{w}_i(s) \; ; i = 1, 2 \ldots, n \tag{B.5.6}$$

where $\mathbf{w}_i(s)$ are vectors, also called *characteristic directions*. If we define a matrix

$$\mathbf{W}(s) = [\mathbf{w}_1(s) \; \mathbf{w}_2(s) \; \mathbf{w}_3(s) \ldots \mathbf{w}_n(s) \,] \tag{B.5.7}$$

and its inverse (which exists because $\mathbf{w}_i(s)$ are linearly independent vectors)

$$\mathbf{V}(s) = \mathbf{W}^{-1}(s) = [\mathbf{v}_1(s) \; \mathbf{v}_2(s) \; \mathbf{v}_3(s) \ldots \mathbf{v}_n(s) \,] \tag{B.5.8}$$

then, by standard algebraic theory, (see, for instance Warner 1965), we can obtain a diagonal matrix $\mathbf{\Lambda}^Q(s)$ whose entries are the eigenvalue transfer functions $q_i(s)$

$$\begin{aligned} \mathbf{\Lambda}^Q(s) &= \mathbf{W}^{-1}(s)\mathbf{Q}(s)\mathbf{W}(s) = \mathbf{V}(s)\mathbf{Q}(s)\mathbf{W}(s) \\ &= \text{diag}[q_1(s), q_2(s), \ldots, q_i(s), \ldots q_n(s)] \end{aligned} \tag{B.5.9}$$

and conversely,

$$Q(s) = W(s)\Lambda^Q(s)V(s) = \sum_{i=1}^{n} q_i(s)w_i(s)v_i^T(s) \tag{B.5.10}$$

Here again, the 'spectrum' of the matrix consists of all eigenvalue functions, and the *spectral radius* of the matrix $Q(s)$ is defined as

$$\rho[Q(j\omega)] \stackrel{def}{=} max\, |q_i(j\omega)| \tag{B.5.11}$$

Here the spectral radius is frequency dependent.

B.6. Linear Fractional Transformation (LFT).

Linear Fractional Transformation is a useful approach for representing uncertainties in matrices and systems, but also in analyzing and designing of the standard regulator problem solved within the H_∞-norm optimization paradigm. Suppose that a matrix M is partitioned into a 2×2 block form represented in Fig. B.6.1,

$$M = \begin{bmatrix} M_{11} & | & M_{12} \\ -- & | & -- \\ M_{21} & | & M_{22} \end{bmatrix} \tag{B.6.1}$$

The original matrix M defines the relation between two vectors, $y = M\,x$. If M is partitioned as in Fig.B.6.1a, then we can write

$$y_1 = M_{11}\,x_1 + M_{12}\,x_2$$

$$y_2 = M_{21}\,x_1 + M_{22}\,x_2 \tag{B.6.2}$$

Next, suppose that Δ relates x_1 to y_1 in Fig.B.6.1b, namely,

$$x_1 = \Delta\,y_1 \tag{B.6.3}$$

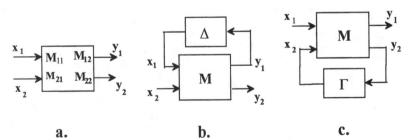

    a.   **b.**   **c.**

Figure B.6.1.   Upper and lower loop of M closed with Δ and Γ respectively

By use of Eq.(B.6.3) we can relate $\mathbf{x}_2$ to $\mathbf{y}_2$ as the *linear fractional transformation* of $\mathbf{M}$ by $\boldsymbol{\Delta}$ as follows:

$$\mathbf{y}_2 = [\mathbf{M}_{22} + \mathbf{M}_{21}\,\boldsymbol{\Delta}(\mathbf{I}\text{-}\mathbf{M}_{11}\boldsymbol{\Delta})^{-1}\mathbf{M}_{12}]\mathbf{x}_2 = F_U(\mathbf{M},\boldsymbol{\Delta})\mathbf{x}_2, \qquad (B.6.4)$$

$$F_U(\mathbf{M}, \boldsymbol{\Delta}): = [\mathbf{M}_{22} + \mathbf{M}_{21}\,\boldsymbol{\Delta}(\mathbf{I}\text{-}\mathbf{M}_{11}\boldsymbol{\Delta})^{-1}\mathbf{M}_{12}] \qquad (B.6.5)$$

$F_U(\mathbf{M}, \boldsymbol{\Delta})$ is defined as the *Upper Linear Fractional Transformation*.
Next suppose that $\boldsymbol{\Gamma}$ relates $\mathbf{x}_2$ to $\mathbf{y}_2$ in Fig.B.6.1c, namely,

$$\mathbf{x}_2 = \boldsymbol{\Gamma}\,\mathbf{y}_2 \qquad (B.6.6)$$

In a similar way, by use of Eq.(B.6.6) we find that for the system in Fig.B.6.1c:

$$\mathbf{y}_1 = [\mathbf{M}_{11} + \mathbf{M}_{12}\boldsymbol{\Gamma}(\mathbf{I}\text{-}\mathbf{M}_{22}\boldsymbol{\Gamma})^{-1}\mathbf{M}_{21}]\mathbf{x}_1 = F_L(\mathbf{M},\boldsymbol{\Gamma})\mathbf{x}_1, \qquad (B.6.7)$$

$$F_L(\mathbf{M}, \boldsymbol{\Gamma}): = [\mathbf{M}_{11} + \mathbf{M}_{12}\boldsymbol{\Gamma}(\mathbf{I}\text{-}\mathbf{M}_{22}\boldsymbol{\Gamma})^{-1}\,\mathbf{M}_{21}] \qquad (B.6.8)$$

$F_L(\mathbf{M},\boldsymbol{\Gamma})$ is defined as the *Lower Linear Fractional Transformation*.

Appendix C

Control Networks For Loopshaping and the Nichols chart

C.1. Introduction

Loopshaping in the frequency-domain is performed by using real and complex poles and zeros, whose transfer functions $G(s)$ are displayed as the usual Bode plots. One is the logarithmic magnitude of $G(j\omega)$ in decibel plotted versus log ω and the other is the phase-angle of $G(j\omega)$ versus log ω (Sections C.2 and C.3).

Although use of individual poles and zeros is sufficient for loopshaping, it is sometimes easier and much more efficient to use combined control networks, such as lead-lag or lag-lead networks, (Section C.4).

More complicated control networks can also be used to facilitate the loop-shaping, such as lead-lag-lag-lead, or lag-lead-lead-lag networks, as presented in Section C.5.

The graphical data in this appendix is mandatory in loopshaping, as was demonstrated in Chapter 2.

The frequency axes for all the graphs of these networks are normalized to the location of the poles or zeros, so that the magnitudes and phase of these networks can be calculated at any desired real frequency. Simple examples are added to explain correct use of the frequency dependent graphs.

Quick graphical calculation of the gain and phase of the unity-feedback closed-loop transfer function $T = L/(1+L)$, for a known loop transmission function L is easily performed graphically by using the Nichols chart, as presented in Section C.6.

Quick graphical calculation of the gain and phase of the sensitivity function $S = 1/(1+L)$, for a known loop transmission function L is easily obtained by using the inverted Nichols chart, as presented in Section C.7.

C.2. Frequency Response of a Real Pole (zero)

$$G_p(s) = \frac{\omega_n}{}$$

(for a real zero, $G_z(s) = 1/\,G_p(s)$, hence, $|G_z| = 1/\,|G_p|$, $|G_z|$ dB $= -\,|G_p|$ dB and arg G_z deg $= -$ arg G_p deg).

The resulting magnitude, magnitude in dB, and phase in degrees are given in table and also in graphical forms as functions of the normalized frequency ω/ω_n

ω/ω_n	$|G_p|$	$|G_p|$ dB	arg G_p deg
0.1	1	−0.04	−5.71
0.2	0.98	−0.17	−11.31
0.3	0.96	−0.37	−16.7
0.4	0.93	−0.64	−21.8
0.5	0.89	−0.97	−26.56
0.6	0.86	−1.13	−30.96
0.7	0.82	−1.73	−34.99
0.8	0.78	−2.14	−38.66
1	0.71	−3.01	−45
1.5	0.55	−5.11	−56.31
2	0.45	−6.99	−63.43
3	0.32	−10	−71.57
4	0.25	−12.31	−75.96
5	0.2	−14.15	−78.69
7	0.14	−16.98	−81.87
10	0.1	−20.04	−84.29
20	0.05	−26.03	−87.14
50	0.02	−33.98	−88.85
100	0.01	−40	−89.43

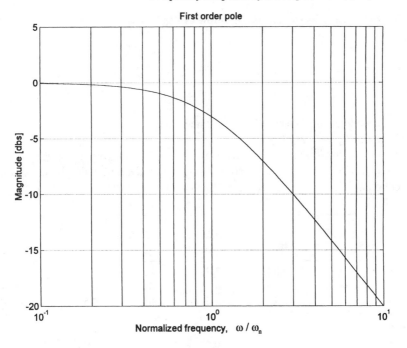

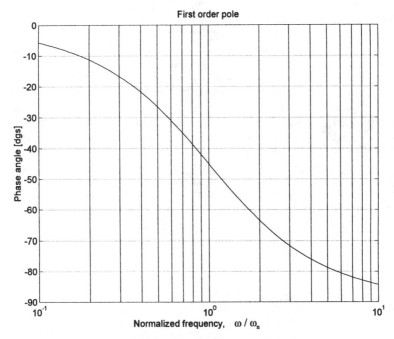

Figure C.2.1.   Frequency response of a real pole.

C.3   Frequency Response of a Complex Pole (zero)

$$G_p(s) = \frac{\omega_n^2}{s^2 + 2\xi\omega_n s + \omega_n^2}$$

(for a complex zero, $G_z(s) = 1/G_p(s)$, hence, $|G_z| = 1/|G_p|$, $|G_z|$ dB $= -|G_p|$ dB and arg G_z deg $= -$ arg G_p deg).

The resulting magnitude, magnitude in dB and phase in degrees are given in table and also in graphical form as functions of the normalized frequency ω/ω_n for different damping coefficients, $\xi = 0.2, 0.4, 0.6$ and 0.8.

	$\xi = 0.2$			$\xi = 0.4$		
ω/ω_n	$|G_p|$	G_p dB	arg G_p deg	$|G_p|$	$|G_p|$ dB	arg G_p deg
0.1	1	0.08	−2.31	1.01	0.06	−4.62
0.2	1.04	0.32	−4.76	1.03	0.24	−9.46
0.3	1.09	0.74	−7.51	1.06	0.53	−14.77
0.4	1.17	1.36	−10.78	1.11	0.93	−20.85
0.5	1.29	2.2	−14.93	1.17	1.42	−28.07
0.6	1.46	3.3	−20.55	1.25	1.93	−36.86
0.7	1.72	4.7	−28.76	1.32	2.41	−47.67
0.8	2.08	6.34	−41.63	1.36	2.68	−60.64
0.9	2.46	7.81	−62.17	1.34	2.56	−75.21
1	2.5	7.96	−90	1.25	1.94	−90
1.5	0.72	−2.84	−154.25	0.58	−4.77	−136.17
2	0.32	−9.84	−165.07	0.29	−10.63	−151.92
3	0.12	−18.15	−171.47	0.12	−18.43	−163.3
4	0.06	−23.57	−173.91	0.07	−23.71	−167.95
5	0.04	−27.63	−175.23	0.04	−27.72	−170.53
7	0.02	−33.63	−176.66	0.02	−33.68	−173.34
10	0.01	−39.9	−177.68	0.01	−39.94	−175.38
20	0	−52.02	−178.85	0	−52.03	−177.7
50	0	−67.96	−179.54	0	−67.96	−179.08
100	0	−79.99	−179.77	0	−79.99	−179.54

$$G_p(s) = \frac{\omega_n^2}{s^2 + 2\xi\omega_n s + \omega_n^2}$$

	$\xi = 0.6$			$\xi = 0.8$		
ω/ω_n	$|G_p|$	$|G_p|$ dB	arg G_p deg	$|G_p|$	$|G_p|$ dB	arg G_p deg
0.1	1	0.02	−6.91	1	−0.02	−9.18
0.2	1.02	0.09	−14.04	0.99	−0.1	−18.43
0.3	1.02	0.19	−21.58	0.97	−0.25	−27.81
0.4	1.03	0.29	−29.74	0.95	−0.47	−37.31
0.5	1.04	0.35	−38.66	0.91	−0.8	−46.85
0.6	1.04	0.32	−48.36	0.87	−1.24	−56.31
0.7	1.02	0.15	−58.73	0.81	−1.8	−65.51
0.8	0.98	−0.22	−69.44	0.75	−2.47	−74.29
0.9	0.91	−0.8	−80.02	0.69	−3.24	−82.48
1	0.83	−1.58	−90	0.63	−4.08	−90
1.5	0.46	−6.82	−124.78	0.37	−8.64	−117.51
2	0.26	−11.69	−141.34	0.23	−12.84	−133.15
3	0.11	−18.86	−155.77	0.11	−19.39	−149.03
4	0.06	−23.94	−162.25	0.06	−24.24	−156.89
5	0.04	−27.86	−165.96	0.04	−28.06	−161.56
7	0.02	−33.75	−170.07	0.02	−33.85	−166.86
10	0.01	−39.97	−173.09	0.01	−40	−170.82
20	0	−52.04	−176.55	0	−52.05	−175.42
50	0	−67.96	−178.62	0	−67.96	−176.17
100	0	−79.99	−179.31	0	−80	−179.08

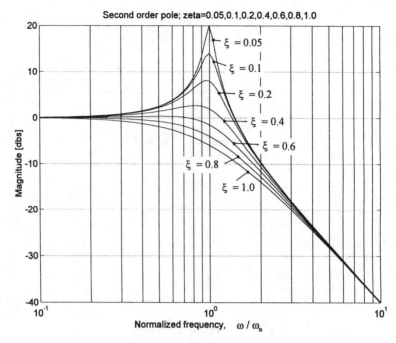

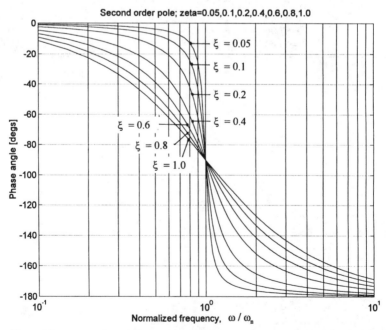

Figure C.3.1.   Frequency response of a complex pole for different damping coefficients.

C.4. Frequency Response of a Lead-Lag Control Network

$$G(s) = \frac{1 + a\tau s}{1 + \tau s}; \quad a > 1, \quad \tau > 0; \quad u = \tau\omega$$

(for a lag-lead control network, $G_1(s) = 1/G(s)$, hence, $|G_1| = 1/\,|G|$, $|G_1|$ dB = $-\,|G|$ dB and arg G_1 deg = $-$ arg G deg).

The resulting magnitude, magnitude in dB and phase in degrees are given in the table and also in graphical forms for different a factors, $a = 2, 3, 4, 5, 7.5, 10, 20$ and 30.

	$a = 2$			$a = 3$		
$u = \tau\omega$	$|G|$	$|G|$ dB	arg G deg	$|G|$	$|G|$ dB	arg G deg
0.01	1	0	0.57	1	0	1.15
0.02	1	0.01	1.15	1	0.01	1.14
0.05	1	0.03	2.84	1.01	0.09	5.66
0.1	1.02	0.13	5.59	1.03	0.33	10.99
0.2	1.06	0.47	10.49	1.14	1.16	19.65
0.3	1.17	0.96	14.26	1.29	2.2	25.28
0.5	1.27	2.04	18.43	1.61	4.15	29.74
0.7	1.41	2.98	19.47	1.91	5.6	29.54
0.8	1.47	3.36	19.33	2.03	6.15	28.72
1	1.58	3.98	18.43	2.24	6.99	26.56
1.5	1.75	4.88	15.25	2.55	8.14	21.16
2	1.84	5.31	12.52	2.72	8.69	17.1
3	1.92	5.68	8.97	2.86	9.13	12.09
5	1.97	5.89	5.56	2.94	9.39	7.49
10	1.99	5.98	2.84	2.98	9.5	3.8
20	2	6.01	1.43	2.99	9.53	1.9

$$G(s) = \frac{1 + a\tau s}{1 + \tau s}; \quad a > 1, \quad \tau > 0; \quad u = \tau\omega$$

$u = \tau\omega$	$a = 4$			$a = 5$		
	$|G|$	$|G|$ dB	arg G deg	$|G|$	$|G|$ dB	arg G deg
0.01	1.01	0.01	1.72	1	0.01	2.29
0.02	1.01	0.03	3.43	1.01	0.04	4.56
0.05	1.02	0.16	8.44	1.03	0.25	11.17
0.1	1.07	0.6	16.09	1.11	0.93	20.85
0.2	1.26	1.98	27.34	1.38	2.84	33.69
0.3	1.49	3.49	33.49	1.73	4.74	39.6
0.5	2	6.02	36.86	2.4	7.63	41.63
0.7	2.43	7.73	35.35	2.98	9.49	39.06
0.8	2.62	8.36	33.98	3.22	10.15	37.3
1	2.91	9.29	30.96	3.6	11.14	33.69
1.5	3.37	10.56	24.23	4.19	12.45	26.09
2	3.6	11.1	19.4	4.49	13.05	20.85
3	3.81	11.62	1,367	4.75	13.54	14.62
5	3.93	11.88	8.44	4.91	13.81	9
10	3.98	12	4.27	4.97	13.94	4.56
20	3.99	12.03	2.14	4.99	13.96	2.28

$$G(s) = \frac{1 + a\tau s}{1 + \tau s}; \quad a > 1, \quad \tau > 0; \quad u = \tau\omega$$

$u = \tau\omega$	$a = 7.5$			$a = 10$		
	$|G|$	$|G|$ dB	arg G deg	$|G|$	$|G|$ dB	arg G deg
0.01	1.01	0.02	3.71	1.01	0.04	5.14
0.02	1.01	0.1	7.38	1.02	0.17	10.16
0.05	1.07	0.56	17.69	1.11	0.96	23.7
0.1	1.24	1.89	31.16	1.41	2.97	39.29
0.2	1.77	4.94	45	2.19	6.81	52.12
0.3	2.35	7.45	49.33	3.03	9.63	54.86
0.5	3.47	10.81	48.5	4.56	13.18	52.12
0.7	4.37	12.82	44.22	5.79	15.25	46.87
0.8	4.75	13.53	41.87	6.29	15.98	44.2
1	5.35	14.56	37.4	7.11	17.03	39.29
1.5	6.26	15.93	28.6	8.34	18.42	29.87
2	6.72	16.55	22.75	8.96	19.05	23.7
3	7.12	17.05	15.89	9.49	19.54	16.52
5	7.36	17.33	9.78	9.8	19.83	10.16
10	7.46	17.45	4.94	9.96	19.95	5.13
20	7.49	17.49	2.48	9.98	19.98	2.57

$$G(s) = \frac{1 + a\tau s}{1 + \tau s}; \quad a > 1, \quad \tau > 0; \quad u = \tau\omega$$

	$a = 20$			$a = 30$		
$u = \tau\omega$	$\|G\|$	$\|G\|$ dB	arg G deg	$\|G\|$	$\|G\|$ dB	arg G deg
0.01	1.01	0.17	10.73	1.04	0.38	16.12
0.02	1.08	0.64	20.65	1.16	1.33	29.8
0.05	1.41	2.99	42.14	1.8	5.1	53.44
0.1	2.25	6.94	57.7	3.14	9.95	65.85
0.2	4.04	12.13	64.65	5.96	15.5	69.2
0.3	5.82	15.3	63.8	8.67	18.76	66.9
0.5	8.98	19.07	57.72	13.44	22.57	59.62
0.7	11.49	21.2	50.9	17.22	24.7	52.2
0.8	12.51	21.95	47.76	18.75	25.46	48.95
1	14.16	23.04	42.13	21.22	26.53	43.09
1.5	16.65	24.42	31.78	24.96	27.94	32.47
2	17.89	25.05	25.13	26.83	28.57	25.6
3	18.97	25.56	17.48	28.46	29.08	17.79
5	19.61	25.85	10.73	29.41	29.37	10.92
10	19.9	25.97	5.42	29.85	29.49	5.52
20	19.97	26	2.72	29.96	29.53	2.76

Two simple examples will illustrate the use of this control network.

Example C.1. We are interested in achieving a maximum lead-angle of 30 deg at $\omega = 5$ rad/sec.

Solution: In Fig.C.4.1, we see on the phase graph that a maximum phase-angle of $+30$ deg is achieved with $a = 3$.

We are interested in locating this phase-lead angle at $\omega = 5$. In the same Fig.C.4.1, we see that the maximum lead angle occurs at the normalized frequency $u = 0.6$. Hence, $\tau = u/\omega = 0.6/5 = 0.12$. The final control network becomes: $G(s) = (1 + 3 \times 0.12\,s)/(1 + 0.12\,s)$.

Example C.2. We wish to achieve a high frequency magnitude attenuation of 14 dB in the region $\omega > 2$ rad/sec. The additional phase-lag angle that will inevitably accompany the magnitude attenuation must be limited to 5 deg.

Solution: From Fig.C.4.1, we see that in order to achieve a high frequency magnitude attenuation of 14 dB, we have to choose $a = 5$. If we want to assure that at $\omega > 2$ rad/sec the added phase-lag angle will be smaller than 5 deg, we have to choose $u = 10$ at $\omega = 2$ rad/sec. This leads to: $\tau = u/\omega = 10/2 = 5$. Finally, the control network becomes: $G(s) = (1 + 5s)/(1 + 5 \times 5s)$.

(Notice that in this case, the pole precedes the zero)

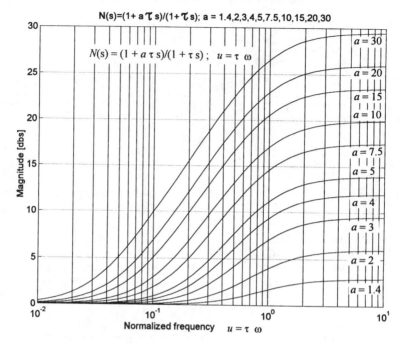

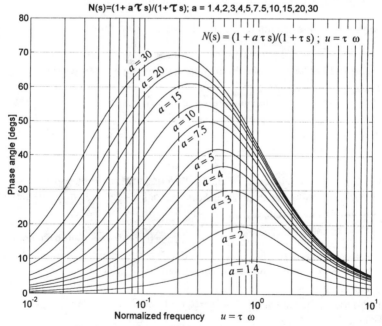

Figure C.4.1. Frequency response of a lead-lag control network for different parameters *a*.

C.5   Frequency Response of a Lead-Lag-Lag-Lead Control network

$$G(s) = \frac{(s + 1/z)(s + z)}{(s + 1/p)(s + p)}; \quad z > p$$

(for a lag-lead-lead-lag control network, $p > z$, $G_1(s) = 1/G(s)$, hence, $|G_1| = 1/|G|$, $|G_1|$ dB $= -|G|$ dB and arg G_1 deg $= -$ arg G deg).

This control network is more difficult to use than the simple lead-lag control network. However, it is useful in more complex problems, as was shown in Example 2.3 in Chapter 2. Example C3 illustrates the use of this control network.

Example C.3.   Suppose that in order to satisfy the phase margin specifications in a loopshaping stage, we need a phase lead angle of 30 deg at $\omega = 5$ rad/sec, with a magnitude attenuation of at least 6 dB.

Solution: Let us try a network of the form

$$G(s) = \frac{(s + p)((s + 1/p)}{(s + z)(s + 1/z)}; \quad p > z.$$

Use Fig.C.5.3. If we choose the normalized poles and zeros such that $p = 24.1$, $z = 7.5$ and we locate the normalized frequency $u = 10$ at $\omega = 5$ rad/sec, then at $\omega = 5$ rad/sec we shall obtain a decrease in gain of 6.5 dB, and a phase-lead of 30 deg.

To locate the actual poles and zeros, note that $\omega = 5$ rad/sec at $u = 10$. Hence, at $u = 1$, $\omega = 0.5$ rad/sec, which is the central frequency of the control network. The real poles and zeros will then be located at $p_1 = 0.5 \times 24.1$, $p_2 = 0.5/24.1$; $z_1 = 0.5 \times 7.5$, $z_2 = 0.5/7.5$, and the final control network becomes:

$$G(s) = \frac{(s + 0.5 \times 7.5)(s + 0.5/7.5)}{(s + 0.5/24.1)(s + 0.5 \times 24.1)} = \frac{(s + 3.75)(s + 0.0666)}{(s + 0.020747)(s + 12.05)}$$

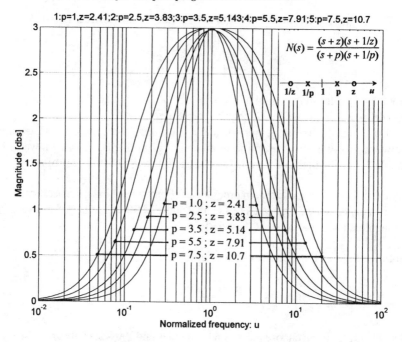

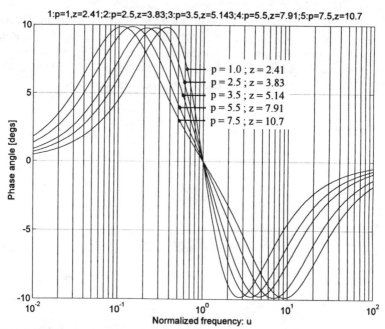

Figure C.5.1. Frequency response of a lead-lag-lag-lead control network for different parameters '*p*' and '*z*'. **Maximum Amplitude: 3 dB; Maximum Phase lead/lag : 9.8 deg.**

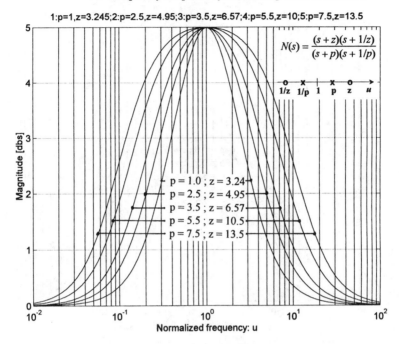

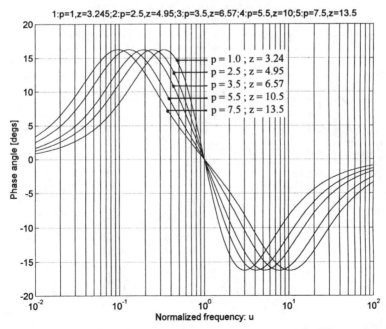

Figure C.5.2. Frequency response of a lead-lag-lag-lead control network for different parameters '*p*' and '*z*'. *Maximum Amplitude: 5 dB; Maximum Phase lead/lag : 16.2 deg.*

1:p=1,z=6.2;2:p=2.5,z=9.1;3:p=3.5,z=11.9;4:p=5.5,z=17.9;5:p=7.5,z=24.1

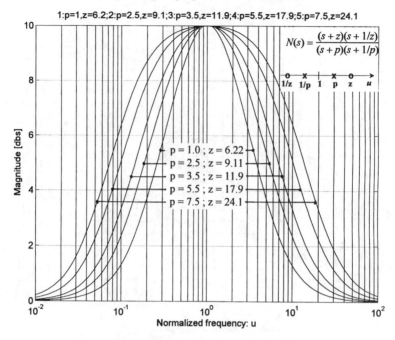

$$N(s) = \frac{(s+z)(s+1/z)}{(s+p)(s+1/p)}$$

p = 1.0 ; z = 6.22
p = 2.5 ; z = 9.11
p = 3.5 ; z = 11.9
p = 5.5 ; z = 17.9
p = 7.5 ; z = 24.1

1:p=1,z=6.2;2:p=2.5,z=9.1;3:p=3.5,z=11.9;4:p=5.5,z=17.9;5:p=7.5,z=24.1

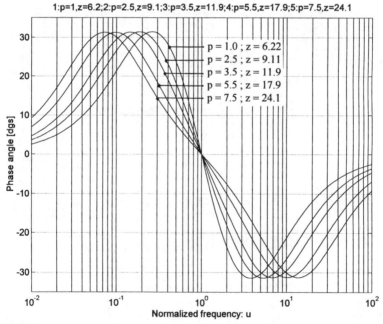

p = 1.0 ; z = 6.22
p = 2.5 ; z = 9.11
p = 3.5 ; z = 11.9
p = 5.5 ; z = 17.9
p = 7.5 ; z = 24.1

Figure C.5.3. Frequency response of a lead-lag-lag-lead control network for different parameters '*p*' and '*z*'. *Maximum Amplitude: 10 dB; Maximum Phase lead/lag : 31.3 deg.*

1:p=1,z=11.2;2:p=2.5,z=16.2;3:p=3.5,z=21.2;4:p=5.5,z=31.9;5:p=7.5,z=42.9

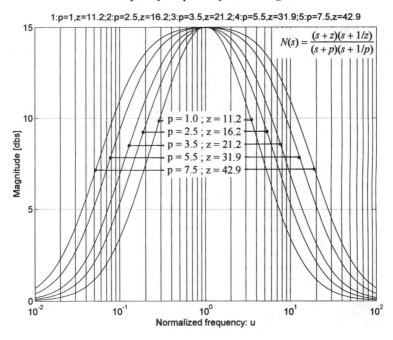

1:p=1,z=11.2;2:p=2.5,z=16.2;3:p=3.5,z=21.2;4:p=5.5,z=31.9;5:p=7.5,z=42.9

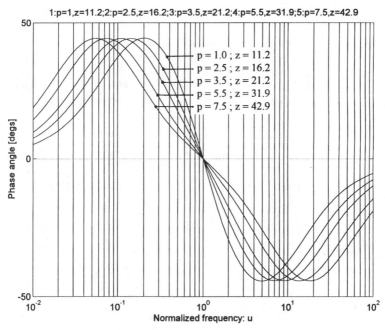

Figure C.5.4. Frequency response of a lead-lag-lag-lead control network for different parameters '*p*' and '*z*'. *Maximum Amplitude: 15 dB; Maximum Phase lead/lag : 44.3 deg.*

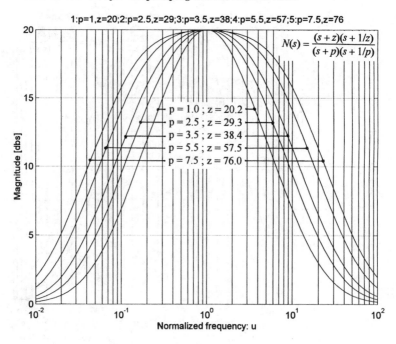

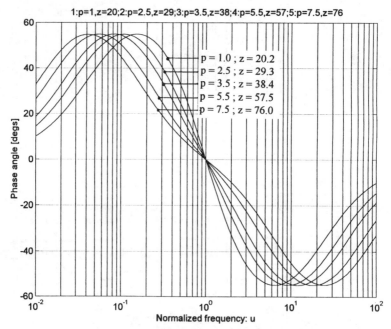

Figure C.5.5. Frequency response of a lead-lag-lag-lead control network for different parameters '*p*' and '*z*'. *Maximum Amplitude: 15 dB; Maximum Phase lead/lag : 55.2 deg.*

C.6. The Nichols chart.

When the one-degree-of-freedom unity-feedback configuration in Fig.C.6.1 is used, we wish to investigate the closed-loop magnitude and phase of $T(j\omega)$ in terms of the open-loop magnitude and phase of $L(j\omega)$ at each frequency. With $L(s) = P(s)\,G(s)$,

$$T(s) = L(s) / [1 + L(s)] \tag{C.6.1}$$

On the complex plane, $L = x + j\,y$, hence,

$$T = |T|e^{j\theta} = \frac{x + jy}{1 + x + jy}$$

from which it follows that

$$|T| = \frac{\sqrt{x^2 + y^2}}{\sqrt{(1 + x)^2 + y^2}} \tag{C.6.2}$$

The above equation can be rearranged as

$$\left(x - \frac{|T|^2}{1 - |T|^2}\right)^2 + y^2 = \left(\frac{|T|}{1 - |T|^2}\right)^2 \tag{C.6.3}$$

which is the equation of a circle of a constant gain $|T|$ on the complex plane (x, jv), centered at $x = |T|^2 /[1 - |T|^2]$, $y = 0$. The radius of the circle is equal to $|[|T| /(1 - |T|^2)]|$. These circles are not shown here because we are interested in designing on the logarithmic complex plane of $\ln L(j\omega) = \ln|L| + j \arg L$, the abscissa in degrees (open-loop phase of L) and the ordinate in decibels (the open-loop magnitude of L). On this plane Nichols has prepared contours of constant unity-feedback gains $|T|$. Such contours of constant $|T|$ are shown in Fig.C.6.2. Using the same procedure, contours of constant argument of T can be also calculated in terms of L. These are also displayed on the Nichols chart as dotted curves. As is discerned in the figure,

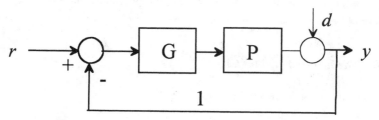

Figure C.6.1. A canonical unity-feedback system structure.

Nichols chart

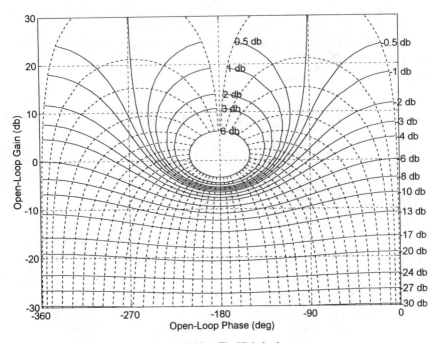

Figure C.6.2.   The Nichols chart

contours of positive constant gains in dB are closed, while contours of negative constant gains in dB are open. The open-loop gain axis of ln $|L|$ is on the left side of the figure. The numbers on the right side of the Nichols chart are the gains in dB of the contours of constant negative $|T|$ in dB.

The Nichols chart is very useful. When the gain and the phase of $L(j\omega)$ are known at some frequency ω, $L(j\omega)$ is located on the Nichols chart according to the open-loop axes $|L|$ dB and arg L in deg. The unity-feedback gain $|T(j\omega)|$ is directly found by reading the value of the constant gain contour passing through the location of $L(j\omega)$ at that frequency. The argument of $T(j\omega)$ is found by reading the value of the unity-feedback contour of constant phase passing through the location of $L(j\omega)$ at the same frequency.

C.7.   The Inverted Nichols Chart.

The sensitivity function is defined as

$$S(s) = 1/[1 + L(s)] \qquad\qquad (C.6.4)$$

We are also interested in graphically finding at each frequency the value of $S(j\omega)$ for a known value of $L(j\omega)$. This can be done by using the inverted Nichols chart. Let us define

$$l(s) = 1/L(s) \tag{C.6.5}$$

With Eq.(C.6.4) we get

$$S(s) = l(s)/[1 + l(s)] \tag{C.6.6}$$

which is the same as Eq.(C.6.1). However, for the newly defined $l(s)$, the interpretation of $l(s)$ is as follows.

$$\text{Set } L(j\omega) = |L(j\omega)|\, e^{j\theta(\omega)} \text{ and } l(j\omega) = |l(j\omega)|\, e^{j\psi(\omega)} \tag{C.6.7}$$

According to Eq.(C.6.5)

$$|l(j\omega)| = 1/|L(j\omega)| \text{ and } \psi(\omega) = \arg l(j\omega) = -\theta(\omega) = -\arg L(j\omega) \tag{C.6.8}$$

Eq.(C.6.6) is in the same form as Eq.(C.6.1) for which the unity-feedback constant gain contours have been plotted in Fig.C.6.2. However, since $l(j\omega) = 1/L(j\omega)$, this means that the gain $|l(j\omega)| = 1/|L(j\omega)|$, and arg $l(j\omega) = -\arg L(j\omega)$. Hence, the range $-360°$ to $0°$ of arg l becomes $+360°$ to $0°$ for arg L. Also, $|l|$ dB $= -|L|$ dB. The final conclusion is that the constant gain contours of $1/[1 + L(j\omega)]$ are the unity-feedback constant gain contours of $L(j\omega)/[1 + L(j\omega)]$, but rotated by $180°$ about the $[0\text{dB}, -180°]$ point. When performing this rotation, we get the constant gain contours of $|S|$ as in Fig.C.6.3, which shows contours for constant $|S| = 3, 1,$ $0.5, 0, -0.5, -3, -6, -12, -16$ and $-2\ 4$ dB. The constant phase contours of $S(j\omega)$ are not shown because generally there is no interest in them. To use the inverted Nichols chart, once the open-loop $L(j\omega)$ is located in the figure according to its magnitude in dB and to its argument, the unity-feedback value of $|S|$ in dB can be read at each frequency.

Example C.6.1. Suppose that an open-loop transmission function is designed, such that at $\omega = 5\text{rad/sec}$, $|L(j5)| = 10\text{dB}$ and arg $L(j5) = -45$ deg. Find the unity-feedback magnitude and phase of $T(j5)$ and the unity-feedback magnitude of $|S(j5)|$.

Solution: First, locate $L(j5)$ on the Nichols chart. From Figure C.6.2. we find that $|T(j5)| = -2$ dB, and arg $T(j5) = -30$ deg. Locating $L(j5)$ on the Inverted Nichols chart in Fig.C.6.3, we find that $|S(j5)| = -12$ dB.

Inverted Nichols chart

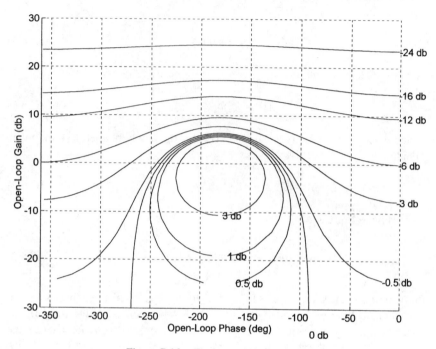

Figure C.6.3. The inverted Nichols chart

Appendix D

Facts about Fourier and Laplace Transforms

D.1   Introduction

Fourier and Laplace transforms are the most important tools in the analysis of linear time invariant systems. There are innumerable books and textbooks that treat these fundamental transforms. Just to mention a few, we have Carslaw and Jaeger (1941), Tichmarsh (1949), Churchill (1958), Cheng (1959), Solodovnikov (1960), Papoulis (1962), Popov (1962) and others.

The present appendix presents here some very useful relationships and formulas to be used in the book.

D.2   Definitions and some General Properties of Fourier Transforms

The *Fourier integral,* or *Fourier transform,* is a linear operator that transforms a function $f(t)$ in the time-domain, into a function $F(j\omega)$ in the frequency-domain:

$$F(j\omega) = \int_{-\infty}^{\infty} f(t)e^{j\omega t}dt \qquad (D.2.1)$$

$F(j\omega)$ is called the Fourier transform of the time function $f(t)$. For the transform to exist, $f(t)$ must be an *absolutely integrable function* that satisfies the condition

$$\int_{-\infty}^{\infty} |f(t)|dt < \infty$$

The *inverse Fourier transform* is defined by:

$$f(t) = \frac{1}{2\pi} \int_{-\infty}^{\infty} F(j\omega)e^{j\omega t} d\omega \tag{D.2.2}$$

The above equation is also called the *inversion integral,* which allows us to obtain $f(t)$ from the known $F(j\omega)$. Eqs.(D.2.1) and (D.2.2) form a Fourier transform pair.

It is well known that in linear dynamic systems, if the frequency characteristics of the linear system is $T(j\omega)$, then the Fourier transform of the output of the system $C(j\omega)$ to a known input $F(j\omega)$ is, (Solodovnikov 1960):

$$C(jw) = T(j\omega)F(j\omega) \tag{D.2.3}$$

Thus, to find the time response $c(t)$, we have to perform the inverse transformation:

$$c(t) = \frac{1}{2\pi} \int_{-\infty}^{\infty} T(j\omega)F(j\omega)e^{j\omega t} d\omega \tag{D.2.4}$$

$F(j\omega)$ is a complex function, so it can be written as:

$$F(j\omega) = R(\omega) + jX(\omega) = A(\omega)e^{j\emptyset(\omega)} \tag{D.2.5}$$

where $R(\omega)$ and $X(\omega)$ are the real and imaginary parts respectively of $F(j\omega)$, $A(\omega) = [R(\omega)^2 + X(\omega)^2]^{0.5}$ and $\emptyset(\omega) = \tan^{-1}[X(\omega)/R(\omega)]$.

Real time functions

For real time functions, which are of interest in engineering, we easily find from Eq.(D.2.1) that

$$R(\omega) = \int_{-\infty}^{\infty} f(t)\cos\omega t\, dt; \; X(\omega) = -\int_{-\infty}^{\infty} f(t)\sin\omega t\, dt \tag{D.2.6}$$

From Eq.(D.2.6) it is easily seen that $R(\omega)$ is even with respect to ω, while $X(\omega)$ is odd:

$$R(\omega) = R(-\omega); \; X(\omega) = -X(-\omega) \tag{D.2.7}$$

By Eqs. (D.2.2) and (D.2.6), a real time functions $f(t)$ can be expressed as:

$$f(t) = \frac{1}{2\pi} \int_{-\infty}^{\infty} [R(\omega)\cos\omega t - X(\omega)\sin\omega t]\, d\omega$$

$$= \frac{1}{\pi} \int_{0}^{\infty} [R(\omega)\cos\omega t - X(\omega)\sin\omega t]\, d\omega \tag{D.2.8}$$

Causal time functions

An important class of time functions is the class of causal time functions $f(t)$, for which:

$$f(t) = 0; \quad t < 0 \qquad (D.2.9)$$

For this class of functions, so important from a practical engineering point of view, it can be concluded that the inversion integral can be simplified to, (Papoulis 1962):

$$f(t) = \frac{2}{\pi} \int\limits_0^\infty R(\omega)\cos \omega t \, d\omega = -\frac{2}{\pi} \int\limits_0^\infty X(\omega)\sin \omega t \, d\omega; \quad t > 0 \qquad (D.2.10)$$

By definition, Eq.(D.2.10) is valid for $t > 0$.

We note here that for this class of functions, $f(t)$ can be obtained solely from the real part or from the imaginary part of its Fourier transform $F(j\omega)$. This important property is used in Chapter 3 to derive, by graphical means, the time response of a function whose real part of $F(j\omega)$ in the frequency-domain is known.

D.3. Definitions and some General Properties of Laplace Transforms

If a function $f(t)$ is defined for all positive values of the variable t, then the Laplace transformation of $f(t)$ is defined as

$$\mathscr{L}\{f(t)\} = F(s) = \int\limits_0^\infty e^{-st} f(t)dt \qquad (D.3.1)$$

where $\mathscr{L}$ is the Laplace transform linear operator. The function $F(s)$ is called the *Laplace transform* of $f(t)$. The *Laplace variable* s is a complex number, generally defined as $s = \sigma + j\omega$. σ should be large enough to make the integral in Eq.(D.3.1) converge. We actually require absolute convergence such that

$$\lim_{T\to\infty} \int\limits_0^T |f(t)|e^{-\sigma t}\, dt < \infty$$

When this convergence exists, we say that the function $f(t)$ is *Laplace transformable*.

Another important relation is the *inverse Laplace transform*, defined as

$$f(t) = \frac{1}{2\pi j} \int\limits_{\sigma - j\omega}^{\sigma + j\omega} F(s)e^{st}ds \qquad (D.3.2)$$

Eqs.(D.3.1) and (D.3.2) form a *Laplace transform pair*.
As an example, let us obtain the Laplace transform of $f(t) = e^{at}$. By Eq.(D.3.1)

$$F(s) = \int_0^\infty e^{at}e^{-st}dt = \left.\frac{1}{a-s}e^{-(s-a)t}\right|_0^\infty$$

hence, as $s > a$,

$$\mathcal{L}\{e^{at}\} = 1/(s\text{-}a)$$

Laplace transform pairs of different time functions are easily obtained and tables of these pairs can be found in most textbooks and handbooks on linear systems and automatic control. A short table of commonly used pairs follows.

Table *D*.3.1. Table of common Laplace transform pairs

	$f(t)$ $(t > 0)$	$F(s) = \mathcal{L}\{f(t)\}$
1	$U(t)$	$1/s$
2	e^{-at}	$1/(s + a)$
3	$\sin \omega t$	$\omega/(s^2 + \omega^2)$
4	$e^{-at}\sin bt$	$b/[(s + a)^2 + b^2]$
5	$(1 - at)\,e^{-at}$	$s/(s + a)^2$
6	$[(b - a)t + 1]\,e^{-at}$	$(s + b)/(s + a)^2$
7	$[(c - a)e^{-at} - (c - b)e^{-bt}]/(b - a)$	$(s + c)/[(s + a)(s + b)]$
8	$\cos \omega t$	$s/(s^2 + \omega^2)$
9	$[1+(c - a)^2/b^2]^{1/2}\,e^{-at}\sin(bt + \psi)$, $\psi = \tan^{-1}[b/(c - a)]$	$(s + c)/[(s + a)^2 + b^2]$
10	$[1 - \cos(at)]/a^2$	$1/[s(s^2 + a^2)]$
11	$[at - \sin(at)]/a^3$	$1/[s^2(s^2 + a^2)]$
12	$t^2/2$	$1/s^3$
13	$t^2 e^{-at}/2$	$1/(s + a)^3$
14	$[1 - (1 + at)e^{-at}]/a^2$	$1/[s(s + a)^2]$
15	$[1 + (be^{-at} - ae^{-bt})/(a - b)]/(ab)$	$1/[s(s + a)(s+b)]$
16	$[e^{-at} + at - 1]/a^2$	$1/[s^2(s + a)]$
17	$(1 - \cos at)/a^2$	$1/[s(s^2 + a^2)]$
18	$1/(a^2 + b^2)+[e^{-at}\sin(bt - \psi)]/[b(a^2 + b^2)^{1/2}]$ $\psi = \tan^{-1}(b/-a)$	$1/\{s[(s + a)^2+b^2]\}$
19	$te^{-at}[1 + (b - a)t/2]$	$(s + b)/(s + a)^3$
20	$b/a^2 + e^{-at}[(1 - b/a)t - b/a^2]$	$(s + b)/[s(s + a)^2]$
21	$e^{-at}[1 + (b - 2a)t+(a^2 - ab + c)t^2/2]$	$(s^2 + bs + c)/(s + a)^3$

D.4. Solution of Linear Differential Equations

An important use of Laplace transforms is the solution of ordinary linear differential equations. This property is gained due to the differentiation and integration theorems:

Differentiation theorem. If a function $f(t)$ and its derivative are both Laplace transformable and if $\mathcal{L}\{f(t)\} = F(s)$, then

$$\mathcal{L}\left[\frac{df(t)}{dt}\right] = sF(s) - f(0_+) \tag{D.4.1}$$

where $f(0_+)$ is the initial value of $f(t)$ at $t = 0_+$.
For the general case of the nth differentiation, the following equality holds,

$$\mathcal{L}\left[\frac{d^n f(t)}{dt^n}\right] = s^n F(s) - s^{n-1}f(0_+) - s^{n-2}f(0_+) - \ldots - sf^{(n-2)}(0_+) - f^{(n-1)}(0_+)$$

$$= s^n F(s) - \sum_{k=1}^{n} s^{n-k} f^{(k-1)}(0_+) \tag{D.4.2}$$

Integration theorem. If $\mathcal{L}f(t) = F(s)$, then

$$\mathcal{L}\left[\int f(t)dt\right] = \frac{F(s)}{s} + \frac{f^{(-1)}(0_+)}{s} \tag{D.4.3}$$

The above definitions and properties of Laplace transforms can be applied to solving linear time invariant ordinary differential equations. The basic idea is to transform the differential equation into an algebraic equation in the Laplace variable s. An example follows.

Example D.4.1. Let us solve the second-order differential equation with known initial conditions and input function $e(t)$:

$$\frac{d^2 f}{dt^2} + b_1 \frac{df}{dt} + b_0 f(t) = e(t)$$

Solution: Let us apply Laplace transformation to both sides of this equation by use of Eq.(D.4.2),

$$s^2 F(s) - sf(0_+) - f'(0_+) + b_1 s F(s) - b_1 f(0_+) + b_0 F(s) = E(s)$$

from which it follows that

$$F(s) = \frac{E(s) + sf(0_+) + f'(0_+) + b_1 f(0_+)}{s^2 + b_1 s + b_0}$$

The solution $f(t)$ of the differential equation is obtained by taking the inverse Laplace transform of $F(s)$. It is very important to observe that we have obtained simultaneously the solutions for both the initial conditions and the excitation signal $e(t)$.

With the initial conditions nullified, we have

$$\frac{F(s)}{E(s)} = T(s) = \frac{1}{s^2 + b_1 s + b_0}$$

which is generally called *the transfer function*, very frequently used in control theory, and in engineering in general. For a known excitation function $e(t)$ having a Laplace transform $E(s)$, $f(t)$ can be obtained by taking the inverse Laplace transform of

$$F(s) = T(s)E(s) = \frac{E(s)}{s^2 + b_1 s + b_0}$$

For instance, if $e(t) = U(t)$, a unity step function beginning at $t = 0$, then

$$F(s) = \frac{1}{s(s^2 + b_1 s + b_0)}$$

and $f(t)$ is obtained by direct use of Table D.3.1, entry No.18.

In a differential equation of a higher order n, the denominator of the transfer function is a polynomial of order n whose inverse transform generally cannot be found in existing tables of Laplace transform pairs. In these cases, the roots of the numerator and the denominator of the transfer function $T(s)$ must be initially found so that it can be expressed in the general form

$$T(s) = \frac{a_m s^m + b_{m-1} s^{m-1} + \ldots + b_1 s + b_0}{a_n s^n + a_{n-1} s^{n-1} + \ldots + a_1 s + a_0} = \frac{\prod_{i=1}^{m} (s - z_i)}{\prod_{j=1}^{n} (s - p_j)}. \tag{D.4.4}$$

z_i are called the zeros of the transfer function $T(s)$. p_j are called the poles of $T(s)$. In order to find the inverse Laplace transform of $T(s)$ from existing tables, it is necessary to expand it in simpler terms such as $T(s) = \sum_{l=1}^{n} \frac{k_l}{(s - s_l)}$. This decomposition is known as Heaviside's expansion (See, for instance, Cheng 1959, or D'Azzo and Houpis 1988). The inverse Laplace transform for these simpler terms can be found in standard tables of Laplace transform pairs.

D.5. Initial and Final Value Theorems

Frequently, it is desirable to be able to determine the initial or the final values of the time response function $f(t)$ from the known $F(s)$ without solving for the complete time response. This can be done by using the following theorems.

Initial-Value Theorem. If $f(t)$ and its first derivative are Laplace transformable, then the initial value of $f(t)$ is

$$f(0_+) = \lim_{t \to 0_+} f(t) = \lim_{s \to \infty} sF(s) \qquad (D.5.1)$$

Final-Value Theorem. If $f(t)$ and its first derivative are Laplace transformable, then the final value of $f(t)$ is

$$\lim_{t \to \infty} f(t) = \lim_{s \to 0} sF(s) \qquad (D.5.2)$$

Example: if $F(s) = 2(s+3)/[s(s+6)]$, find the initial and final values of $f(t)$.

Solution: By Eq.(D.5.1) $f(0_+) = 2$; by Eq.(D.5.2), $f(\infty) = 1$.

D.6. Time Convolution Theorem

The time convolution theorem is of utmost importance in the analysis of linear systems. It permits the easy derivation of many important results in linear system theory. It is defined in the following way: If $f_1(t)$, $f_2(t)$, and their respective Laplace transforms $F_1(s)$ and $F_2(s)$ are known, then $F_1(s)F_2(s)$ is the transform of the time convolution $f_1(t)* f_2(t)$, defined as each one of the integral operations in the following equation:

$$F(s) = F_1(s)F_2(s) = \mathscr{L} \int_0^t f_1(\tau)f_2(t - \tau)d\tau = \mathscr{L} \int_0^t f_1(t - \tau)f_2(\tau)d\tau \qquad (D.6.1)$$

This equality holds only if $f_1(t)$ and $f_2(t)$ have finite energy, which means

$$\int_{-\infty}^{\infty} |f_i(t)|^2 dt < \infty; \; i = 1,2$$

D.7 Frequency Convolution Theorem

The frequency convolution theorem states as follows: The Fourier transform $F(\omega)$ of the product $f_1(t)f_2(t)$ of two time functions equals the convolution $F_1(\omega)*F_2(\omega)$ of their respective transforms $F_1(\omega)$ and $F_2(\omega)$ divided by 2π (See Papoulis 1962),

$$f_1(t)f_2(t) \Leftrightarrow \frac{1}{2\pi} \int_{-\infty}^{\infty} F_1(x)F_2(\omega - x)dx \tag{D.7.1}$$

D.8 Parceval's Formula

A very important relation between the square of time-domain and frequency-domain functions follows:

If $F(j\omega) = A(\omega)e^{j\varnothing(\omega)}$ is the Fourier transform of $f(t)$, then

$$\int_{-\infty}^{\infty} |f(t)|^2 dt = \frac{1}{2\pi} \int_{-\infty}^{\infty} A^2(\omega)d\omega \tag{D.8.1}$$

_____

The Bode Formulae and Transform Relations

E.1 Introduction

Feedback control theory deals with analytic functions $F(s)$ in the 's' domain, $s = \sigma + j\omega$. $F(s)$ can be functions describing the dynamic behaviour of linear process, usually called *plants,* or they might stand for the open or closed-loop transmission functions in feedback systems. In fact, all control theories in the s-domain are based on these kind of functions. When treated in the practical frequency domain, a value of the function in the complex plane corresponds to each value of s. If we put $s = j\omega$, then, $F(j\omega) = A(\omega) + j\,B(\omega)$. The real and imaginary parts of $F(j\omega)$, which are $A(\omega)$ and $B(\omega)$ respectively, play an important part in the analysis of linear systems. Moreover, there are some very important relationships between the real and the imaginary parts of such functions, these relationships have a strong impact on feedback design philosophy from a practical point of view, such as maximum achievable bandwidth etc.

The present appendix intends to summarize some important results concerning restrictions on real and imaginary parts of analytic functions used in control theory as well as some of the relations between them.

The material follows closely the very fundamental work of Bode (1945). Use is also made of the works of Guillemin (1949), Seshu and Balabanian (1959) and Horowitz (1963). Proofs are omitted in this context.

E.2. Preliminary Definitions and Facts

Lumped, linear, time invariant physical systems are described mathematically in the s-domain by rational functions with real coefficients. Since sums, products, subtraction's and quotients of rational functions are also rational functions, it follows that forming a complete system by several sub-systems leads to a system that is represented by a rational function. This is indeed a fortunate situation, because real rational functions are analytical. Transfer functions, loop transmission functions and so on are rational functions which can be represented in the following form

$$F(s) = \frac{a_m s^m + a_{m-1} s^{m-1} + \ldots + a_1 s + a_0}{b_n s^n + b_{n-1} s^{n-1} + \ldots + b_1 s + b_0}. \tag{E.2.1}$$

The coefficients in the numerator and the denominator of the rational functions of physical systems are all real numbers. By observing the rational function in Eq.(E.2.1) it is easily deduced that all transmission functions are real on the real axis in the s-plane. If a function of a complex variable is real on the real axis, it is called a *real function*. Thus, all transfer functions and loop-transmission function used intensively in analysis and design of feedback systems are *real rational functions*. This leads immediately to the known identity

$$F(s^*) = F^*(s) \tag{E.2.2}$$

which determines that transmission functions will assume conjugate values at conjugate points in the s-complex plane. Transmission functions will take on complex values for complex values of s.

However, we are seldom interested in calculating the transmission functions at each s. We are rather interested in the behavior of the transmission functions on the $j\omega$ axis. We are generally interested in the real part, imaginary part, magnitude, or its logarithm, and the phase for purely imaginary values of s. Each one of these is referred to as *frequency response function* in ω,

$$F(s)|_{s=j\omega} = F(j\omega) = A(\omega) + jB(\omega) = |F(j\omega)|e^{j\emptyset(\omega)} \tag{E.2.3}$$

An important additional approach in representing physical transmission functions is to take the natural logarithm of $F(j\omega)$, namely,

$$\ln F(j\omega) = \ln|F(j\omega)| + j\emptyset(\omega) = A(\omega) + jB(\omega) \tag{E.2.4}$$

where $A(\omega)$ is the attenuation function in Neper, $B(\omega)$ is the phase function in radians. In practical use of attenuation functions, it is common to use *decibel* (dB) units. If so, the gain in Neper is transformed to gain in dB by multiplying $\ln|F(j\omega)|$ by the factor 8.686.

From Eqs.(E.2.1) and (E.2.4) it also follows that for real frequencies, $s = j\omega$, the real part $A(\omega)$ of $F(j\omega)$ is an even function in ω, and the imaginary part $B(\omega)$ is an odd function in ω.

Having represented any transmission function either by its real and imaginary parts, or by its magnitude and phase functions, we next wish to proceed further and find some general important restrictions on the above functions. We are also interested in finding relations between them.

E.3.   Some Restrictions on Physical Transmission Functions at Real Frequencies.

E3.1.   Cauchy's Integral Theorems.

The material in this section is based heavily on Cauchy's integral theorems. Two important theorems are used extensively in this appendix.

Theorem E.3.1:   If a function $F(s)$ is analytic within a closed curve and also on the curve itself, the integral of $F(s)$ taken around that curve is equal to zero.

For our purposes, the closed curve will encompass the closed RHP of the Laplace variable s. In order to keep the analyticity of the function on this curve, poles located on the $j\omega$ axis are indented by small semicircles in order to prevent any singularity in the integrand. See Figure E.3.1.

Another important theorem to be used in this appendix is Cauchy's Residue Theorem that states:

Theorem E.3.2:   If a function $F(s)$ is single valued and analytic within a closed curve and also on the curve itself, except for poles of any finite number and mul-

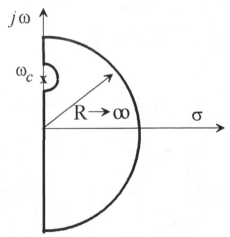

Figure E.3.1.   A closed path in the s-plane enclosing the RHP, and indentation of a pole located on the imaginary axis.

tiplicity, then the integral of $F(s)$ taken around that curve is related to the residues of those poles of $F(s)$ located inside the region as follows

$$\oint F(s)ds = 2\pi j \sum residues. \qquad \text{(E.3.1)}$$

Both theorems cited here will be used to obtain some important restrictions on analytic functions used in automatic control theory. They will be used as well to derive basic relations between the real and the imaginary parts of transfer functions, so that when one of them is given, the other one can be calculated as well.

Some analytic conditions to be defined next are necessary prior to using these basic theorems. In terms of Bode's terminology, define the functions of interest by $F(\omega) = A(\omega) + jB(\omega)$, with $F(\omega)$ satisfying the following conditions:

1. The real part $A(\omega)$ is an even function of frequency.
2. The imaginary part $B(\omega)$ is an odd function of frequency.
3. There are no singularities in the interior of the RHP.
4. Singularities on the imaginary axis at finite points (for instance at $s = j\omega_1$) are such that $(s - j\omega_1)F(\omega)$ vanishes as s approaches $j\omega_1$. This admits branch points as well as logarithmic singularities, but means that no poles on the imaginary axis are allowed.
5. $F(s)$ is assumed to be analytic at infinite frequencies, as well as at the origin. In this case, it can be defined at these frequencies in the following power series expansions:

The expansion of $F(s)$ at the origin is:

$$F(s) = A_0 + B_0' s + A_0'' s^2 + B_0''' s^3 + \ldots \qquad \text{(E.3.2)}$$

The expansion of $F(s)$ at infinity is:

$$F(s) = A_\infty + B_\infty'/s + A_\infty''/s^2 + B_\infty'''/s^3 + \ldots \qquad \text{(E.3.3)}$$

Knowledge of the behavior of $F(s)$ at the origin and at infinity allows us to obtain some very important relations and restrictions on physical transmission functions.

E3.2   Integral of the Sensitivity Function

First, let us obtain a relation between the real part of the frequency area of $F(j\omega)$ defined previously, and the behavior of $F(s)$ at infinity. We apply Cauchy's Theorem E.3.2 on $F(s) - F(\infty)$ over the s-variable right-half-plane whose boundary consists of the $j\omega$ axis, and of the right half semicircle with infinite radius, so that

$$\oint [F(s) - A_\infty]ds = 0 \qquad \text{(E.3.4)}$$

By taking into consideration that $A(\omega)$ is even, $(A(\omega) = A(-\omega))$, and that $B(\omega)$ is odd, $(B(\omega) = -B(-\omega))$, it is easily shown that after integration of Eq.(E.3.4) we obtain the important result

$$\int_0^\infty [A(\omega) - A_\infty] \, d\omega = \frac{\pi}{2} B'_\infty \tag{E.3.5}$$

The interpretation of this result is as follows: If the analytical function drops off as a higher power than the first, then $B'_\infty = 0$, and the right side of the above equation vanishes. The above results lead to a very important theorem which Bode (1945) phrased as:

Theorem E.3.3: In a single-loop feedback amplifier of more than one stage, the average regeneration or degeneration over the complete frequency spectrum is zero.

This theorem was primarily used in feedback amplifier design. But, its meaning is exactly the same when used in the design of feedback control systems. In this context, it is illuminating to illustrate it in the following way:

Let us define the function $F(s) = \ln [1 + L(s)]$, where $[1 + L(s)]$ is the return difference in feedback systems, as defined in Chapter 2. It is assumed that $L(s)$ has no RHP poles, and the roots of the numerator of $[1 + L(s)]$ are stable, i.e. that there are no zeroes of $[1 + L(s)]$ in the RHP. Also, we admit that $L(s)$ goes to zero as s approaches infinity, which is always true in any practical system, since the number of poles outnumbers the number of zeros in such systems, at least by $e \geq 2$ as $L(s) \to 1/s^e$ at high frequencies. For such functions, according to Eqs.(E.3.2) and (E.3.3), $A_\infty = B'_\infty = 0$. After applying the result of EQ.(E.3.5), we get

$$\int_0^\infty A(\omega) d\omega = \int_0^\infty \ln|1 + L(j\omega)| \, d\omega = 0 \tag{E.3.6}$$

The meaning of the result is very simple: in almost all feedback systems, ($e \geq 2$), the net feedback area is zero. This means that if in the frequency band in which $|1 + L(j\omega)| \geq 1$ a positive definite area under the integrand of the sensitivity function $\ln|1 + L(j\omega)|$ is obtained, then there must be an equal area with negative sign of $\ln|1 + L(j\omega)|$ spread over the rest of the frequency range. Fortunately, the area with negative sign can be spread over a much larger frequency band, while the positive area is concentrated in the useful frequency band to achieve an adequate sensitivity reduction. (Remember that the sensitivity function was defined by Bode as

$S_k^T = \dfrac{d \, lnT}{d \, lnk} = \dfrac{dT/T}{dk/k} = \dfrac{1}{1 + L(s)}.$ With this definition, the larger $|1 + L(j\omega)|$ is,

the smaller the sensitivity function S_k^T is.

E3.3. Phase Integral

Another important result, known as the *phase integral,* can be obtained from Eq.(E.3.5). $F(j\omega)$ is first manipulated so that it becomes a manageable integrand at high frequencies, namely $F(j\omega)/\omega$. After subtracting A_∞ from $F(j\omega)$, we perform the integration:

$$\oint \frac{F(j\omega)}{\omega}\, d\omega = 0 \tag{E.3.7}$$

where the path of integration encloses the entire RHP in the s-plane. The final result is

$$\int_{-\infty}^{\infty} B\, du = \frac{\pi}{2}\, (A\infty - A_0) \tag{E.3.8}$$

where $du = d(\log \omega)$ stands for $d\omega/\omega$. Here the integration is taken on a logarithmic frequency scale. The importance of Eq.(E.3.8) is best illustrated by Fig.E.3.2. The behaviors of three real characteristics named 1 to 3 are shown in Fig.E.3.2a. they have the same initial and final values A_0 and A_∞. An imaginary characteristic, shown in Fig.E.3.2.b, corresponds to each real characteristic. The areas under each imaginary characteristic are equal on a logarithmic frequency scale. The practical importance of these results is that by achieving a finite change in gain in any loop transmission, an inevitable finite integral change in the phase of the loop transmission can be anticipated. The phase area shall be proportional A_0-A_∞. In other words, there is no way to obtain, for instance, a finite phase-lead needed in the loopshaping stage of a loop transmission, without at the same time changing adversely its gain function, and vice versa.

Additional relations of contour integral formulas can be found in Bode (1945).

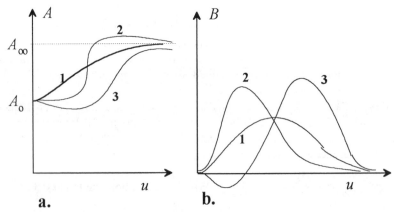

Figure E.3.2. Graphical illustration of Eq.(E.3.8).

E.4.　Formulas Relating the Real and Imaginary Parts of Transmission Functions

Basically, knowing one part of a transmission function (real or imaginary) on the entire frequency spectrum permits us to calculate the other part (imaginary or real) also on the entire frequency spectrum. In engineering terms, if the gain function is completely known for the entire frequency spectrum, the phase of this function can be exactly calculated at all frequencies, and vice versa.

Another important problem arises when the real part is prescribed in some bands of the frequency spectrum, and the imaginary part is prescribed in the remaining frequency bands. In such cases, the missing characteristics of the real and imaginary parts can be calculated in their related frequency bands. The practical importance of this problem lies in the fact that the real and the imaginary parts of an analytical transmission function are not independent. There is no way to manipulate independently its gain and phase characteristics.

It is important to remind the reader that the functions treated in this appendix are of minimum-phase nature. In very general terms, a minimum-phase function is characterized by the property that for a given attenuation characteristic, its phase is minimal. Transfer functions containing right-half-plane poles and zeros are not minimum-phase for this reason.

Some important relations between real and imaginary parts of practical nature in feedback system design will be stated in the remaining part of this appendix. Most of the results are obtained by an extension of Eq.(E.3.4) and (E.3.7). (See Bode 1945 and Horowitz 1963).

E.4.1.　Phase Characteristic Corresponding to a Prescribed Attenuation Characteristic.

The solution to this problem is obtained by first creating a pole at the frequency at which the correlation between the real and the imaginary (attenuation and phase) parts are to be calculated. The contour used to derive the relations is shown in Fig.E.3.1. We apply the residue theorem

$$\oint \frac{F(s)}{s - j\omega_x} \, ds = 0 \tag{E.4.1}$$

and perform the integration on the contour shown in Fig.E.3.1. After integration we obtain the important result

$$B(\omega_c) = \frac{j2\omega_c}{\pi} \int_0^\infty \frac{A(\omega) - A(\omega_c)}{\omega^2 - \omega_c^2} \, d\omega \tag{E.4.2}$$

In the above equation, ω_c is the frequency at which the phase (imaginary part) is sought, knowing the attenuation characteristic (real part) in the entire frequency spectrum. Note that in the above equation $A(\omega_c)$ can be removed at will

since $A(\omega_c) \int_0^\infty \dfrac{d\omega}{\omega^2 - \omega_c^2} = 0$. The practical meaning is that the constant gain of

an attenuation function can be changed at will without disturbing the phase characteristics. This is a well-known fact to all control engineers.

Eq.(E.4.2) is a basic relation, but some of its variations can be also useful in certain conditions. For instance, there is an alternative to writing the above equation on a logarithmic frequency scale. By using the definition $u = \log(\omega/\omega_c)$, the expression in Eq.(E.4.2) becomes

$$B(\omega_c) = \frac{1}{\pi} \int_{-\infty}^{\infty} \frac{dA}{du} \log \coth \frac{|u|}{2} \, du. \tag{E.4.3}$$

It is important to look at the graphical nature of $\log \coth |u/2|$, as shown in Fig.E.4.1.
From Eq.(E.4.3) we see clearly that the phase argument is proportional to the derivative of the attenuation function dA/du on a logarithmic frequency scale. However, as per Fig.E.4.1, the relative importance of the derivative increases as $\omega/\omega_c \to 1$; $\log[\coth|u/2|]$ is a weighting factor.

Use of Eq.(E.4.3) allows us to find relations between the phase characteristics and different attenuation characteristics. Some of these relations are summarized next.

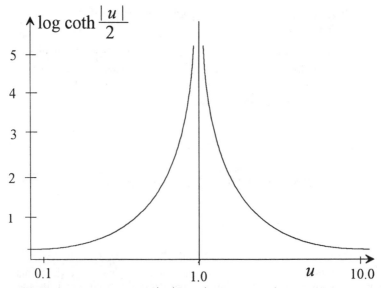

Figure E.4.1.   Plot of $\log \coth |u/2| = \log |(\omega+\omega_c)/(\omega-\omega_c)|$ versus $\log(\omega/\omega_c)$.

Phase characteristic corresponding to constant slope attenuation characteristic

Let us suppose a constant slope attenuation characteristic, $dA/du = k$. In this case Eq.(E.4.3) reduces to

$$B(\omega_c) = \frac{k}{\pi} \int_{-\infty}^{\infty} \log \coth \frac{|u|}{2} \, du = k \frac{\pi}{2} \tag{E.4.4}$$

The meaning of this equation is that the phase characteristic is constant for a constant slope attenuation characteristic. This is shown in Fig.E.4.2.

Eq.(E.4.4) shows that for a *unit slope* of the attenuation function $A(\omega)$, the phase characteristic will be also constant, and equal to $B(\omega) = \pi/2$ rad. When u is the natural logarithm, A is in Neper units. When designing feedback systems in practice, we prefer to use the dB units. Within this unit scale, a unit slope is the same as 20 dB/decade or 6 dB/octave. The unit slope characteristics reminds of an 'integration' in the s-domain. In various theoretical applications, we use attenuation characteristics having slopes of non integer values.

The semi-infinite constant slope characteristics

Another characteristic of practical importance is the semi-infinite constant slope shown in Fig.E.4.3. For this attenuation characteristic, the slope is null in the low frequency range, and becomes constant in the remaining part of the frequency spectrum. The phase characteristics tend to be very low at very low frequencies, where the attenuation slope is null. However, at the very high frequency range, where the slope is constant, the phase characteristic reaches a constant value, for instance, a value of $\pi/2$ radians for the unity slope. For a slope of k units, the phase will reach its final value of $k\pi/2$ radians.

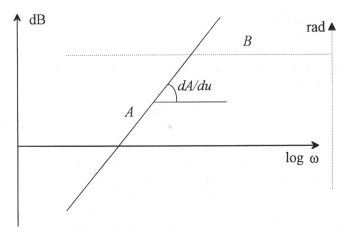

Figure E.4.2.   Constant slope attenuation characteristics

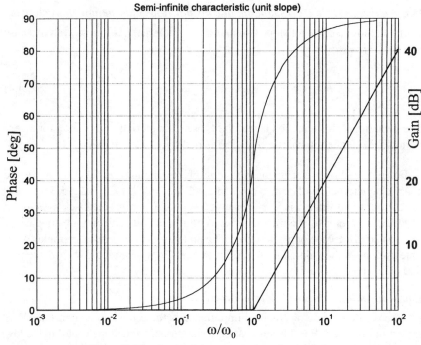

Figure E.4.3. Semi-infinite constant slope characteristic.

Note that the phase characteristic is in a way symmetric on a logarithmic scale about the $\omega/\omega_o = 1$ point.

E.4.2. Attenuation Characteristic Corresponding to a Prescribed Phase Characteristic

By use of Eq.(E.4.1), we can also obtain the attenuation characteristic when the phase characteristic is given

$$A(\omega_c) - A_\infty = -\frac{2}{\pi} \int_0^\infty \frac{\omega B(\omega)}{\omega^2 - \omega_c^2} \, d\omega \qquad (E.4.5)$$

Eq.(E.4.5) is the basic relation, but some variations can be also useful in different situations. For instance, we may express it in logarithmic scale in the frequency ω.

$$A(\omega_c) - A_\infty = -\frac{1}{\pi\omega_c} \int_{-\infty}^\infty \frac{d(\omega B)}{du} \log \coth \frac{|u|}{2} \, du \qquad (E.4.6)$$

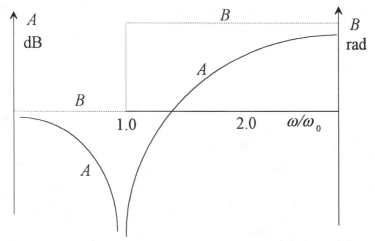

Figure E.4.4.   Attenuation characteristic related to an abrupt phase characteristic

Abrupt step change in phase characteristic

It is interesting to plot the attenuation characteristic A versus an abrupt step change in the phase characteristic B on a normalized linear frequency axis ω/ω_o. These relations are sketched in Fig.E.4.4. In this case, too, the final slope of $A(\omega)$ will be proportional to the level of the phase characteristic $B(\omega)$.

Another important phase-attenuation relation is sketched in Fig.E.4.5.

Finite line phase segment.

The finite-line phase segment is very useful in practical derivations of optimal loop transmission functions (Bode 1945). This $B(\omega)$ segment is shown in Fig.E.4.6, in

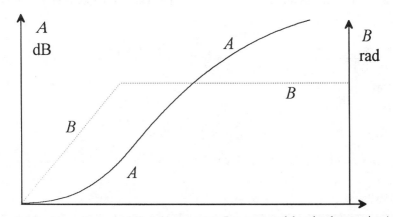

Figure E.4.5.   Linear B segment followed by a constant B segment, and the related attenuation A

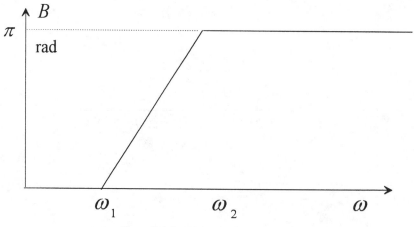

Figure E.4.6.   Finite-line phase segment.

which the β factors are defined as $\beta = \omega_2/\omega_1$ on a linear frequency axis. The related attenuation characteristic $A(\omega)$ is shown in Fig.E.4.7 on logarithmic frequency scale for different β factors.

The above relations between attenuation and phase characteristics are used in the derivation of the Ideal Bode Characteristic.

E.5.   *A* and *B* prescribed in Different Frequency Ranges.

The analytical solution of this problem can be carried out by dividing $F(j\omega)$ by $[1-\omega^2/\omega_o^2]^{0.5}$ to obtain

$$\frac{F(\omega)}{\sqrt{1 - \omega^2/\omega_o^2}} = \frac{A(\omega)}{\sqrt{1 - \omega^2/\omega_o^2}} + j\,\frac{B(\omega)}{\sqrt{1 - \omega^2/\omega_o^2}}\,;\,\omega < \omega_o \qquad \text{(E.5.1)}$$

$$= \frac{B}{\sqrt{\omega^2/\omega_0^2 - 1}} - j\,\frac{A}{\sqrt{\omega^2/\omega_0^2 - 1}}\,;\,\omega > \omega_o$$

By integrating Eq.(E.4.2) into the two frequency ranges, we get

$$\frac{2\omega_c}{\pi} \int_0^{\omega_0} \frac{A}{\sqrt{1-\omega^2/\omega_0^2}} \frac{d\omega}{\omega^2 - \omega_c^2} + \frac{2\omega_c}{\pi} \int_{\omega_0}^{\infty} \frac{B}{\sqrt{\omega^2/\omega_0^2-1}} \frac{d\omega}{\omega^2 - \omega_c^2}$$

$$= \frac{B_c}{\sqrt{1 - \omega_c^2/\omega_0^2}}; \; \omega_c < \omega_0$$

$$= \frac{-A_c}{\sqrt{\omega_c^2/\omega_0^2 - 1}}; \; \omega_c > \omega_0 \qquad \text{(E.5.2)}$$

The above equation is exemplified with the following characteristic function. Let us suppose that $B(\omega) = a\omega_0$ in the frequency range $\omega/\omega_0 < 1$ and $A(\omega) = K$ in the range $\omega/\omega_0 > 1$, as shown in Fig.E.5.1. The problem is to derive the missing B and A in their respective ranges. This can be done by using Eq.(E.5.2). After solving this integral for B we get

$$B(\omega_c) = a\omega_0 \left(\frac{\omega}{\omega_0} - \sqrt{\frac{\omega_c^2}{\omega_0^2} - 1} \right) \qquad \text{(E.5.3)}$$

and also

$$A(\omega_c) = K - a\omega_0 \sqrt{1 - \frac{\omega_c^2}{\omega_0^2}} \qquad \text{(E.5.4)}$$

Thus, the $A(\omega)$ and $B(\omega)$ functions are derived for the entire frequency spectrum. Generally, the A function can be specified in more than 3 frequency regions, and B in the remaining regions. Formulas permitting us to find the missing functions in the remaining regions were also obtained by Bode (1945).

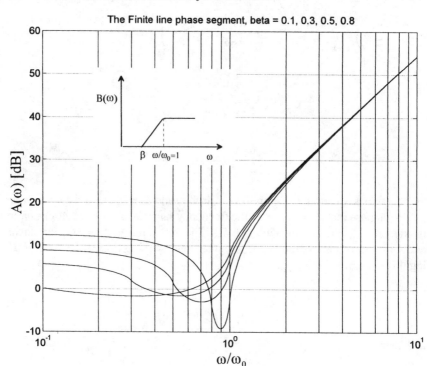

Figure E.4.7.   Attenuation characteristic $A(\omega)$ for the finite-line phase segment on logarithmic frequency scale.

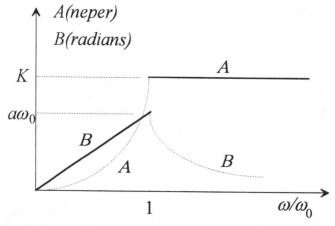

Figure E.5.1.   Phase and attenuation functions defined in different frequency ranges.

Appendix F

Order of Compensator
for Pole Placement

There is a vast literature dealing with pole placement techniques for stabilizing linear time invariant plants: Wonham (1967), Brasch and Pearson (1970), Jameson (1970) and others. The purpose of the present appendix is to clarify the notion of order regarding the compensating network necessary to stabilize a plant of given order by a straightforward pole placement design procedure used in this book.

Assume a plant $P(s)$ whose transfer function is proper or strictly proper at infinity and is of the order $n = \delta(P)$. Suppose also there are assigned q arbitrarily chosen stable poles to the closed-loop system. The compensator $G(s)$ that stabilizes the closed-loop feedback system by the pole placement procedure has the general form

$$G(s) = \frac{n_G(s)}{d_G(s)} = \frac{a_r s^r + a_{r-1} s^{r-1} + \ldots a_1}{s^m + b_{m-1} s^{m-1} + \ldots + b_0} \qquad (\text{F.1})$$

which is proper, if $r = m$, and strictly proper, if $r < m$. If $r = m$, then, the proper transfer function comprises at most $r + m$ free parameters which are $a_r, a_{r-1}, \ldots a_1, b_m, b_{m-1}, \ldots, b_0$. If $r < m$, then the strictly proper transfer function comprises at most $m + r - 1$ free parameters which are

$$a_{r-1}, \ldots a_1, b_m, b_{m-1}, \ldots, b_0.$$

A straightforward procedure to place q arbitrarily chosen poles within the SISO closed-loop feedback system is to equate the coefficients of the numerator polynomial of $1 + G(s)P(s)$ to the coefficients of the characteristic polynomial obtained from the assigned closed-loop poles.

Call $m = \delta(d_G)$—the polynomial order of the denominator, and r—the number of free parameters a_r of the numerator of $G(s)$. With these definitions, $q = n + m$ from which it follows that

$$m = q - n \tag{F.2}$$

Since the order of the characteristic polynomial of the closed loop is q, it follows that the number of free parameters provided by $G(s)$ must be $m + r = q$, or

$$r = q - m = n \tag{F.3}$$

Eqs.(F.1) and (F.3) fix the compensator's structure that provides the closed-loop system the arbitrarily assigned closed-loop poles.

Since for a dynamic compensator, $r \geq 1$ is a practical necessity, it follows by Eq.(F.3) that

$$q \geq n + 1 \tag{F.4}$$

and the closed-loop characteristic polynomial must be of an order at least by one higher than that of the plant (n), namely, $q = n + 1$. With this condition, it finally follows, by Eqs.(F.2) and (F.3) that

$$\begin{aligned} m &= q - n = n + 1 - n = 1 \text{ and} \\ r &= q - m = n. \end{aligned} \tag{F.5}$$

Example F.1.   Suppose that the order of the plant is $n = 3$, and $q = 5$ poles are to be assigned to the closed-loop system. Find the form of the compensator to be used.

Solution: By Eq.(F.2) $m = q - n = 2$ and by Eq.(F.3) $r = n = 3$, the compensator will have the form

$$G(s) = \frac{a_3 s^2 + a_2 s + a_1}{s^2 + b_2 s + b_1}$$

The five free parameters of $G(s)$ suffices to locate five arbitrarily chosen poles to the closed-loop system.

Appendix G _____

Steady-State Error Coefficients

G.1 Introduction

One of the important reasons for using feedback is its ability to decrease the steady-state error for different inputs to the system.

The time response of a feedback system to any input command consists of two important regions: A), the transient part of the output response; B), the steady-state part of the output response. For instance, the time response of a feedback system to a step command is shown in Fig.G.1.

The transient part of the output response is due to the dynamic properties of feedback system, the closed-loop frequency response, phase and gain margins of the loop transmission function, the frequency bandwidth and so on. These parameters are responsible for the rise time, damping coefficient, overshoot and undershoot of the response. The steady-state error of the output response depends only on the behaviour of the loop transmission function at $s \to 0$, as shown in the next sections.

G.2 The Steady-State Error Equation

Let us find the steady-state error equation of the unity-feedback system in Fig.G.2. $L(s)$ is the usual loop transmission function, consisting of both the plant $P(s)$, and the control network $G(s)$. We easily find that the error in the s-domain is:

$$E(s) = \frac{R(s)}{1 + L(s)} \tag{G.1}$$

in which $R(s)$ is the Laplace transform of the input signal to the unity-feedback structure, and $L(s) = P(s)G(s)$, where $L(s)$ is the loop transmission function, represented here as

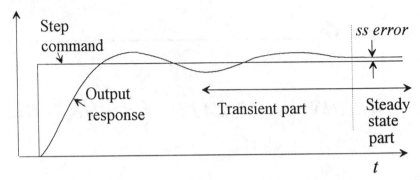

Figure G.1.   Transient and steady-state parts of the output response.

$$L(s) = K \frac{\prod\limits_{i=1}^{m} (s + z_i)}{s^I \prod\limits_{j=1}^{n} (s + p_j)}. \tag{G.2}$$

In the general case, $L(s)$ consists of m zeros, of n poles and of I integrators. We see that as the Laplace variable s approaches zero, the loop transmission $L(s)$ depends on I. I identifies the *type* of the system. If $I = 0$, the feedback system is type 0. If $I = 1$, the system is type 1, and so on.

The steady-state error in the time-domain is then:

$$\lim_{t \to \infty} e(t) = e_{ss} = \lim_{s \to 0} \frac{s R(s)}{1 + L(s)}. \tag{G.3}$$

It is of practical importance to determine the steady-state error for the three standard inputs commands: *step*, *velocity* and *acceleration*.

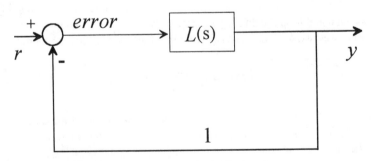

Figure G.2.   Canonical unity-feedback system.

Step input

If the amplitude of the step input is R_{ST}, $(R(s) = R_{ST}/s)$, then according to Eq.(G.3):

$$e_{ss} = \lim_{s \to 0} \frac{s(R_{ST}/s)}{1 + L(s)} = \frac{R_{ST}}{1 + \lim_{s \to 0} L(s)} = \frac{R_{ST}}{1 + L(0)}. \quad \text{(G.4)}$$

Clearly, the form and parameters of $L(s)$ will determine the steady-state error. For a *type zero* system, $I = 0$, $L(0)$ is finite, and the steady-state error is:

$$e_{ss} = \frac{R_{ST}}{1 + L(0)}. \quad \text{(G.5)}$$

For a higher type system, $I \geq 1$, we find that $\lim_{s \to 0} L(s) = L(0) = \infty$, so that, according to Eq.(G.4), the steady-state error is clearly zeroed.

The constant $L(0)$ is usually denoted by K_p, *the position error coefficient*. To be more precise

$$K_p = \lim_{s \to 0} L(s) \quad \text{(G.6)}$$

and Eq.(G.5) becomes

$$e_{ss} = \frac{R_{ST}}{1 + K_p}. \quad \text{(G.7)}$$

In a feedback system in which $I < 0$, which means that there is at least one differentiator in the loop transmission function, $K_p = 0$, and the steady-state-error approaches the step input amplitude.

Velocity input

The steady state error for a velocity input $r(t) = R_v \, t \, U(t)$ $(R(s) = R_v /s^2)$ is:

$$e_{ss} = \lim_{s \to 0} \frac{s(R_v/s^2)}{1 + L(s)} = \lim_{s \to 0} \frac{R_v}{s + sL(s)} = \lim_{s \to 0} \frac{R_v}{sL(s)} = \frac{R_v}{\lim_{s \to 0} sL(s)} = \frac{R_v}{K_v}. \quad \text{(G.8)}$$

Here we define the *velocity error coefficient* as :

$$K_v = \lim_{s \to 0} sL(s). \quad \text{(G.9)}$$

The steady-state error is proportional to the input velocity slope R_v and inversely proportional to the velocity error constant K_v.

Note that for velocity input, if the system is type 1, then K_v is finite, as is the steady-state error (Eq.(G.8)). For a zero type system, K_v is null, hence, the veloc-

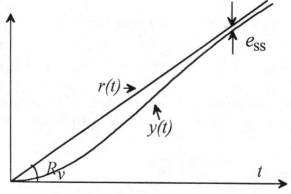

Figure G.3.   Steady-state error for a velocity input.

ity steady-state error tends to infinity. For a system in which $I \geq 2$, K_v becomes infinite, hence the steady-state error is nullified.

Acceleration input

When the system input is $r(t) = R_a\, t^2/2\, U(t)$, where R_a is the acceleration constant of the input, ($R(s) = R_a/s^3$), then the steady-state error becomes:

$$e_{ss} = \lim_{s \to 0} \frac{s(R_a/s^3)}{1 + L(s)} = \lim_{s \to 0} \frac{R_a}{s^2 + s^2 L(s)} = \frac{R_a}{\displaystyle\lim_{s \to 0} s^2 L(s)} = \frac{R_a}{K_a} \qquad (G.10)$$

We define the *acceleration error coefficient* as:

$$K_a = \lim_{s \to 0} s^2 L(s) \qquad (G.11)$$

In this case, the steady-state error is infinite for $I < 2$, since for this case $K_a = 0$, (Eq.(G10)). In order to nullify the steady-state error, we must change the system so that it is at least type 3. Only then will the acceleration error coefficient become infinite.

The results for the steady-state errors for different type systems and inputs are summarized in Table G.1

Table G.1. Steady-state errors for systems with different type number.

Type number I	Step $r(t)$ $= R_{ST} U(t)$ $r(\text{s}) = R_{ST}/s$	Velocity $r(t)$ $= R_v t U(t)$ $r(\text{s}) = R_v/s^2$	Acceleration $r(t)=R_a t^2/2 U(t)$ $r(\text{s}) = R_a/s^3$
0	$e_{ss} = R_{ST}/(1 + K_p)$	Infinite	Infinite
1	$e_{ss} = 0$	R_v/K_v	Infinite
2	$e_{ss} = 0$	$0 R_a/K_a$	

We shall clarify the obtained results with an example.

Example G.1. $L(s) = 5 (s + 3)/ [s (s + 1) (s + 10)]$. Find the different error constants and the steady-state errors for $R_{ST} = 5$, $R_v = 15$ and $R_a = 1$.

Solution: According to Eqs.(G.6), (G.9) and (G.11) we find that $K_p = \infty$, $K_v = 15 / 10 = 1.5$ and $K_a = 0$ respectively. Hence, according to Eqs.(G.7), (G.8) and (G.10) we find that $e_{ss} = 0$ for the step input, that the steady-state error for the velocity input is $e_{ss} = 15 / 1.5 = 10$, and that the steady-state error for the acceleration input is $e_{ss} = \infty$.

References

Anderson B., and Moore J., (1971), *Linear Optimal Control,* Englewood Cliffs, NJ: Prentice-Hall.

Anderson B., and Moore J., (1990) , *Optimal Control:Linear Quadratic Methods,* Englewood Cliffs, NJ: Prentice-Hall.

Asseo S., (1970), "Application of Optimal Control to Perfect Model Following," J.Aircraft 7(4): 308–313

Athans M.,(Guest Editor), (1971), Special Issue on Linear-Quadratic- Gaussian Problem, IEEE Transaction on Automatic Control., AC-16.

Athans M., and Falb P.,(1969), *Optimal Control,* N.Y.:McGraw-Hill Book Company.

Balas G., Doyle J., Glover K., Packard A., and Smith R., (1995), "μ-Analysis and Synthesis Toolbox", For Use with Matlab. The MathWorks, Inc.,Cochituate Place, 24 Prime Park Way, Natick, MA 01760; MUSYN Inc., P.O.Box 1337, Minneapolis, MN 55414-5377.

Barman J., Katzenelson J., (1973), "A generalized Nyquist-type stability criterion for multivariable feedback systems," Int.J.Control, Vol.20: 593.

Bellman R., (1952), "The theory of dynamic programming", Proc. Nat. Acad. Sci. USA 38: 716–719.

Benshabat D., Chait Y.,(1993), "Application of Quantitative Feedback Theory to a class of Missiles", Journal of Guidance, Control and Dynamics, 16(1): 47–58.

Black S., (1934), "Stabilized Feedback Amplifiers", Bell Syst. Tech.

Blakelock J., (1991), *Automatic Control of Aircraft and Missiles,* John Wiley & Sons, Inc., New York/London/Sydney

Bliss G., (1966), *Algebraic functions,* Dover, New York.

Bode , H. W., (1945), *Network Analysis and Feedback Amplifier Design,* D. Van Nostrand Company Inc., Princeton, N.J.

Bongiorno J., and Youla D., (1977), "On the Design of Single-Loop single Input-Output Feedback Control Systems in the Complex-Frequency Domain", IEEE Transactions on Automatic Control, AC-22, No.3: 416–423.

Borghesani, Chait, and Yaniv, (1995), Quantitative Feedback Theory Toolbox. For Use with MATLAB, The MATHWORKS Inc.

Brasch F. , and Pearson J., (1970),'Pole Placement Using Dynamic Compensators', IEEE Transactions on AC-15(1) February: 34–43

Bryson A., and Ho Y., (1969), *Applied Optimal Control,* Blaisdell Publishing Company, Waltham, Massachussets/Toronto/London.

Chait Y., and Yaniv O. (1993), "MULTI-INPUT/SINGLE-OUTPUT COMPUTED-AIDED CONTROL DESIGN USING THE QUANTITATIVE FEEDBACK THEORY", International Journal of Robust and Nonlinear Control, 3(1): 47–54

Cheng D. K., (1960), *Alalysis of Linear Systems,* Addison-Wesley Publishing Company, Inc, Reading, Masschusetts, Palo Alto; London.

Chiang R., and Safonov M., (1988), *Robust Control Toolbox, User's Guide,* Sherborn, MA: MATHWORKS

Churchill R.,(1960), *Complex variables and applications,* McGraw-Hill Book Company,Inc., New York,Toronto London.

D'Azzo J., and Houpis C., (1988), *Linear Control System Analysis & Design-Conventional and Modern,* McGraw Hill Book Company, New York

Desoer C., Liu R., Murray J., and Saeks R., (1980), " Feedback System Design: The Fractional Representation Approach to Analysis and Synthesis", IEEE Transaction on Automatic Control, AC-25(3), :399–412.

Desoer J., and Vidyasagar M., (1975), *Feedback Systems: Input-output Properties,* Academic Press, New York.

Desoer C., and Wang Y., (1980), "On the generalized Nyquist stability criterion", IEEE Transactionson Automatic Control, AC-25: 187–96.

Dorato P., Abdallah C., and Cerone Vito, (1995), *Linear-Quadratic Control, An Introduction ,* Prentice Hall, Englewood Cliffs, N.J.

Doyle J., (1978), "Robustness of Multiloop Linear Feedback Systems", Proc. 17th IEEE Conference Decision and Control, :12–18.

Doyle J., (1983), "Synthesis of robust controllers and filters" , Proc.IEEE Conf. on Decision and Control, San Antonio, Texas, :109–114.

Doyle J., (1986), "Quantitative Feedback Theory (QFT) and Robust Control", Am. Control Conf., : pp.1691–1698.

Doyle J., and Glover K. (1989), " State-Space Solutions to Standard H_2 and Control Problems, IEEE Trans. on Automatic Control, AC-34(8) : pp.831–845

Doyle J., Glover, K., Khargonekar P., and Francis B. (1989), "State-Space Solutions to Standard H_2 and H_∞ Control Problems", IEEE Transactions on Automatic Control, 34(8) :831–845.

Doyle J., Francis B., and Tannenbaum A., (1992), *Feedback Control Theory,* Macmillan Publishing Company.

Doyle J., and Stein G., (1979), "Robustness with Observers", IEEE Trans. on Automatic Control, AC-24(4) : pp.607–611.

Doyle J., and Stein G., (1981), "Multivariable Feedback Design: Concepts for a Classical/Modern Synthesis", IEEE Trans.on Automatic Control, AC-26(1): pp.4–16.

Doyle J., Wall J., and Stein G., :"Performance and robustness analysis for structured uncertainty", Proc. IEEE Conf. Dec. Contr., :629–636.

Edmunds J., and Kouvaritakis B., (1979),'Extensions of the frame alignment technique and their use in the characteristic locus design method', International Jopurnal of Control, 29: 787–96.

Evans R., (1954), *Control System Dynamics,* McGraw-Hill, New York.

Francis B., (1986), *A Course in H_∞ Control Theory,* Springer-Verlag.

Francis B., and Doyle J., 1987, "Linear control theory with an optimality criterion", SIAM J. Control Opt.vol.25, :815–844.

Franklin G.,F. and Powel J.D., (1990), *Digital Control of Dynamic Systems,* Addison-Wesley

Freudenberg J. S., and Looze D., P, (1985), "Right Half Plane Poles and Zeros and Design Tradeoffs in Feedback Systems", IEEE Trans. AC, 30(6) : 555–565.

Freudenberg J. S., and Looze D. P., (1987), *Frequency Domain Properties of Scalar and Multivariable Feedback Systems,* Springer-Verlag, Berlin, Heidelberg, New York, London, Paris, Tokyo

Garnett J., (1981), *Bounded Analytic Functions,* Academic Press, New York, London, Toronto

Glover K., and Doyle J., (1988), "State-space formulae for all stabilizing controllers that satisfy an H_∞ norm bound and relations to risk sensitivity", Syst. Contr. Lett.,vol.11:167–172.

Goldberg R.,(1970), *Fourier Transforms,* Cambridge University Press

Gourishankar V., and Ramar K., (1976), 'Pole assignment with minimum eigenvalue sensitivity to plant parameter variations', INT.J.Control 23(4): 493–504

Green M.,(1992), "H_∞ controller synthesis by *J*- lossless coprime factorization", SIAM J. Control and Optimization,vol.28, :522–547.

Green M., and Limebeer D.,(1995), *Linear Robust Control,* Prentice Hall, Englewood Cliffs, New Jersey

Guillemin, E., A., (1949), *The Mathematics of Circuit Analysis,* The M.I.T. PRESS , Massachusetts Institute of Technology, Cambridge, Massachusetts

Harvey C., and Stein G.,(1978), "Quadratic Weights for Asymptotic Regulator Properties", IEEE Transactions on Automatic Control, AC-23(3) :378–387.

Hirzinger G., (1974), "Application of advanced model-following techniques to the design of flight control systems for control configured vehicles", AGARD 11–1,11–15.

Horn R., Johnson C.,(1991), *Topics in Matrix Analysis,* Cambridge University Press.

Horowitz I.,(1962), " Design of multiple-loop feedback systems", Trans.IRE AUT.Control AC-7 : 47–57.

Horowitz I., (1963), *Synthesis of Feedback Systems,* Academic Press, New York , London

Horowitz I.,(1973), "Optimum loop transfer function in single-loop feedback systems", INT.J.CONTROL, vol. 18: 97–113.

Horowits I., (1976), "Synthesis of Feedback Systems with Nonlinear Time-Varying Uncertain Plants to Satisfy Quantitative Performance Specifications", Proc. of the IEEE, Vol.64(1), :123–130.

Horowitz I., (1979,a), "Design of feedback systems with non-minimum-phase unstable plants", INT. J. Systems Sci., 10(9):1025–1040

Horowitz I., (1979,b), "Quantitative synthesis of uncertain multiple input-output feedback system" INT.J.Control, 30(1): 81–106.

Horowitz I., (1982), "Improved design technique for uncertain multiple-input-multiple-output feedback systems", Int.J.Control, vol.36: 155–171

Horowitz I.,(1992), *Quantitative Feedback Design Theory,* Vol.1, QFT Publications, 4470 Grinnel Ave., Boulder, Colorado, 80303.

Horowitz et al, (1983) :"Multivariable Flight Control Design with Uncertain Parameters (YF16CCV)", AFWAL-TR-83–3036, Air Force Wright Aeronautical Laboratories, Wright-Patterson AFB, Ohio.

Horowitz I., and Bor-Chyun Wang, (1979), "A synthesis theory for a class of multiple-loop systems with plant uncertainty", INT.J. CONTROL, 30( ) :, 837–862.

Horowitz I., and Breiner, M., (1981), "Quantitative synthesis of feedback systems with uncertain nonlinear multivariable plants", Int.J.Systems, vol. 11: 851

Horowitz I., Golubev B., and Kopelman Z. (1980), "Flight Control Design Based on Nonlinear Model with Uncertain Parameters", AIAA J. Guidance Control, vol. 3, :113–118.

Horowitz I.,and Liau Y.,(1984), "Limitations of Non-Minimum- Phase Feedback Systems", Int., J. Cont., 40(5): 1003–1015.

Horowitz I., and Liao, (1986), "Quantitative feedback design for sampled-data systems", INT.J.Control, 44(3): 665–675.

Horowits I., and Loecher C., (1981), "Design of a 3 × 3 multivariable feedback system with large plant uncertainty", INT.J.Control, 33(4) : 677–699.

Horowitz I., and Sidi M., (1972), "Synthesis of feedback systems for prescribed time-domain tolerances", INT.J. CONTROL, 16(2) : 287–309.

Horowitz I., Sidi M, (1973), "Synthesis of Cascaded Multiple-Loop Feedback Systems with Large Plant Parameter Ignorance", Automatica, Vol. 9 : 589–600.

Horowitz I., Sidi M., (1978)a, :"Synthesis of linear time-varying nonminimum phsase systems with plant uncertainty", INT.J.CONTROL, 27(3) : 351–359

Horowitz I., Sidi M., (1978)b, "Optimum synthesis of non-minimum phase feedback systems with plant uncertainty", INT.J.CONTROL, 27(3) : 361–386

Horowitz I., and Sidi M., (1980), "Practical design of feedback systems with uncertain multivariable plants", INT.J.Systems Sci,, 11(7): 851–875

Horowitz I., Sidi M., and Erickson R., 1894, "Quantitative synthesis for non-linear switched-mode uncertain regulators, INT.J. CONTROL, 57(4): 461–476.

Horowitz I., and Te-Shing Wang, 1979, "A synthesis theory for a class of multiple-loop systems with plant uncertainty", INT.J. CONTROL, 29(4): 645–668.

Houpis H., and Lamont G.,(1992), *Digital Control Systems-Theory, Hardware, Software* McGraw-Hill International Editions

Hvostov H., (1990), "Simplifying Controller Synthesis Via Classical Feedback System Structure", IEEE Trans. on Automatic Control, 35(4) : 485–488.

Jameson A., (1970), "Design of a Single-Input System for Specified Roots Using Output Feedback", IEEE, AC-15: 345–347.

James H., Nichols N., and Phillips R., (1948), *Theory of Servomechanisms,* MIT Radiation Laboratories Series, Vol 25, McGraw-Hill Company, Inc.

Kailath T., (1980), *Linear systems,* Prentice Hall, Englewood Cliffs, N.J.

Kalman R., (1964), "When is a Linear Control System Optimal?", Journal of Basic Engineering, Transaction of the ASME, March: 51–60.

Kalman R., (1965), "Mathematical description of linear dynamical systems", J.S.I.A.M. Control, Ser. A, Vol 1(2): 152–192.

Kalman R., and Bucy R., (1961), "New results in linear filtering and prediction theory", Trans. ASME Ser. D. (J. Basic Engr.) 83 :95–107.

Kalman R., Englar T., and Bucy R., (1964),'Fundamental Study of Adaptive Control Systems,' ASD-T R-61–27, Vol.II, Wright-Patterson Air Force Base, Ohio.

Kolmogorov A., Fomin S., (1970), *Introductory Real Analysis,* Dover Publications, Inc., N.Y.

Korn G. and Korn T.(1968), *Mathematical Handbook for Scientists,* McGraww-Hill Book Company.

Kouvaritakis B., A., (1974), "Characteristic locus method for multivariable feedback systems design", Ph.D. thesis, University of Manchester, England.

Kouvaritakis B., A., (1979), "Theory and practice of the characteristic locus design method", PROC.IEE 126(6) : 542–547.

Kouvaritakis B., A., and Edmonds J., (1978), "The characteristic frequency and characteristic gain design method for multivariable feedback systems", Alternatives for linear multivariable control', National Engineering Consortium, Inc., Chicago: 229–246.

Kreindler E., and Rothschild D.,(1974), "New methods for command augmentation via optimal control", Grumman Reasearch Department RE-472.

Kreindler E., and Rothschild D., (1976), "Model-Following in Linear-QuadraticOptimization", AIAA Journal , 14(7) : 835–842.

Krishnan K., and Cruickshanks A., (1977), "Frequency-domain design of feedback systems for specified insensitivity of time-domain response to parameter variation", INT.J.CONTROL, 25(4): 609–620.

Kuo B., (1980), *Didital Control Systems,* Holt, Reinehart and Winston, Inc., New York.

Kwakernaak H., (1990a): "The polynomial approach to H_∞-optimal regulation". In E.Mosca and L.Pandolfi (Eds.), H_+-Control, Como 1990, Lecture notes in Mathematics, 1996, Springer-Vellag, Heidelberg.

Kwakeraak H., (1990b), *"Matlab macros for polynomial H control system optimization.* Memorandum No. 881, Department of Applied Mathematics, University of Twente, Enschede, The Netherlands

Kwakernaak H.,(1993), "Robust Control and -Optimizartion-Tutorial Paper", Automatica, 29(2): 255–273.

Kwakernaak H., and Sivan R., (1972), *Linear Optimal Control Systems,*Wiley Interscience,N.Y.

Laub A., and Wette M., (1984), "Algorithms and Software for Pole Assignment and Observers", UCRL-15646 Rev.1, EE Dept, Univ of Calif., Santa Barbara, CA, September.

Lehtomaki N.,(1981), "Practical robustness measures in multivsariable control',Ph.D. dissertation, Mass. Inst. Technol., Cambridge, MA, May.

Leithead W., and O'Reilly J. ,(1991), "Uncertain SISO systems with fixed stable minimum-phase controllers:relationship of closed-loop systems to plant RHP poles and zeros", INT.J.Control , 53(4): 771–798.

Luenberger D.,(1964), "Observing the State of a Linear System", IEEE Transactions on Military Electronics:74–80.

Luenberger D., (1966), "Observers for Multivariable Systems", IEEE Transactions on Automatic Control , AC-11(2) : 596–602.

Luenberger D., (1971), "An Introduction to Observers", IEEE Transactions on Automatic Control , AC-16(6) :190–197.

Macfarlane A.G., (1970), "Return-difference and return-ratio matrices and their use in analysis   and design of multivariable feedback control systems", PROC.IEE, 117(120): 2037–2049.

Macfarlane A.G.,:(1977), "Relationships Between Recent Developments in Linear Control Theory and Classical Design Techniques" in'*Control System Design by Pole-Zero Assignments,* Academic Press, London, :51–122.

MacFarlane A.,G., and Belletrutti J.,(1973), "The Characteristic Locus Design Method", Automatica, Pergamon Press, Vol.9: 575–588,

MacFarlane A.,G., and Kouvaritakis B., A., (1977), "'A design technique for linear multivariable feedback systems'", INT.J.Control, 25(6): 837–874. MacFarlane A.,G., Kouvaritakis B., A., and Edmunds J.,(1978), "Complex variable methods for multivariable feedback systems analysis and design", in '*Alternatives for linear multivariable control':* 189–228, Nationbal Engineering Consortium, Inc., Chicago

MacFarlane A.,G., and Postlethwaite I., (1977), "The generalized Nyquist stability criterion and multivariable root loci", INT.J.Control, 25(1) : 81–127.

Maciejowski J., 1989, *Multivariable Feedback Design,* Addison-Wesley Publishing Company.

Mason S., (1953),.: "Feedback theory-Some properties of flow graphs", Proc. IRE 41 (9) :1144–1156.

Mason S.J, (1956), "Feedback Theory-Further Properties of Signal Flow Graphs" Proceedings of the IRE, 44(7) :920–926.

Mayne D. Q., (1979), "Sequential design of linear multivariable systems", Proceedings of the Institute of Electrical Engineers, 126: 586–572.

McRuer D., Ashkenas I., and Graham D., (1973), *Aircraft Dynamics and Automatic Control,* Princeton University Press, Princeton, New Jersey.

Middelton R. H.,(1991), "Tradeoffs in Linear Control Systems Design", Automatica, 27(2) :281–292.

Moore J., Glover K., and Telford A., (1990), "All Shaped Controllers as Frequency-Shaped State Estimate Feedback, IEEE Trans. on Automatic Control, vol. AC-35(2): 203–208.

Morari M., and Zafiriou E., (1989), *Robust Process Control,* Prentice-Hall, Englewood Cliffs, N.J.

Motyka P., (1974), "A classical approach to the design of model-following control systems", AIAA Mechanics and control of flight conference., August 5, Anaheim, Cal.:.1–9.

Net C., Jacobson C., and Balas M., (1984), "A connection between state-space and doubly coprime fractional representation", IEEE trans. Auto. Control, AC-29: 831–832.

Newton G., Gould L., and Kaiser J, (1957), *Analytic Design of Linear Feedback Controls,* Wiley, New York.

Niewoehner R., Kaminer I.,(1996), "Design of an Autoland Controller for an F-14 Aircraft Using H_∞ Synthesis", Journal of Guidance, Control and Dynamics, 19(3): 656–663.

Nyquist H.,(1932): "Regeneration Theory", Bell System Tech.J.,vol. 11, January, :126–147.

Ogata K.,(1967), *State space analysis of control systems,* Prentice Hall, Englewood Cliffs, N.J.

Olson D., and Horowitz I.,(1970), " Design of dominant-type control systems with large parameter variations, INT.J.CONTROL, 12(4): 545–554.

Owens D., H.,(1981), *Multivariable Optimal Systems,* Academic Press, London

Papoulis A., 1962, *The Fourier Integral and its Applications,* McGraw-Hill Electronic Sciences Series,

Petit Bois G., (1961), *Tables of Indefinite Integrals,* Dover Publications, Inc., New York., p.4.

Postlethwaite I. and MacFarlane A., (1977), *A Complex VariableApproach to the Analysis of Linear Multivariable Feedback Systems,* Springer-Verlag, Berlin

Rogers W. and Collins D., (1992), "X-29 Controller Synthesis, J. Guidance, Control and Dynamics, 15(4) : 962–967.

Rosenblum M., Rovnyak J.,(1994), *Topics in Hardy Classes and Univalent Functions,* Birkhauser Verlag, Basel-Boston-Berlin

Rosenbrock H.,(1970), "Design of multivariable control systems using the inverse Nyquist array", PROC.IEE, 116(11) :1929–1936

Rosenbrock H., (1974), *Computer-aided control system design,* Academic press.

Rosenbrock H., and Munro N., 1978 "The inverse Nyquist Array Method", in*Alternatives for linear multivariable control,*Nationbal Engineering Consortium, Inc., Chicago: 101–188.

Safonov M., and Athans M.,(1977), "Gain and Phase Margin for Multiloop LQG Regulators", IEEE Transactions on Automatic Control AC-22(2) : 173–179.

Saucedo R., Schiring E., (1968); *Introduction to Continuous and Digital Control Systems,* Mac Millan.

Seshu S., and Balabanian N., (1959), *Linear Network Design,* John Wiley and Sons, Inc., New York.

Skogestad S., and Postlethwaite I.,(1996), *Multivariable Feedback Control-Analysis and Design,* John Wiley & Sons, Chichester, New Tork, Brisbane, Toronto, Singapore

Sidi M., (1973), 'Synthesis of Feedback Systems with Large Plant Ignorance for prescribed Time-Domain Tolerances', Ph.D Dissertation, Weizman Institute of Science, Rehovot, Israel

Sidi M.,(1976), "Feedback Synthesis with Plant Ignorance, Nonminimum-Phase, and Time-Domain Tolerances", Automatica, Vol. 12: 265–271.

Sidi M.,(1977), "Synthesis of sampled feedback systems for prescribed time domain tolerances, 26(3) :445–461.

Sidi M., (1997a), *Dynamics and Control of Spacecraft-practical engineering approach,* Cambridge University Press.

Sidi M.,(1997b), "Gain-bandwidth limitations of feedback systems with non-minimum-phase plants", Int.J.Control, 67(5) :731–743.

Sidi M., (1999), "A Combined QFT/H_∞ Design Technique for TDOF uncertain Feedback Systems", The 7th IEEE Mediterranean Conference on Control & Automation, MED99 Conference, paper No. MED034, 28–30 June, Haifa, Israel :21–45.

Sidi M., and Yaniv O.,(1999), "Margins and Bandwidth Limitations of NMP SISO Feedback systems", The 7th IEEE Mediterranean Conference on Control & Automation, MED99 Conference, paper No. MED050, 28–30 June, Haifa, Israel: 674–688.

Simmons G., (1963), *Topology and Modern Analysis,* McGRAW-HILL BOOK COMPANY, INC.

Skogestad S., and Postlethwaite I., (1996), *Multivariable Feedback Control-Analysis and Design,* John Wiley & Sons, Chichester, New Tork, Brisbane, Toronto, Singapore

Smith M.,(1984), Applications of algebraic function theory in multivariable control, in *Mulivariable Control: New Concepts and Tools* (Tzafestas S., ed.) pp.3–26, Dordrecht:Reidel.

Solodovnikov V. V.,(1960), *Introduction to the Statistical Dynamics of Automatic Control Sysems,* Dover Publications, Inc, New York.

Stein G.,(1979), "Generalized quadratic weights for asymptotic regulator propertied", IEEE Trans. Automatic Control, AC-24: 559–566.

Stein G. and Athans M., (1987), "The LQG/LTR Procedure for multivariable Feedback Control Design", IEEE Trans. on Automatic Control, AC-32(2) : 4–16.

Stein G., and Doyle J., (1991), "Beyond Singular Values and Loop Shapes", J. Guidance, Control and Dynamics, 14(1) : 5–16.

Stevens P., (1981), "A Generalization of the Nyquist Stability Criterion", IEEE Transactions on Automatic Control, AC-26(3) :664–669.

Tichmarsh E. C. (1937), *Introduction to the Theory of Fourier Integrals,* Oxford University Press, New York.

Thompson D., and Pruyn J., (1999), "On characteristic sensitivity-based and traditional formulation for quantitative feedback theory., INT.J. CONTROL, 72(6): 536–543.

Truxal J., (1953), *Automatic Feedback Control System Synthesis,* McGraw-Hill Book Company, Inc., New York.

Tyler J., and Tuteur F., (1966), "The use of a quadratic performance index to design multivariable control systems", IEEE Trans. Automatic Control, AC-11: 84–92.

Valley G., and Wallman H.,(1948), *Vacum tube amplifiers,* Radiation Lab. Series, Vol.18, McGraw Hill , N.Y.

Verma M. and Jonckheere E., (1984), "H_∞compensation with mixed sensitivity as a broadband matching problem", Systems and Control Letters, 4 :125–130 .

Vidyasagar M., (1985), *Control System Synthesis- A Factorization Approach,* The MIT Press, Massachusetts Institute of Technology, Cambridge, Massachusetts 02142

Vincent J., Emami-Naeini A., Khraishi N., (1994), "Case Study Comparision of Linear Quadratic Regulator and H∞ Control Synthesis", Journal of Guidance, Control and Dynamics, 17(5) :958–965.

Voulgaris P., and Valavani L., (1991), "High performance Linear-Quadratic and H-Infinity Design for a "SupermaneuveraBLE" Aircraft", Journal of Guidance, Control and Dynamics, 14(1): 157–165.

Warner S., (1965), *Modern algebra,* Prentice-Hall

Weinmann A., (1991), *Uncertain Mode and Robust Control,* Springer-Verlag, Berlin.

Weyl H., (1955), *The concept of a Riemann surface,* Addison Wesley, Reading, Mass.

Wonham W.,(1967), "On Pole Assignment in Multi-Input Controllable Linear Systems", IEEE Transactions on Automatic Control, AC-12(6) : 660–665

Yaniv O., (1991), "Robust Design of MIMO Feedback systems Having an Uncertain Non-linear Plant", Int.Journal Contr., 53(6): 1283–1294.

Yaniv O., (1995), "MIMO QFT Using Non-Diagonal Controllers", Int.J.Control, 61(1): 245–253.

Yaniv O., Chait Y.,(1993), "Direct Control Design in Sampled-data Uncertain Systems", Automatica, 29(2): 365–372.

Yaniv O., and Horowitz I., (1986), " A quantitative design method for MIMO linear feedback systems having uncertain plants", Int.J.Control, 43(2) : 401–421.

Yaniv O., and Horowitz I.,(1987), "Quantitative feedback theory -reply to criticism", Int.J.Control, 46(3): 945–962.

Youla D., Bongiorno J., and Jabr H.,(1976a), "Modern Wiener-Hopf Design of Optimal Controllers; Part I : The Single-Input-Output Case", IEEE Transactions on Automatic Control, AC-21(1): 3–13.

Youla D., Bongiorno J., and Jabr H.,(1976b), "Modern Wiener-Hopf Design of Optimal Controllers; Part II: The Multivariable Case", IEEE Transactions on Automatic Control, AC-21(3): 319–338.

Youla D., Bongiorno J., and Lu C.,(1974), "Single-Loop Feedback-Stabilization of Linear Multivariable Dynamical Plants", Automatica, Vol.10: 159–173, Pergamon Press.

Zames G., (1979), "Feedback and optimal sensitivity: Model reference transformations, weighted seminorms, and approximate inverses", Proc. 17th Allerton Conf.,:744–752.

Zames G., (1981),"Feedback and Optimal Sensitivity: Model reference transformations, multiplicative seminorms, and approximate inverse", IEEE Transactions on Automatic Control AC-26,: 301–320.

Zhou K. with Doyle J.,(1998), *Essentials of Robust Control,* Prentice Hall, Upper Saddle River, New Jersey

Zames G., and Francis B.,(1983), "Feedback, minimax sensitivity, and optimal robustness", IEEE Trans. Auto. Contr., AC-28 :585–601.

Zhao Y. and Jayasuriya S., (1998), "An $H\infty$ Formulation of Quantitative Feedback Theory" , Journal of Dynamics Systems, Measurements, and Control, September, Vol.120: 305–313.

Zhou K., Doyle J., and Glover K., (1996), *Robust and Optimal Control,* Prentice Hall,Upper Saddle River, New Jersey

Index